B R I T I S H
ARCHIVES
A GUIDE TO ARCHIVE RESOURCES IN THE UNITED KINGDOM

BRITISH

ARCHIVES

A GUIDE TO ARCHIVE RESOURCES IN THE UNITED KINGDOM

JANET FOSTER &
JULIA SHEPPARD

MACMILLAN PRESS
LONDON

MACMILLAN REFERENCE BOOKS

First published by MACMILLAN PUBLISHERS LTD (Journals Division) 1982
Distributed by Globe Book Services Ltd,
Brunel Road, Houndmills, Basingstoke,
Hants RG21 2XS, England

Reprinted 1983
Paperback edition 1984

British Library Cataloguing in Publication Data

Foster, Janet
  British archives.
  1. Archives – Great Britain – Directories
  I. Title   II. Sheppard, Julia
  941   CD1040

  ISBN 0-333-32999-6
  ISBN 0-333-37868-7 Pbk
  ISSN 0265-3915

Consulting Editor: KLAUS BOEHM

Typeset by Leaper & Gard Ltd, Bristol
Printed in Hong Kong

CONTENTS

Introduction

Archival holdings available for research of all kinds in the UK are among the most rich and extensive in the world. They range over the records of medieval and modern government, both central and local, the archives of the Church and universities, the papers of great dynastic landed families, and collections made from various sources by scholarly or aristocratic antiquarians, collections which often form the basis of the modern national libraries of England, Scotland and Wales. The rescue of much 19th- and 20th-century archival material, usually on a subject basis, has been undertaken by recently established specialist repositories.

Despite, or perhaps because of, this wealth of historical source material, there has never been an attempt to provide an exhaustive list of repositories which hold archives and manuscript collections of historical interest. In this Guide, county and city record offices, national, university and polytechnic libraries, local government libraries, institutions and so-called specialist repositories have all been covered.

Concept of the book

The book was originally conceived as a guide to the specialist repositories which have proliferated over the past two decades, excluding national and local authority repositories. However, while the interests of many repositories are obvious, the wealth and scope of their holdings are frequently underestimated since no general guide exists to archive resources as a whole in the UK. It was therefore decided that *British Archives* would be most useful if it embraced all types of repository. Thus it consolidates information for the historian and the archivist and provides a starting point for the first-time user of archives. Archives are not normally arranged or catalogued on a subject basis; for this reason it can be difficult to trace records held in unlikely or lesser-known repositories. Therefore, another primary aim was to give a subject approach to the information in the Guide by means of a key subject word list. It was also decided that a general index to the names of individuals, bodies and collections appearing in the entries would be useful.

Criteria for selection

'Archives', in the purest sense, are documents which have been created in the normal course of the life of an institution or an individual and contribute to their historical record. Thus, an archive is a body of material produced over a period of time which has its own coherence and related interest. Recently, the usage of the word has been stretched to cover any primary documentary material, including individual pieces gathered into artificial collections, photographs and other non-manuscript material. Moreover, it is also used to describe the physical place where public records or historical documents are held.

Inevitably this Guide cannot be comprehensive, since any organization holding its own non-current records selected for preservation can claim to have an archive. Our approach has been to cover as many places as we could learn of where archives, in the widest sense of the word, are held and are made relatively accessible. Our sources have been *Record Repositories in Great Britain* (5th–7th editions); British Records Association additional list in *Archives* vol. xiv, no.63 (1980); membership list of the Specialist Repositories Group of the Society of Archivists; *Libraries in the United Kingdom and the Republic of Ireland*; reference works on library special collections; responses to requests for information in *The Local Historian, Museums Bulletin*, the

Newsletter and Calendar of the Council for British Archaeology. The many local history, archaeology, literary and philosophical societies have not been systematically included, both because of the numbers involved and because information about them is normally available from the local athority record office. We also decided to exclude businesses, which are the specific concern of the Business Archives Council (*see* List of Useful Addresses). Privately held collections of estate and family records have not been extensively covered, since many of these collections have been listed by the Historical Manuscripts Commission.

Methods

The main problem with a reference work of this kind is that its contents are frequently out of date by the time of publication. But the editors decided that, if the Guide could be produced quickly, the advantages would outweigh the disadvantages. Restrictions on time and finance made it necessary to use questionnaires to obtain the information required and, with hindsight, a tight schedule proved helpful in eliciting responses. Approximately 750 questionnaires were sent out between September and December 1981, requesting information as outlined below. Sample entries were provided for guidance, with a checklist of key subject words. Briefer information was requested from local authority record offices, the Public Record Office and larger national libraries, for reasons explained later in this introduction. Where no reply was received a reminder card was sent and, if this failed, it was followed by telephone enquiries. The Guide is essentially based on information received, since the editors had not the resources to make visits to repositories. Returns obviously varied, and although editorial persistence achieved a substantial measure of improvement in many cases, there remain differences in the quality and detail of entries. Of course the larger the office the more sweeping and general will be the description of its holdings. In other cases a slight return may reflect lack of knowledge of the archives held, impatience with filling in questionnaires, or fear of encouraging an influx of researchers. In some cases 'minimal' entries have been given where it was impossible or inappropriate to have a full entry. We have included lists of those places which did not reply and those which declined to contribute to the Guide.

Briefly the information sought, apart from address and phone number, was:

Enquiries: To whom enquiries should be addressed – title and, in most cases, name. Qualifications have not been included.

Open: Opening times. It is assumed that places will be closed on Bank and other public holidays. Academic institutions are normally closed for longer periods over Easter and Christmas. Many smaller places close for lunch. A prior appointment is *always* advisable.

Access: Arrangements regarding availability of the archives, whether the user needs to provide a reference, and details of any restriction or closure periods on material. Since archives are *not* available on loan, 'reference only' is to be understood throughout. Unless otherwise stated, charges are not normally made.

Historical background: Outline history of the organization including details of its predecessor bodies where applicable and/or the background to the collecting of manuscript material.

Acquisitions policy: Aims of the collecting policy where applicable and areas of particular interest.

Major collections: The major archive holdings of the oganization and/or its deposited collections, where possible naming significant collections with covering dates.

Non-manuscript material: Any other archival material such as plans, drawings, photographs, maps, sound archives, films and, occasionally, printed material.

Finding aids: Types of aids available in the office which facilitate access to the archives, such as indexes, handlists, catalogues.

Facilities: Reading room provisions, usually specifying the availability of reprographic facilities (charges have not been included). Reading aids and on-site conservation have not been noted.

Publications: Details of guides or information about the repository or its collections which have been published or can be consulted elsewhere.

If any section is not included in an entry, this indicates that no information of relevance was supplied.

Local Authority Record Offices and Libraries

Every county in England and Wales, with the exception of Powys, has at least one record office maintained by a local government authority. In England these began to be formally established by county councils from the 1930s and in Wales from the 1950s. Until local government reorganization in 1974 there were no equivalent repositories in Scotland, thus there and, to a certain extent, in Wales the responsibility for acquiring and housing archives fell to the respective National Libraries.

Local authority record offices, that is county, city and some borough record offices, provide a comprehensive record service to the general public, collecting material, official and unofficial, which is of relevance to the history of the locality. Such record offices can be expected to produce a wide range of lists, indexes and catalogues which may also be available at the National Register of Archives. For these reasons the entries for local authority record offices were modified to save endless repetition of similar information. The formula 'the usual local authority record holdings and deposited collections' has been used, with additional information when necessary on collections which the offices deemed were of wider significance. *Access, Acquisitions policy* and *Finding Aids* have been omitted and, for similar reasons, *Major Collections* was omitted from the entries for certain national repositories whose collections by definition cover all types of archival material and subjects.

Usual local authority record office holdings can be categorized as local government and related records (including Quarter Sessions records); family and estate archives (including manorial records); business records; solicitors' and estate agents' records; ecclesiastical, probate, parish and non-conformist records; records of political parties, unions, societies and voluntary organizations; antiquarian collections.

Public libraries may hold a miscellany of documents, but we found that the 'usual local history collection of non-manuscript material' consisted (apart from the books) of some or all of the following: census returns; Ordnance Survey and other maps;

postcards and photographs; drawings; newspapers and cuttings; details of local functions; ephemera including programmes, theatre bills, advertising, etc. Where manuscript material is held this might include rate books; local business records; papers of local residents and celebrities; written and oral memoirs; journals and correspondence.

Advice to the user of archives

Researchers should bear in mind that consulting archives is not the same as looking up information in a book. Archives are unique; the reader cannot assume that they are freely available, easily accessible or even that the originals can be consulted. They are never 'loaned', and copies are not necessarily obtainable. Finding aids – lists and indexes – vary greatly in style and detail; there is no single classification system; in some places finding aids or guides may not exist. All this will depend greatly on the type of repository/library the reader visits, and the facilities and services of, for example, a large and well-staffed county record office cannot be expected everywhere. It will be obvious from consulting the entries in this Guide that some of the archives are administered by librarians, clerks, secretaries, honorary archivists or other individuals whose chief priorities or duties may be elsewhere. Moreover the archives are frequently not stored readily to hand. It is, therefore, always advisable to make a prior appointment.

Background reading and preparation are essential if the reader is to grasp the significance of the archives and the types of documentation likely to be encountered. It must be remembered that records were not normally created with the needs of historical research in mind. It is easy to fall into the trap of assuming that the records will directly answer a specific query; rather it is necessary to understand how and why the records were created before embarking on any research into them. Archivists, being primarily custodians, are not necessarily authorities on all that the records contain, although they will do everything possible to direct the researcher towards the relevant material. If the enquiry is lengthy and a personal visit to the archive is impossible, the services of a professional researcher may be recommended. Some record offices maintain lists of approved professional researchers and the Society of Genealogists publishes a list of members indicating those who are willing to undertake research.

Finally, users are reminded that this Guide is a first step to discovering where to locate archives since the entries do not comprise every place in the United Kingdom where archives and manuscripts are held. Nevertheless the editors hope that the publication of *British Archives* will stimulate interest in expanding and improving the contents of the Guide. To this end we would welcome any additions, suggestions or comments.

Note from the editors

Every effort has been made to incorporate changes to addresses and telephone numbers and opening hours but we would be grateful to receive any further amendments or suggestions.

Janet Foster
Julia Sheppard

March 1984

Acknowledgements

We acknowledge and thank the contributors to *British Archives*, without whom this book would not exist. Many went out of their way to help us and, indeed, made us wish that we could have incorporated some of their informal comments. We are grateful to Klaus Boehm of Macmillan London for his advice during the planning of the book, also to Māra Vilčinskas at Macmillan for her help throughout the editorial stages. Joan Auld and Trevor Parkhill made useful suggestions for entries. Rowan Watson, in particular, has given thoroughly helpful comments and information. We are especially indebted to the Wellcome Trustees and the staff of the Wellcome Institute for the History of Medicine for their support. Thanks are due to Lesley Hall, who has shown the utmost patience during several months of feverish activity. Tracy Saul and Heather Edwards have kindly deciphered and typed the manuscript. More recently Janet Browne has given us invaluable aid with proofs and we are greatly in her debt. Finally, our thanks go to our many colleagues and friends who have encouraged us when all seemed overwhelming, in particular to Bill Bynum and Stevie Holland.

Arrangement

The Guide contains 708 entries arranged alphabetically by town. The title of each repository has normally been that given by the repository itself. A complete list of repositories with cross references is also included. For local historians interested in the repositories in a wider catchment area than the city or town, a list of repositories within each county has also been included.

To facilitate use of the Guide by the subject or name approach, a list of key subject words and a general index can be found at the end of the book. There are limitations to both of these, and the introductory remarks to each index should be read.

List of Useful Addresses

The Royal Commission on Historical Manuscripts (incorporating the National Register of Archives)
Quality House, Quality Court, Chancery Lane, London WC2A 1HP
Tel (01) 242 1198
The central collecting point for information about manuscript sources; holds catalogues and indexes to records and papers in Great Britain and Northern Ireland. Search room open Mon–Fri 9.30–5.00.

The National Register of Archives (Scotland)
General Register House, Edinburgh EH1 3YY
Tel (031) 556 6585
Counterpart of the NRA in London and forms a branch of the Scottish Record Office.

The Principal Registry of the Family Division
Somerset House, Strand, London WC2R 1LP
Tel (01) 405 7641 ext 3097
Holds all wills admitted to probate in England and Wales since 1858. Open Mon–Fri 10.00–4.30.

The British Records Association
Master's Court, The Charterhouse, Charterhouse Square, London EC1M 6AU
Tel (01) 253 0436
A national organization founded to co-ordinate and encourage the work of individuals, authorities, institutions and societies interested in the conservation and use of records.

The Business Archives Council
Denmark House, 15 Tooley Street, London SE1 2PN
Tel (01) 407 6110
Assists in locating business records and also gives guidance with records management and listing.

The Business Archives Council of Scotland
Glasgow University Archives, The University, Glasgow G12 8QQ
Tel (041) 339 8855 ext 7516
Does similar work to the Business Archives Council in England.

List and Index Society
The Secretary, c/o the Public Record Office, Chancery Lane, London WC2A 1LR
Distributes copies of Public Record Office lists and lists from other public archives to subscribing members.

British Association for Local History
43 Bedford Square, London WC1B 3DP
Tel (01) 636 4066
Promotes knowledge and understanding of local history.

Society of Genealogists
37 Harrington Gardens, London SW7 4JX
Tel (01) 373 7045
Information about regional genealogical societies and the work of individuals in this field. Reference library open to non-members on payment of a fee.

The Catholic Archives Society
Hon. Secretary, c/o 4A Polstead Road, Oxford OX2 6TN
Promotes the care and preservation of records and archives of the dioceses, religious foundations, institutions and societies of the Roman Catholic Church in UK and Eire.

Contemporary Scientific Archives Centre
16 Wellington Square, Oxford OX1 2HY
Locates and catalogues papers of distinguished contemporary British scientists, placing collections in appropriate repositories after cataloguing.

Institutions Not Included

We were unable to obtain any reply from the following:

Broadlands Archive Trust, Broadlands, Romsey, Hampshire; Ealing Borough Libraries, Central Library, Walpole Park, Ealing, London W5 5EQ; Haileybury School, Hertford SG13 7NU; Harrow Borough Libraries, Civic Centre Library, PO Box 4, Station Road, Harrow HA1 1UU; Isle of Wight County Libraries, Parkhurst Road, Newport, Isle of Wight PO30 5TX; Leicester Polytechnic, Kimberlin Library, PO Box 143, Leicester LE1 9BH; Liverpool Polytechnic, The Library, Walton House, Tithebarn Street, Liverpool L2 2NG; Loughborough University of Technology, Pilkington Library, Loughborough, Leicestershire LE11 3TU; Motherwell District Council Libraries, Motherwell Public Library, Hamilton Road, Motherwell ML1 3BZ; National Gallery of Scotland, The Mound, Edinburgh EH2 2EL; North East London Polytechnic, Waltham Forest Precinct, Forest Road, London E17 4JB; North Staffordshire Polytechnic, The Library, College Road, Stoke-on-Trent, Staffordshire ST4 2DE; Northampton Libraries, 27 Guidehall Road, Northampton, NN1 1EF; Oxfordshire County Libraries, Headquarters, Holton, Oxford OX9 1QQ; Queen's University of Belfast, University Library, Belfast BT7 1LS; Royal College of Nursing, The Library, Henrietta Place, London W1; Royal Dental Hospital School, The Library, 32 Leicester Square, London WC2H 7LJ; Royal Institution of Chartered Surveyors, 29 Lincolns Inn Fields, London WC2; Royal Photographic Society, The Octagon, Milsom Street, Bath, Avon; St. Bride's Printing Library, Bride Lane, London EC4; Society of Genealogists, 37 Harrington Gardens, London SW7; South Eastern Education and Library Board, Windmill Hill, Ballynahinch, Co. Down BT24 8DH; Southern Education and Library Board, Brownlow Road, Legahory, Craigavon Co. Armagh BT65 8DP; Spanish and Portuguese Synagogue, 8 St. James Gardens, London W11; Stirling District Library, Administration HQ, Spittal Street, Stirling FK8 1DY; Strathkelvin District Council Libraries, 170 Kirkintilloch Road, Bishopbriggs, Glasgow G64; Teesside Polytechnic, Main Site Library, Borough Road, Middlesborough, Cleveland TS1 3BA; Trinity College, Cambridge; Thames Polytechnic, The Library, Wellington Street, London SE18 6PF; Trafford Borough Council Libraries, Birch House, Talbot Road, Old Trafford, Manchester M16 0GH; Wandsworth Borough Libraries, Battersea District Library, Lavender Hill, London SW11 1JB; Western Education and Library Board, Library Headquarters, Dublin Road, Omagh, Co. Tyrone, BT78 1HG.

The following are known to have archives, but preferred not to provide an entry:

Bedford Estates, Bedford Office, 29A Montague Street, London WC1B 5BL; Drapers' Company, Clerk's Office, Drapers' Hall, London EC2N 2DQ; Middle Temple Library, Middle Temple, London EC4; North Devon Athenaeum, Library and Museum, The Square, Barnstaple, Devon; Northumberland Estates, Estates Office, Alnwick Castle, Alnwick, Northumberland NE66 1NQ; Royal Archives, The Library, Windsor Castle, Berkshire; Trinity House, Tower Hill, London EC3.

Alphabetical List of Repositories

Aberdeen City District Libraries 2
Aberdeen University Library 3
Abingdon Town Council 13
Air Photo Library, University of Keele 261
Alan Ramsay Library 53
Andover Borough Archives 18
Angus District Council 198
Arbroath Library and Art Gallery 19
Arbroath Signal Tower Museum 20
Archives of the English Province of the Society of Jesus 306
Argyll and Bute District Council 304
Armagh County Museum 22
Army Museums Ogilby Trust (AMOT) 16
Ashmolean Museum 564
Avon County Library, Bath 34
Avon County Reference Library, Bristol 72

Baillie Library 204
Balfour Library 576
Bank of England 307
Baptist Missionary Society 308
Baptist Union Library 309
Barbers' Company see Worshipful Company of Barking and Dagenham Public Libraries see London Borough of
Barnet Public Libraries 393
Barnsley Metropolitan District Council 32
Bath City Record Office 35
Bath Reference Library 34
BBC Written Archives Centre 597
Bearsden and Milngavie District Libraries 39
Bedfordshire County Library 42
Bedfordshire Record Office 43
Belfast Education and Library Board 45
Belfast Library and Society for Promoting Knowledge 46
Berkshire County Libraries 598
Berkshire Record Office 599
Berwick upon Tweed Record Office 50
Bethlem Royal Hospital and the Maudsley Hospital 41
Bexley Libraries and Museums Department 52
Birkbeck College 311
Birmingham Polytechnic see City of Birmingham Polytechnic
Birmingham RC Diocesan Archives 55
Birmingham Reference Library 56
Blackburn Museum 60
Bodleian Library, Department of Western Manuscripts 565
Bolton Metropolitan Borough Archives 61
Borders Regional Library 630
Borthwick Institute of Historical Research 702
Boston Borough Council 63
BP Library of Motoring 40
Bradford Archives Department 65
Brechin Public Library and Museum 67
Brian O'Malley Central Library and Arts Centre 612
Brighton Polytechnic 69
Bristol Polytechnic 73
Bristol Record Office 74
Britannia Royal Naval College 139
British and Foreign Bible Society 312
British Antarctic Survey 84
British Architectural Library 313
British Institute of Recorded Sound 315
British Library, Department of Manuscripts 316
British Library, Department of Oriental Manuscripts 317
British Library, Library Association Library 318
British Library of Political and Economic Science 319
British Museum (Natural History) 320
British Steel Corporation, Cardiff 103

British Steel Corporation, Deeside 140
British Steel Corporation, Glasgow 205
British Steel Corporation, Middlesbrough 530
British Steel Corporation, Wellingborough 687
British Telecom Museum 321
Bromley Public Library, Archives Section 76
Brotherton Collection, University of Leeds 279
Brotherton Library, University of Leeds 280
Bruce Castle 400
Brunel University 678
Brynmor Jones Library, University of Hull 250
Buckinghamshire County Libraries 25
Buckinghamshire Record Office 26
Burnley District Library 78
Burton Library 79
Bury Central Library see Metropolitan Borough of Bury
Business Statistics Office Library 545

Calderdale Metropolitan Borough Archives Department 230
Cambridge County Record Office, Cambridge 85
Cambridge County Record Office, Huntingdon 252
Cambridge University Library 87
Cambridgeshire Collection 86
Camden see London Borough of
Canterbury Cathedral, Library and Diocesan Record Office 99
Cardiff Central Library see County of South Glamorgan Libraries
Carlisle Cathedral Library 112
Castle Howard 703
Central Regional Council Archives Department 651
Centre for English Cultural Tradition and Language 114
Centre for South African Studies, University of York 704
Centre of South Asian Studies 88
Charing Cross Hospital Medical School 322
Charity Commission for England and Wales 294, 323
Charterhouse 220
Chelsea College Library 324
Cheshire County Council, Libraries and Museums Department 118
Cheshire Record Office 119
Chester City Record Office 120
Chesterfield Central Library see Derbyshire Library Service
Chetham's Library 517
Christ's College Archives 89
Christ's Hospital 14
Church Commissioners 325
Church House Record Centre 326
Church Missionary Society 327
Churchill College Archives Centre 90
City and Hackney Health Authority 328
City of Birmingham Polytechnic Library 57
City of London Polytechnic 329
City of London School 330
City of Manchester Archives Department 518
City University 331
Clackmannan District Library 17
Cleveland County Archives Department 531
Clothworkers' Company 332
Clwyd Library Service 533
Clwyd Record Office, Hawarden 238
Clydebank District Libraries 124
Clydesdale District Libraries 275
College of Arms 333
College of Librarianship Wales 8
Commonwealth Institute Library and Research Centre 334
Congregational Library 335

Contemporary Medical Archives Centre 336
Cornwall County Library 675
Cornwall County Library, Redruth 604
Cornwall County Record Office 676
Corporation of London Record Office 337
Costume and Fashion Research Centre 36
Council for the Care of Churches 338
Country Life Archive 167
County of South Glamorgan Libraries, Cardiff 104
Courtauld Institute of Art 339
Coventry (Lanchester) Polytechnic Library 129
Coventry City Record Office 128
Cranfield Institute of Technology 44
Cromwell Museum 253
Croydon Public Libraries 131
Cumbernauld and Kilsyth District Council 132
Cumbria County Library, Carlisle 113
Cumbria County Record Office, Barrow-in-Furness 33
Cumbria County Record Office, Carlisle 114
Cumbria County Record Office, Kendal 265
Cumnock and Doon Valley District Library Headquarters 133
Cunninghame District Library Headquarters 21
Cusworth Hall Museum 145
Cynon Valley Borough Libraries 1

Darlington Library 137
Dartford Central Library see Kent County Library
David Owen Centre for Population Growth Studies 105
Department of Educational Studies Library, University of Oxford 580
Derby Central Library see Derbyshire Library Service
Derbyshire Library Service, Chesterfield 121
Derbyshire Library Service, Derby 141
Derbyshire Record Office 528
Devon Library Services, Exeter 192
Devon Library Services, Plymouth 587
Devon Record Office 193
Devonshire Collection 28
Dick Institute 266
Doncaster Archives Department 143
Doncaster Metropolitan Borough Council, Central Library 144
Dorchester Reference Library see Dorset County Libraries
Dorset County Libraries Local Studies Collection 146
Dorset Record Office 147
Douai Abbey 600
Dr William's Library 340
Duchy of Cornwall Office 341
Dudley Archives and Local History Department 150
Duke of Norfolk's Library and Archives 23
Dumbarton District Libraries 151
Dumfries and Galloway Regional Council Library Service 152
Dumfries Burgh Archives 153
Duncan of Jordanstone College of Art 155
Dundee College of Technology 156
Dundee District Archive and Record Centre 157
Dundee District Libraries 158
Dunfermline District Library 160
Durham City Reference Library 162
Durham County Record Office 163
Durham Dean and Chapter Library 161
Durham University, Department of Palaeography and Diplomatic 164
Dyfed Archives Service, Aberystwyth 9

County List of Repositories

Antrim
North-Eastern Education and Library Board 29
Ulster Polytechnic Library 548

Armagh
Armagh County Museum 22

Avon
Avon County Library, Bath 34
Avon County Reference Library, Bristol 72
Bath City Record Office 35
Bath Reference Library 34
Bristol Polytechnic 73
Bristol Record Office 74
Costume and Fashion Research Centre 36
University of Bath Library 37
University of Bristol Library 75

Bedfordshire
Bedfordshire County Library 42
Bedfordshire Record Office 43
Cranfield Institute of Technology 44

Belfast
Belfast Education and Library Board 45
Belfast Library and Society for Promoting
    Knowledge 46
General Register Office, Northern Ireland 47
Linen Hall Library 46
New University of Ulster Library 127
Public Record Office of Northern Ireland 48
Ulster Museum 49

Berkshire
BBC Written Archives Centre 597
Berkshire County Libraries 598
Berkshire Record Office 599
Douai Abbey 600
Eton College Records 693
Institute of Agricultural History and Museum
    of English Rural Life 601
National Meteorological Archive 64
St George's Chapel, Windsor 694
University of Reading, Department of Archives
    and Manuscripts 602
Windsor Muniment Rooms 695

Borders
Borders Regional Library 630

Buckinghamshire
Buckinghamshire County Libraries 25
Buckinghamshire Record Office 26
University College at Buckingham 77

Cambridgeshire
British Antarctic Survey 84
Cambridge County Record Office, Cambridge
    85
Cambridge County Record Office, Huntingdon
    252
Cambridge University Library 87
Cambridgeshire Collection 86
Centre of South Asian Studies 88
Christ's College Archives 89
Churchill College Archives Centre 90
Cromwell Museum 253
East Asian History of Science Library 91
Fitzwilliam Museum 92
Gonville and Caius College 93
Institute of Astronomy Library, University of
    Cambridge 94
Institute of Education, University of
    Cambridge 95
Norris Library and Museum 621
Peterborough Cathedral 585
Peterborough Museum and Art Gallery 586
St John's College 96
Scott Polar Research Institute 97
Seeley Historical Library 98

Central
Central Regional Council Archives
    Department 651
Clackmannan District Library 17
Falkirk District Council 196
University of Stirling Library 652

Channel Islands
Judicial Greffe 619
Société Guernesiaise 623
Société Jersiaise 620
The Greffe 622

Cheshire
Cheshire County Council, Libraries and
    Museums Department 118
Cheshire Record Office 119
Chester City Record Office 120
Metropolitan Borough of Stockport Archives
    Service 653
Warrington Library 684

Cleveland
British Steel Corporation, Middlesbrough 530
Cleveland County Archives Department 531

Clwyd
British Steel Corporation, Deeside 140
Clwyd Library Service 533
Clwyd Record Office, Hawarden 238
St Deiniol's Library 239

Cornwall
Cornwall County Library 675
Cornwall County Library, Redruth 604
Cornwall County Record Office 676
Royal Institution of Cornwall 677

Cumbria
Carlisle Cathedral Library 112
Cumbria County Library, Carlisle 113
Cumbria County Record Office, Barrow-in-
    Furness 33
Cumbria County Record Office, Carlisle 114
Cumbria County Record Office, Kendal 265

Derbyshire
Derbyshire Library Service, Chesterfield 121
Derbyshire Library Service, Derby 141
Derbyshire Record Office 528
Devonshire Collection 28

Devon
Britannia Royal Naval College 139
Devon Library Services, Exeter 192
Devon Library Services, Plymouth 587
Devon Record Office 193
Exeter Cathedral Library and Archives 194
Exeter University Library 195
Plymouth Polytechnic 588
West Devon Record Office 589

Dorset
Dorset County Libraries Local Studies
    Collection 146
Dorset Record Office 147
Poole Borough Council 591
Tank Museum 683

Down
Ulster Folk and Transport Museum 245

Dumfries and Galloway
Dumfries and Galloway Regional Council
    Library Service 152
Dumfries Burgh Archives 153

Durham
Darlington Library 137
Durham City Reference Library 162
Durham County Record Office 163
Durham Dean and Charter Library 161
Durham University, Department of
    Palaeography and Diplomatic 164

Sudan Archive, University of Durham 166
University Library, Durham 165

Dyfed
College of Librarianship, Wales 8
Dyfed Archives Service, Aberystwyth Office 9
Dyfed Archives Service, Carmarthen 115
Dyfed Archives Service, Haverfordwest 237
Dyfed County Library Headquarters 116
Llanelli Public Library 302
National Library of Wales 10
National Monuments Record, Wales 11
Saint David's University College 274
University College of Wales Library 12

East Sussex
Brighton Polytechnic 69
East Sussex County Library, Hove Area 247
East Sussex Record Office 290
Hastings Museum and Art Gallery 234
Royal Greenwich Observatory 229
Tom Harrisson Mass-Observation Archive 70
University of Sussex Library 71
Wolseley Collection 247

Essex
Essex County Libraries 125
Essex Record Office 117
Essex Record Office, Southend Branch 642
Saffron Walden Town Council 614
University of Essex 126

Fife
Dunfermline District Library 160
Hay Fleming Reference Library 615
Kirkcaldy District Libraries 271
Kirkcaldy Museum and Art Gallery 272
North East Fife District Library 134
St Andrews University Library, Manuscript
    Department 616
St Andrews University Muniments 617

Gloucester
Gloucester Cathedral Library 217
Gloucestershire Collection 218
Gloucestershire Record Office 219

Grampian
Aberdeen City District Libraries 2
Aberdeen University Library 3
Gordonstoun 191
Grampian Regional Archives 4
Moray District Council, Record Office 200
MRC Medical Sociology Unit 5
North East of Scotland Library Service 6
Robert Gordon's Institute of Technology
    Library 7

Greater London
Archives of the English Province of the Society
    of Jesus 306
Bank of England 307
Baptist Missionary Society 308
Baptist Union Library 309
Barnet Public Libraries 393
Birkbeck College 311
British and Foreign Bible Society 312
British Architectural Library 313
British Institute of Recorded Sound 315
British Library, Department of Manuscripts
    316
British Library, Department of Oriental
    Manuscripts 317
British Library, Library Association Library 318
British Library of Political and Economic
    Science 319
British Museum (Natural History) 320
British Telecom Museum 321
Bruce Castle 400
Brunel University 678

(xxi)

1   Cynon Valley Borough Libraries

Address   Central Library
Greefach
Aberdare
Mid-Glamorgan CF44 7AG

Telephone   (0685) 872441 ext. 47

Enquiries to   The Borough Librarian

Open   Mon–Thurs: 9.00–6.00
Fri: 9.00–8.00
Sat: 9.00–12.00

Access   Generally open to the public.

Historical background   The Public Library Act was adopted in 1904.

Acquisitions policy   To collect any available material appertaining to the history of
the Cynon Valley.

Major collections   Local History Collection of MSS.

Non-manuscript material   Rev. Ivor Parry Collection: a local historian's collection,
mainly notes and articles from local newspapers, c1950–70.
W.W. Price Collection.
Extensive photograph collection including c5000 relating to Cynon Valley.

Finding aids   Pamphlets and MSS are listed in a separate schedule.

Facilities   Microfilm reader.

2   Aberdeen City District Libraries

Address   Central Library
Rosemount Viaduct
Aberdeen

Telephone   (0224) 634622

Enquiries to   City Librarian, Mr Peter Grant

Open   Mon–Fri: 9.00–9.00
Sat: 9.00–5.00

Access   Generally open, except where depositors have stipulated
otherwise.

Historical background   The Public Library Acts were adopted for Aberdeen in
1884, and the Library Service began in 1886 in the Mechanics' Institute building,
Market Street. The present Central Library was opened in 1892, with extensions

in 1905 and 1981–2. The Library includes a well-stocked reference library and Local Studies Department.

Acquisitions policy   Items relating to Aberdeen and the surrounding area are considered for acquisition by donation or purchase. Archive deposits by local societies are welcomed.

Major collections   Aberdeen Airport, aircraft movement log-books from 1972.
Aberdeen Mechanics' Institute, reports, rules and regulations, library catalogues, handbills.
Papers relating to the Bruce Family of Heatherwick Farm, Inverurie.
Journals and letter-books of George Sim (1835–1908), naturalist.

Non-manuscript material   Aberdeen city plans, 1661–.
George Washington Wilson Photographic Collection (11 vols).
Photographs of places, people and events in Aberdeen and its local newspapers, 1759–.

Finding aids   Typescript lists only. Cataloguing to be undertaken in the near future.

Facilities   Photocopying. Microfilm/fiche readers. Study areas.

3   Aberdeen University Library
Manuscript and Archives Section

Address   University of Aberdeen
                 King's College Library
                 Aberdeen AB9 2UB

Telephone   (0224) 40241 ext. Old Aberdeen 5112

Enquiries to   Archivist, Mr C.A. McLaren

Open   Mon–Fri: 9.15–4.30
                 The Section opens by pre-arrangement with readers on Tuesday evenings during term

Access   Approved readers. Written application preferred.

Historical background   For over 200 years there were two separate universities in Aberdeen, each with its own statutory rights and degree-granting privileges. The first, King's College, was founded in Old Aberdeen in 1495. The second, Marischal College, was founded in New Aberdeen by George Keith, fifth Earl Marischal of Scotland, in 1593. The two colleges remained rival institutions until 1860, when a royal ordinance united them under the title of the University of Aberdeen.
The Manuscripts and Archives Section of the University Library was established in its present form in November 1969.

Acquisitions policy   The principal function of the Section is the systematic accumulation and preservation of the University's archives. Non-archival material relating to the University is acquired as often as possible. Until 1976 the University acted as a repository for local historical material in the absence of a local authority record office in the region, under the terms of the agreement reached between the Scottish universities and the National Register of Archives (Scotland). Since 1976 it has shared this activity with the Regional and District Record Offices.

Major collections   Archives of the Universities of Aberdeen.
Individual MSS and archival collections bought by the Library, given to it, or deposited in it on loan.
Collections of papyri, ostraca and non-European MSS.
There are in all *c*4000 separate items and collections.

Non-manuscript material   Collections of photographic prints and drawings are administered by the Department of Special Collections. The Section holds a quantity of pamphlets and printed ephemeral literature as part of the deposited papers of local branches of trade unions and of political organizations.

Finding aids   All collections are catalogued briefly by title. Standardized descriptive or summary lists, 1969–, are circulated via the National Register of Archives (Scotland).

Facilities   Photocopying. Photography. Microfilm/fiche reader/printers.

Publications   *Guide to Sources of Information: Manuscripts and Archives* (Aberdeen, 1979–).
M.R. James: *A Catalogue of the Medieval Manuscripts in the University Library Aberdeen* (Cambridge, 1932)
E.G. Turner: *Catalogue of Greek and Latin Papyri and Ostraca in the Possession of the University Library, Aberdeen*, Aberdeen University Studies, no.116 (Aberdeen, 1939)
L. Macfarlane: 'William Elphinstone's Library', *Aberdeen University Review*, xxxvii (1957–8), 253
C. Roth: *The Aberdeen Codex of the Hebrew Bible*, Aberdeen University Studies, no.138 (Edinburgh, 1958)
N.R. Ker: *Medieval Manuscripts in British Libraries*, ii (Oxford, 1977) 2
Other descriptions can be found in *Aberdeen University Library Bulletin*, *Aberdeen University Review*, and *Northern Scotland*, *passim*, and in Scottish Records Association *Datasheet* no.6

4   Grampian Regional Archives

Address   Woodhill House,
                Ashgrove Road,
                West Aberdeen AB9 2LU

Telephone   (0224) 682222, ext. 2130

Enquiries to   Regional Archivist, Mrs Brenda Cluer

Open   Mon–Fri: 9.00–5.00, by appointment

Historical background   The Archive was established following local government reorganization in 1976.

Virtually all records are local government archives and of purely local interest.

Major collections   Regional records and records of three districts: Banff/Buchan, Kincardine/Deeside, Gordon.

Facilities   Photocopying. Photography.

5   MRC Medical Sociology Unit

Address   Institute of Medical Sociology
                    Westburn Road
                    Aberdeen AB9 2ZE

Telephone   (0224) 681818 ext. 2420

Enquiries to   Director of Unit, Prof. Raymond Illsley

Open   By appointment

Access   Bona fide research workers on written application, sponsored by academic supervisor or director.

Historical background   The Medical Research Council's Medical Sociology Unit was offered these archives in 1971, subject to certain conditions, when the Abortion Law Reform Association (ALRA) was disbanded. In 1982 the archives were transferred to the Contemporary Medical Archives Centre (*see* entry **336**).

Major collections   The entire archives of the Abortion Law Reform Association, comprising campaign material, parliamentary papers, press cuttings and correspondence dating back to the mid-1930s.
Evidence to numerous committees up to the passing of the Abortion Act 1967 and subsequently to the Lane Committee on the Working of the Abortion Act.
Further material on the campaigns associated with the Abortion (Amendment) Bills up to 1980.

Finding aids   All material has been sorted into broad categories and is catalogued up to 1971.

6   North East of Scotland Library Service

Address   14 Crown Terrace
                    Aberdeen

Telephone	(0224) 572658
Enquiries to	Local History Librarian, Mr E. Russell
Open	Mon–Fri: 9.00–5.00
Access	Generally open to the public.

Historical background The service was formed in May 1975 on local government reorganization to serve Banff and Buchan, Gordon, and Kincardine and Deeside Districts.

Acquisitions policy To strengthen existing primary and secondary collections of material on the local area by purchase and donation.

Major collections Strichen Collection: Strichen estate records and plans; records of local societies and Auchmedden estate papers and a small collection of late 19th-century and early 20th-century photographs.
George Macdonald Collection: MSS, letters, books and photographs relating to Macdonald. Held at Huntly Library.

Non-manuscript material The local history collection includes maps and photographs of the area.
Council minutes, valuation rolls and voters' rolls for the area.
Community council newsletters and minutes of meetings, since 1975.

Finding aids The Collection is catalogued and classified. Maps index. Index to magazine articles, proceedings of local societies. Index to major reference sources.

Facilities Photocopying. Microfiche reader.

7   Robert Gordon's Institute of Technology Library

Address   St Andrew Street
Aberdeen AB1 1HG

No archives are held.

8   College of Librarianship Wales

Address   The Library
Llanbadarn Fawr
Aberystwyth
Dyfed SY23 3AS

Telephone   (0970) 3181

Enquiries to   The Librarian

Open   Term: Mon–Fri: 9.00–10.00
                  Sat: 10.00–4.30
                  Vacation: Mon–Thurs: 9.00–5.30
                  Fri: 9.00–5.00

Access   Bona fide researchers. Written application preferred.

Historical background   The College was founded in 1964.

Acquisitions policy To seek material at all levels on library and information science. The Library also acquires material in the related fields of printing, management, education, communication etc.

Major collections   The Library has one of the most comprehensive collections on library and information science in the world, principally non-MS material.
Ranganathan/Palmer correspondence, 1949–72.
College archives not yet organized or available for research.

Non-manuscript material   c250 16mm films, 1922–.
c500 sound recordings (some on video), including interviews with distinguished librarians, visiting lecturers.
c2500 slides/photographs of library buildings.
c650 architect drawings/plans of libraries.
Collection of materials produced by libraries, including annual reports.
Posters produced by libraries.

Finding aids   Special bibliography of films and video-recordings.

Facilities   Photocopying. Microform readers. 16mm film viewing table. Video cassette recorders.

Publications   Library Guide
Library Link (Bulletin and Acquisitions List)

9   Dyfed Archives Service
Aberystwyth Office

Address   Swyddfa'r Sir
                  Marine Terrace
                  Aberystwyth
                  Dyfed SY23 2DE

Telephone   (0970) 617581 ext. 2120

Enquiries to   The Records Assistant

Open   Tues and Thur: 9.00–4.45

Historical background   The Office was established in 1974. Previously records for the area had been collected by the National Library of Wales (*see* entry **10**). The Office also acts as the Diocesan Record Office for St Davids (parish registers).

Major collections Usual local authority record holdings and deposited collections.

Facilities Photocopying. Photography. Microfilming. Microfilm readers.

10 National Library of Wales
Department of Manuscripts and Records

Address	Aberystwyth Dyfed SY23 3BU
Telephone	(0970) 3816
Enquiries to	The Keeper of Manuscripts
Open	Mon–Fri: 9.30–6.00 Sat: 9.30–5.00
Access	By reader's ticket.

Historical background The Library was established by royal charter in 1907 and is a copyright library.

Acquisitions policy Manuscript and archival material relating to Wales.

Major collections General series of the National Library of Wales MSS (*see* 'Publications').
Records of Great Sessions in Wales, 1542–1830.
Official records for the county of Powys.
Diocesan and capitular archives of the Church in Wales; many of the parish records.
Archives of the Welsh Calvinistic Methodist Church; substantial holdings for other non-conformist denominations.
Many large archives of Welsh estates, families, institutions, politicians, writers.

Non-manuscript There are two other departments: that of Printed books and that of Prints, Drawings and Maps (including MS maps).

Finding aids Some 600 vols of calendars, schedules and lists, mostly typescript, a few printed, kept in the Reading Room, with associated card indexes. (*See also* 'Publications'.)

Facilities Photographic department. Microfilm readers.

Publications *Annual Report* [includes detailed list of accessions]
National Library of Wales Journal (1939–) [articles on the Library's holdings]
Handlist of Manuscripts in the National Library of Wales (1943–) [describes MSS acquired up to 1940 in the general series of National Library of Wales MSS]
A Brief Guide to the Department of Manuscripts and Records (in preparation)

11 The Royal Commission on Ancient and Historical Monuments in Wales
National Monuments Record

Address	Edleston House Queen's Road Aberystwyth Dyfed SY23 2HP
Telephone	(0970) 4381/2
Enquiries to	Secretary, Mr Peter Smith
Open	Mon–Fri: 9.30–12.30; 2.00–5.00
Access	Generally open to the public.

Historical background   The Commission was founded in 1908 by royal warrant to compile inventories of all man-made structures within Wales from earliest times up to 1750. It now includes later and industrial structures and, if necessary, areas outside Wales.

Acquisitions policy   Vast majority of material acquired by staff field-work; donations accepted.

Major collections   Field-work archive, 1908–.
Some deposited collections; including that of Herbert L. North (1871–1941), concerning arts and crafts movements in North Wales.

Non-manuscript collections   Extensive photographic material, including photographs of the Welsh Section of the former National Building Record (originally a charitable trust), c1940–65.
Many thousands of plans, including modern architects' dyeline copies of listed buildings (poorly catalogued).
Incomplete collection of Ordnance Survey maps (25" = 1 mile).

Facilities   Photocopying. Photography.

Finding aids   Almost comprehensive internal index system.

Publications   Inventories for most old counties of Wales (1908–) [HMSO has list of those currently available].

12 University College of Wales Library

Address	Huw Owen Building Penglais Aberystwyth Dyfed SY23 3DZ

Telephone   (0970) 3111

Enquiries to   Librarian, Mr W.W. Dieneman

A few archives are held. The Registrar's Office holds some internal records.

13   Abingdon Town Council

Address   Stratton Lodge
                 52 Bath Street
                 Abingdon
                 Oxfordshire OX14 3QH

Telephone   (0235) 22642

Enquiries to   The Town Clerk

Open   By prior arrangement

Major collections   Borough minutes, 1556–1974; charters, leases, burial records and other miscellaneous documents concerning the history of the borough, 16th–20th centuries.
Chamberlain's accounts, 16th–17th centuries.
Obientiar's accounts of Abingdon Abbey.
Most records are at the Berkshire Record Office (*see* entry **599**).

14   Christ's Hospital

Address   33 Bath Street
                 Abingdon
                 Oxfordshire

Enquiries to   The Clerk to the Governors of Christ's Hospital

Open   By prior arrangement

Major Collections   Records of the Fraternity of the Holy Cross and the Guild of Our Lady, 1165–1547.
Records of Christ's Hospital, 1533–1918.
Records (minutes and accounts) of other charities, deriving from 17th-century benefactors, administered by the Governors.

15   Monklands District Local Collection

Address   Monklands District Council
                   Airdrie Library
                   Wellwynd
                   Airdrie
                   Strathclyde ML6 0AG

Telephone   (02364) 63221

Enquiries to   Local History Librarian, Mr C.E. Smith

Open   Mon, Tues, Thurs, Fri: 9.30–7.30
                   Sat: 9.30–12.30; 1.30–5.00

Access   Generally open to the public.

Historical background   Airdrie Library was established in 1853 and local history material has been collected spasmodically since that date. In 1980 the Local Collection was set up to house the collections from Airdrie and Coatbridge.

Acquisitions policy   To provide a comprehensive collection of local material from Airdrie, Coatbridge and the surrounding district.

Major collections   Airdrie Weavers Friendly Society minutes. Gartsherrie Estate minute books.

Non-manuscript material   Books, pamphlets, photographs, maps.

Finding aids   Subject index in preparation.

Facilities   Photocopying. Photography. Microfilm/fiche reader.

Publications   Monklands 1980 [produced by Monklands District Libraries]

16   Army Museums Ogilby Trust (AMOT)

Address   Connaught Barracks
                   Duke of Connaught Road
                   Aldershot
                   Hampshire GU11 2LR

Telephone   (0252) 24431 ext. 2102

Enquiries to   The Secretary

Open   Mon–Fri: 10.00–4.00

Access   On written application

Historical Background   AMOT is a charitable educational private trust, set up by the late Colonel R.J.L. Ogilby in 1954 to support and encourage British Army regimental museums.

Acquisitions policy   Acquires papers and books allied to its interests, principally military costume.

Major collections   1000 box files of papers arranged regimentally, dealing mainly with dress of British and Commonwealth forces.
Some biographical material, of which most significant is the collection of the military historian and journalist Henry Spenser Wilkinson (1853–1937) and includes correspondence with Lord Roberts etc (13 boxes).

Non-manuscript material   The Library holds regimental material etc, histories, journals, army lists (British, Indian and Commonwealth).
Some photographs.

Finding aids   Card index on various matters.

Facilities   Photocopying.

Publications   *Index to British Military Costume Prints 1500–1914* (1972)
Military Drawings in the Royal Collection [with Phaidon Press]
The Evolution of the Victoria Cross (1975) [with Midas Books]
The Uniforms of the British Yeomanry Force 1794–1914 [a continuing series of booklets; 3 pubd to date]

17   Clackmannan District Library

Address   17 Mar Street
Alloa
Central FK10 1HT

Archives are neither held nor acquired.

18   Andover Borough Archives

Address   Hampshire County Library
Chantry Way
Andover
Hampshire SP10 1LT

Telephone   (0264) 52807

Enquiries to   The Senior Librarian

Open   Mon, Tues, Thurs, Fri: 10.00–7.00
Sat: 10.00–4.00

Access   Intending readers must apply for permission to The Borough Secretary and Solicitor, Test Valley Borough Council, Beech Hurst, Weyhill Road, Andover, Hampshire SP10 3AJ

Historical Background   Documents accumulated during the life of Andover Borough Council.

Acquisitions Policy   In general no further acquisitions are made.

Major Collections   Royal charters; court records; Town Council minutes and other records; legal records; charity and other local bodies' records.

Finding aids   Catalogue of Andover Borough Archives.

Facilities   Photocopying.

Publications   Various pamphlets and other publications of the Andover Local History Society, formerly the Andover Local Archives Committee.

19   Arbroath Library and Art Gallery

Address   Hill Terrace
                 Arbroath
                 Angus

Telephone   (0241) 72248

Enquiries to   Librarian, Mr Alistair Sutherland

Open   Mon–Sat: 9.30–6.00

Access   Generally open to the public, on written application.

Historical background   The Library was opened 1896 and in 1975 became part of Angus District Libraries and Museums. The local collection was created by a former librarian.

Acquisitions policy   To collect any local material.

Major collections   Miscellaneous Arbroath Town Council records, 1741–1891.
Arbroath Incorporated Trades: Glovers, Hammermen, Shoemakers and Guildry records, 18th–20th centuries.
Local labour movements records, 1886–1971.
Friendly and charitable societies records, 18th–19th centuries.
Arts, scientific, musical and sporting associations records, 20th century.
Miscellaneous private papers, 18th–20th centuries.

Non-manuscript material   Local maps and plans, 18th–20th centuries.
Published local monographs etc, rules and proceedings of local societies, local periodicals, 19th–20th centuries.

Finding aids   Archive list.

Facilities   Photocopying by arrangement.

20   Arbroath Signal Tower Museum

Address   Ladyloan
                   Arbroath
                   Angus DD11 1PU

Telephone   (0241) 75598

Enquiries to   Curator, Ms Gillian Zealand

Open   Mon–Sat: 9.30–1.00; 2.00–5.00

Access   Generally open to the public on written application.

Historical background   The Museum was opened in 1974 by Arbroath Town
   Council; since 1975 it has been part of Angus District Libraries and Museums.

Acquisitions policy   Any local material.

Major collections   Arbroath Burgess records, 1790–1849.
   Arbroath Museum Society, 1843–1918.
   Miscellaneous local private records, 18th–20th centuries.
   Alex Shanks Dens Ironworks: engineers' catalogues of boilers, steam engines and
   lawnmowers and papers 1859–c1900.

Finding aids   Archive list.

21   Cunninghame District Library Headquarters
Local Collection

Address   39/41 Princes Street
                   Ardrossan
                   Strathclyde KA22 8BT

Telephone   (0294) 69137/39

Enquiries to   Chief Librarian, Miss J.G. MacMillan

Open   Mon–Fri: 9.00–5.00

Access   Generally open to the public.

Historical background   The collection was developed after local government
   reorganization in 1975. The Alexander Wood Memorial Library was donated to the

new council by the old Burgh of Ardrossan and now forms an integral part of the Library's local material.

Acquisitions policy   To acquire all possible material relating to the history of the area.

Major collections   Principally non-MS material (*see* below).
Alexander Wood Memorial Library: collection of material with local connections through publisher, topic, author; includes MSS, maps and pamphlets.

Non-manuscript material   Small collection of maps and photographs.
Newspaper *Ardrossan and Saltcoats Herald*, 1857–1966 (one third is on microfilm).

Finding aids   Subject index.

Facilities   Photocopying. Microfilm reader/printer.

Publications   Local collection catalogue under consideration.

22   Armagh County Museum

Address	The Mall East
	Armagh
	Co. Armagh BT61 9BE
Telephone	(0861) 523070
Enquiries to	Curator, Mr D.R.M. Weatherup
Open	Mon–Sat: 9.00–1.00; 2.00–5.00
Access	Bona fide students.

Historical background   Around 1839 the Armagh Natural and Philosophical Society started a museum which moved to the present address in 1857. Armagh County Council took over the building and collections in 1931 and opened Armagh County Museum in 1935. The Museum was rebuilt and enlarged in 1962 and transferred to the Ulster Museum trustees as a regional branch on local government reorganization in 1973.

Acquisitions policy   To increase the collections selectively, so as to illustrate the history of Co. Armagh and build up a supporting library and archive for student reference.

Major collections   T.G.F. Paterson collection of MSS and typed scripts on local history etc.
Correspondence of George Russell, 'AE' (1867–1935).
Sundry items of MSS, typed scripts and annotated published pamphlets etc, of local historical interest.

Non-manuscript material   Books and pamphlets forming a reference collection to assist the study of Museum collections in the fields of history, local history, pre-history, social history, art, genealogy etc.

Finding aids   Card index.

Facilities   Photocopying and photography can be arranged subject to management discretion.

Publications   D.R.M. Weatherup: 'The published writings of T.G.F. Paterson', *Seanchas Ardmacha*, vi/2 (1972)
————: 'Armagh County Museum – The Reference Library', *Irish Booklore*, ii/1 (1972)

23   Duke of Norfolk's Library and Archives

Address   Arundel Castle
                  Arundel
                  West Sussex BN18 9AB

Telephone   (0903) 882173

Enquiries to   Librarian, Dr J.M. Robinson

Open   By written appointment
                  Tues, Wed and some Sats

Access   To all accredited scholars. A daily research fee is charged. Personal
                  papers less than 100 years old are not normally available.

Historical background   The Duke of Norfolk's archives form one of the largest and most complete family collections in England and cover a period from the 13th century to the present day. They reflect the roles played by generations of the Fitzalan-Howard family in political, religious and other affairs in England. There is a large series dealing with the office of Earl Marshal and an enormous quantity of records concerning the family estates in various counties. The archives have a unique importance for the study of English Catholic history.

Non-manuscript material   Recusant collection: a large series of 17th-century printed pamphlets.

Facilities   Limited photocopying.

Publications   F.W. Steer (ed.): *Arundel Castle Archives* (Chichester, 1968–80) [4 vols]

24   Wye College

Address   University of London
                   Wye
                   Ashford
                   Kent TN25 5AH

No collections of archival material of note are held.

25   Buckinghamshire County Libraries

Address   Walton Street
                   Aylesbury
                   Buckinghamshire HP20 1UU

Archives are neither held nor acquired.

26   Buckinghamshire Record Office

Address   County Hall
                   Aylesbury
                   Buckinghamshire HP20 1UA

Telephone   (0296) 5000 ext. 588

Enquiries to   County Archivist, Mr Hugh Hanley

Open   Mon–Fri: 9.00–5.00

Historical background   The office was established in 1938 with the appointment of its first archivist. It also acts as the Diocesan Record Office for Oxford (archdeaconry of Buckingham).

Major collections   Usual local authority record holdings and deposited collections of which the following contain correspondence of wider significance: Fremantle; Bulstrode Park (Seymour, Ramsden); Earl of Buckinghamshire (Hobart, Trevor); Spencer Bernard; Howard Vyse; Roscoe; E. Gomme Ltd, Furniture Manufacturers (G-Plan).

Facilities   Photocopying. Photography and microfilming by arrangement. Microfilm reader.

Publications   *Education Records* (1961) [typescript]
     Records of the Archdeaconry of Buckingham (1961) [typescript]

27   Kyle and Carrick District Libraries and Museums

Address   Carnegie Library (Reference Library)
                 12 Main Street
                 Ayr
                 Strathclyde KA8 8ED

Telephone   (0292) 81511 ext. 229

Enquiries to   The Director of Libraries and Museums

Open   Mon–Fri: 9.00–7.30

Access   Generally open to the public.

Historical background   The collection originally covered the whole of Ayrshire, but since local government reorganization in 1974 has been restricted to Kyle and Carrick.

Acquisitions policy   To obtain, when possible, further material on Kyle and Carrick and Robert Burns.

Major collections   Kyle and Carrick Collection: minute books of various local societies, committees, etc.
Robert Burns (1759–96) Collection: the only original MS is the Visitors' Book for Burns's Cottage.
Other MS items are still being processed.

Non-manuscript material   Robert Burns (1759–96) Collection: c1200 books by and about Burns.
Kyle and Carrick Collection: photographs, slides, cassette recordings; newspapers, 1803–, some on microfilm/fiche.

Finding aids   Catalogue to Burns Collection. Newspaper index being completed. Local collection being catalogued.

Facilities   Photocopying. Microfilm reader/printer.

28   Devonshire Collection

Address   Chatsworth
                 Bakewell
                 Derbyshire DE4 1PP

Telephone   (024 688) 2204

Enquiries to   Keeper of Collections, Mr P.J. Day
                 Librarian and Archivist, Mr M.A. Pearman

Open   By written appointment

Access   Accredited postgraduate students or scholars only.
              Reading fees and search fees payable.

Historical background   There are now concentrated at Chatsworth the collections of art, books, estate archives and political and personal correspondence of the Cavendish family, Earls of Devonshire from 1618 to 1694, and Dukes of Devonshire from 1694 onwards. The family fortune and estates were founded by Sir William Cavendish and his wife Bess of Hardwick in the mid-16th century, who built the first Chatsworth. The house was rebuilt by the first Duke of Devonshire (1640–1707), a strong supporter of William of Orange, and the collections of art founded by his son the second Duke, a celebrated connoisseur. The third and fourth Dukes served as Lords Lieutenant of Ireland, and the fourth Duke briefly as Prime Minister of England. The sixth Duke greatly extended the house and collections at Chatsworth, and the eighth Duke, as the Marquis of Hartington, was a prominent Liberal politician.

Acquisitions policy   To acquire works of art, books or archives that help to document the history of the family, their houses and collections.

Major collections   MSS of the philosopher Thomas Hobbes, tutor to the Earls of Devonshire.
MSS of the scientist Henry Cavendish.
Political correspondence of the third, fourth and eighth Dukes of Devonshire.
Correspondence of Sir Joseph Paxton, gardener to the sixth Duke of Devonshire.
Building and household accounts for Chatsworth, Hardwick, Chiswick and Devonshire Houses.
Estate archives for present and former family estates in England and Ireland.

Non-manuscript material   c2000 Old Master drawings and prints, 15th–17th centuries.
c400 designs for court masques by Inigo Jones.
c50,000 rare printed books, 15th–19th centuries.
c1000 paintings.

Finding aids   Calendars of MSS and correspondence copied by Royal Commission on Historical MSS. Paintings, sculpture and drawings listed by Photographic Survey of the Courtauld Institute of Art.

Facilities   Photocopying. Photography.

Publications   International Exhibition Foundation: *Treasures from Chatsworth: The Devonshire Inheritance* (Washington, DC, 1978–9)

29   North-Eastern Education and Library Board

Address　　　　Area Library
　　　　　　　　Demesne Avenue
　　　　　　　　Ballymena
　　　　　　　　Co. Antrim BT43 7BG

No archives are held.

30   Normal College

Address　　　　Bangor
　　　　　　　　Gwynedd

Telephone　　　(0248) 53316

There are no deposited collections. Internal records are held.

31   University College of North Wales
Department of Manuscripts

Address　　　　The Library
　　　　　　　　University College of North Wales
　　　　　　　　Bangor
　　　　　　　　Gwynedd LL57 2DG

Telephone　　　(0248) 51151 ext.316

Enquiries to　　Archivist and Keeper of Manuscripts, Mr A. Giles Jones
　　　　　　　　or
　　　　　　　　Deputy Archivist and Keeper of Manuscripts, Mr T. Roberts

Open　　　　　Term: Mon, Tues, Thurs, Fri: 9.15–4.45
　　　　　　　　Wed: 9.15–8.50
　　　　　　　　Vacation: Mon–Fri: 9.15–4.45

Access　　　　Generally open to the public. Prior arrangement preferred.

Historical background　　The Library of University College of North Wales has been an approved repository since 1927, and was therefore the first Record Office in North Wales (the Caernarvonshire Record Office opened in 1947, and the Flintshire Record Office in 1952).

Acquisitions policy　　Deposits and donations are not solicited, but are gratefully accepted. Papers relating to all aspects of life in North Wales, past and present, are particularly welcome.

Major collections　　Holdings run to some 500,000 items, and include family and

estate papers; mine and quarry papers; Quarter Sessions records (Borough of Beaumaris, acquired by purchase during World War II; literary MSS in Welsh and English; personal papers; deposits by solicitors, etc.
Bangor (General) MSS; Baron Hill MSS; Beaumaris and Anglesey MSS; Bodorgan MSS; Bodrhyddan MSS; Carter Vincent MSS; Kinmel MSS; Lligwy MSS; Maesyneuadd MSS; Maenan MSS; Mostyn MSS; Nannau MSS; Penrhyn Castle MSS; Plas Coch MSS; Plas Newydd MSS; Porth yr Aur MSS.

Non-manuscript material Printed ephemera, all topics.
O.S. maps, 2½ and 6 inch: Wales and borders.

Finding aids Catalogues and indexes. (Bangor MSS catalogue is continually in progress.) Provisional Guide to Special Collections, 1962 (typescript).

Facilities Photocopying. Photography. Microfilm/fiche reader.

32 Barnsley Metropolitan District Council

Address Central Library
Local Studies Department
Shambles Street
Barnsley
South Yorkshire S70 2JF

Telephone (0226) 83241

Enquiries to The Local History Librarian

Open Mon, Wed: 9.30–8.00
Tues, Thurs, Fri: 9.30–6.00
Sat: 9.30–5.00
Advance notice preferred

Access Generally open to the public.

Historical background The Library holds archives relevant to the Barnsley Metropolitan District and tended to keep archival material in the absence of a county record office before reorganization. Most estate and business records were placed in Sheffield Central Library (*see* entry **633**).

Aquisitions policy Archival material is purchased. Donations and deposits of relevant material covering the Barnsley Metropolitan District are accepted.

Major collections Borough minutes with rate books and papers from the early 19th century.
Records of Barnsley British Co-operative Society and West Riding Miners' Permanent Relief Fund Friendly Society.
Local Methodist records.

Non-manuscript material Collection of illustrations including:

*c*1000 photographs from Barnsley Borough Engineers, 1950s–60s, and the Biltclisse collection of postcards (*c*200).
Books relating to Barnsley Metropolitan District and by local authors.

Finding aids Lists of some collections. Other collections are still being listed.

Facilities Photocopying. Microfilm reader.

33   Cumbria County Record Office
Barrow-in-Furness Office

Address   Duke Street
                 Barrow-in-Furness
                 Cumbria LA14 1XW

Telephone   (0229) 31269

Enquiries to   The Archivist-in-charge

Open   Mon–Fri: 2–5
                 Other times by appointment

Historical background The present office was opened in 1979, but archives had been acquired from 1975. It also acts as the Diocesan Record Office for Carlisle (archdeaconry of Furness).

Major collections Usual local authority record holdings and deposited collections including the following which have a wider significance:
Duke of Buccleuch's Furness estate records reflecting the iron-ore trade, 1854–1963.
Gun-mounting drawings, 1890–1950.

Facilities Photocopying. Photography and microfilming by arrangement. Microfilm reader.

34   Avon County Library
Bath Reference Library

Address   18 Queen Square
                 Bath
                 Avon

Telephone   (0225) 28144

Enquiries to   Librarian-in-charge, Mrs M. Joyce

Local History Collection of non-MSS material.

35   City Record Office

Address	Guildhall Bath Avon BA1 5AW
Telephone	(0225) 61111 ext. 201
Enquiries to	City Archivist, Mr Robert Bryant
Open	Mon–Thurs: 8.30–1.00; 2.00–5.00 Fri: 8.30–1.00; 2.00–4.30

Historical background   The office was established by the Bath City Council in 1967.

Major collections   Usual local authority record holdings and deposited collections.

Facilities   Photocopying.

36   Costume and Fashion Research Centre

Address	Bath Museums Service 4 Circus Bath Avon BA1 2EW
Telephone	(0225) 61111 ext. 425
Enquiries to	Keeper of Costume, Miss P.C. Byrde
Open	Mon–Fri: 10.00–1.00; 2.00–5.00
Access	Generally open to the public.

Historical background   The Centre was opened in 1974 as an extension to the Museum of Costume in Bath to make available study facilities in the history of dress. The aim is to provide a centre for reference and research from both documentary material and actual specimens of costume maintained in a Study Collection. The collections at both the Museum and Research Centre deal mainly with fashionable dress in Europe for men, women and children from the late 16th century to the present day.

Acquisitions policy   To expand and strengthen existing primary and secondary collections in the history of costume and related subjects by donations and occasional purchases.

Major collections   Principally non-MSS material.

Non-manuscript material   Fashion periodicals: *c*100 titles of fashion magazines, 1802–.

Trade catalogues: *c*600 catalogues from British firms, *c*1900–.
Sunday Times Fashion Archive: *c*2000 fashion photographs, 1957–72.
Worth/Paquin Archives: designs, photographs and press cuttings from house records of both firms, 1902–56.
*c*1000 fashion plates, late 18th century–1920.
Photographs: *c*10,000 19th and 20th-century *cartes-de-visite* and photograph albums; fashion photographs; photographs of works of art from the medieval period to the 20th century.
*c*300 paper dressmaking patterns, 1875–1900.
Miscellaneous designs and fashion illustrations.
Works of reference: *c*500 works of reference related to the history of costume, textiles and needlework.

Finding aids Catalogues and indexes (e.g. to fashion designers represented in *Sunday Times* Fashion Archive or *Vogue* magazine, 1930–).

Facilities Photocopying. Photography.

37   University of Bath Library

Address   University of Bath
                 Claverton Down
                 Bath
                 Avon BA2 7AY

Telephone   (0225) 61244

Enquiries to   Librarian, Mr J. H. Lamble

Open   Mon–Fri: 9.00–5.00

Access   Approved readers.

Historical background The University of Bath received its charter in 1966, having developed from the Bristol College of Science and Technology. At present the Library houses the Feminist Archive, but enquiries should be directed c/o St Saviour's Terrace, Larkhill, Bath.

Acquisitions policy To maintain a collection in support of the University's teaching and research interests.

Major collections The University Library acquired the Pitman Collection, which is the library of Sir Isaac Pitman (1813–97), the inventor of the Pitman Shorthand System. This covers the international development of the use of shorthand and contains MS material as yet uncatalogued.
The library of the Initial Teaching Alphabet Foundation was received following the closing of that institution
The Centre for the History of Technology, Science and Society at the School of Humanities and Social Sciences houses the Watkins Collection of documents and

photographs on the role of steam power in the British economy, 1850–1914.

Facilities   Photocopying. Microfilm.

38   West Lothian District Library

Address   Wellpark
                    Marjoribanks Street
                    Bathgate
                    West Lothian EH48 1AN

Telephone   (0506) 52866/630300

Enquiries to   Chief Assistant, Mrs Jane Brady

Open   Mon–Thurs: 8.30–5.00
                    Fri: 8.30–4.00

Access   Generally open to the public.

Historical background   The Library service was started in 1924 and local material has probably been collected since that date.

Acquisitions policy   To improve existing collections relating to local history.

Major collections   Local Authority Minutes for Armadale Town Council; Bathgate Town Council; Linlithgow Town Council; Whitburn Town Council and West Lothian County Council, 19th and 20th centuries.
District Council Minutes for Torphichen and Bathgate; East Calder; West Calder; Uphall and Whitburn, 19th and 20th centuries.

Non-manuscript material   Local newspapers, 1883–.

Finding aids   Catalogue of all holdings. Various lists and indexes

Facilities   Photocopying. Microfilm/fiche reader.

39   Bearsden and Milngavie District Libraries

Address   "Brookwood"
                    166 Drymen Road
                    Bearsden
                    Glasgow

Telephone   (041) 942 6811

Enquiries to   Chief Librarian, Mrs Sheena Peters

Open   Mon–Fri: 9.00–5.00

Access   Generally open to the public.

Historical background   Bearsden and Milngavie joined together to form one district in 1975.

Major collection   Minutes of Milngavie and of Bearsden Burghs.

40   The BP Library of Motoring

Address   National Motor Museum
              Beaulieu
              Hampshire SO4 7ZN

Telephone   (0590) 612345

Enquiries to   Reference Librarian, Mr Peter Brockes
              or
              Photographic Librarian, Mr Philip Scott

The Reference Library was formed in 1961 and the photographic library the following year. Although there is some correspondence from the motor industry and sporting personalities the bulk is mostly printed material (magazines, manuals, handbooks etc.) and there are several important collections of motor sporting photographs. The Sound Archive contains *c*2800 reels of film, 1903–.

41   The Bethlem Royal Hospital and the Maudsley Hospital

Address   The Bethlem Royal Hospital
              Monks Orchard Road
              Beckenham
              Kent BR3 3BX

Telephone   (01) 777 6611

Enquiries to   Archivist, Miss Patricia Allderidge

Open   Mon–Fri: 9.30–5.00, preferably by appointment

Access   100-year closure on medical and other records relating to individual patients. 30-year closure on other public records. Otherwise fully open to the public.

Historical background   The Bethlem Royal Hospital (originally 'Bedlam') was founded in 1247 as the Priory of St Mary of Bethlehem. It has occupied four separate sites: Bishopsgate (the original priory); Moorfields (building designed by Robert Hooke); St George's Fields, Southwark (now the Imperial War Museum); and, since 1930, its present site. By the mid-14th century it was serving as a hospital, and by 1400 as a hospital for the insane. It came under the control of the

City of London in 1547, and from 1557 was administered jointly with Bridewell Hospital (now King Edward's School, Witley) under a single Court of Governors. In the 19th century it housed the first State Criminal Lunatic Asylum, later replaced by Broadmoor Hospital. It was taken over by the National Health Service in 1948, when it was united with the Maudsley Hospital, Denmark Hill. The Maudsley was opened in 1923 as a London County Council mental hospital. Since 1948 the two have formed a single postgraduate psychiatric teaching hospital, administered by a Board of Governors. In April 1982 the Board was replaced by a Special Health Authority.

Acquisition policy   The Hospital is a recognized place of deposit under The Public Records Act 1958 for all its own records. Other acquisitions of MSS and pictures are restricted to those relating to the Hospital, its staff and patients; books on these subjects, the history of psychiatry and the development of insane asylums and hospitals are also collected.

Major collections   Records of Bethlem Hospital: admission books 1683–; administrative records from the 18th century; records of the Criminal Department, 1816–64; endowment estates (various dates including medieval).
Minute Books of the Court of Governors of Bridewell and Bethlem 1599–, and of the General Committee of Bridewell and Bethlem 1737– (on microfilm only).
Records of Maudsley Hospital, 1923–.
Records of the Joint Hospital, Bethlem and Maudsley, 1948–.

Non-manuscript collections   Maps, plans and architectural drawings.
Photographs and engravings, including photographs of patients in the mid-1850s.
Watercolours by Richard Dadd (1817–86); photographs and slides of his other works.
In 1982 the department took responsibility for part of the Guttman-Maclay Collection of paintings and drawings by psychiatric patients, some of which are on display in the small museum which is run by the archives department. It is hoped to include tape/slide presentations of other material for which there is no display space at present.

Finding aids   NRA lists 1958/9 (these are very out-of-date for everything except material relating to endowment estates; advice should be sought from the archivist). Parts of the collection are listed on cards. Court Books, General Committee Books, Casebooks and Admission Registers have contemporary index at present.

Facilities   Photocopying. Photography by arrangement. Microfilm/fiche reader. Microfilm material may not be copied.

42 Bedfordshire County Library

Address   County Hall
                 Bedford
                 Bedfordshire MK42 9AP

Archives are neither held nor acquired.

43 Bedfordshire Record Office

Address   County Hall
                 Bedford MK42 9AP

Telephone   (0234) 63222 ext. 277

Enquiries to   County Archivist, Miss P.L. Bell

Open   Mon–Fri: 9.15–1.00; 2.00–5.00

Historical background   There was no formal policy before the establishment of the
   Record Office in 1913, although a Records Committee was active from 1898. The
   Office covers the whole county with the exception of early Bedford borough
   material which is housed in Bedford Muniment Room, and some pre-1974 district
   council material, the most important of which, Luton, is still housed there. The
   Office also acts as the Diocesan Record Office for St Albans (archdeaconry of
   Bedford) and provides administrative assistance to Luton Museum and the Bedford
   Settled Estates Office.

Major collections   Usual local authority record holdings and deposited collections.

Facilities   Photocopying. Photography. Microfilm/fiche reader.

Publications   *Guide to the Bedfordshire Record Office*, (1957), *Guide Supplement
   1957–62*
   Guide to the Russell Estate Collections for Bedfordshire and Devon to 1910
   (1966)

44 Cranfield Institute of Technology

Address   Cranfield
                 Bedford
                 Bedfordshire MK43 0AL

Telephone   (0234) 750111 ext. 203/223

Enquiries to   The Librarian

Open　　　　Mon–Fri: 9.00–9.00

Access　　　Generally open to the public.

Historical background　Founded in 1946 as The College of Aeronautics for the education of aeronautical engineers, the Institute became Cranfield Institute of Technology in 1970 with the power to award degrees. It now deals with many aspects of applied science.

Acquisitions policy　To acquire books, periodicals and published material (e.g. reports) on those subjects taught at Cranfield. There is no formal acquisitions policy on historical material.

Major collections　c4500 reports on aerodynamics and aeronautical engineering.

Non-manuscript material　The Institute has recently acquired the Library of the Aeronautical Research Council.

Facilities　Photocopying. Microfiche readers/printer.

45　Belfast Education and Library Board

Address　　　Irish and Local Studies Department
　　　　　　　Central Library
　　　　　　　Royal Avenue
　　　　　　　Belfast BT1 1EA

Telephone　　(0232) 43233

Enquiries to　Senior Reference Librarian, Mr H. Russell

Open　　　　Mon, Thurs: 9.30–8.00
　　　　　　　Tues, Wed, Fri: 9.30–5.30
　　　　　　　Sat: 9.30–1.00

Access　　　Generally open to the public.

Historical background　Since the 1920s the Library has acquired the papers of local antiquarians and literary figures.

Acquisitions policy　To acquire material relating to the work of local historians and writers.

Major collections　Irish antiquarian and bibliographical studies: F.J. Bigger (1863–1926), 40,000 items; J.S. Crone (1858–1945), 10,000 items; A.S. Moore (1870–1961), 1000 items; A. Riddell (1874–1958), 5000 items.
Gaelic MSS: Bryson MacAdam collection of 44 MS vols of Ulster Gaelic writings, 17th–18th centuries.
MSS, typescripts and/or correspondence of the following: Lynn Doyle (1873–1961); Alexander Irvine (1863–1941); Amanda McKittrick Ros, 1897–1939; Forrest Reid (1876–1947); Sam Thompson, 1956–65.

Non-manuscript material c5000 theatre and cinema posters and programmes, mainly relating to Belfast.
Photographs, political ephemera, postcards relating to Ireland.

Finding aids Various lists and indexes.

Facilities Photocopying. Limited photography. Microfilm/fiche reader/printer.

Publications *Guide to Irish and Local Studies Department* (1980) [free on postal application]
B. O'Buachalla: *Clar na Lamhscribhinni Gaeilge. 1 Leabharlainn Phoibli Bheal Feirste,* (Baile Atha Cliath: An Chead Chlo, 1962)

46 Belfast Library and Society for Promoting Knowledge
Linen Hall Library

Address	17 Donegall Square North Belfast
Telephone	(0232) 21707
Enquiries to	Mr John Gray
Open	Mon–Fri: 9.30–6.00 Sat: 9.30–4.00
Access	Members. Approved readers on application to the Librarian.

Historical background The Library was founded in 1788 as the Belfast Reading Society, its stated aim being the 'collection of an extensive library, philosophical apparatus, and such productions of nature and art as tend to improve the mind and excite a spirit of general inquiry'. The Library holdings cover the humanities and sciences, in particular the field of Irish history.

Acquisitions policy To strengthen existing collections of Irish material.

Major collections Blackwood Collection of local genealogies of Co. Down families. Minute books of local societies, including Belfast Burns Society, from the early 20th century; Natural History and Philosophical Society from the early 19th century; Belfast Anacreontic Society from the late 18th century.

Facilities Photocopying.

47   General Register Office, Northern Ireland

Address	Oxford House 49–55 Chichester Street Belfast BT1 4HL
Telephone	(0232) 35211
Enquiries to	Deputy Registrar-General, Mr L.H. Anderson Assistant Registrar-General, Miss D. Stephens
Open	Mon–Fri: 9.30–3.30
Access	Generally open to public. Fees vary.

Historical background   The Registrar General's Office was set up for the whole of Ireland and at the date of partition (1921) divided into General Register Office (Northern Ireland) and General Register Office (Republic of Ireland). Since 1973 the Registrars of births, deaths and marriages have been local authority staff, paid for by the Department of Finance, Northern Ireland.

Acquisitions policy   The Registrar General is required by statute to arrange for the registration of all births, marriages and deaths in Northern Ireland, and for the storage and safe keeping of all such records.

Major collections   Marriage records (Northern Ireland), 1844–.
Birth and death records (Northern Ireland), 1863–.

Non-manuscript material   Some pre-1921 birth and death indexes on microfilm. Post-1973 birth and death records on microfiche.

Finding aids   Indexes to all records available.

Facilities   Index search facilities. Microfilm/fiche readers.

Publications   Registrar General's Annual Reports, Quarterly Reports.

48   Public Record Office of Northern Ireland

Address	66 Balmoral Avenue Belfast BT9 6NY
Telephone	(0232) 661621
Enquiries to	Director, Mr B. Trainor
Open	Mon–Fri: 9.30–4.45. Documents are not produced after 4.15 Closed: first two weeks in December
Access	Official records normally after 30 years. Private records open to public inspection except where the depositor has imposed restrictions.

Historical background The Public Record Office of Northern Ireland was set up by the Public Records Act (Northern Ireland) 1923, to be responsible for the custody of official records – those of government departments, courts of law, statutory bodies etc. Provision was also made for the deposit of imperial records (i.e. those relating to Northern Ireland created by government at Westminster) and for the Record Office to accept records from private depositors.

Acquisitions policy Official records are transferred to the Public Records Office of Northern Ireland under the terms of the 1923 Act. The Office seeks to acquire a wide range of private records, in particular family, estate and business archives; ecclesiastical records; papers of clubs and societies; emigrant letters etc.

Non-manuscript material Very small collection of tapes and files.
Several large (glass plate negative) photographic collections.

Finding aids Catalogues. Indexes. Deputy Keeper's Reports, 1954–65.

Facilities Photocopying. Photographic copies. Microfilm. Genealogical searching carried out on fee-paying basis by Ulster Historical Foundation.

Publications A large number of publications, some published by HMSO, others by the Public Records Office. These include Education Facsimile Packs, calendars, catalogues of selected papers. A booklist is available.

49 Ulster Museum

Address Botanic Gardens
Belfast BT9 5AB

Telephone (0232) 668251

Enquiries to Librarian, Department of Local History, Mr J.N.H. Nesbitt

Open Mon–Thurs: 10.00–12.45; 2.00–5.00
Fri: as above, but by prior appointment only.

Access Bona fide enquirers, by prior application in writing, by telephone or in person at the Museum.

Historical background The Ulster Museum has its roots in the Museum of the Belfast Natural History and Philosophical Society, founded in 1831, and the Belfast Municipal Art Gallery and Museum, founded in 1890, whose collections were amalgamated in 1910. In 1929 the Belfast Museum and Art Gallery was opened on the present site, and in 1962 it was transferred to a statutory board of trustees as the Ulster Museum. That part of the archive which does not relate to museum specimens is soon to be handed over to the Public Record Office of Northern Ireland (*see* entry **48**).

Acquisitions policy To build up comprehensive collections relating to the north of Ireland (and, where appropriate, to Ireland as a whole) in the fields of antiquities, art, botany and zoology, geology, industrial archaeology, local history and numismatics. In some areas, such as art, ethnography, botany, zoology and numismatics, major collections of non-Irish material exist.

Major collections   Templeton MSS: *c*25 vols of MSS of John Templeton (1766–1825), botanist; including his journal, 1806–25, several vols of an unpublished Irish flora illustrated by himself, records of mosses and ferns and a list of Irish shells.
Hyndman MSS: numerous notes by George C. Hyndman (1796–1868), Belfast marine biologist; also dredging papers, Belfast Bay, 1844–57.
Thompson MSS: several folders of notes and correspondence of William Thompson (1805–52), Belfast naturalist and author of *Natural History of Ireland*.
Welch MSS: *c*20 vols of personal and excursion diaries, natural history notes, memoranda and lists of negatives of Robert J. Welch (1859–1936), photographer and amateur naturalist.
Botany and Zoology Department: small but important collections, including notebooks of P.H. Grierson (1859–1952) on Mollusca and one letter of Dr Alexander Henry Halliday (?1728–1802) relating to Insecta.
Local History Department: extensive archive of MS and printed material, including the Barber MSS (Rev. Samuel Barber of Rathfriland, United Irishman) and the Tennant Collection (Robert J. Tennant, early 19th-century Liberal politician from Belfast).

Non-manuscript material   Posters and other ephemera, chiefly playbills and programmes of Belfast theatres (*c*200–250 items).
Belfast and other locally printed books, pamphlets, chapbooks and broadsides (*c*500 items).
Welch Collection: *c*6000 glass plate negatives by R.J. Welch of Irish subjects, covering topography, industries, rural crafts, antiquities, geology, botany and zoology.
Historical and Topographic Collection: *c*1000 negatives, modern and copied from old prints and negatives (constantly growing); a few other collections, large and medium-sized (uncatalogued or in process of being catalogued).
A growing collection of several hundred slides made in the field and from specimens and photographs.
Departments other than Local History keep their own specialized collections of negatives and slides.
Local History Department: *c*250 maps; *c*1500 topographical drawings, paintings and prints; *c*250 portraits.
Art Department: *c*2000 drawings and watercolours.
Botany and Zoology Department: various watercolours and drawings.

Finding aids   The Thompson MSS are at present being catalogued. A topographical index to the Art and Local History collection (not confined to Irish views) is in preparation.

Facilities   Photocopying. Photography.

Publications   Various, including:
A.W. Stelfox: 'John Templeton's notes on Irish land and freshwater Mollusca', *The*

Irish Naturalist, xxiii (1914), 29

N. Fisher: 'George Crawford Hyndman's MSS', *Journal of Conchology*, xix (1931), 164

B.S. Turner and others: *A List of the Photographs in the R.J. Welch Collection in the Ulster Museum, 1: Topography and History* (Belfast, 1979)

50 Berwick upon Tweed Record Office

Address   Berwick upon Tweed Borough Council Offices
Wallace Green
Berwick upon Tweed
Northumberland

Telephone   (0632) 362680

Enquiries to   The County Archivist, Northumberland Record Office, Melton Park, North Gosforth, Newcastle upon Tyne NE3 5QX.

Open   Thurs: 10.00–12.45; 2.15–5.00

Historical background This branch repository of the Northumberland Record Office (*see* entry 542) was opened in 1981.

Major collections The usual local authority record holdings and deposited collections.

51 Humberside County Record Office

Address   County Hall
Beverley
North Humberside HU17 9BA

Telephone   (0482) 867131 ext. 3393/4

Enquiries to   County Archivist, Mr K.D. Holt

Open   By appointment
Mon, Wed, Thurs: 9.00–4.45
Tues: 9.00–8.00
Fri: 9.00–4.00

Historical background East Riding County Record Office was established in *c*1953. Following reorganization in 1974 it became Humberside County Record Office, holding the same material with the exception of some private deposits placed in North Yorkshire Record Office. The Office incorporates the East Riding Registry of Deeds, 1709–1974. It also acts as the Diocesan Record Office for York (parish records of the archdeaconry of East Riding). *See also* South Humberside Area Record Office (entry 223).

Major collections   Usual local authority record holdings and deposited collections.

Facilities   Photocopying. Photography. Microfilming. Microfilm readers.

52   Bexley Libraries and Museums Department
Local Studies Section

Address   Hall Place
Bourne Road
Bexley
Kent DA5 1PQ

Telephone   (0322) 526574

Enquiries to   Local Studies Officer, Mr J.C.M. Shaw

Open   Mon–Sat: 9.00–5.00
Winter: 9.00–dusk

Access   Generally open to the public.

Historical background   The section was established in 1972 to preserve the records of former local and semi-official authorities in the area and to collect documentary material relevant to local studies. The section includes a local history library and museum.

Acquisitions policy   To increase holdings of material of local relevance.

Major collections   Minutes of local bodies. Rate-books, 1790–. Archives of Danson and Hall Place Estates.

Non-manuscript material   Ordnance Survey and tithe maps.
Large collection of local photographs and prints.

Finding aids   Catalogues and indexes are being compiled.

Facilities   Photocopying. Microfilm reader/printer.

Publications   Duplicated papers on local houses, industries, transport, persons etc.

53   Allan Ramsay Library
Leadhills Miners' Library

Address   Main Street
Leadhills
Biggar
Strathclyde ML12 6XP

Enquiries to   The Secretary, The Library Committee

Open   Easter–October: Sat, Sun: 2.30–4.00
                 Other times by appointment

Access   Generally open to the public.
                 The Library is run by a committee of voluntary workers.
                 There is a yearly subscription and donations are welcomed.

Historical background   The Leadhills Miners' Reading Society was founded in 1741 and is the oldest subscription library in the British Isles. Allan Ramsay, poet, was born in Leadhills in 1686, and his name commemorates the library. Members included a number of celebrated men including William Symington (1763–1831), mining engineer; Dr John Brown (1786–1854), Edinburgh author; and Dr James Braid (?1795–1860), surgeon. The lead mines in the village closed in the 1930s and the membership of the Reading Society declined. In 1940 the Lanarkshire County Council took over the building but by 1965 the local authority withdrew financial support. In 1969, with the help of grants, the restoration of the building was started and the library re-opened in 1972. The Library also has a small exhibition of relics.

Acquisitions policy   The Library does not purchase, but from time to time receives gifts of books, photographs etc.

Major collections   Library records including MS 'Members' Roll', 1741–1903; minute books, 1821–, ledgers of book loans, 1903–.
Mining records, 1738– (Leadhills).
Minute books of the local Curling Club, early 19th century.

Non-manuscript material   Photographs. Maps of mining grounds.

Finding aids   It is hoped that the collection will be catalogued in the near future.

Facilities   Photography permitted on written application to the Committee.

Publications   Information leaflets on the library are available.

54   Wirral Archives

Address   Reference and Information Services
                 Birkenhead Central Library
                 Borough Road
                 Birkenhead
                 Merseyside L41 2XB

Telephone   (051) 652 6106/7/8

Enquiries to   Archivist, Mr D.N. Thompson

Open   Mon, Tues, Thurs, Fri: 10.00–8.00
                 Sat: 10.00–1.00; 2.00–5.00

Historical background   The archives department was established at the time of local goverment reorganization in April 1974, to administer the historical records inherited by the Wirral Metropolitan Borough Council. The service is, however, based at a reference library which has been collecting material of local interest, including manuscripts, since 1856. In 1967 records were also transferred from the Town Clerk's Department. Wallasey Reference Library (Earlston Road, Wallasey L45 5DX) is a dependent repository.

Major collections   Usual local authority holdings and deposited collections including the following which have a wider significance:

Birkenhead Improvement Commission 1833–79, which includes records of the first park to be laid out at public expense, 1843–7 (designed by Sir Joseph Paxton) and the first street tramway in Great Britain, 1860.

Archives of Unichema Chemicals Ltd, formerly the Bromborough, Wirral, branch of Price's Patent Candle Co Ltd. This includes material relating to the candle-making industry in general and Price's Workers' Village at Bramborough Pool founded in 1853.

Some antiquarian collections (e.g. John Stafford, a mid-18th-century Macclesfield attorney), including a wide range of documents relating to the history of Macclesfield and villages throughout Cheshire, mainly 15th–18th centuries.

Facilities   Photocopying. Photography by arrangement. Microfilm reader/printer.

55   Birmingham RC Diocesan Archives

Address   Cathedral House,
                     St Chad's Queensway
                     Birmingham
                     West Midlands B4 6EU

Telephone   (021) 236 2251

Enquiries to   Archivist, Rev P. Dennison, 243 Jockey Road, Sutton Coldfield, West
                     Midlands B73 5US

Holds records of the Vicars Apostolic of the Midland District, 1700–1850, and of the Bishops of Birmingham, 1850–1900, which may be consulted on written application.

56   Birmingham Reference Library

Address   Central Libraries
                     Chamberlain Square
                     Birmingham
                     West Midlands B3 3HQ

Telephone   (021) 235 4219

Enquiries to   Senior Archivist, Mr J.D. Warner-Davies

Open   Mon–Fri: 9.00–6.00
                 Sat: 9.00–5.00

Access   Unrestricted except to those categories of record controlled by the
                 Public Records Act or by agreement with the record owner.

Historical background   The Library was first opened in 1866 but was completely
    destroyed by fire in 1879. Re-opening later that year, it moved into new premises
    which it occupied until 1973 when it was moved into its present building. It is
    particularly noted for its unique Shakespeare Library and for a number of special
    collections of printed books and archives. It also acts as the Diocesan Record Office
    for Birmingham (parish records).

Acquisitions policy   The Library seeks to ensure the preservation of all important
    archives within the post-1974 City boundary, that is, the old City together with the
    former County Borough of Sutton Coldfield. The Library's function as archive
    keeper to the City and the Diocese of Birmingham forms an integral part of this.

Major collections   Business archives include the Boulton and Watt Collection, a
    major source for the history of the Industrial Revoution; the Assay Office
    Collection, relating to the Birmingham toy and silver trade and to the Mint;
    Metropolitan Cammell engineering drawings; records of B.S.A., Cadbury's and
    many small Birmingham firms.
    Private archives include large collections of family papers relating to Birmingham
    and surrounding counties, with considerable deposits of medieval material.
    Religious archives include Anglican and Non-conformist records for Birmingham,
    16th–20th centuries.

Non-manuscript material   Local Studies Department collection. Seals. Maps.

Finding aids   Individual handlists available for archive collections. Indexes by
    personal name, place name and subject. Special indexes for seals, apprenticeship
    and maps.

Facilities   Photocopying. Photography. Microfilm/fiche readers.

Publications   Birmingham Public Libraries: *Catalogue of the Birmingham Collection*
    (Birmingham 1918; Suppl. 1931)
    A. Andrews: 'The Birmingham Reference Library', *Archives*, v (1951)
    U. Rayska: 'The Archives Section of Birmingham Reference Library', *Archives*, liv
    (1978)

57   City of Birmingham Polytechnic Library

Address   Westbourne Road
                 Edgbaston
                 Birmingham B15 3TN

Telephone	(021) 454 5106
Enquiries to	Librarian, Mr D. Cadney
Open	Term: Mon–Thurs: 9.00–9.00
	Fri: 9.00–5.00
	Vacation: Mon–Fri: 9.00–5.00
Access	By application (telephone in the first instance) to Library staff.

Historical background   The Polytechnic was founded in 1975 by the amalgamation of the City of Birmingham Emergency Training College (1946–1957), the City of Birmingham College of Education (1957–1975) and Bordesley College of Education (1965–1975).

Acquisition policy   Donations are gratefully accepted. All archival records relating to the institution, including photographs, prospectuses, programmes, newspaper clippings etc, are collected.

Major collections   Material relating to predecessor institutions.

Non-manuscript material   Small collection of newspaper cuttings; prospectuses; minutes of meetings; student magazines; programmes; and photographs.
Other collections, including antiquarian books, are held by Art and Design Library, Gosta Green, Birmingham B4 7DX (telephone: (021) 359 6721 ext.236).

Facilities   Photocopying.

58   University of Aston in Birmingham

Address	University Library
	Gosta Green
	Birmingham B4 7ET

No archives are held.

59   University of Birmingham Library

Address	PO Box 363
	Birmingham B15 2TT
Telephone	(021) 472 1301
Enquiries to	Sub-Librarian (Special Collections), Dr B.S. Benedikz
Open	Mon–Fri: 9.00–5.00 (5.15 in term)
Access	Bona fide researchers. All new users of MSS and archives must supply a formal letter of introduction from an appropriate person; all would-

be researchers must apply first by letter. Special Collections are
made available in the Heslop Room.

Historical background The Library began as the library of Mason College in 1880; it
was gathered on one site in 1959–60.

Acquisitions policy To build and strengthen existing collections and to collect in
the fields where active academic research is taking place in the University, by
purchase, deposit or donation.

Major collections Political archives (*c*200,000 items): papers of the Chamberlain
family; Sir Anthony Eden, first Earl of Avon; William Harbutt Dawson; Nikolai
Shishkin.
Literary papers of Harriet Martineau (1802–76) and Francis Brett Young (1884–
1954); some papers of John Galsworthy (1867–1933), Edward Arber (1836–
1912) and Margaret Galway.
Local archives: papers of Bishop E.W. Barnes; Eyton papers of Shropshire local
history; several smaller collections of local companies and personalities, including
non-psychic papers of Sir Oliver Lodge (1851–1940).
Other archives: selected Church Missionary Society papers, from beginnings to
20th century (*c*50,000 items, in process of transfer); philosophical papers of
Professor J.W. Harvey and Professor A.E. Duncan-Jones.

Non-manuscript material *c*15,000 Birmingham University theses.
Alma Tadema collection of sketches and photographs (*c*30,000).

Finding aids Typed handlists to the individual collections.

Facilities Very limited photocopying (at the discretion of the University Librarian).

Publications D.W. Evans: *Catalogue of the Cadbury papers* (1973)
B.S. Benedikz: *The Chamberlain Collection Introduction and Guide* (1978)
————: *The Galsworthy Papers; handlist of papers – by the bequest of R.H.
Sauber Esq* (1978)
————: *Handlist of the Papers of Sir Oliver Lodge* (1979)

60   Blackburn Museum

Address   Library Street
Blackburn
Lancashire

Telephone   (0254) 667130

Enquiries to   The Borough Recreation Services Officer, Town Hall, Blackburn
(postal)

Open   Mon–Sat: 9.30–6.00

Access   Bona fide scholars.

Historical background   The Blackburn Museum was founded 1862, and has been in its present premises since 1874. The Museum maintains the collections of the East Lancashire Regimental Museum, founded in 1934, and Lewis Textile Museum, founded in 1938.

Acquisitions policy   Interests restricted to local history, regimental history and the textile trade.

Major collections   The Feilden Papers: documents relating to the Feilden properties in Blackburn, 16th–20th centuries.
The Regimental Museum collection includes records of the East Lancashire Regiment.

Non-manuscript material   Local history collection includes some films.
Textile history collection includes a number of 19th-century pattern books.

Finding aids   Handlists.

Facilities   Photocopying. Photography and microfilming by arrangement.

61   Bolton Metropolitan Borough Archives

Address   Central Library and Museum
                 Le Mans Crescent
                 Bolton
                 Greater Manchester BL1 1SA

Telephone   (0204) 22311 ext. 318/351

Enquiries to   Archivist, Mr T.K. Campbell

Open   Mon, Tues, Thur, Fri: 9.00–5.00
                 Wed: 9.00–1.00
                 Wed p.m., Sat and evenings by arrangement

Historical background   The archives department was established in 1974. It includes some collections from Bolton Libraries and Museums.

Major collections   Usual local authority record holdings and deposited collections including the following which have a wider significance:
Compton family of Tonge and Bolton, c1780–1943.
Heywood family of Bolton, c1784–1938.
Records of Messrs Hick, Hargreaves & Co, Engineers and Iron Founders, Bolton, c1819–1959.

Facilities   Photocopying. Photography. Microfilm/fiche reader/printer.

62   The Haberdashers' Aske's School

Address   Butterfly Lane
             Elstree
             Borehamwood
             Herfordshire WD6 3AF

Telephone   (01) 207 4323

Enquiries to   The School Librarian/Archivist

Some archives are held at the school but no details are available.

63   Boston Borough Council

Address   Municipal Buildings
             West Street
             Boston
             Lincolnshire PE21 8QR

Telephone   (0205) 64601

Enquiries to   The Chief Executive

Open   Mon–Fri: 9.30–12.30; 2.30–4.30

Access   Written or personal application.

Major collections   Council and Committee minutes, 1545–.
    Contracts, conveyances and deeds.

Non-manuscript material   Printed books on Council and Committee minutes.

Finding aids   Comprehensive printed index.

64   National Meteorological Archive

Address   Meteorological Office Met O 18e
             Eastern Road
             Bracknell
             Berkshire RG12 2UR

Telephone   (0344) 20242 ext. 2521

Enquiries to   The Archivist

Open   Mon–Thurs: 9.00–5
             Fri: 9.00–4.30

Access   Generally open to the public by appointment.

Historical background   The office was established in 1865 by Admiral Fitzroy as part of the Department of Trade. The archives are officially designated public records.

Acquisitions policy   Apart from the office's own archives, records from private bodies or administrations, and the papers of individuals which are relevant are accepted.

Major collections   Synoptic charts and upper air charts covering the Western northern hemisphere and climatological data covering the British Isles, mainly from 1941–42, but some from 1900.
Autographic records (e.g. thermographs) of sunshine, temperature, pressure, rainfall etc.

Non-manuscript material   Published material is at the National Meteorological Library.

Finding aids   Assistance of staff.

Facilities   Photocopying by arrangement.

65   Bradford Archives Department

Address   Central Library
                   Prince's Way
                   Bradford
                   West Yorkshire BD1 1NN

Telephone   (0274) 33081 ext. 57

Enquiries   District Archivist, Mr D. James

Open   Mon–Fri: 9.00–1.00; 2.00–5.00
                   Arrangements can be made for material to be consulted in the Local
                   Studies Department of the Central Library:
                   Mon–Fri: 5.00–8.00
                   Sat: 9.00–5.00

Access   Generally open to the public.

Historical background   The Archives Department was established as a separate entity in 1974. Prior to that date the library had acquired collections of manuscripts and these are the basis of the Department's holdings. Many records have since been acquired from local government and other sources. The Department also acts as the Diocesan Record Office for Bradford.

Acquisitions policy   To acquire MS material relating to the history of the area covered by Metropolitan Bradford Council.

Major collections   Records of Bradford Council and other defunct authorities which comprise Metropolitan Bradford Council.

Religious records for c90 churches and chapels.

Records of leading local families, including the Tempests of Tong and the Ferrands of Bingley.

Records of local worsted and woollen firms; coal and iron companies and other businesses; chambers of commerce.

Records of local trade union branches and trades councils.

Records of local political parties, particularly the Conservative party; some Independent Labour Party material.

Records of local charities and voluntary organizations.

Finding aids   Catalogues for c250 collections. Some indexes. Much material remains unlisted.

Facilities   Photocopying. Microfilm reader/printer.

66   University of Bradford

Address   University Library
Bradford
West Yorkshire BD7 1DP

Telephone   (0274) 33466

Enquiries to   Librarian, Mr F. Earnshaw

Archive resources are not extensive and no details are available.

67   Brechin Public Library and Museum

Address   St Ninean's Square
Brechin
Angus

Telephone   (03562) 2687

Enquiries to   Librarian, Mrs P. Robertson

Open   Mon–Sat: 9.30–6.00

Access   Generally open to the public on written application.

Historical background   The Library opened in 1890. MS material was collected by honorary curators of the museum and libraries; certain records of Brechin Town Council were donated in 1975. The Library and Museum became part of Angus District Libraries and Museums in 1975.

Acquisitions policy   To collect any local material.

Major collections   Brechin Town Council papers, 1805–1906; Burgess rolls, 1710–

1971; Roll of Honour, 1914–1951; Burgh charters, 1306–1685.
Trades incorporation records: Bakers, Glovers, Hammermen, Shoemakers, Tailors, Weavers, Wrights, 17th–19th centuries.
Local charity, friendly and voluntary society records 19th–20th centuries.
Miscellaneous local private papers 18th–20th centuries. Records of D. & R. Duke, linen manufacturers, 1845–1935.

Non-manuscript material   Local maps and plans, 18th–20th centuries.
Published local monographs; rules and regulations of local societies; some local periodicals.

Finding aids   Archive list.

Facilities   Photocopying by arrangement.

68   Mid Glamorgan County Library

Address   Coed Parc
                 Park Street
                 Bridgend
                 Mid Glamorgan CF31 4BA

Telephone   (0656) 57451

Enquiries to   County Librarian, Mr R.W. Davies

Local History Collection, principally of non-MS material. The Charles Evans Collection, containing a few MSS, is at Pontypridd Branch Library.

69   Brighton Polytechnic

Address   Moulsecoomb
                 Brighton
                 East Sussex BN2 4GJ

No archives are held.

70   Tom Harrisson Mass-Observation Archive

Address   Arts Building D
                 University of Sussex
                 Falmer
                 Brighton
                 East Sussex BN1 9QN

Telephone   (0273) 606755 ext. 1054

Enquiries to   Archivist, Ms Dorothy E. Sheridan

Open   Mon–Thurs: 9.15–5.15, by appointment

Access   Bona fide researchers on written application. Reference/sponsorship
                     required.

Historical background   Mass-Observation was a social science research organization
set up in 1937 by Tom Harrisson and Charles Madge. They aimed to create what
they called an 'anthropology of ourselves' using two main approaches: (*a*) the
recruiting of a panel of volunteer 'observers' to record their everyday lives in
diaries and to respond to detailed monthly questionnaires; and (*b*) the
establishment of a core of full-time investigators based in London. During World
War II Mass-Observation was used by the Ministry of Information for a short period
to monitor civilian morale. The papers generated by this work (which continued
into the 1950s) were brought to the University of Sussex in 1970. The Archive was
officially opened in 1975 when it became a charitable trust.

Acquisitions policy   The original Mass-Observation collection is virtually complete,
but a small amount of complementary material relating to the period 1937–50 has
been accepted. A new Mass-Observation project has been set up by Professor D.F.
Pocock, Director of the Archive, and material resulting from this project is being
added to the main Archive. Expansion of the Archive is being currently considered.

Major collections   Mass-Observation Records: personal diaries, 1937–63; detailed
questionnaire replies, 1937–53; papers resulting from a wide range of
investigations into British social life before, during and immediately after World
War II.
Mary Adams collection: personal papers donated by Mary Adams relating to her
work at BBC Television, 1936–9, 1942–58; as Director of Home Intelligence,
Ministry of Information, 1939–41; and as Deputy Chairman of the Consumers'
Association 1958–70.

Non-manuscript material   c400 photographs taken by Humphrey Spender of Bolton
and Blackpool, 1937–8, for Mass-Observation's 'Worktown Project'.
The Library includes Mass-Observation and related publications; these may not be
borrowed.
Newspaper cuttings relating to Mass-Observation's history.
Ephemera including posters, pamphlets, leaflets etc which related to topics
investigated by Mass-Observation.

Finding aids   Lists and indexes available in the Archive. Sections of the collection still
being catalogued.

Facilities   Photocopying. Microfilm reader.

Publications   T. Jeffery: *Mass-Observation: a Short History* (1978) [Occasional Paper
no. 55]
   D. Sheridan: *The Mass-Observation Records 1937–49* (1981)

——————: *Guide to the Mass-Observation File Reports* (1981)
Details of early Mass-Observation publications and further proposed publications available from the Archive.

71   University of Sussex Library

Address	University of Sussex
	Falmer
	Brighton
	East Sussex BN1 9QL
Telephone	(0273) 606755 ext. 884
Enquiries to	Librarian, Ms Elizabeth M. Rodger
Open	Mon–Fri: 9.00–5.30
Access	Academic researchers on written application.

Historical background   The University Library was opened to readers in 1964. In 1970 a section was created within the Library to handle the special materials acquired to support research projects which had arisen from the curriculum. In 1973 these special collections were divided into two groups, official published papers and manuscripts, and thereafter the Manuscripts Section has maintained and serviced the manuscript collections, together with small supporting collections of printed books.

Acquisitions policy   To collect papers which support research and teaching in the University, especially literary, political, sociological, and scientific papers of the late 19th and 20th centuries.

Major collections   Collections include the following: Benn Levy MP, c1930–70; Charles W. Gibson MP, c1910–70; James Gerald Crowther papers on scientific journalism and politics; Federal Union papers, 1938–73; Sir Richard Gregory, c1880–1952; John Hilton Bureau papers – *News of the World* readers' problems, 1945–68; Kenneth Allsop, 1940–68, Kingsley Martin, 1910–69; Rudyard Kipling and family, c1860–1940; Leonard and Virginia Woolf, 1890–1969; Rosey Pool – American Negro Literature, 1945–70; Sir Lawrence Dudley Stamp, 1910–65.

Non-manuscript material   Printed books associated with individual collections (e.g. works and studies of Virginia Woolf, Leonard Woolf, Rudyard Kipling, etc.)

Finding aids   Descriptive handlists to each collection. Indexes of letter writers for main collections in progress. Handlists are lodged with the National Register of Archives.

Facilities   Usual reprographic facilities.

72   Avon County Reference Library

Address   County Central Library
College Green
Bristol
Avon BS1 5TL

Telephone   (0272) 276121

Enquiries to   The County Reference Librarian

Open   Mon–Fri: 9.30–8.00
Sat: 9.30–5.00

Access   Generally open to the public but advance notice is required for the use of MSS, early printed material and some other valuable items.

Historical background   The City Library of Bristol has been in existence since 1613. In 1974 Bristol Public Libraries became part of Avon County Library and much of the early stock survives in the County Reference Library, which also contains the books of the Bristol Library Society, founded in 1772. Most MS material relevant to the history of Bristol is housed in the Bristol Record Office (*see* entry 74).

Acquisitions policy   To strengthen the existing collections, especially those relating to local history and local literary figures, by purchase and donation.

Major collections   MS and printed material relating to Thomas Chatterton (1752–70) and Samuel Taylor Coleridge (1772–1834).
The Richard Smith Collection: MS and printed material relating to the history of the theatre in Bristol.
Letters and papers relating to the Southwell family.
Small collection of documents relating to slavery in the West Indies and the slave trade generally.
The Ellacombe Collection: MSS and other material relating to the history and topography of south-east Gloucestershire (now part of Avon).

Non-manuscript material   Extensive collections on the history of Bristol and its environs, including books, pamphlets, pictorial material, colour and monochrome transparencies, sound archives.
Braikenridge Collection: c9000 items on the history of the city including engravings, ephemera and other pre–1850 material.
Emanuel Green collection of books on the history of Somerset.

Finding aids   Full card catalogues and lists.

Facilities   Photocopying. Photography. Microfilm/fiche readers.

73   Bristol Polytechnic

Address   Bolland Library
                 Coldharbour Lane
                 Bristol
                 Avon BS15 1QY

There are no deposited collections; only administrative records are held.

74   Bristol Record Office

Address   Council House
                 College Green
                 Bristol
                 Avon BS1 5TR

Telephone   (0272) 26031 ext. 441/2

Enquiries to   City Archivist, Miss Mary E. Williams

Open   Mon–Thurs: 8.45–4.45
                 Fri: 8.45–4.15
                 Sat: 9.00–2.00, by appointment

Historical background   The Record Office was established in 1924. It is one of the
   few offices set up to look after Council records, but from the early days acquired
   other material. It also acts as the Diocesan Record Office for Bristol.

Major collections   Usual local authority record holdings, from 12th century, and
   deposited collections. There are not many landed family archives.

Facilities   Photocopying. Photography by arrangement. Microfilming. Microfilm
   reader. Microfilm printouts by arrangement.

Publications   I. Kirby: *Diocese of Bristol: A Catalogue of the Records...* (1970)
   E. Ralph: *Guide to the Bristol Archives Office* (1971)
   Lists of parish registers and bishop's transcripts deposited in the Record Office

75   University of Bristol Library

Address   Tyndall Avenue
                 Bristol
                 Avon BS8 1TJ

Telephone   (0272) 24161 ext. 941

Enquiries to   The Librarian

Open   Mon–Fri: 9.15–4.45

Access   Members of the University of Bristol; others on written application.

Historical background   University College Bristol was founded in 1876 and became a University on Grant of Charter in 1909. MS collections were built up by deposits, gifts and purchase as opportunity offered; the range of material is wide and miscellaneous. Bristol University Library is a recognized repository for West Indies MSS.

Acquisitions policy   Acquisitions are mainly by donation or deposit. Occasionally an item is purchased to add to an existing collection.

Major collections   Bristol Moravian Church: minute books and items of church history, 1760–1893.
University College and University of Bristol: incomplete archives of the institution, 1876–1982; papers relating to individuals connected with it, including Dr Heinz London (1886–1972), Professor Conwy Lloyd Morgan, 1875–1938, Sir Philip Robert Morris, 1942–80, Professor Cecil Frank Powell, 1916–69, Philip John Worsley.
Letter-books, sketchbooks, calculations and accounts of Isambard Kingdom Brunel, (one of the major collections of material on I.K. Brunel), 1830–66.
Letter-books and accounts of Henry Marc Brunel, 1860–88.
Correspondence, notes, papers and publications of Edward Conze in the field of Oriental Theology.
Autograph scores and correspondence of Philip Napier Miles, 1884–1951.
National Liberal Club: membership records, 1882–1955; minute books, miscellaneous papers, 1882–1973.
Paget Papers: accounts, correspondence, family and estate papers, mainly relating to Somerset and Staffordshire, 1270–1920.
Pinney Papers: accounts, letter-books, family and estate papers, mainly relating to Dorset and the West Indies, 1650–1948.
Somerset Miners Association: minutes, accounts, correspondence etc, 1868–1964.
John Addington Symonds: correspondence and family papers, 1884–1980.
West Indies Papers: miscellaneous personal and estates records, 1663–1929.

Non-manuscript material   Recordings, cassettes, photographs, films, plans and drawings referring to the history of University College Bristol and Bristol University, 1870s–1982.

Finding aids   Indexes. Lists. Catalogues. Calendars.

Facilities   Photocopying. Photography. Microfilm/fiche reader/printer.

76   Bromley Public Library
Archive Section

Address   Central Library
                 Bromley
                 Kent BR1 1EX

Telephone   (01) 460 9955

Enquiries to   Archivist, Miss E. Silverthorne

Open   Tues, Thurs: 9.30–8.00
                 Wed, Fri: 9.30–6.00
                 Sat: 9.30–5.00, by appointment

Historical background   The Greater London borough of Bromley was formed in
    1965 by the amalgamation of Bromley, Beckenham, Penge, Orpington and
    Chislehurst, all of which had previously been part of Kent; Penge had been in
    Surrey until 1900. The first archivist was appointed in 1970. Previously there had
    been haphazard collection of material at all libraries, with the largest at Bromley,
    the result of the activities of a committee of local historians in the 1920s. There is
    close liaison with Kent Archives Office (*see* entry **515**) which has transferred some
    local material.

Major collections   Usual local authority record holdings and deposited collections.

Facilities   Photocopying. Photography by arrangement. Microfilm/fiche reader and
    reader/printer.

77   The University College at Buckingham

Address   Buckingham
                 Buckinghamshire MK18 1EG

No archives are held.

78   Burnley District Library

Address   Grimshaw Street
                 Burnley
                 Lancashire BB11 2BE

Telephone   (0282) 37115 ext. 25

Enquiries to   District Librarian, Mr R. Pickles

Holds local authority archives including water board and court records; also business
and non-conformist records.

79 Burton Library

Address   Riverside
High Street
Burton on Trent
Staffordshire DE13 9HD

Telephone   (0283) 43271

Enquiries to The Librarian

Open   Mon, Tues, Thurs, Fri: 9.30–6.00
Wed, Sat: 9.30–1.00
Previous notification of visit to Archive Collection would be
appreciated

Access   Generally open to the public.

Historical background   The present building was opened in 1976 and material was
transferred there from the former County Borough of Burton and Tutbury Urban
District Councils.

Acquisitions policy   Local archives are accepted on deposit or as gifts.

Major collections   The Anglesey Documents, relating to Burton Abbey, deposited by
the Marquess of Anglesey.
Local authority records from local councils.
Board of Guardians records.
Burton Methodist archives.
Education records from the former County Borough of Burton.

Facilities   Microfilm reader.

Publications   *Historical Collections of Staffordshire* [list of Anglesey documents]

80 Metropolitan Borough of Bury
Central Library

Address   Manchester Road
Bury
Lancashire BL9 0DG

Archives are held but no details are available. Access is difficult and there are no
facilities for readers.

81

Suffolk Record Office
Bury St Edmunds Branch

Address   Schoolhall Street
                Bury St Edmunds
                Suffolk 1P33 1RX

Telephone   (0284) 63141 ext. 384

Enquiries to County Archivist, Miss Amanda Arrowsmith

Open   Mon–Thurs: 9.00–5.00
                Fri: 9.00–4.00
                Sat: 9.00–1.00; 2.00–5.00
                Material required on Sat must be ordered before 1.00 on Fri

Historical background   The Suffolk Record Offices at Bury St Edmunds and Ipswich (*see* entry **257**) were originally established in 1950 by the East and West Suffolk County Councils respectively, jointly with the Borough of Bury St Edmunds and the County Borough of Ipswich. In 1974 the two offices were amalgamated. The office also acts as the Diocesan Record Office for St Edmundsbury and Ipswich (archdeaconry of Sudbury).

Major collections   Usual local authority record holdings and deposited collections.

Facilities   Photocopying. Photography. Microfilming. Microfilm reader.

82

Gwynedd Archives Service
Caernarfon Area Record Office

Address   Postal: County Offices
                Shirehall Street
                Caernarfon
                Gwynedd LL55 1SH
                (Archives situated at Victoria Dock, Caernarfon)

Telephone   (0286) 4121

Enquiries to County Archivist, Mr Bryn R. Parry
                or
                Area Archivist, Mr G. Haulfryn Williams

Open   Mon, Tues, Thurs: 9.30–12.30; 1.30–5.00
                Wed: 9.30–12.30; 1.30–7.00
                Fri: 9.30–12.30; 1.30–4.30

Historical background   Merioneth County Record Office was founded in 1952 and Gwynedd Record Office was established in 1974, incorporating Anglesey and

Merioneth. The Office also acts as the Diocesan Record Office for Bangor and St Asaph (parish records). It gives administrative assistance to the Royal Welsh Fusiliers Regimental Museum, Caernarfon Castle. There are Gwynedd Archives Service Record Offices also at Dolgellau (*see* entry **142**) and Llangefni (*see* entry **303**).

Major collections   Usual local authority record holdings and deposited collections including the following which have a wider significance:
Records of the slate quarrying industry; shipping and other maritime history collections; major collection of prints and photographs.

Facilities   Photocopying. Photography.

Publications   W. O. Williams: *Guide to the Caernarvonshire Record Office* (1952)

83   Gwynedd County Council
Library Headquarters

Address   Maesincla
                 Caernarfon
                 Gwynedd LL55 1LH

No archives are held.

84   British Antarctic Survey

Address   Madingley Road
                 Cambridge
                 CB3 0ET

Telephone   (0223) 61188 ext. 200

Enquiries to   Archivist, Mrs G.J. Smith

Open   Mon–Fri: 10.00–4.00

Access   Approved readers on written application only.

Historical background   In 1943 'Operation Tabarin' was organized by the navy to keep a British presence in the Antarctic during wartime. Of the bases establised in the ensuing years, five are currently occupied. Scientific work was undertaken from the beginning starting with meteorology and surveying; this has subsequently expanded into all branches of atmospheric, earth and life sciences. After World War II 'Operation Tabarin' was renamed the Falkland Islands Dependencies Survey and control was transferred to the Colonial Office. In 1950 a Scientific Bureau was established in London and from 1956 Units were set up at various universities. The Antarctic Treaty, which sought to open Antarctica to scientific investigation with territorial claims in abeyance, came into force in 1962, when the Antarctic part of the Falkland Islands Dependencies was designated the British Antarctic Territory and the name of the survey changed to the British Antarctic Survey (BAS). In 1967 BAS was made a component institute of the Natural Environment Research Council and moved into its new headquarters in Cambridge.

Acquisitions policy   Normal internal administrative accruals.

Major collections   Administrative papers of the London and present head office and of Port Stanley office [closed].
*c*4000 internal reports on the maintenance and scientific work of all British bases in the Falkland Islands Dependencies and British Antarctic Territory.
Field notes, maps, satellite photographs, processed data and draft papers of scientific staff in the fields of earth, atmospheric and life sciences.
Personal reminiscences of staff.
Copies of 'Operation Tabarin' scientific papers.

Non-manuscript material   Large film and photographic collection in charge of Publications Officer in use (open for consultation with permission).
Limited selection of historical books and extensive collection of relevant scientific publications in the Library.

Finding aids   MS card index pending transfer to computer for production of lists and indexes (in preparation).

Facilities   Photocopying. Photography.

Publications   Annual Reports (1967/8–)

85   Cambridge County Record Office
Cambridge Office

Address   Shire Hall
                 Castle Hill
                 Cambridge CB3 0AP

Telephone   (0223) 317281

Enquiries to   County Archivist, Mr J.M. Farrar

Open   Mon–Thurs: 9.00–12.45; 1.45–5.15 (Tues evening to 9.00, by appointment)
                 Fri: 9.00–12.45; 1.45–4.15

Historical background   The office was established for receipt of records in 1930, but had no staff until 1948. Before 1930 Cambridge University Library (*see* entry **87**) acted as a local repository and still has Diocesan and other ecclesiastical records. The office also acts as the Diocesan Record Office for Ely (parish records of archdeaconries of Ely and Wisbech). There is a Branch Office at Huntingdon (*see* entry **252**).

Major collections   Usual local authority record holdings and deposited collections including the following which have a wider significance:
Records of Bedford Level Corporation, 1663–1920 (with some earlier records): nearly complete series relating to land drainage of Fens and adjoining counties.
Records of various women's rights organizatons, of which Cambridge was particularly prolific, 1885–1981.

Facilities   Photocopying. Photography by arrangement. Microfilming. Microfilm/ fiche reader.

Publications   A. Black: *Guide to Education Records* (1972)
M. Farrar: *Genealogical Sources in Cambridgeshire* (1979)

86   Cambridgeshire Collection
Cambridgeshire Libraries

Address   Central Library
                     7 Lion Yard
                     Cambridge CB2 3QD

Telephone   (0223) 65252 ext. 30

Enquiries to   Local Studies Librarian, Mr M.J. Petty

Open   Mon–Fri: 10.00–5.30
                     Sat: 9.00–5.00

Access   Generally open to the public.

Historical background   Cambridge Free Library opened in June 1855 and from that date collected material relating to Cambridge and Cambridgeshire, both current and retrospective. In 1974 material from the local collection of Cambridgeshire and Isle of Ely County Library was incorporated with the City Library collection to form the current collection.

Acquisitions policy   To collect material, principally published, relating to the City of Cambridge and the former county of Cambridgeshire and Isle of Ely past, present and future.

Non-manuscript material   Photographic record of the Cambridge Antiquarian Society.
Industrial archaeological record of the Cambridge Society for Industrial Archaeology.
Various photographic collections.
Books, articles, annual reports, periodicals and associated monograph material.
Handbills and posters, 1734–.
Maps, principally printed, 1574–.
Newspapers, 1770–.
*c*60,000 illustrations, 1688–.

Tape recordings and gramophone records relating to Cambridgeshire.
Printed ephemera.

Finding aids   Catalogues. Indexes.

Facilities   Photocopying. Photography. Microfilm reader/printer. Tape play-back
facilities.

Publications   *Guide for Users*
    Guide to Catalogues and Indexes
    Cambridgeshire Newspapers and the Local Researcher
    Village Projects: A Guide for Users
    Local Studies in Your Library

87   Cambridge University Library

Address   University of Cambridge
    West Road
    Cambridge CB3 9DR

Telephone   (0223) 61441

Enquiries to   Library Manuscripts Department:
    Senior Under-Librarian for Special Collections, Mr A.E.B. Owen
    University Archives:
    Keeper of the Achives, Mrs D.M. Owen

Open   Manuscripts Room:
    Mon–Fri: 9.00–6.45
    Sat: 9.00–12.30
    Closed one week in September and certain other days

Access   Non-members of the University may be admitted on production of
    satisfactory references. Intending readers are advised to write in
    advance.

Historical background   Cambridge University is known to have possessed a library
    since the second decade of the 14th century. It retains few MSS from its pre–
    Reformation holdings, but since 1574 the MS collections have been continuously
    enlarged. The present Library building was opened in 1934. An extension was
    added in 1972 when the University Archives, until then separately housed, were
    brought into the Library.

Acquisitions policy   MSS of all types are acquired, with the emphasis on
    strengthening existing collections.

Major collections   The older collections, both Western and Oriental, are mainly of a
    literary character.
    The Taylor-Schechter Genizah Collection of Hebraica.
    Major Western MSS acquired over the past 100 years include: records of the

Diocese and Dean and Chapter of Ely; several East Anglian family and estate archives; private papers of Cambridge men e.g. Adam Sedgwick (1785–1873) and Charles Darwin (1809–82); records of University societies.
Commercial records of Jardine Matheson & Co., 19th century.
University archives (separately administered).

Non-manuscript material   The Manuscripts Department holds microfilms of MSS in other locations (e.g. the papers of Field Marshal J.C. Smuts (1870–1950)).

Finding aids   Lists and indexes.

Facilities   Photocopying. Photography. Microfilming. Microfilm readers.

Publications   *Catalogue of the (Western) Manuscripts preserved in the Library of the University of Cambridge* (Cambridge, 1856–67/R1980) [The preface to the reprint contains details of the principal catalogues of both Western and Oriental MS collections since 1867]
Various published lists and indexes

88   Centre of South Asian Studies

Address   University of Cambridge
Laundress Lane
Cambridge CB2 1SD

Telephone   (0223) 65621 ext. 202

Enquiries to   Archivist, Miss T.M. Thatcher

Open   Mon, Tues, Thurs, Fri: 9.30–5.30

Access   Written application two weeks in advance, with references and statement of study, preferred.

Historical background   The archive was begun in 1966 to collect papers relating to economic, social and political conditions during the period of British rule in India. Contact was made with persons whose papers would not otherwise have found their way into a collection. This was done through the Indian Civil Service Pensioners' Association, and later all recipients of a pension from the former Indian Empire were contacted. Funding has come from various sources.

Acquisitions policy   Contacts made by word of mouth are the main source of material, which is personally collected by the archivist.

Major collections   Papers of Sir Edward Benthall (1893–1961); Sir Malcolm Darling (1880–1969); J.T. Gwynn (1881–1956) and J.P.L. Gwynn, Indian Civil Service, Madras; P.T. Mansfield (1892–1975), ICS Bihar and Orissa; Sir Reginald (1882–1967) and Lady Maxwell, ICS Madras etc.
Collection of writings (memoirs, letters, etc) by British women who lived and worked in India, and a series of answers to questionnaires.

Non-manuscript material   Tape recordings made in India of people who knew Ghandi and were connected with the early days of the Independence Movement; the conditions in Delhi and the Punjab in 1947; Anglo-Indians; Roman Catholic missionaries and those who remained in India after 1947. Tape recordings made in England of wives and widows of Indian Civil Servants, and other Government Officers (Forestry etc) missionaries and educationalists.

Ciné films: home movies (16mm, 9.5mm and 8mm) covering aspects of domestic and social life, ceremonial, engineering, indigenous village life, people, crafts, tribals.

The Library includes 3555 pamphlets and offprints, 256 maps on South and South-east Asia, an Indian Newspaper Collection on microfilm and relevant indexes on South and South-east Asia in other libraries of the University.

Finding Aids   Typescript lists of unpublished material.

Facilities   Microfilm/fiche readers.

Publications   M. Thatcher, ed.: *Cambridge South Asian Archive: Records of the British period in South Asia relating to India, Pakistan, Ceylon, Burma, Nepal,* etc... (1973; 1980)
Catalogues (1980) [microfiche]
Paper on the film collection in *Internationales Asienforum* and British women in India 7th European Conference on Modern South Asian Studies (in preparation)

89   Christ's College Archives

Address   University of Cambridge
                   Cambridge CB2 3BU

Telephone   (0223) 67641

Enquiries to   College Archivist, Mr Edward A. Carson

Open   Mon–Fri: 9.00–1.00, by arrangement

Access   Subject to approval of Governing Body of Christ's College.

Historical background   The College was founded in 1439 as God's House, licensed by Henry VI and refounded in 1505 by the Lady Margaret Beaufort by whom the College was richly endowed.

Acquisitions policy   To receive gifts and bequests of MSS and photographic material from Fellows.

Major collections   Large number of archives from the 12th century onwards, including deeds, grants, manorial rolls, confirmations, conveyances, terriers, grants of advowsons, college account books, student admission books and numerous other records relating to the administration of the College.

Non-manuscript material   Some photographic material from the mid-19th century. A few tape recordings.

Maps and plans of College present and former estates.
Architectural plans and drawings of College buildings.

Finding aids   Lists and catalogue in preparation.

Facilities   Photocopying.

Publications   J. Peile: *Christ's College Bibliographical Register* (Cambridge, 1910)
[2 vols]
H. Rackham: *Early Statutes of Christ's College* (1927)

90   Churchill College Archives Centre

Address   Churchill College
University of Cambridge
Cambridge CB3 0DS

Telephone   (0223) 61200 ext.378 (Archivist)/287 (Search Rooms)

Enquiries to   The Archivist

Open   Mon–Fri: 9.30–12.30; 1.30–5.00

Access   This varies as certain collections have special conditions of access. In
all cases, the Archivist should be consulted first, in writing.

Historical background   The Archives Centre was built and endowed in 1973 by a
group of American wellwishers, including all the American Ambassadors to the
Court of St James's from 1925 until 1974, as the American tribute to the memory of
Sir Winston Churchill in the College which was the British and Commonwealth
memorial to him.

Acquisitions policy   As the chosen repository of the papers of Sir Winston Churchill
and his family, collections are acquired relating to all the phases of his career,
political and military, and to the statesmen, military leaders, government officials
and others who served with him or whose careers began in his time. As the College
was founded, by Sir Winston's wish, to concentrate on scientific studies (70
per cent science), scientific papers of members of the College or other
distinguished scientists are also collected.

Major collections   300 accessions of papers of political, military, naval, diplomatic
and scientific figures, mainly 20th century.

Non-manuscript material   Some microfilms.
The Roskill Library, occupying the two search rooms and comprising books about
Sir Winston Churchill and his era.

Finding aids   Most of the collections that are available have catalogues.

Facilities   Photocopying. Microfilm readers. Search room for use of typewriters or
dictaphones. Luncheon tickets can be purchased for use in the College.

Publications   *A Guide to the Holdings of Churchill College Archives Centre*, (1980)
[a complete list of collections, reprinted regularly]
Copies of the catalogues are sent to the National Register of Archives and are available from the College, for the cost of copying.

91   East Asian History of Science Library

Address   16 Brooklands Avenue
                 Cambridge CB2 2BB

Telephone   (0223) 311545/69252

Enquiries to   Librarian, Dr Michael Salt

Open   Mon–Fri: 9.30–6.00, by appointment only

Access   Bona fide scholars and research workers.

Historical background   The personal collection of Dr Joseph Needham (b. 1900) forms the nucleus round which the Library is developing. Dr Needham has been working, with a number of collaborators, for over 40 years on the history of Chinese science, technology, and medicine. The Library, as part of the Science and Civilization in China Project, became a recognized Educational Charity in 1963. It belongs to, and is governed by, the East Asian History of Science Trust.

Acquisitions policy   Chinese material of all periods connected with the history of science, technology and medicine is constantly being added, together with Japanese and Western material on the same subjects.

Major collections   There is little or no old MS material in the Library, but much archival and photographic material from 1940. There is a quantity of MSS in European and Asian languages, especially Chinese and Japanese, comprising notes, maps, etc.

Non-manuscript material   Printed books (including many rare Chinese editions), periodicals and offprints.
Microfilm and microfiche collections contain much Chinese material not widely available in the West.

Finding aids   Card catalogues.

Facilities   Photocopying. Microfilm/fiche reader.

Publications   J. Needham and others: *Science and Civilization in China* (Cambridge, 1954–) [11 vols to date].

92   Fitzwilliam Museum

Address   Department of Manuscripts and Printed Books
Trumpington Street
Cambridge CB2 1RB

Telephone   (0223) 69501

Enquiries to   The Keeper

Open   Tues–Thurs: 10–1.00; 2.15–4.45
Fri: 10.00–1.00; 2.15–4.15

Access   Museum staff, members of the University of Cambridge; others with special research enquiries on written application.

Historical background   The Museum was founded in 1816 by Richard, seventh Viscount Fitzwilliam of Merrion, when he bequeathed to the University of Cambridge, in which he took his MA in 1764, his fine art collections, his library, and the sum of £100,000 to build a museum. The Museum now has six curatorial departments: Antiquities, Applied Arts, Coins and Medals, Manuscripts and Printed Books, Paintings and Drawings, Prints.

Acquisitions policy   To strengthen the collection by purchase, gifts, bequests, loans.

Major collections   Illuminated MSS (Western and Oriental).
MS and printed music.
Literary and historical MSS.
Autograph letters.
McClean collection of illuminated MSS and incunabula.

Non-manuscript material   Lord Fitzwilliam's Library. Exhibition catalogues. Dealers' catalogues. Sale catalogues. Incunabula. Private Press books.

Finding aids   Card and slip catalogues.

Facilities   Photocopying. Photography. Microfilm/fiche reader/printer.

Publications   J.A. Fuller-Maitland and A.H. Mann: *Catalogue of the Music in the Fitzwilliam Museum* (London, 1893)
M.R. James: *A Descriptive Catalogue of the Manuscripts in the Fitzwilliam Museum* (Cambridge, 1895)
————: *A Descriptive Catalogue of the McClean Collection of Manuscripts in the Fitzwilliam Museum* (Cambridge, 1912).
F. Wormald and P.M. Giles: *A Descriptive Catalogue of the additional Illuminated Manuscripts in the Fitzwilliam Museum acquired between 1895 and 1979* (Cambridge, 1982)

93   Gonville and Caius College

Address   University of Cambridge
                Cambridge CB2 1TA

Telephone   (0223) 12211

Enquiries to   The Bursar
                or
                The Archivist

Muniments are held within the College Bursar's Office. There are no facilities for readers and no finding aids, apart from the *Registrum*, a MS volume of 17th-century provenance. The College will try to answer written enquiries. Maps are in process of being listed.

94   Institute of Astronomy Library

Address   University of Cambridge
                The Observatories
                Madingley Road
                Cambridge CB3 0HA

Telephone   (0223) 62204

Enquiries to   Librarian, Dr D.W. Dewhirst

Open   Term: Mon–Fri: 9.00–1.00; 2.00–5.00
                Vacation: enquiry necessary

Access   Members of the University. Accredited readers by prior written request.

Historical background Founded in 1823 as the Library of the University Observatory, it then acquired many earlier books; later the libraries of the former Solar Physics Observatory and Institute of Theoretical Astronomy were incorporated.

Acquisitions policy Now mostly books, conference proceedings, periodicals and serials on modern astronomy; also material relating to history of astronomy.

Major collections MSS archives and observational records of Cambridge Observatories, 1823–.
Correspondence and some scientific papers of former Directors and staff members, especially G.B. Airy (1801–1892), R.S. Ball (1840–1913), J. Challis (1803–1882), A. Hinks (1873–1945).

Non-manuscript material 800 periodical and serial titles relating to astronomy (8500 vols). 4500 monographs. Sky surveys, star maps and catalogues. Offprint and pamphlet collection.

Finding aids   Finding list to 19th century MS letters etc.

Facilities   Photocopying. Microfilm readers.

Publications   *Notes on the Use of the Library*.

95   Institute of Education

Address   University of Cambridge
Shaftesbury Road
Cambridge CB2 2BX

There are no deposited collections. Internal records are held.

96   St John's College

Address   University of Cambridge
Cambridge CB2 1TP

Telephone   (0223) 354688/61621

Enquiries to   Archivist, Mr M. Underwood

Open   Mon–Fri: 10.00–1.00; 2.15–5.30, by appointment

Access   Open to those having a letter of reference, subject to the discretion of the archivist. 50-year closure on personal and administrative records unless otherwise approved by the college.

Historical background   The college was founded in 1511 by the executors of Lady Margaret Beaufort, mother of Henry VII, as successor to, and on the site of the hospital of St John the Evangelist. Statutes made for its government by Bishop Fisher from 1516 to 1530 were all superseded by new ones given by the crown in 1545 and these in turn by others in 1580, until the 19th–century commissions ushered in a period of frequent reform and reorganization. The college is now governed by statutes made in 1926–7 (under powers given to the Universities Commission in 1923), as subsequently amended by the governing body of the college.

Acquisitions policy   Acquisitions are restricted to records relating directly to the college and to members of it.

Major collections   Administrative and financial records of the college from its foundation, including accounts and correspondence of college officers and records of admissions of members (regularly from 1545).
Title deeds of college estates and those of the hospital of St John, the hospital of Ospringe, Kent, the priory of Higham, Kent, and the priory of Broomhall, Berkshire. Some household accounts of Lady Margaret Beaufort (1443–1509).

Non-manuscript material   Printed bills and Acts of Parliament relating to college properties.

Printed matter relating to the University's affairs in the late 18th century and 19th century.

Numerous maps, plans and surveys; architectural drawings relating to the college site.

A few photographs of the college buildings and certain properties.

Ordnance Survey 6" and 25" maps of Cambridge city and areas in which the college holds property; a few other printed maps.

Finding aids   Calendar with supplementary card index. General catalogue in preparation.

Facilities   Photocopying, subject to discretion of archivist.

Publications   T. Baker: *History of St John's College Cambridge*, ed. J.E.B. Mayor, i (Cambridge, 1869) [Calendars of college registers c1545–1671]

J.E.B. Mayor and R.F. Scott: *Admissions to the College of St John the Evangelist, Cambridge* i–iv (Cambridge, 1882–1931)

Records printed by R.F. Scott in *Notes from the College Records* [extracts from *The Eagle*, 1889–1915, college magazine]

97   Scott Polar Research Institute

Address   University of Cambridge
Lensfield Road
Cambridge CB2 1ER

Telephone   (0223) 66499

Enquiries to   Curator, Mr Clive Holland

Open   Mon–Fri: 9.00–1.00; 2.15–5.30

Access   Bona fide students on application.

Historical background   The Scott Polar Research Institute was founded in 1920 as a memorial to Captain Robert Falcon Scott and his four companions who died returning from the South Pole in 1912. The MS collection was started in the same year with a deposit of papers relating to Scott's two Antarctic expeditions, and has continued to expand ever since with the acquisition of documents relating to all aspects of Arctic and Antarctic exploration and research, particularly expedition diaries and correspondence.

Acquisitions policy   To continue to extend the collection by donations, deposits, and occasional purchases.

Major collections   Records of Captain Scott's Antarctic expeditions, 1901–4 and 1910–13, and of numerous other expeditions in the heroic era of Antarctic exploration, 1900–20.

Records of the search for the North–west Passage in the 19th century, notably the personal papers of Sir John Franklin (1786–1847), Lady Jane Franklin (1792–1875), Sir George Back (1796–1878), Sir William Parry (1790–1855), Sir John (Clark) Ross (1777–1856) and Sir James Clark Ross (1800–62).

Non-manuscript material   Extensive collections of watercolours, drawings and prints, photographs, films, sound recordings, press cuttings.

Finding aids   Author/biographical catalogue. Index of expeditions and voyages.

Facilities   Photocopying. Photography and microfilming by arrangement. Microfilm/fiche reader.

Publications   Ann Savours: 'The Manuscript collection of the Scott Polar Research Institute, Cambridge', *Archives*, iv/22 (1959), 102
A catalogue of the collection is in preparation.

98   Seeley Historical Library

Address   University of Cambridge
               Faculty of History
               West Road
               Cambridge CB3 9EF

The Library holds little archival material but has microfilms of Kenya National Archive.

99   Canterbury Cathedral, City and Diocesan Record Office

Address   The Precincts
               Canterbury
               Kent CT1 2EG

Telephone   (0227) 63510

Enquiries to   Archivist and Director, Miss Anne M. Oakley

Open   Mon–Fri: 9.30–12.45; 2.00–4.30, by appointment
               Closed one week in each quarter

Access   Fees are charged for some categories of diocesan records.

Historical background   Cathedral records have been kept here since the foundation of the Cathedral in 597.
   From 1884 to 1915 and 1956 to 1970 the office acted as the City Record Office, and from 1970 it has been run as the joint City and Chapter Record Office. It became the Diocesan Record Office in 1959 and the Archive Filing Unit for Council was

opened in 1981.

Acquisitions policy   Normal statutory acquisitions from all three authorities; no purchases are made but deposits or gifts are accepted.

Major collections   Records of:
Dean and Chapter of Canterbury, 742–
City of Canterbury 1200–
Diocese of Canterbury c1400–1869; parish records for the Archdeaconry of Canterbury.

Finding aids   Catalogues are available for most records.

100   Institute of Heraldic and Genealogical Studies

Address   Northgate
                 Canterbury
                 Kent CT1 1BA

Telephone   (0227) 68664

Enquiries to   Hon. Librarian, Mr Frank Higenbottam

Open   Mon–Fri: 9.30–6.00

Access   Approved readers on written application. Times restricted except for full-time students.

Historical background   A school for the study of the history and structure of the family was founded by Cecil Humphery-Smith on the suggestion of the late Canon K.J.F. Bickersteth in 1957. The Institute opened in Canterbury in 1961 and was established as an educational trust. Subsequently it moved into its present premises (which date from 1283 with 16th-century and later additions). Full-time and other courses of instruction are held to train and qualify members of the genealogical profession and provide researchers into the applications of family history studies.

Acquisitions policy   To build a corpus of original material for the study of social, economic and environmental changes and historical structures of family life.

Major collections   Family History, unpublished MSS collections relating to some 15,000 family groups.
Case histories and genealogical tracings.
Estate maps, collections of deeds and related documentation, manorial incidences and papers, 13th–20th centuries.
Tyler Collection: extracts from Kentish parish records, wills, marriage settlements, local history material. Several hundred MS notebooks by eminent antiquary and family historian, and related documents.
Hackman Collection: similar material for Hampshire.
Humphery-Smith Collection: extensive MS notes on Sussex families, records of

coats of arms in all churches of Sussex county, in Canterbury Cathedral and elsewhere, with related research notes; very large British and European armorial indexes; transcripts of rolls of arms and heraldic treatises with related notes; several original heralds' notebooks, painted and blazoned armorials (16th and 17th centuries).

Culleton Papers: four large bound MS books of working papers of 19th-century genealogical and heraldic practice.

MS Indexes: The Augmented Pallot Index to several million London marriages. Andrew's Index to British overseas.

Non-manuscript material c5000 pamphlets relating to parish and local histories. A collection of European heraldic works unique in the UK.

Finding aids Lists, indexes and guides. A comprehensive classified catalogue is in preparation.

Facilities Photocopying. Microfilm/fiche. Palaeographic aids.

Publications *Family History* (1962–) Journal of the Institute
Guide to Pallot Index
Maps of the parishes and probate jurisdictions of the UK and other research aids.

101 St Augustine's Library

Address Monastery Street
Canterbury
Kent CT1 1NL

No archives are held; the MS collections have been dispersed to various national repositories.

102 University of Kent at Canterbury Library

Address Canterbury
Kent CT2 7NU

Telephone (0227) 66822 ext. 289

Enquiries to Librarian, Mr W.J. Simpson
or
Special Collections Librarian, Mr R.S. Holland

Open Mon–Fri: 9.00–5.00

Access Approved readers on written application.

Historical background The University was founded in 1963.

Acquisitions policy Selected acquisitions of material related to existing collections.

Major collections   The Frank Pettingell Collection of Nineteenth-Century Drama. This includes 1296 MSS and typescripts of plays, only 36 of which are known to have been published. Several hundred MSS related to productions at the Britannia Theatre, Hoxton.

Non-manuscript material   The Frank Pettingell Collection contains *c*7000 items. Apart from the MSS noted above, there are *c*3000 printed texts, separately bound (with many prompt-books and actors' copies); 1800 printed texts in composite vols; 331 pantomime libretti; and over 300 playbills.
A collection of popular literature, chiefly ballads and popular poetry, with some chap-books.
The Grace Pettman Collection, including her writings in 20th-century popular magazines and religious tracts.
Kingsley Wood Press Cuttings: 25 large press cutting books covering the career of the politician and cabinet minister, 1903–40.

Finding aids   A catalogue to the Frank Pettingell Collection exists in typescript in the Library. Other material is in the process of being catalogued.

Facilities   Photocopying. Photography. Microfilm/fiche printer.

Publications   G.S. Darlow: 'A Brief Description of the Frank Pettingell Collection of Plays in the University Library, Canterbury, Kent', *Theatre Notebook*, xxxi/3 (1977), 2

103   British Steel Corporation
Records Services Section

Address   South Wales Regional Records Centre
               Gabalfa
               Cardiff

Telephone   (0222) 62161

Enquiries to   Western Region Manager, Mr P. Emmerson

The archive covers South Wales and the southwest of England. For enquiries covering more than one region write to The Director, Secretariat, at the Corporation's Head Office, 33 Grosvenor Place, London SW1.
For other information in common with each Records Centre *see* East Midlands Regional Records Centre, Wellingborough (entry **687**).

104   County of South Glamorgan Libraries

Address   Central Library
              South Glamorgan Library Service
              The Hayes
              Cardiff CF1 2QU

Telephone   (0222) 22116

Enquiries to   County Librarian, Mr G.A.C. Dart

Open   Mon–Fri: 9.30–8.00
              Sat: 9.30–5.30
              (MS material not available after 4.30)

Access   Apply in advance for special reader's ticket.

Historical background   The Library was founded in 1862 as the Cardiff Free Library
   with the following foundation collections: (a) MSS acquired with the Town
   Library, purchased from the Rees family of Llandovery in 1891; (b) literary and
   historical MSS and deeds of Welsh interest, purchased from the collection of Sir
   Thomas Phillips in 1896. Subsequent additions by purchase (especially in the
   1920s–1950s) and gift from a variety of sources.

Acquisitions policy   Acquisitions have virtually ceased. Some items, plus the
   majority of deeds and manorial documents (which relate to all Welsh counties and
   Cheshire, Gloucester, Hereford and Shropshire) are currently being transferred to
   Glamorgan Archives Service, Cardiff (*see* entry **106**).

Major collections   c100 vols Welsh literary MSS, mostly poetry, medieval to the 18th
   century.
   c50 vols of non-Welsh medieval MSS, mostly religious.
   c4300 groups of historical MSS, mostly relating to Wales and including 19th- and
   20th-century literary MSS.
   Papers of Alfred Thomas, Lord Pontypridd (1840–1927); papers of the third earl of
   Bute and the marquesses of Bute, 12th–19th centuries.

Non-manuscript material   Mackworth Collection of early music includes MSS and
   printed music, mostly 18th century (c500 printed items, 60 MSS).
   Large collection of maps, photographs, prints, original drawings etc, relating to
   Wales (c20,000 items).

Finding aids   Card index and shelf list. Typescript catalogue of Mackworth
   Collection.

Facilities   Photocopying. Microfilm readers.

Publications   N.R. Ker: 'Cardiff Public Library', *Medieval Manuscripts in British
   Libraries*, ii (Oxford, 1977), xx, 331–77
   MSS are described in various Library reprints, and brief details of recent
   acquisitions are in *Morgannwg* ii–xv (1958–71)

105   David Owen Centre for Population Growth Studies

Address	University College PO Box 78 Cardiff CF1 1XL
Telephone	(0222) 44211 ext. 2610/2690
Enquiries to	Technical Information Officer, Ms V. Blakey
Open	Mon–Fri: 9.30–5.00
Access	Bona fide researchers. Readers for Family Planning Association (FPA) archives should seek prior written approval from the FPA at 27–35 Mortimer Street, London W1.

Historical background   The archives of the FPA were deposited with the David Owen Centre in 1976.

Acquisitions policy   Acquisitions cover primary and secondary material relating to the FPA. Since 1973 acquisitions have mainly included material relating to the FPA's press and information department.

Major collections   FPA records, relating to the development of birth control services, 1920s–72 (the bulk of the archive relates to the period 1930–68). Records of the International Planned Parenthood Federation.

Finding aids   Class list. Index.

Facilities   Photocopying.

106   Glamorgan Archive Service

Address	Mid Glamorgan County Hall Cathays Park Cardiff CF1 3NE
Telephone	(0222) 28033 ext. 282
Enquiries to	Glamorgan Archivist, Mrs Patricia Moore
Open	Tues–Thurs: 9.00–5.00 Fri: 9.00–4.30

Historical background   The office was established in 1939 to serve the county of Glamorgan, which was split into the counties of West Glamorgan, Mid Glamorgan and South Glamorgan on local government reorganization in 1974; these three authorities now jointly fund the Glamorgan Archive Service. Since local government reorganization, the office administers the archive collection of the former City Library, Cardiff, now the County of South Glamorgan Library (*see* entry **104**). It also acts as the Diocesan Record Office for Llandaff, Swansea and Brecon (parish records). Pending the establishment of an area office, there are temporary search-room facilities in Swansea, West Glamorgan, on the third Thursday of each month.

Major collections   Usual local authority records and deposited collections including the following which have a wider significance:

South Wales Coalfield, pre-1947 records received from National Coal Board.

Dowlais Iron Company collection, containing extensive correspondence, 1792–.

Society of Friends records relating to the whole of Wales, 1650–.

Bruce Collection, containing correspondence received by the first Lord Aberdare (1815–95).

Papers of John Singleton Copley, Baron Lyndhurst (1772–1863), Lord Chancellor.

Facilities   Photocopying. Photography. Microfilming. Microfilm reader.

Publications   *Dowlais Iron Company. Calendar of the London House Letter-book Series, 1837–1867* [42 schedules; reproduced typescript]

107   National Museum of Wales
Welsh Industrial and Maritime Museum

Address   Bute Street
                 Cardiff CF1 6AN

Telephone   (0222) 371805

Enquiries to   The Curator, Mr J. Geraint Jenkins

Open   By appointment
                 Museum open: Mon–Sat: 10.30–5.00
                 Sun: 2.00–5.00

Access   Generally open to the public.

Historical background   The Museum was recently established within the framework of the National Museum of Wales and deals with the industrial and maritime history of Wales.

Acquisitions policy   To collect relevant MSS, artefacts and photographs relating to industrial Wales.

Major collections   Records of shipping companies and Welsh railways etc; also of coal mines and other industrial undertakings.

Non-manuscript material   An extensive collection of photographs, prints and drawings relating to Wales.

Plans, drawings and maps included in the above collections.

Finding aids   Card index.

108   University College, Cardiff

Address	The Library University College PO Box 78 Cardiff CF1 1XL
Telephone	(0222) 44211
Enquiries to	The Librarian *or* Archivist to Youth Movement Archive, Mr Michael Breaks
Open	Mon–Fri: 9.00–5.00, appointment preferred At other times when the Library is open prior appointment is essential.
Access	Members of University College, Cardiff; others on written application.

Historical background   The College was founded in 1883; during the century of its existence the Library has accumulated a number of archival collections, as well as miscellaneous individual documents. The Youth Movement Archive, housed in the Library, was founded in 1973.

Acquisitions policy   There is no acquisitions policy except in relation to the Youth Movement Archive, for which there is an active policy of collecting research materials on the full range of youth movement history.

Major collections   Youth Movement Archive (the main components being records of Kibbo Kift and the Woodcraft Folk).
Cardiff Trades Council records.
Letters and scrapbooks of Edward Thomas (1878–1917), poet.
Papers and printed ephemera of E.G.R. Salisbury (1819–90).
Library archive.
Papers of deceased members of the College including Cyril Brett, Professor of English (*d* 1936); B.J. Morse, lecturer in Italian (*d* 1977); C.M. Thompson, Professor of Chemistry (*d* 1932).

Finding aids   The various archive collections are in process of being sorted and listed. A handlist of the Youth Movement Archive should be available in 1982/3.

Facilities   Photocopying. Photography. Microfilm/fiche readers.

109 University of Wales Institute of Science and Technology (UWIST)

Address   King Edward VII Avenue
Cardiff CF1 3NU

No archives are held.

110 Welsh Folk Museum

Address   St Fagans
Cardiff CF5 6XB

Telephone   (0222) 569441 ext.37

Enquiries to Archivist, Mr A. Lloyd Hughes

Open   Mon–Fri: 9.30–1.00; 1.45–4.30

Access   Bona fide researchers, preferably by prior arrangement.

Historical background   In March 1946, the Earl of Plymouth offered St Fagans Castle, some four miles north-west of Cardiff, with its 18 acres of gardens and grounds, to the National Museum of Wales as a centre for a Folk Museum. A further 80 acres of St Fagans Park immediately adjacent to the gardens were also transferred on very acceptable terms. Through Lord Plymouth's generosity, therefore, Wales was provided with approximately 100 acres of land in situation and character ideal as a site for the development of the Welsh Folk Museum. It was opened to the public in 1948.

Acquisitions policy   To complement existing collections in the fields of Welsh ethnology by donations or deposits, in co-operation with other archival institutions in Wales.

Major collections   Ty'n-y-pant MSS: *c*800 MSS in the Welsh language relating to the history and folklore of Cantref Buallt, Breconshire (now Powys).
T.C. Evans and T.H. Thomas MSS, relating to Glamorgan folklore and dialect, the National Eisteddfod, Gorsedd of Bards, heraldry etc.
W. Meredith Morris MSS, relating to the folklore and dialect of Pembrokeshire (now Dyfed), musicology etc.
Farmers' and craftsmen's account books, diaries, eisteddfodic essays etc.
Questionnaires on aspects of Welsh folk cultures.

Non-manuscript material   Pamphlets and broadsides.
*c*60,000 photographs; *c*200 cine-films.
Sound archives (*c*6000 tapes).
The library houses a unique collection of some 20,000 books and periodicals of historical and ethnological interest with special emphasis on Wales.

Facilities   Photocopying. Photography. Microfilm/fiche reader. Playback tape recorders.

Publications   A. Lloyd Hughes: 'The Welsh Folk Museum Manuscripts', *Folk Life*, xvii (1979), 68
Catalogue of Welsh Folk MSS 1–3000 (1979, 1981) [3 vols to date]

111   Welsh National School of Medicine Library

Address   Heath Park
                 Cardiff CF4 4XN

No archives are held.

112   Carlisle Cathedral Library

Address   c/o The Cathedral
                 Carlisle
                 Cumbria CA3 8TZ

Telephone   (0228) 35169

Enquiries to   The Librarian

Open   By arrangement

Access   Responsible and qualified persons.

Historical background   The Library is based on the theological library of a 17th-century bishop.

Acquisitions policy   Occasionally MSS are accepted.

Major collections   Ecclesiastical muniments and MSS of the Cathedral and Diocese of Carlisle.

Finding aids   Index.

Facilities   Table. Chairs. No reprographic facilities.

113   Cumbria County Library

Address   County Library Headquarters
                 18–19 Portland Square
                 Carlisle
                 Cumbria CA1 1PS

Telephone   (0228) 48481

Enquiries to   The Assistant County Librarian (Bibliographic Services)

Local History Collection, principally of non-MSS material.

114   Cumbria County Record Office
Carlisle Office

Address   The Castle
                 Carlisle
                 Cumbria CA3 8UR

Telephone   (0228) 23456 ext. 314/316

Enquiries to   County Archivist, Mr B.C. Jones

Open   Mon–Fri: 9.00–5.00

Historical background   The Office was officially opened in 1962 although archives had been collected before then and staff appointed from c1944. It also acts as the Diocesan Record Office for Carlisle. Administrative assistance is given to Carlisle Dean and Chapter Library and Egremont Estate Office, Cockermouth Castle. There are branch offices at Kendal and Barrow-in-Furness (*see* entries **264** and **33** respectively).

Major collections   Usual local authority record holdings and deposited collections of which the following have a wider significance:
Political and other personal papers of Sir Esme Howard (Lord Howard of Penrith), diplomat, 1780–1961.
Papers of Catherine Marshall, suffragist and pacifist, of Hawse End, Keswick, c1880–1956.

Facilities   Photocopying. Photography. Microfilming. Microfilm reader.

Publications   R.C. Javis: *The Jacobite Rising of 1715 and 1745*, Cumberland County Council Record Series, *i* (Carlisle, 1954)
E. Hughes, ed.: *The Fleming Senhouse Papers,* Cumberland County Council Record Series, *ii* (Carlisle, 1961)
B.C. Jones: 'Cumberland Westmorland and Carlisle Record Office, 1960–65', *Archives*, vii/34 (1965), 80
H.W. Hodgson: *A Bibliography of the History and Topography of Cumberland and Westmorland* (Carlisle, 1968)
B.C. Jones: 'Cumberland and Westmorland Record Offices, 1968', *Northern History*, iii (1968), 162

115   Dyfed Archives Service
Carmarthen Office

Address   County Hall
                 Carmarthen SA31 1JP

Telephone   Headquarters: (0267) 233333 ext. 4182

Enquiries to   County Archivist, Miss M. Patch (at Headquarters)
                 or
                 Archivist-in-charge, Miss S.G. Beckley

Open   Mon–Thurs: 9.00–4.45
                 Fri: 9.00–4.15
                 Sat (1st and 3rd in each month, except Bank holiday weekends):
                 9.30–12.30, by appointment

Historical background   The office was established as Carmarthenshire Record Office in 1959. It also acts as the Diocesan Record Office for St David's (parish registers). There are branch offices at Aberystwyth and Haverfordwest (*see* entries **9** and **237** respectively).

Major collections   Usual local authority record holdings and deposited collections including the following which has a wider significance:
Cawdor Collection, containing the *Golden Grove Book*, an 18th-century collection of pedigrees relating to the whole of Wales.

Facilities   Photocopying. Photography. Microfilming. Microfilm reader.

Publications   S.G. Beckley: *Carmarthen Record Office Survey of Archive Holdings* (1980)

116   Dyfed County Library Headquarters

Address   St Peter's Street
                 Carmarthen
                 Dyfed SA31 1IN

Archives are neither held nor acquired.

117   Essex Record Office

Address   County Hall
                 Chelmsford
                 Essex CM1 1LX

Telephone	(0245) 267222 ext. 2104
Enquiries to	County Archivist, Mr V.W. Gray
Open	Mon: 10.00–8.45
	Tues–Thurs: 9.15–5.15
	Fri: 9.15–4.15

Historical background   The Record Office opened formally in 1939, although parish and other records had been collected from 1936. Before the reorganization of London in 1964 the office covered old Essex, which included the boroughs of Havering, Barking and Dagenham, Waltham Forest, Newham and Redbridge. The office also acts as the Diocesan Record Office for Chelmsford. There is a branch office at Southend (*see* entry **642**).

Major collections   Usual local authority record holdings and deposited collections including the following which have a wider significance:
Papers of Sir Thomas Smith relating to the colonization of the Ards in Ulster, 1572–77.
Correspondence of the Cornwallis and Bacon families, 1622–80.
Record book and papers of William Holcroft as JP, verderer and captain of militia, 1661–8.
Antiquarian and literary correspondence of Charles Gray, 1728–76.
Journals and correspondence of James Paroissien, relating to South America, 1806–27.

Facilities   Photocopying. Photography. Microfilming. Microfilm reader.

Publications   F.G. Emmison: *Guide to the Essex Record Office* (1969)

118   Cheshire County Council
Libraries and Museums Department

Address	91 Hoole Road
	Chester
	Cheshire CH2 3NG

Most archives previously held have been transferred, principally to Cheshire Record Office (*see* entry **119**), but archives are held by the North Division in Warrington Library (*see* entry **684**).

119   Cheshire Record Office

Address	The Castle
	Chester
	Cheshire CH1 2DN
Telephone	Enquiries: (0244) 602574

County Archivist: (0244) 602560

Enquiries to   County Archivist, Mr B.C. Redwood

Open   By appointment
Mon–Fri: 9.00–5.00; 1st and 3rd Mon of each month: 9.00–9.00

Historical background   There was no formal collecting policy before 1933, when a voluntary archivist started to work on the records. The first archivist was appointed in 1949. The office also acts as the Diocesan Record Office for Chester. Administrative assistance is given to Grosvenor of Eaton, Estate Office, Chester.

Major collections   Usual local authority record holdings and deposited collections.

Facilities   Photocopying. Photography and microfilming by arrangement. Microfilm readers.

Publications   Source sheets to main series of records are available singly or combined as *Summary Guide*
County Record Office and Chester Diocesan Record Office, Summary Guide 1975 [typescript; periodically revised]

120   Chester City Record Office

Address   Town Hall
Chester
Cheshire CH1 2HJ

Telephone   (0244) 40144 ext. 2108

Enquiries to   City Archivist, Miss A.M. Kennett

Open   Mon: 9.00–1.00; 2.00–9.00 (after 5.00 by appointment)
Tues–Fri: 9.00–1.00; 2.00–5.00

Historical background   Chester City Record Office was established by Chester County Borough Council in 1948. Since 1974 it has served the new City of Chester, one of eight districts of Cheshire. The City Archivist is Honorary Archivist to the Freemen and Guilds of the City of Chester. Administrative assistance is given to the Grosvenor Estates (Duke of Westminster's MSS), Eaton Estate Office, Eccleston, Chester. The office houses Chester Archaeological Society Library and MSS (the City Archivist is Honorary Archivist to the Society).

Major collections   Usual local authority record holdings and deposited collections including:
Archives of ten of the city guilds; Chester Bluecoat Hospital; Chester College; Chester Royal Infirmary.
MSS of J.P. Earwaker, antiquarian.

Facilities   Photocopying. Photography.

Publications   A.M Kennett: *Chester Schools, A Guide to the School Archives* (1973)

121 Derbyshire Library Service
Local Studies Department

Address Chesterfield Central Library
Corporation Street
Chesterfield
Derbyshire S41 7TY

Telephone (0246) 32047

Enquiries to Reference Librarian, Mr J. Lilley

Open Mon, Tues, Thurs, Fri: 10.00–7.00
Wed: 10.00–5.30
Sat: 9.30–1.00

Access Generally open to the public, but since archives are housed in a separate building it is advisable to write in advance.

Historical background The Library was established in 1879 with a strong engineering background, due to George Stephenson's influence. It has gradually accumulated archival material over the years. The Library came under Derbyshire County Council with reorganization in 1974 and it is hoped that it will move into a new central library in 1984.

Acquisitions policy To strengthen and enlarge existing primary and secondary collections on the history of Derbyshire and environmental studies within the country.

Major collections Collections of family papers including: Barnes family, landowners and owners of Grassmore colliery, including bills and accounts, 18th–19th centuries (c1000 items); Twigg family, from Ashover area, some material relating to local mining, mostly 18th century (c500 items).
Records of local businesses including Plowrights Brothers Ltd, engineering firm; Greaves, chemist shop, from mid-19th century.
Methodist records for Chesterfield; Unitarian church records.
Education records including school log books, Chesterfield School Board and Chesterfield Education Committee.

Non-manuscript material Stephenson Collection of books, pamphlets etc, showing contribution of George Stephenson to railway history.
Census returns, 1841–71.
Newspapers: *Derbyshire Times*, 1854–; *Derbyshire Courier*, 1831–53.
Maps, historical and current, of various scales covering Chesterfield area.

Finding aids Various lists and indexes.

Facilities Photocopying. Microfilm/fiche reader.

Publications *Derbyshire Local Studies Collection: a Guide to Resources* (rev., 1982)

122   West Sussex County Council
Library Headquarters

Address   Administration Centre
                 Tower Steet
                 Chichester
                 West Sussex PO19 1QJ

Archives are neither held nor acquired.

123   West Sussex Record Office

Address   West Street
                 Chichester
                 West Sussex PO19 1RN

Telephone   (0243) 777100 ext. 2770/777983

Enquiries to   County Archivist, Mrs P. Gill

Open   Mon–Fri: 9.15–12.30; 1.30–5.00

Historical background   The Records Committee was set up in 1939 and took in
   records from that date, although an archivist was not appointed until 1946.
   Since reorganization in 1974 the Office has covered the old West Sussex area and
   part of what was East Sussex. The office also acts as the Diocesan Record Office
   for Chichester.

Major collections   Usual local authority record holdings and deposited collections
   including the following which have a wider significance:
   Wilfred Scawen Blunt MSS: Irish and Middle Eastern politics, and literary, 19th
   and 20th centuries.
   Cobden MSS: politics, 19th century.
   Eric Gill Collection: works of art, 20th century.
   Goodwood MSS: political and cultural, 18th and 19th centuries.
   Maxse MSS: politics, 20th century.
   Petworth House Archives: Thomas Harriott astronomical papers, 17th century.
   Royal Sussex Regiment MSS: military, 18th–20th centuries.

Facilities   Photocopying. Photography. Microfilming. Microfilm reader/printers.

Publications   *Official Guide and Report on the East and West Sussex Record Offices*
   (1954)
   F.W. Steer and I.M. Kirby: *Catalogue of the Records of the Bishop, Archdeacons
   and Former Exempt Jurisdictions* (1966)
   P.M. Wilkinson: *Genealogists Guide to the West Sussex Record Office* (1979)
   Over 50 publications [list available]
   See also 'Publications' under East Sussex Record Office (entry **290**)

124 Clydebank District Libraries

Address   Central Library
Dumbarton Road
Clydebank
Strathclyde G81 1XH

Telephone   (041) 952 1416

Enquiries to   District Chief Librarian, Mr John Hood

Local History Collection of non-MSS material, including the Singer Sewing Machine Company collection.

125 Essex County Libraries
Local Studies Department

Address   Colchester Central Library
Trinity Square
Colchester
Essex CO1 1JB

Telephone   (0206) 62243

Enquiries to   Local Studies Librarian, Mr P.R. Gifford

Open   Mon–Wed, Fri: 9.00–8.00
Thurs, Sat: 9.00–5.00

Access   Generally open to the public. Notice is preferred for access to special collections.

Historical background   The department was established in 1974 for the acquisition of local material.

Acquisitions policy   To strengthen, augment and continue the furtherance of knowledge relating to all aspects of Essex, by means of purchase, donations etc.

Major collections   c400 Committee Minute Books, mid-19th century to 1950.
2000 Colchester MS indentures, releases etc, c1600–c1900.
Rebow papers (5000) c1600–1931.
Taylor MSS with letters (261).
Various local studies MSS (c200), 16th–20th centuries.

Non-manuscript material   Harsnett Library: personal library of Archbishop Samuel Harsnett (1561–1631) comprising c900 books of bibliographical and religious rarity and interest.
Sound archives: c30 tapes of local material.
Maps and illustrations.

Finding aids Catalogues and indexes.

Facilities Photocopying. Photography. Microfilm/fiche reader/printers.

Publications Essex Libraries leaflet: *Local Studies. Guide to Resources*

126 University of Essex

Address   The Library
PO Box 24
Colchester
Essex CO4 3UA

Telephone   (0206) 862286

Enquiries to   The Librarian

Open   Term: Mon–Fri: 9.00a.m.–10.00p.m.
Sat: 9.00–6.00
Sun: 2.00–7.00
Vacation: Mon–Fri: 9.00–5.30

Access   On written application to the Librarian.

Historical background   The University of Essex was founded in 1963.

Acquisitions policy   Donation or deposit of records either relevant to the teaching and research at the University or of local interest.

Major collections   Archives of the Colchester and Coggeshall Meetings of the Society of Friends, including correspondence of Steven Crisp.
Papers of the Rowhedge Iron Works.
Letters and papers of Henri and Sophie Gaudier-Brzeska.
Diaries, papers and work-ledger of John Hassall, poster artist and book illustrator.
Diaries of Samuel Levi Bensusan (1872–1958), author.
Papers of Professor Donald Davie (*b* 1922), author.

Finding aids   Handlist to the Archives of the Colchester and Coggeshall Meetings of the Society of Friends (cf. S.H.G. Fich, *Colchester Quakers*; Colchester, 1962), and to the papers of the Rowhedge Iron Works.

Facilities   Photocopying.

127 New University of Ulster Library

Address   Coleraine
County Londonderry BT52 1SA

Telephone   (0265) 4141

Enquiries to   Librarian, Mr F.J.E. Hurst

Open   Term: Mon–Fri: 9.00–10.00
               Sat: 9.30–1.00
          Vacation: Mon–Fri: 9.30–5.30
          Special collections available only up to 5.00 or by arrangement

Access   Anyone establishing a serious interest.

Historical background   The New University of Ulster was established on the recommendation of the *Lockwood Report on Higher Education in Northern Ireland* (1965) and accepted its first students in 1968. The University now incorporates Magee University College in Londonderry, which houses The Institute of Continuing Education.

Acquisitions policy   To strengthen relevant research areas.

Major collections   Papers of George Shiels (1881–1949), playwright.
    Papers of Denis Johnston (*b* 1901), playwright and author.
    Papers of George Stelfox (1884–1972), naturalist.
    Papers of E. Norman Carrothers (1898–1977), botanist and railway engineer.
    Headlam–Morley collection of World War I material.
    Paul Ricard collection of World War II material.

Non-manuscript material   Henry Davis Gift of early books and incunabula.
    Henry Morris collection of Irish material.
    E.N. Carrothers bookplates.
    Study of Conflict archive.
    Considerable runs of newspapers and other material in microtext form.
    European Documentation Centre.
    Co-operative Documentation Centre.

Facilities   Photocopying. Photography by arrangement. Microtext readers.

Publications   *Guide to the Libraries* [annual]

128   Coventry City Record Office

Address   Room 220
          Broadgate House
          Broadgate
          Coventry
          West Midlands CV1 1NG

Telephone   (0203) 25555 ext.2768

Enquiries to   City Archivist, Mr D.J. Rimmer

Open   Mon–Thurs: 8.45–4.45
          Fri: 8.45–4.15
          One day's notice required

Historical background   The St Mary's Hall Muniment Room was constructed in 1892. The City Record Office was established when the first City Archivist was appointed in 1938. In 1974 the Record Office was transferred from the Associate Town Clerk's Department to the Department of Libraries, Arts and Museums. In 1979 the public and staff areas were moved to purpose-adapted offices in Broadgate House.

Major collections   Usual local authority record holdings and deposited collections including archives of the medieval city, craft guilds and manufacturing firms.

Non-manuscript material   The Local Studies Library, on the same site, holds an extensive photographic collection and also collections of films and tape recordings.

Facilities   Photocopying. Photography. Microfilm/fiche reader.

Publications   J.C. Jeaffreson: *A Calendar of the Books, Charters ... in ... the New Muniment Room of St Mary's Hall* (1896)
F. Smith: *Supplementary Catalogue* (1931)
A.A. Dibben: *Coventry City Charters* (1969)

129   Coventry (Lanchester) Polytechnic Library

Address   Much Park Street
                   Coventry
                   West Midlands CV1 2HF

Telephone   (0203) 24166 ext. 435

Enquiries to   Polytechnic Librarian, Mr J. Fletcher

Open   Term: 9.00–8.45
                   Vacation: 9.00–5.15

Access   Approved readers on application to the Polytechnic Librarian.

Historical background   The family of F.W. Lanchester, aeronautical and automotive engineer, presented books and papers to the College (afterwards Polytechnic) named in his honour. Mr E.G. Baxter (1918–79), first Librarian of the College and Polytechnic, catalogued the papers in 1966.

Acquisitions policy   To receive, by gift or purchase, any relevant material offered.

Major collections   Papers of F.W. Lanchester (1868–1946).

Non-manuscript material   Books written by F.W. Lanchester.
   A few historic engineering books, not written but owned by F.W. Lanchester.

Finding aids   Catalogue of papers of F.W. Lanchester.

Facilities   Photocopying. Microfilm/fiche readers.

130   Modern Records Centre

Address   University of Warwick Library
                 Coventry
                 West Midlands CV4 7AL

Telephone   (0203) 24011 ext. 2014

Enquiries to   The Archivist

Open   Mon–Thurs: 9.00–1.00; 1.30–5.00
                 Fri: 9.00–1.00; 1.30–4.00
                 Other times by arrangement
                 A few days' notice of a visit is advisable

Access   All serious researchers. Some accessions subject to restricted
                 access.

Historical background   The Centre was established in October 1973 on the initiative
of a group of academics at the University of Warwick and with the aid of a grant
from the Leverhulme Trust Fund. Its objects are to ensure the preservation (where
necessary by collecting) of original sources for British political, social and
economic history, with particular reference to labour history, industrial relations
and industrial politics, and to make such sources available for research.

Acquisitions policy   To build on existing strengths, especially in industrial relations
and industrial politics.

Major collections   Confederation of British Industry Predecessor Archive; also some
other trade and employers' association records.
    Trade union archives: including Association of Scientific, Technical and Managerial
Staffs; National Graphical Association; National Union of Railwaymen; Transport
and General Workers' Union; Union of Construction, Allied Trades and
Technicians; also unions in the fields of education and the Post Office and
Telecommunications, as well as in a variety of other occupations.
    Pressure groups: including Campaign for Nuclear Disarmament; Howard League
and NACRO; also comprehensive holdings of public documents of Amnesty
International and Anti-Concorde Project.
    Individuals' papers: including those of Lady Allen of Hurtwood (1897–1976);
R.H.S. Crossman (1907–74) (full transcripts of published diaries); R.A. Etheridge,
convenor at Austin Motor Company, Longbridge; Sir Victor Gollancz (1893–
1967), publisher and humanitarian (personal papers); Reg Groves, socialist activist
and historian.

Non-manuscript material   Numerous accessions include printed reports, journals
and pamphlets.
    Individual items and small groups of ephemera over a wide range of political, social
and economic activity.
    The University Library has an extensive collection of journals, reports and

pamphlets of trade unions and employers' and trade associations which may be consulted in the Centre.

Historical Library of the Howard League (owned by the University Library).

Finding aids   Typescript catalogues or interim finding aids exist for some accessions (copies of most of these are in the National Register of Archives); search-room card indexes are based on these.

Facilities   Limited photocopying and photography.

Publications   R.A. Storey and J. Druker: *Guide to the Modern Records Centre* (1977)
C. Woodland and R.A. Storey: *The Taff Vale Case: a Guide to the ASRS records* (1978)
————: *The Osborne Case Papers and other Records of the Amalgamated Society of Railway Servants* (1979)
J. Bennett and R.A. Storey: *Trade Union and Related Records* (1979; rev., 1981);
S. Edwards and R.A. Storey: *Women at Work and in Society* (1980)
R.A. Storey and S. Edwards: *Supplement to the Guide to the Modern Records Centre* (1981)
Also *Information Bulletin, Annual Report* and *Information Leaflet* series

131   Croydon Public Libraries
Local Studies Library

Address   Central Library
                    Katharine Street
                    Croydon
                    Surrey CR9 1ET

Telephone   (01) 688 3627 ext.48

Enquiries to   Local Studies Librarian, Mrs D. Garrett

Open   Mon: 9.30–7.00
                    Tues–Fri: 9.30–6.00
                    Sat: 9.00–5.00
                    Appointment preferred

Access   Generally open to the public.

Historical background   The Croydon Collection was begun in the 1890s, soon after the public library was opened. It was established as a separate department under the supervision of a Local Studies Librarian in 1973. The Purley Collection was begun in the 1930s with the formation of the Coulsdon and Purley Libraries. The two collections remain separately housed.

Acquisitions policy   To acquire primary and secondary sources related to the London Borough of Croydon and general secondary sources related to the county of Surrey.

Major collections Croydon Collection: printed and MS records relating to the ancient parish of Croydon and its later extensions (now a London borough), including manorial, 1532–; parochial, 1741–; workhouse, 1842–; and local government, 1849–; deeds, 1329–; rate books, 1744–; Mills' collection of notebooks, drawings and plans on the history of Addington and Shirley; Paget's collection of notebooks on the history of Croydon; items relating to Addiscombe College, military seminary for the East India Company, 1809–61.

Non-manuscript material *c*5000 pamphlets and cuttings.
Printed council minutes etc.
Local church and society periodicals (*c*350 titles).
*c*6000 paintings; *c*16,000 prints, photographs and postcards.
Maps, 1785–.
Local newspapers, 1855–.
*c*2000 Sales Particulars for land and properties.
Census returns, 1841–(on microfilm).
Purley Collection: mainly printed materials covering the area of the former Urban District Council of Coulsdon and Purley (housed in the Reference department of the Purley Branch Library).

Finding aids Catalogue. Various indexes.

Facilities Photocopying. Microfilm readers.

Publications Duplicated handlist of the main archive holdings [available free of charge from the Local Studies Librarian]

132 Cumbernauld and Kilsyth District Council

Address 8 Allander Walk
Cumbernauld
Strathclyde

Telephone (023 67) 25664

Enquiries to District Librarian, Miss Jean Dawson

Virtually no archives are held apart from minutes of Cumbernauld Town Council, 1968–75, and of Cumbernauld and Kilsyth District Council, 1975–.

133 Cumnock and Doon Valley District Library Headquarters

Address Bank Glen
Cumnock
Strathclyde KA18 1PH

Telephone   (0290) 22024

Enquiries to   District Librarian, Mr I.C. Crawford

Open   Mon–Fri: 9.00–4.30

Access   Generally open to the public.

Historical background   Formerly part of Ayr County, the Cumnock and Doon Valley District was formed in 1975 on local government reorganization.

Acquisitions policy   To build up the archival collection for all parishes within the district.

Major collections   Local Authority department records, 1887–.
Parochial records for Mauchline, New Cumnock and Sorn, 19th and 20th centuries.
Dalmellington District Council Minutes, 1932–.

Non-manuscript material   Pamphlets.
Photographs, prints, glass negatives.

Finding aids   Catalogue of archival material.

Facilities   Photocopying.

134   North East Fife District Library

Address   County Buildings
                   Cupar
                   Fife

Telephone   (0334) 53722

The Library administers the archives at the Hay Fleming Reference Library (*see* entry 615).

135   Gwent County Record Office

Address   County Hall
                   Cwmbran
                   Gwent NP4 2XH

Telephone   (06333) 67711

Enquiries to   County Archivist, Mr W.H. Baker

Open   Mon–Thurs: 9.30–5.00
                   Fri: 9.30–4.00

Historical background   Monmouthshire Record Office was founded in 1938 and

Gwent Record Office was established following local government reorganization in 1974. It also acts as the Diocesan Record Office for Monmouth, Swansea and Brecon (parish records).

Major collections   Usual local authority record holdings and deposited collections, all of purely local interest.

Facilities   Photocopying. Microfilm.

Publications   W.H. Baker: *Guide to the Monmouthshire Record Office* (1959)

136   London Borough of Barking and Dagenham Public Libraries

Address	Valence Reference Library
	Becontree Avenue
	Dagenham
	Essex RM8 3HT
Telephone	(01) 592 2211 ext. 5
Enquiries to	Curator/Archivist, Mr James Howson
Open	Mon, Tues, Thurs, Fri: 9.30–7.00
	Wed, Sat: 9.30–1.00
Access	Approved readers on written application.

Historical background   Dagenham Public Libraries acquired certain parish and urban district records and in 1963 were given the family papers of the late Captain A.B. Fanshawe, RN. In 1965, on the amalgamation of Barking and Dagenham, a council decision to provide an archive store, to be administered by the libraries department, awaits implementation (material therefore remains dispersed and difficult of access), though a curator/archivist was appointed in 1974.

Acquisitions policy   Non-current records of the London Borough of Barking and Dagenham and its predecessors, and of local firms and organizations etc, by donation or deposit.

Major collections   Local Government records: Barking, 1666–; Dagenham, 1838–.
Local property title deeds, 15th–19th centuries.
Business archives of Lawes Chemical Co. Ltd, 1872–1969.
Fanshawe Family MSS, including genealogical papers and pedigree, and correspondence and papers of Sir Richard Fanshawe (1600–66), mainly as ambassador to Portugal, 1662–3, and Spain, 1664–6 (housed at Valence House Museum, Dagenham, Essex RM8 3HT, with the Fanshawe Family Portraits).

Non-manuscript material   Photographs; drawings, paintings and prints (in the parallel Valence House Museum collections).

Maps and plans (including some in the parallel Reference Library Local Studies Collection).

Facilities   Photocopying. Microfilm reader.

Publications   Guide to Local History Resources [cyclostyled typescript]

137   Darlington Library

Address   Branch Library
                Crown Street
                Darlington
                Co. Durham DL1 1ND

Telephone   (0325) 69858

Enquiries to Mrs J. Campbell
                or
                County Librarian, Mr S.C. Dean (County Hall, Durham)

Open   Mon–Fri: 9.00–1.00; 2.15–7.00
                Sat: 9.00–1.00; 2.15–5.00

Access   Generally open to the public. Closure on material less than 30 years
                old.

Historical background   Most of the material was part of the stock of the local history study room, Darlington Branch Library, until June 1979. Responsibility for the archives was then transferred to the Durham County Record Office and an Archivist appointed to work at Darlington. It was agreed that the material would always be retained at Darlington, which is a dependent repository of Durham County Record Office (*see* entry **163**).

Acquisitions policy   To add to the collection any archival material on the Darlington area that becomes available.

Major collections   Darlington Borough Council archives.
Pease/Stephenson papers, 1825–1923.
Darlington Union records, 1837–1947.
Stockton and Darlington Railway Company minutes, 1832–49.
Pease family and business papers.

Non-manuscript material   Photographs and prints of the Darlington area; local newspapers; tape recordings of local people; posters.

Finding aids   Lists and indexes.

Facilities   Photocopying. Microfilm readers.

Publications   Guides produced by Durham County Library, Darlington Local History Department, include archive and local history stock.

Local History Guide, no.1, *Darlington before 1800*; no.3, *Stockton and Darlington Railway*; no.10, *The Pease Family*

138 Kent County Library
Dartford Division

Address   Divisional Reference Library
Central Library
Central Park
Dartford
Kent

Telephone   (0322) 21133/4

Enquiries to   Divisional Reference Librarian, Mr J. Ayers

Local History Collection of non-MS material, including Youens Collection of glass negatives, c1910.

139 Britannia Royal Naval College

Address   Dartmouth
Devon TQ6 0HJ

Telephone   (08043) 2141 ext.328

Enquiries to   Librarian, Mr R.J. Kennell

Open   Weekday working hours, by appointment, (frequently closed during naval leaves)

Access   By written application in advance.

Historical background   The College was established in the 1860s on two hulks on the river and moved to its present premises c1905. It is a working college involved in the initial training of officers and therefore is not equipped to deal with general naval historical enquiries, for which *see* Naval Historical Branch Library (entry **430**) and National Maritime Museum (entry **425**). There has been gradual accrual of archival material in the library.

Acquisitions policy   The College will accept material of relevance to its history, but does not normally seek to collect it.

Major collections   Records relating to the College and its history, naval history in general and the development of naval training, including papers of individuals, copies of treaties and battle plans.
Midshipmen's logs (Victorian and World War II).

Non-manuscript material   Extensive photographic collection.

Finding aids   MS material is largely uncatalogued at present, but members of the History and English Departments are at hand if required.

Facilities   Limited photocopying.

Publications   E.L. Davies and E.J. Grove: *The Royal Naval College Dartmouth: 75 Years in Pictures* (1980)

140   British Steel Corporation
Records Services Section

Address   North Western Regional Records Centre
                   Shotton Works
                   Deeside
                   Clwyd CH5 2NH

Telephone   (0244) 912345

Enquiries to   Western Region Manager, Mr P. Emmerson

The archive covers South Wales and the southwest of England. For enquiries covering more than one region write to The Director, Secretariat, at the Corporation's Head Office, 33 Grosvenor Place, London SW1.
For other information in common with each Records Centre *see* East Midlands Regional Records Centre, Wellingborough (entry **687**).

141   Derbyshire Library Service
Local Studies Department

Address   Derby Central Library
                   The Wardwick
                   Derby DE1 1HF

Telephone   (0332) 31111 ext.2184

Enquiries to   The Local Studies Librarian

Open   Mon–Fri: 9.00–7.00
                   Sat: 9.00–1.00

Access   Generally open to the public.

Historical background   The collection is based on two family libraries, the Devonshire and Bemrose libraries, acquired in 1878 and 1914 respectively. The Devonshire collection consisted of books, pamphlets, prints, election addresses and MSS; the Bemrose library included some MS items and early editions of the works of Derbyshire authors. There have subsequently been a number of deposits, some quite large, prior to the establishment of the local record office.

Acquisitions policy To strengthen and enlarge existing primary and secondary collections on the history of Derbyshire and environmental studies within the county.

Major collections c1000 Derby Corporation deeds, 17th–19th centuries.
Borough Court records.
Derby Union Board of Guardians records, 1837–1915.
Collections of the Catton, Pares and Mundy families.
Duesbury collection of records of Derby China Factory, 1780–1800.
Wyatt collection relating to lead mining, 1810–50.
Derby Canal Company records, 1793–1974.

Non-manuscript material Large collections of illustrative material; broadsides; tapes; maps.
Newspapers: *Derby Mercury*, 1732–1933; *Derby and Chesterfield Reporter*, 1828–1930, *Derbyshire Advertiser*, 1876–; *Derby Evening Telegraph*, 1879–.
Census returns, 1841–71, for Derbyshire and some small portion of surrounding counties.

Finding aids Various lists and indexes.

Facilities Photocopying. Microfilm/fiche reader/printer.

Publications *Derbyshire Local Studies Collections* (1976)

142 Gwynedd Archives Service
Dolgellau Area Record Office

Address   Cae Penarlag
Dolgellau
Gwynedd

Telephone   (0341) 422341 ext. 261

Enquiries to   Archivist-in-charge, Miss Ann Rhydderch

Open   Mon–Fri: 9.30–1.00; 2.00–4.30

Historical background The Office was set up in 1952 as the Record Office for the County of Merioneth.

Major collections Usual local authority record holdings and deposited collections.

Facilities Photocopying. Photography.

Publications K. Williams-Jones: *Calendars of The Merioneth Quarter Session Rolls* (1965)

143   Doncaster Archives Department

Address   King Edward Road
                   Balby
                   Doncaster
                   South Yorkshire DN4 0NA

Telephone   (0302) 859811

Enquiries to   Borough Archivist, Mr T.S. Alexander-Macquiban

Open   Mon–Fri: 9.00–12.00; 1.30–4.30

Access   Generally open to the public.

Historical background The Doncaster Archives Department was formally established in 1973 after many years of employing an Honorary Archivist to the Doncaster Corporation. It started operating from the Priory Place Offices of the Doncaster Metropolitan Borough Council, but moved in 1977 to the first floor of Bentley Library which it occupied until a move to the former Balby Junior School in 1982. The Archives Department also acts as the Diocesan Record Office for the Archdeaconry of Doncaster.

Acquisitions policy Acquisitions of deposited records from within the Doncaster Metropolitan Borough Council area and church records from the Archdeaconry of Doncaster, as well as official records of superseded authorities whose functions were inherited by the Doncaster Metropolitan Borough Council.

Major collections Davies-Cooke family of Owston: family and estate records over a continuous period of 400 years for a large estate to the north of Doncaster, comprising over 3000 MSS.
Ancient Borough of Doncaster: charters, deeds and administrative records, 15th–19th centuries.
Warde-Aldam family of Frickley: political and social papers of William Aldam, MP, JP, relating to 50 years' public service in the West Riding, 1840–90.

Non-manuscript material Maps and plans of the district are housed in the Archives Department and also in the Local History Section of the Central Library (which specializes in material relating to railways and racing).
Microfilms of bishop's transcripts, census returns, newspapers, pamphlets and other local history material are also held by the Local History Section.

Finding aids Various lists and indexes, including detailed lists of each of the classes of records described in the *Guide* (*see* 'Publications') and indexes for the following: parish register names, tithe awards, main name index, place index. Also a list of sources for family historians and notes for their guidance.

Facilities Photocopying. Microfilm reader.

Publications *A Survey of School Archives: Part One – Doncaster County Borough* (1978)
Guide to the Archives Department (2/1981)

144 Doncaster Metropolitan Borough Council
Central Library

Address   Waterdale
               Doncaster
               South Yorkshire DN1 3JE

Telephone   (0302) 69123/4/5

The Library has a local history collection mainly of non-MS material. All archival holdings have been transferred to Doncaster Archives Department (*see* entry **143**).

145 South Yorkshire Industrial Museum
Cusworth Hall Museum

Address   Doncaster
               South Yorkshire DN5 7TU

Telephone   (0302) 782342

Enquiries to Curator, Miss A.V. Morrish

No MS collections are held. Some examples of printed ephemera (e.g. advertising material).

146 Dorset County Library Local Studies Collection

Address   Reference Library
                 Colliton Park
                 Dorchester
                 Dorset DT1 1XJ

Telephone   (0305) 63131

Enquiries to   County Reference Adviser, Mr N.G. Lawrence

Open   Mon, Wed, Fri: 9.30–7.00
                 Thurs: 9.30–5.00
                 Sat: 9.00–1.00

Access   Generally open to the public.

Historical background   Much material was acquired in the 1960s on the building of the new library. The Thomas Hardy Society Library is housed here.

Acquisitions policy   Material relating to the area and to Thomas Hardy (1840–1928) in particular.

Major collections   Lock Collection (deposited on semi-permanent loan by Henry Lock of the family firm of solicitors who dealt with the Hardy family): includes correspondence of the Hardy and Hand families; letters from literary figures, 1868–1940; press cuttings; photographs; play programmes etc.
Typescripts, mainly taken from MSS, connected with the Powys family; primarily T.F. Powys (1875–1953), but also John Cowper Powys (1872–1963).
Scripts with MS annotations of BBC Radio programme *Country Magazine*, 1942–53 (owned by Ralph Wightman, one of the participants).

Non-manuscript material   Maps; illustrations.
Microfilms of census returns.

Facilities   Photocopying. Microfilm/fiche reader/printer.

147   Dorset Record Office

Address   County Hall
                 Dorchester
                 Dorset DT1 1XJ

Telephone   (0305) 63131 ext. 4411

Enquiries to   County Archivist, Miss M.E. Holmes

Open   Mon–Fri: 9.00–1.00; 2.00–5.00

Historical background   The office was established in 1955. The County Museum collected documents before then, and these were transferred to the Record Office in 1957. The office also acts as the Diocesan Record Office for Salisbury (parish records for archdeaconries of Sherborne and Dorset).

Major collections   Usual local authority record holdings and deposited collections including the following which have a wider significance:
State papers of Sir John Trenchard, Chief Secretary of State, 1693–5.
Accounts etc of Sir Stephen Fox and others as Paymasters of the Forces and in other public offices, 1638–1712.
War Office letter-books of Sir W. Yonge, 1741–5, and Henry Fox, Lord Holland, 1746–55; Army Agent's accounts, 1755–64; court of enquiry relating to Gibraltar, 1749–50.

Facilities   Photocopying. Photography. Microfilming. Microfilm reader.

Publications   A.C. Cox: *Index to the Dorset County Records* (1938)
M.E. Holmes: 'The Dorset Record Office', *Archives* vii (1966), 207:

148   General Registry, Isle of Man

Address	Finch Road Douglas Isle of Man
Telephone	(0624) 3358
Enquiries to	Chief Registrar, Mr G.A. Kissack
Open	Mon–Fri: 9.00–1.00; 2.15–4.30
Access	Generally available to the public. A search fee is charged.

Historical background   Established under the General Registry Act, 1965, it carries out the functions of the Rolls Office, Registry of Deeds and Registrar General's Department. Its functions include the issue of summonses and processes for all divisions of the High Court; the making of Grants of Probate, Administration and other Grants of Representation, and the registration of all deeds and documents leading to title to real estate in the Island. It also acts as the Diocesan Record Office for Sodor and Man.

Major collections   Wills, 1847–.
Statutory records of registered births, 1878–.
Church of England baptisms, 1611–1878.
Marriage records: Church of England, 1629–1849; Church of England and dissenters, 1849–1883; statutory records 1884–.
Statutory records of death, 1878–.
Church of England burial records, 1610–1978.
Records of legal adoptions registered in Isle of Man, 1928–.
Deeds of property, 1847–.
High Court Records, original Acts and Resolutions of Tynwald; Grants of Representation to the estates of descendants; original plans and valuations of Manx estates; many other documents relating to the history and development of the Isle of Man.

Facilities   Photocopying. Microfilming. Microfilm reader.

149   Manx Museum Library

Address	Kingswood Grove Douglas Isle of Man
Telephone	(0624) 5522
Enquiries to	Librarian-Archivist, Miss A.M. Harrison
Open	Mon–Sat: 10.00–5.00

Access   Generally open to the public.

Historical background   The Manx Museum Trustees have pursued a policy of collecting Manx books and MS material since their institution in the 1880s. The Library, open to the public since 1922, holds certain classes of Manx public records by Act of Tynwald as well as the records of Manx families and private agencies.

Acquisitions policy   Records relating to the Isle of Man, both public and private.

Major collections   Isle of Man Government: court records; registered deeds, 1600–1846.
Archidiaconal and episcopal wills, 1629–1846.
Papers of the Derby family, 17th–18th centuries.
Papers of the Atholl family, 18th–19th centuries.

Non-manuscript material   Photographs, prints, printed ephemera, printed maps.
Manx newspapers, 1793–.
Manx printed books.
Microfilms of census records, 1841–81.

Finding aids   Various lists and indexes.

Facilities   Photocopying. Photography. Microfilm readers/printer.

Publications   *The Journal of the Manx Museum* [contains many articles on the Library and its collections]

150   Dudley Archives and Local History Department

Address   St James's Road
                 Dudley
                 West Midlands DY1 HR

Telephone   (0384) 55433 ext.5514 (Archivist)/5526 (Search room)
                 After 5.00 and Sats: (0384) 56321

Enquiries to   Archivist and Local History Librarian, Mrs K.H. Atkins

Open   Mon, Wed, Fri: 9.00–1.00; 2.00–5.00
                 Tues, Thurs: 2.00–7.00
                 Prior notice advisable. Other times by arrangement.

Historical background   Archives have been collected since 1947 and the first qualified archivist was appointed in 1972. The department also acts as the Diocesan Record Office for Worcester (Deaneries of Dudley and Stourbridge parish records) and Lichfield (Deanery of Himley parish records).

Major collections   The usual local authority record holdings and deposited

collections, of which the following is of wider significance:
Archive of the Earls of Dudley, 12th–20th centuries.

Non-manuscript material   The Local History Library includes newspapers, cuttings, and over 12,000 local photographs.
Local history collections can also be found at the following area libraries: Brierley Hill Library, Halesowen Library, Kingswinford Library, Stourbridge Library.

Facilities   Photocopying. Photography. Microfilm reader/printer, by arrangement.

151   Dumbarton District Libraries

Address   Dumbarton Library
                 Strathleven Place
                 Dumbarton

Telephone   (0389) 63129

Enquiries to   Librarian, Mr M.C. Taylor

Open   Mon–Sat: 10.00–5.00

Access   Generally open to the public.

Historical background   After the reorganization of local government, in 1975 Dumbarton Library became a recognized repository for archives, and the Library has collected the records of the various local authorities which were in existence up to that time. Since 1881 the Library has collected any records of societies, institutes, individuals and business organizations which were present in the area.

Acquisitions policy   To collect records relating to the area covered by the District Libraries.

Major collections   Dumbarton Burgh records, 1599–1975.
Collection of charters, documents, letters pertaining to the town of Dumbarton, 15th century–.
Helensburgh Burgh records, 1807–1975.
Records of the Dennystown Forge Company, 1854–1979.

Non-manuscript material   Maps and plans of the district.
c250 drawings, paintings and prints.
c3550 photographic prints; c1000 photographic negatives; c200 photographic slides.
Local newspapers, 1851–.

Finding aids   Various lists and indexes.

Facilities   Photocopying. Photography. Microfilm/fiche reader.

152 Dumfries and Galloway Regional Council Library Service Archives

Address   Ewart Library
              Catherine Street
              Dumfries
              Dumfries and Galloway DG1 1JB

Telephone   (0387) 3820/2070

Enquiries to Regional Librarian, Mr J. Preston

Open   Mon–Wed, Fri: 10.00–7.30
              Thurs–Sat: 10.00–5.00

Historical background   The Archives department was established in 1975 with local government reorganization; before that local authorities held their own records and there was no formal collecting policy. All records came to Dumfries in 1975.

Major collections   Usual local authority record holdings and deposited collections primarily of local interest, with the exception of early militia records.

Facilities   Photocopying. Photography. Microfilm reader/printer.

153 Dumfries Burgh Archives

Address   Municipal Chambers
              Buccleuch Street
              Dumfries
              Dumfries and Galloway DG1 2AD

Telephone   (0387) 3374

Enquiries to Nithsdale District Archivist and Curator of Museums, Mr David Lockwood, Dumfries Museum, The Observatory, Church Street, Dumfries.

Open   Mon–Fri, by arrangement

Historical background   Records were 'rediscovered' after a fire in the Town Hall in 1908; they were transferred to the County Library on the closure of the Town Hall in 1931 and were boxed and catalogued. They were moved back to the Town Hall in 1956, and in 1978 were finally housed in the Municipal Chambers. The Scottish Record Office has assisted with cataloguing.

Major collections   Usual local authority record holdings and some deposited collections, all of purely local interest.

Facilities   Photocopying.

Publications   A number of museum leaflets based on the archives.

154   Leighton Library, Dunblane

Enquiries to   The Librarian
c/o Rare Books Department
Stirling University Library
Stirling GK9 4LA

Telephone   (0786) 3171 ext. 2230

The library was founded in the late 17th century by Robert Leighton to meet the needs of the local clergy. The library acted as a subscription library in the 18th and early 19th centuries. MSS items are made available at Stirling University Library (*see* entry **652**).

155   Duncan of Jordanstone College of Art

Address   The Library
Perth Road
Dundee
Angus DD1 4HT

No archives are held.

156   Dundee College of Technology

Address   The Library
Bell Street
Dundee
Tayside DD1 1HG

There are no deposited collections. Internal records, mainly minutes, are held.

157   Dundee District Archive and Record Centre

Address   City Chambers
Dundee
Tayside DD1 3BY

Telephone   (0382) 23141 ext.494

Enquiries to   Archivist, Mr Iain Flett

Open   Mon–Fri: 9.00–1.00; 2.00–5.00

Historical background   Formerly Dundee City Record Office, the Archive was renamed a district office following reorganization in 1974, but acts on an agency basis for Tayside Regional Council.

Major collections   Usual local authority record holdings and deposited collections including the following which have a wider significance:
Dundee Chamber of Commerce (formerly Forfarshire Chamber of Commerce, and Baltic Coffee House and Chamber of Commerce) records, 1819–1960.
Dundee Harbour Trustees and various shipping company records, 19th–20th centuries.
Dundee Jute and Flax Union records, 1906–1971 (including references to jute industry in India).
Geekie Family, Keillor, Co. Angus: correspondence etc, 1646–1850 (includes letters from Alexander Geekie, surgeon in London, c1678–1724).
Papers of David Greig, FRCSEd. (*fl* 1850s): copies of his letters written while serving as assistant surgeon in the Crimea.
Papers of Dr Thomas Dick, LL.D, FRAS (1774–1857), 1814–1908.
Account books covering voyages of the brigantines *Flora* and *Tagus*, Dundee, 18th century.

Facilities   Photocopying.

158   Dundee District Libraries

Address   Central Library
The Wellgate
Dundee
Tayside DD1 1DB

Telephone   (0382) 23141

Enquiries to   Chief Librarian, Mr D.M. Torbet

Open   Mon–Fri: 9.30–9.00
Sat: 9.30–5.00
Readers requiring items from special collections are advised to make prior arrangement.

Access   Generally open to the public.

Historical background   The Library was established in 1869 after the adoption of the Public Libraries Act 1867, since when the library service in Dundee has steadily been developed. Various special collections, including archival material, have been donated over the years.

Acquisitions policy   The special and archival collections are strengthened by donations or, in special cases, by purchase.

Major collections   Letters and other MS material of local persons, including Edwin Scrymgeour, William McGonagall, Mary Slessor.
Dundee Trades Council Collection, MS and printed material, to *c*1960.
Miscellaneous MS material relating to local authors and organizations.
Some personal whaling log-books.

Non-manuscript material   Wilson Collection of Photographs, *c*1888–*c*1910.
Local History Library (Dundee and District) includes the 'Lamb Collection' of ephemeral material; books; pamphlets; posters; newspapers; prints; maps; plans.
Wighton Collection of early national music.

Finding aids   Library catalogues and indexes.

Facilities   Photocopying. Photography. Microfilm/fiche readers. Study carrels.

Publications   J. MacLauchlan: *A Brief Guide to the old Dundee Historical Collection* ... (Dundee, 1901)
E.B. Schnapper: *British Union-Catalogue of Early Music* (1957)

159   University Library, Dundee

Address   Archive Department
The Library
University of Dundee
Dundee
Tayside DD1 4HN

Telephone   (0382) 23181 ext. 245

Enquiries to   Archivist, Mrs Joan Auld

Open   Mon–Fri: 9.00–5.00
Evenings and Sat mornings during term by arrangement

Access   Generally open to the public.

Historical background   The University has its origins in University College, Dundee, founded in 1881. The College became part of St Andrews University in 1897, was renamed Queens College in 1954 and was granted its charter as a University in 1967.

Acquisitions policy   To strengthen the Library's MSS collection, particularly as it relates to the textile industry and medical history, and to accumulate records of the University and Queens College and prominent staff and students.

Major collections   Library MSS:
Records of local textile industry, particularly relating to jute and flax, *c*1840–1978.
Records of Dundee hospitals, 1855–1948, and local medical associations, 1864–1927; R.C. Buist collection of papers relating to the history of medicine in Angus,

16th century–; army medical notebooks of R.C. Alexander, 1914–18.

Glassite church sermons and correspondence, 1728–1885; papers relating to the College and Collegiate Church of the Holy Spirit, Isle of Cumbrae, c1850–c1926.

MSS and correspondence of Thomas Campbell, poet, 1797–1854.

Papers of Alexander Mackenzie, c1896–1936; Alexander Scott, 1851–1935; Sir Robert Robertson, 1894–1949; A.D. Walsh, c1930–1970.

Brechin Diocesan Library MSS:

Correspondence of Bishop Alexander Penrose Forbes, 1844–74.

Transcripts of episcopal registers, c1681–1890; records of Diocese of Brechin, c1744–1904.

Diary and commonplace book of William Drummond of Hawthornden, 1606–49.

Psalter, Book of Hours, sermons, 15th century.

University Archives: records of the University, 1967–, and its predecessors University College and Queens College, c1875–1966.

Non-manuscript material   Thornton collection and others, maps and plans (some MS), particularly Dundee and Angus railway plans, c1770–1960.

George H. Bell collection of photographs of eminent visitors (particularly physiologists and other medicals) to University and Queens College and the University of Dundee, c1950–1970.

Herbert Watt Torrence, medical missionary in Tiberias, photographic slides of the hospital at Tiberias, other views in Palestine and flora and fauna, c1880–1970.

Miscellaneous photographs relating to Library MS collections, particularly local industry, c1870–1980.

Finding aids   Descriptive lists. Card indexes.

Facilities   Photocopying. Photography.

160   Dunfermline District Library

Address   Dunfermline Central Library
Abbot Street
Dunfermline
Fife KY12 7NW

Telephone   (0383) 23661/2

Enquiries to   Director of Libraries, Museums and Art Galleries, Mr James K. Sharp

Open   Mon, Tues, Thurs, Fri: 10.00–7.00
Wed, Sat: 10.00–1.00; 2.00–5.00

Access   Generally open to the public.

Historical background   In 1975, at the time of local government reorganization in Scotland, Dunfermline Burgh Library and a part of the former Fife County Library were amalgamated to form the present District Library Service. The Central Library was opened in 1883; it was the first Carnegie Free Library in the world. The donation of materials by Dr Erskine Beveridge in 1931 formed the basis of the local history collections.

Acquisitions policy   All records and published material relating to the locality.

Major collections   Municipal and official records: including parish records, 1561–1685, extracts from the Burgh records, valuation rolls and voters rolls, 1850s–.
Local History Collection: includes records of Dunfermline Incorporation of Weavers, Dunfermline Co-operative Society, local churches etc.
George Reid Collection of medieval MSS and early printed books. A donation by a local linen manufacturer. Most of Reid's collection was given to the Victoria and Albert Museum. The Dunfermline Library's MSS are listed in N.R. Ker: *Medieval Manuscripts in British Libraries.*

Non-manuscript material   Maps, photographs, prints, drawings – all relating to the West Fife area.

Finding aids   Card catalogues. Various indexes.

Facilities   Photocopying. Microfiche reader/printer.

Publications   *Guide to Local History Room* (rev. edn., 1976)
A Guide to Local Maps and Plans (1978)
Coalmining in West Fife: a Bibliography of Material held in Dunfermline Central Library (1979)

161   The Dean and Chapter Library

Address   The College
Durham DH1 3EH

Telephone   (0385) 62489

Enquiries to   Deputy Librarian, Mr Roger Norris

Open   Mon–Fri: 9.00–1.00; 2.15–5.00
Closed: whole of August

Access   Bona fide students; references are required, together with means of identification.

Historical background   The Library of the Dean and Chapter of Durham descends in direct historic continuity from the library of the Benedictine house (*fd* 10th century in Durham) which was dissolved in 1540 and then changed into a capitular foundation of a Dean and 12 residentiaries.

Acquisitions policy   Archives are not acquired but some are held.

Major collections   Extensive collection of medieval MSS (*see* 'Publications' below). Papers include those of the following:
I.T. Ramsey, Bishop of Durham, 1966–72.

General Synod, i.e. Liturgical Commission, 1960s–1970s.

J.B. Lightfoot, Bishop of Durham, 1879–89.

H.H. Henson, Bishop of Durham, 1920–39.

Antiquarian collections of the following: Christopher Hunter (1675–1757); Thomas Randall, headmaster, Durham School, 1761–8; George Allan (1736– 1800); Robert Surtees (1779–1834); Sir Cuthbert Sharp (1781–1849); James Raine (1791–1858).

Music MSS, early 17th century–19th century.

Non-manuscript material   Extensive iconographic material.

Finding aids   Card indexes.

Facilities   No photocopying of MS material. Photography by arrangement.

Publications   *See* N.R. Ker: *Monastic Libraries in Great Britain* (1964) and Sir Roger Mynors: *Durham Cathedral Manuscripts* (1939)

162   Durham City Reference Library

Address   Branch Library
South Street
Durham DH1 4QS

Telephone   (0385) 64003

Enquiries to   District Librarian, Mr J. Main

Local History Collection of non-MS material.

163   Durham County Record Office

Address   County Hall
Durham DH1 5UL

Telephone   (0385) 64411 ext. 2474/2253

Enquiries to   County Archivist, Mr D. Butler

Open   By appointment
Mon, Tues, Thurs: 8.45–4.45
Wed: 8.45–8.30
Fri: 8.45–4.15
Documents required for Wed evening must be ordered by the previous day.

Historical background   The office was established in 1961 to cover the whole county; previously no archive service had existed. The department moved to its new building in 1964. It also acts as the Diocesan Record Office for Durham (parish records). There is a branch office at Darlington Library (*see* entry **137**).

Major collections   Usual local authority record holdings and deposited collections including the following which have a wider significance:
Londonderry records: estate and business papers, including those relating to Seaham Harbour and coal interests in east Durham; family and personal papers.
Strathmore records: estate records and records relating to 'Grand Allies' and the development of Durham Coalfield in the 18th century.
National Coal Board records: pre-nationalization records.

Facilities   Photocopying. Photography and microfilming by arrangement. Microfilm reader.

Publications   W.A.L. Seaman: *Durham County Record Office* (1969)

164   Durham University
Department of Palaeography and Diplomatic

Address   5 The College
                 Durham DH1 3EQ
                 and

                 The Prior's Kitchen
                 The College
                 Durham DH1 3EQ

Telephone   (0385) 61478/64561

Enquiries to   Reader in Palaeography and Diplomatic, Mr J.E. Fagg

Open   Mon–Fri: 10.00–1.00; 2.00–5.00
                 Sat: 9.30–12.30 (term only)
                 Closed: one week at Christmas and Easter; three weeks during summer

Access   Generally open to the public.

Historical background   The Department was established in 1948 under a joint scheme of Durham University and the Dean and Chapter of Durham for the care of archives, mainly from the northern counties, and for the promotion of the study of MS material.

Acquisitions policy   To accept limited further deposits of appropriate archives, particularly administrative records of the diocese and the palatinate of Durham.

Major collections   Durham Dean and Chapter Muniments: records of Durham Cathedral, 11th–19th centuries (monastic to 1539).
Durham Diocesan Records: central administrative records, 16th–20th centuries.
Durham Bishopric Records: financial and estate records deposited by the Church Commissioners, 14th–20th centuries.
Probate records, Durham Diocese, 16th–19th centuries.

Earl Grey Papers: political, private and estate papers of the Greys of Howick, 18th–20th centuries.

Howard of Naworth Papers: family and estate papers, relating mainly to Cumberland and Northumberland, 18th–19th centuries.

Baker Baker Papers: family, estate and business papers, relating mainly to Durham and North Yorkshire, 18th–19th centuries.

Non-manuscript material Pamphlets, personal photographs etc, among papers of the Earls Grey, 19th century.

Stud books and veterinary publications (Baker Baker Papers), 18th–19th centuries.

Ordnance Survey maps of Durham and Northumberland, various dates.

Finding aids Various lists and indexes in Search Rooms.

Facilities Photocopying. Microfilming.

Publications 44 lists of documentary collections including Durham Diocesan and Durham Bishopric, Halmore Court records, records deposited by the Church Commissioners, Baker Baker, Howard, Grey and Shipperdson papers and Land Tax records.

Lists of Deans and Major Canons of Durham 1541–1900 (1974)

165   University Library, Durham

Address   Palace Green
                 Durham DH1 3RN

Telephone   (0385) 61262

Enquiries to   The Keeper of Rare Books

Open   Mon–Fri: 9.00–12.45; 2.00–4.45
                 Sat: 9.00–12.00 (except July, Aug)

Access   Preferably by written enquiry in advance and adequate identification
                 on visit.

Historical background The University Library, founded in 1833, incorporated Bishop Cosin's Library, founded in 1668. Until 1950 it was the only official archive repository in Co. Durham, apart from Gateshead Borough Library.

Acquisitions policy Material relating to the County, City and University of Durham, but no large archives if they can be accommodated in the County Record Office (*see* entry **163**) or the University Department of Palaeography (*see* entry **164**); and smaller groups only if they are connected with material already in the Library's custody, or if the depositor insists, or if another suitable local repository cannot find the money for a purchase.

Major collections Correspondence of John Cosin, 1660–72; letters to other

Durham churchmen, 1593–1662.

Collections of the Mickleton and Spearman families, Durham lawyers and antiquaries, including original documents, 17th and early 18th centuries.

Letters and papers of the Clavering family of Greencroft, Co. Durham, 16th–18th centuries.

Letters and diaries of the Wharton family of Dryburn, Co. Durham, 18th–19th centuries.

Astronomical papers of Thomas Wright (1711–86) of Byers Green, Co. Durham.

Letters and papers of Charles Thorp, first warden of the University, 1831–62.

University Observatory records and correspondence, 1838–1953.

Correspondence and papers of William Plomer (1903–71).

Non-manuscript material Plans, photographs, accounts etc, for the restoration of Durham Castle, 1920–39.

Durham County parliamentary election poll-books and contest literature in pamphlet and broadside form (with some MS material), 1675–1874.

Playbills for City of Durham theatres, 1769–1859.

Finding aids Chronological lists of John Cosins and Durham churchmen collections. Incomplete catalogues of Mickleton and Spearman families. Interim lists of letters of Clavering family. Calendar and index of Charles Thorp papers. List of University Observatory records in progress. Interim lists of William Plomer papers. Interim catalogues of additional MSS, including miscellaneous items and small groups.

Facilities Photocopying if condition of material suitable; photostat, microfilm and bromide prints can be arranged.

Publications H.R. Klieneberger: *Durham elections; a List of Material Relating to Parliamentary Elections in Durham, 1675–1874* (1956)

D. Ramage: *A Summary List of the Additional Manuscripts accessioned and listed between September 1945 and September 1961* (1963)

166   University of Durham
Sudan Archive

Address   University Library
Oriental Section
Elvet Hill
Durham DH1 3TH

Telephone   (0385) 64971

Enquiries to   Keeper of Oriental Books, Miss L.E. Forbes

Open   Mon–Fri: 9.00–5.00
Sat: 9.00–12.30 (excluding Aug)
Appointment preferred

Access   Bona fide scholars and researchers. Students must provide a letter of introduction from their supervisor, preferably in advance. 30-year closure on certain documents. Copies of microfilm copies are available for Abbas Hilmi II papers (originals available only in exceptional circumstances).

Historical background   The Sudan Archive was set up in 1957 by R.L. Hill as a repository for the papers of British men and women who had served in the Anglo-Egyptian Sudan, 1899–1956 and earlier. It was handed over to the custody of the Oriental Section of the University Library in 1966. It is a collection of private papers, not restricted to members of the Sudan Political Service and Government officers.

Acquisitions policy   To add to existing primary and secondary collections on the Sudan, especially during the Condominium period, 1899–1956.

Major collections   Sudan Archive: c300 Mahdist documents in Arabic; a substantial amount of material relating to Egypt, Arabia, Palestine, Transjordan, Syria and African states bordering on the Sudan; papers of General Sir Reginald Wingate (1861–1953), Sir Rudolf Baron Slatin (1857–1932), Brigadier-General Sir Gilbert Clayton (1875–1929), Sir Harold MacMichael (1882–1969), Sir James Robertson, and the Gordon Memorial College Trust Fund.
Abbas Hilmi II Papers: papers of Abbas Hilmi II (1874–1944) covering the period of his Khedivate, 1892–1914, and after his deposition until his death; the papers are in three sections: (a) official, political, diplomatic, (b) estates, business interests, property, (c) personal. (c326 files, principal languages: French, Arabic, German, English, Ottoman Turkish).

Non-manuscript material   Maps of the Sudan (complete 1:250,000 series); plans of some towns and buildings.
Collection of printed material relating to the Sudan (particularly 1899–1956), including Sudan Government publications.
c15,000 photographs plus slides and cine films; paintings, drawings.
Small collection of contemporary pamphlets (with Abbas Hilmi papers) in several languages.

Finding aids   Card index of personal and place names, some subjects, and inventory, of material deposited up to 1966 (half the material). Later deposits, and some earlier, listed alphabetically by collection, with an indication of a person's career at the beginning of each list. (It is hoped that these lists may be published soon.) Computerized index of photographs being compiled.

Facilities   Photocopying and photography by arrangement. Microfilm reader.

Publications   R.L. Hill: *Handlist of Arabic Manuscripts and Lithographs* (3rd draft, 1966; rev. and amended D. Grimwood-Jones, 1973 [mimeograph])
L.E. Forbes: 'The Sudan Archive of the University of Durham', *Middle East Studies and Libraries* (London, 1980) [felicitation vol. for Professor J.D. Pearson, ed. B.C. Bloomfield]
Papers of Abbas Hilmi II (1874–1944) on Deposit with the University of Durham, Summary List (Durham, 1980)

167   Country Life Archive

Address	National Museum of Antiquities of Scotland Queen Street Edinburgh EH2 1JD
Telephone	(031) 556 8921
Enquiries to	The Country Life Section
Open	Mon–Fri: 9.00–5.00 (subject to availability of staff), by appointment Closed: 2nd–4th weeks of June
Access	Generally open to the public.

Historical background   The Archive was founded in 1959, as a development within the County Life Section and a working tool for the Museum, to collect and organize information on the material culture of the countryside of Scotland and the Northern Isles.

Acquisitions policy   Reinforcement of existing material.

Major collections   Memoirs, diaries and letters, scrapbooks and recorded MS evidence gathered from a variety of sources.

Non-manuscript material   Photographs: copies of old photographs, fieldwork photographs; Alasdair Alpin MacGregor photographic collection.
Small amount of oral information recorded on tape.

Finding aids   Material arranged by subject, then county (self-indexed)

Facilities   Limited. No photography.

168   Edinburgh City Libraries
Edinburgh Room and Scottish Library

Address	George IV Bridge Edinburgh EH1 1EG
Telephone	(031) 225 5584
Enquiries to	City Librarian, Mr A.P. Shearman
Open	Mon–Fri: 9.00–9.00 Sat: 9.00–1.00
Access	Generally open to the public. Restrictions on certain categories of material.

Historical background   Edinburgh Public Library opened in 1890 with a Reference

Library, newsroom and Home Reading Library serving the City of Edinburgh. The Edinburgh Room opened in 1932 (the Fine Art and Music Libraries also opened in the 1930s), and the Scottish Library in 1961. At local government reorganization they became Edinburgh City Libraries, serving the Edinburgh District.

Acquisitions policy   Edinburgh Room: collects some MSS illustrating the life of the City but does not compete with the District Archives (*see* entry **170**) and the National Library of Scotland (*see* entry **177**).

Scottish Library: comprehensive coverage of printed sources and non-book materials illustrating the life of Scotland.

Major collections   Edinburgh Room: 1000 MSS, including school log-books, school board minutes, letters, account books, minutes of local societies and trade unions.

Scottish Library: principally non-MS material (see below).

50 MSS, including Smith's poems, *Old Scottish Clockmakers* and *Surfaceman*.

Non-manuscript material   Edinburgh Room: *c*2000 broadsides, including playbills, political broadsides, acts and proclamations, ballads.

Large collection of press cuttings.

*c*2600 maps and plans, 16th century–.

*c*9000 prints and drawings, excellent for costume and architecture.

*c*9000 photographs, including large callotype collection from the 1840s of the work of D.O. Hill and Robert Adamson, and Dr Thomas Keith.

Films and tapes.

Scottish Library: Large collection of press cuttings.

Extensive map and print collections, 17th century–.

*c*700 photographs, 800 negatives and 900 lantern slides, including Dr I.F. Grant's Highland Folklife collection, 19th century; and Dr Thomas Keith's collection, 1855–6.

Finding aids   Indexes to much of non-MS material.

Facilities   Photocopying. Photography by arrangement. Microfilm reader/printer.

169   Edinburgh College of Art

Address   Lauriston Place
                 Edinburgh EH3 9DF

The college was founded in 1907 from predecessor institutions dating from the early 19th century. There was no attempt to save archives and therefore very insubstantial material survives.

170   Edinburgh District Archives

Address   City Chambers
                   High Street
                   Edinburgh EH1 1YJ

Telephone   (031) 225 2424 ext. 5196

Enquiries to   City Archivist, Dr W.H. Makey

Open   By appointment

Historical background   The Burgh of Edinburgh official records were accumulated
   and held by Edinburgh City Archives, which was renamed City of Edinburgh
   District Council Archives on reorganization in 1974.

Major collections   Usual local authority record holdings including a small number of
   deposited collections. (Midlothian County Council records are not included.)

Facilities   Photocopying.

171   Edinburgh University Library
Special Collections Department

Address   George Square
                   Edinburgh EH8 9LJ

Telephone   (031) 667 1011 ext. 6628

Enquiries to   Sub-Librarian (Special Collections), Dr J.T.D. Hall

Open   Mon–Fri: 9.00–5.00
                   Closed: 2nd week of August; approximately two weeks at Christmas
                   and New Year; Good Friday; Scottish spring and autumn holidays

Access   By written application to the University Librarian.

Historical background   The Library was founded by the bequest of books from the
   library of Clement Little in 1580 to the Town and Kirk of Edinburgh; it was
   transferred to the Town's College (later University) in 1584.

Acquisitions policy   To strengthen existing collections in certain fields by purchase
   and donation.

Major collections   Laing collection: rich in material relating to Scottish letters and
   history.
   Oriental MSS: includes MSS transferred from New College (*see* entry **179**), and a
   small collection of palm-leaf MSS.
   Western MSS: c260 medieval items, and MSS and papers relating chiefly to Scottish
   or University personalities; Modern Scottish literary collections include Hugh

MacDiarmid (1892–1978), George Mackay Brown (*b* 1921).
Deposited collections: business archives, papers of John Wain (*b* 1925) and of the Scottish Liberal Association.
University archives: historical collections relating to students and teaching in the University.
Small collections are also housed in the Reid Music Library and the Veterinary Library.

Non-manuscript material   Rare book collections in all fields, 15th–20th centuries.
Thomson-Walker collection of engraved portraits of medical men.
University medals.
Kennedy-Fraser wax cylindrical recordings.

Finding aids   Index to MSS, with separate files relating to individual collections.
Shelf-lists of business and University archives.

Facilities   Photocopying. Photography. Microfilm/fiche reader.

Publications   *Index to Manuscripts* (Boston, 1964 [2 vols]); *First Supplement* (Boston, 1981)
Rev. J. Anderson (ed.): *Calendar of the Laing Charters AD 854–1837 belonging to the University of Edinburgh* (Edinburgh, 1899)
Report on the Laing Manuscripts preserved in the University of Edinburgh, Historical Manuscripts Commission (London, 1914–25) [2 vols]
C.R. Borland: *A Descriptive Catalogue of the Western Medieval Manuscripts in Edinburgh University Library* (Edinburgh, 1916)
M.A. Hukk, H. Ethé and E. Robertson: *A Descriptive Catalogue of the Arabic and Persian Manuscripts in Edinburgh University Library* (Hereford, 1925)
R.B. Serjeant: *A Handlist of the Arabic, Persian and Hindustani MSS of New College* (London, 1942)
J.R. Walsh: 'The Turkish Manuscripts in New College, Edinburgh', *Oriens*, xii (1959), 171
N.R. Ker: *Medieval Manuscripts in British Libraries*, ii (Oxford, 1977), 589

172   Fettes College

Address   Carrington Road
             Edinburgh EH4 1QX

Telephone   (031) 332 2281

Enquiries to   The Headmaster

Open   School hours, by appointment only

Access   Generally open to the public.

Historical background   The College was founded in 1870 under the terms of the will of Sir William Fettes, Bart., of Comely Bank and Redcastle (1750–1836): 'It is my intention that the residue of my whole Estate should form an Endowment for the maintenance, education and outfit of young people whose parents have either died without leaving sufficient funds for that purpose, or who from innocent misfortune during their lives, are unable to give suitable education to their children.' He very wisely gave his Trustees ample and unlimited powers for the making of regulations and general management of the funds.

Acquisitions policy   Records directly relating to the history of the College and to prominent Old Fettesians.

Major collections   School records.
Minutes of meetings of Governors of the Fettes Trust.

Non-manuscript material   Photographs, plans, maps.
Portraits.
Selwyn-Lloyd Memorial Library.

Publications   *The Fettesian* [annual]
A Hundred Years of Fettes (1970)

173   Free Church College

Address   The Mound
Edinburgh EH1 2LS

Telephone   (031) 226 4978

Enquiries to   The Secretary of Senate

Open   Mon–Fri: 9.00–4.30

Access   Approved readers on written application.

Historical background   The College became the Free Church College in continuity from New College, subsequent to the reorganization of the Free Church College and Offices by the Executive Commission after the emergence of the United Free Church in 1900. The building originally comprised luxury flats occupied by leading notables of Edinburgh society.

Major collections   Many documents of historical and antiquarian significance, relating mainly to the Scottish Church.

Non-manuscript material   Portraits of leading Scottish Churchmen; D.O. Hill's famous painting, *The First Free Church General Assembly*, 1843.
Celtic library, housed in Senate Hall.

Finding aids   Lists of archives.

Facilities   Photocopying by arrangement.

174   General Register Office for Scotland

Address   New Register House
                  Edinburgh EH1 3YT

Telephone   (031) 556 3952 ext.26

Enquiries to   Curatorial Officer, Dr I.D. Grant

Open   Mon–Thurs: 9.30–4.30
                  Fri: 9.30–4.00

Access   Generally available to the public on payment of a fee (list of charges
                  available). Free to approved researchers on written application.

Historical background   The Office was established in 1855 on the introduction of
     compulsory registration of births, deaths and marriages in Scotland. New Register
     House was designed by Robert Mathieson, an assistant surveyor of HM Office of
     Works. The Office provides a facility for record searching thought to be unique in
     the UK, housing under one roof the old parochial records, the later statutory
     registers and census records.

Acquisitions policy   Intake of statutory or closely allied material only.

Major collections   Statutory records of births, deaths and marriages, 1855–.
     Old parish records of Church of Scotland, 1553–1854 (incomplete).
     Open census records, 1841–91.
     Minor records of births, deaths and marriages registered abroad, 1855– (Scottish
     nationals only).

Non-manuscript material   Microfilm and microfiche of records.
     Registrar Generals' weekly, monthly, quarterly and annual reports, 1855–.
     Census reports, 1841–1981.

Finding aids   Old parochial records: lists and some indexes. Open census records:
     lists and street indexes for larger towns. Minor records: index. Glasgow street
     indexes.

Facilities   Microfilm/fiche readers.

175   Heriot-Watt University Library

Address   Riccarton
                  Edinburgh EH14 4AS

Telephone   (031) 449 5111 ext. 2283/2014

Enquiries to   Librarian and Keeper of Historical Records, Mr Alex Anderson
                  or
                  The Historical Records Section

Open   Term: Mon–Fri: 9.15 a.m.–9.45 p.m.
              Sat, Sun: 10.00–5.00, by appointment only
              Vacation: Mon–Fri: 9.15–5.00

Access   By application to the Librarian. Discretionary access to certain
              administrative and personal records.

Historical background   The institution founded in 1821 as an evening school by
  Leonard Horner (1785–1864), under the title School of Arts, became the Watt
  Institution and School of Arts, incorporating the Edinburgh memorial to James
  Watt, in 1852. As the Heriot-Watt College, 1885–1928, it offered day and evening
  classes to university level, under the Governors of George Heriot's Trust (founded
  1623). From 1928 to 1966 it was an autonomous Scottish Central Institution, and
  in 1966 became the Heriot-Watt University. Situated in the Chambers Street area of
  Edinburgh from 1837 to 1968, since 1969 it has also occupied a new site on the
  Riccarton Estate, formerly (1610–1969) the property of the Craig and Gibson-
  Craig families.
  Houses Scottish Brewing Archive (*see* entry **185**).

Acquisitions policy   To strengthen (by purchase, donation, deposit or the
  acquisition of micro-copies or photocopies) existing collections on the history of
  the Institution and its background from 1821, including material by or relating to
  persons prominently connected with it as staff, students and otherwise, and
  material relevant to existing interests, e.g. Leonard Horner, technical education,
  the history of Riccarton and of the Craig and Gibson-Craig families.

Major collections   University Collection: MS and printed items, including
  foundation, governing bodies', principals', administrative, academic, staff and
  student records, and those of associated bodies including the Watt Club, 1854–,
  staff and student societies, publications and papers of prominent staff and members
  and alumni; these include papers and correspondence, official and private
  (research etc), of Arthur Pillans Laurie (Principal, 1900–28; art historian and
  pigment chemist; 51 vols), Hugh Bryan Nisbet (Principal, 1950–67, chemist; 50
  vols and 12 boxes), Robert Allan Smith (Principal, 1968–74, physicist).
  Leonard Horner (1785–1864), founder of the Institution, educationalist, geologist,
  factory inspector; small collection of MSS and printed material (contact is
  maintained with the private owner of the major collection of Horner material;
  listing of the latter is projected).
  Watt Club Collection: books, some MSS, pamphlets, ephemera, by or relating to
  James Watt, the Watt family, Matthew Boulton, Thomas Telford, James Nasmyth
  (alumnus).
  Riccarton Collection: history of Riccarton estate, 15th century–; Craig and Gibson-
  Craig families including (Sir) Thomas Craig (?1538–1610), jurist, and Sir James
  Gibson-Craig, First baronet (1765–1850), Whig politician.
  Blair MSS: papers (semi-official and private) of Sir Robert Blair (1859–1935), first
  Chief Education Officer of London County Council, 1904–24, on education,
  especially further and technical, in Ireland, London and UK generally; includes
  papers of Liberal Advisory Education Committee, 1920s; Haldane Committee on

Education, 1916–; Royal Commission on London Government 1922; and drafts of works on education by Blair, and on Blair by James Cameron Small. Blair's official papers are deposited in the Greater London Record Office, entry 348.

Non-manuscript material University Collection: includes *c*1000 vols printed material, e.g. calendars, annual reports etc, of School of Arts, Watt Institution; maps, plans, illustrations.
Iconographic Collection: paintings, sculptures, drawings, prints, photographs (prints, negatives, slides) relating to Institution, associated persons, Riccarton etc.
Sound/Vision Archives: 50 cassettes of recordings of reminiscences of past staff and students, *c*1910–; *c*25 films and video-cassettes of events in recent college/university history.
*c*90 medals, mainly of Heriot-Watt College, 1886–1966.

Finding aids Various lists and indexes, some of printed material included in general library catalogue, of which a microfiche key-word index is available. Major listing/indexing project now under way will produce, inter alia, full index of past students etc, 1821–.

Facilities Photocopying. Microfilm reader. Audio-visual and TV equipment.

Publications *Heriot-Watt University: from Mechanics' Institute to Technological University, 1821–1973* (1973) [updated version by A. Anderson in progress]
National Register of Archives (Scotland) Lists nos 877–9

176   Leith Nautical College

Address   24 Milton Road East
             Edinburgh EH15 2PP

Telephone   (031) 669 8461 ext.209

Enquiries to Chief Librarian, Mr Paul F. Burton

Open   Term: Mon–Thurs: 8.45–8.00
             Fri: 8.45–5.00
             Vacation: Mon–Fri: 9.00–5.00

Access   On application to the Chief Librarian

Historical background The College was founded in 1855, following the 1850 Merchant Shipping Act. It became a Central Institution in 1903 and moved to new purpose-built premises in 1978, with three academic departments for marine electronics marine engineering and navigation. A specialized unit for hazardous cargo handling was created in 1978.

Acquisitions policy The main emphasis is on the acquisition of current textbooks. However, it is also policy to retain or acquire examples of texts and teaching materials for the education and training of merchant seamen, from 1850 onwards.

Major collections Historical collection of texts and teaching materials, including former students' log-books, examination primers and notebooks.

Non-manuscript material Selected examples of navigation instruments.

Finding aids Card catalogue to historical collection (a printed catalogue is planned). List of navigation instruments.

Facilities Photocopying. Microfilm/fiche readers.

177 National Library of Scotland
Department of Manuscripts

Address	George IV Bridge
	Edinburgh EH1 1EW
Telephone	(031) 226 4531
Enquiries to	The Keeper of Manuscripts
Open	Mon–Fri: 9.30–8.30
	Sat: 9.30–1.00
Access	All MSS and documents are available for consultation by serious researchers, except for a few items which are under restriction.

Historical background The National Library of Scotland came into being in 1925 when the Faculty of Advocates of Scotland gave to the Scottish nation the contents of the Advocates' Library (except legal books and MSS). The Advocates' Library had collected a wide range of MS material since the 1680s, and after 1925 this policy was continued and expanded by the Manuscript Department of the National Library.

Acquisitions policy As a general principle the Department acquires MS material relating to the history and literature of Scotland and the activities of Scots throughout the world. In recent years emphasis has been given to family papers, business records (especially of Scottish publishers), papers of political interest (including the archives of Scottish trade unions), and the papers of contemporary Scottish literary and cultural figures. Projects are in force to collect documents of individual famous Scots such as Sir Walter Scott (1771–1832), Thomas Carlyle (1795–1881) and David Livingstone (1813–73).

Non-manuscript material There is very little non-MS material in the Department, apart from some oral history tapes compiled and deposited by *Scotland's Record*.

Finding aids Typescript catalogues, indexes and inventories.

Facilities Photocopying. Photography. Microfilming. Provision for researchers who wish to use their own typewriters and tape-recorders.

Publications *Catalogue of Manuscripts acquired since 1925*, i (1938); ii (1966); iii

(1968)[iv, in press]
Summary Catalogue of the Advocates' Manuscripts (1971)

178   National Trust for Scotland

Address	5 Charlotte Square Edinburgh EH2 4DV
Telephone	(031) 226 5922
Enquiries to	Deputy Director, Mr J. Davie

The Trust holds only its own archives dealing with internal matters. Any archives acquired with properties are usually deposited with the appropriate local record office.

179   New College Library

Address	Edinburgh University Library Mound Place Edinburgh EH1 2LU
Telephone	(031) 225 8400 ext. 256
Enquiries to	Librarian, Mr J.V. Howard
Open	Term: Mon–Thurs: 9.00–9.00 Fri: 9.00–5.30 Vacation: Mon–Fri: 9.00–5.00 Closed: 25 Dec–3 Jan; Good Friday; Victoria Day; Scottish spring and autumn holidays
Access	By written application to the Librarian.

Historical background   The College was founded in 1843 when training for the Free Church ministry began. The Library has become one of the chief British research collections in theological, religious, historical and other subjects. After the Church Union of 1900, a large proportion of the Library of the United Presbyterian Church College (Synod Hall) was acquired and in recent years the General Assembly (Tolbooth) Library of the Church of Scotland has been incorporated. In 1935, as a result of the 1929 Reunion, New College formally became also the University's Faculty of Divinity, and in 1963 the Library was placed on permanent deposit with the University. It is now administered as a detached section of the University Library.

Acquisitions policy   To add to the Thomas Chalmers archive by purchase or gift. To add to existing collections of papers of Scottish church leaders, and, selectively, other material relevant to the religious life of Scotland, and to the Ecumenical and Hymnology collections.

Major collections   Archive of Thomas Chalmers (1780–1847), leader of Free Church of Scotland, social reformer, c1760–1890.

New College archives and historical papers.

Papers of principals and professors of New College, 19th and 20th centuries.

MSS relating to individuals and events in Scottish church history, including Alexander Thomson (1798–1868) of Banchory; papers of John White (1867–1951) relating to reunion of Church of Scotland and United Free Church of Scotland, 1929; James King Hewison papers on the Covenanters, 17th century; letters, journals and sermons of Robert Baillie, 1637–62; James Kirkwood, provision of the Irish Bible in Scotland, and establishment of Highland Libraries, 1676–1709.

Westminster Assembly of Divines minutes, 1643–52.

Sermons of Covenanters, 17th century; and Secession ministers, 18th century.

Ecumenical Collection including: Church of Scotland Special Committee on Anglican-Presbyterian relations, 1961–6; Christian Unity Association, 1904–56; Balfour of Burleigh papers on church reunion, to 1913.

Non-manuscript material   Ecumenical collection of printed books, pamphlets and microfilm of the World Council of Churches, British Council of Churches and Scottish Council of Churches.

James Thin hymnology collection (7000 printed items).

Finding aids   Chronological inventories and author indexes to the Thomas Chalmers archive.

Facilities   Photocopying. Microfilm/fiche readers. Microfilming and photography in main University Library building.

Publications   Guide to New College Library [annual]
H. Watt: *New College, Edinburgh, a Centenary History* (1946)

180   Royal Botanic Garden Library

Address   Inverleith Row
                   Edinburgh EH3 5LR

Telephone   (031) 552 7171

Enquiries to   Librarian, Mr M.V. Mathew

Open   By appointment only
                   Mon–Thurs: 8.30–1.00; 2.00–5.00
                   Fri: 8.30–1.00; 2.00–4.30

Access   Bona fide researchers.

Historical background   The Garden was founded in 1670. Its large archival collection is the result of its long history and activities, particularly in the field of botany and horticulture.

Acquisitions policy   No active acquisition, but any relevant material is accepted.

Major collections   Archives of the Garden and its predecessors: administrative records and scientific papers, including papers of Regius Keepers and staff.
Records of botanical clubs and societies, including the Botanical Society of Edinburgh minute books, 1836–, and the Royal Caledonian Horticultural Society.
Transcribed material and notes made by historians of the Garden.
Papers including J.F. Rock's diaries and photographs; James MacNab's journals and scrapbooks; several files of papers and letters related to expeditions to different parts of the world.
Collection of *c*30,000 letters including John Hutton Balfour's worldwide correspondence (*c*4000); George Forrest's letters from China (*c*4000).

Non-manuscript material   Extensive collection of plant drawings, paintings and prints.

Finding aids   No catalogue or index: a first sort of the collection is being attempted.

Facilities   Photocopying. Photography. Microfilm/fiche reader.

Publications   H.R. Fletcher and W.H. Brown: *The Royal Botanic Garden, Edinburgh, 1670–1970* (1970)
I.C. Hedge and J.M. Lammond (eds): *Index of Collectors in the Edinburgh Herbarium* (1970)

181   Royal College of Physicians of Edinburgh Library

Address   9 Queen Street
                 Edinburgh EH2 1JQ

Telephone   (031) 225 5968

Enquiries to   Librarian, Miss J.P.S. Ferguson

Open   Mon–Fri: 9.00–5.00

Access   Fellows, members of the College and bona fide researchers.

Historical background   The Library was founded in 1681 by Sir Robert Sibbald, the principal founder of the College, and has had a continuous existence as a working medical library since then. It also contains good collections of works on botany and natural history down to the mid-19th century.

Acquisitions policy   To fill gaps in historical collections and augment the history of medicine section.

Major collections   College archives relating to the constitution, with lists of members, minutes, accounts and records, general correspondence, College buildings, Fellows' petitions etc, 1681–.

Reports and correspondence concerning Lunatic Asylums in Scotland, 1814–85.

Records and papers of the Medical Provident Institution of Scotland, 1826–34.

MSS Collection: c1000 vols, including 18th-century lecture notes of lecturers in Edinburgh medical school; MSS of William Cullen (1710–90), including consultation letters; MSS of Sir James Young Simpson (1811–70); MSS of the three Alexander Monros (1697–1767, 1733–1817, 1773–1859).

Non-manuscript material   College portraits.

Albums of engravings of medical men, 18th and 19th centuries.

Other prints, engravings, photographs, including those from the collection of J.D. Comrie.

Finding aids   Index to muniments. Various other indexes.

Facilities   Photocopying. Microfilm/fiche reader.

Publications   *Inventory of Muniments*, 2 vols (1914) [at Scottish Record Office]
   W.J. Robertson: *A Checklist of Manuscripts in the RCP of Ed* (1965)

182   Royal Commission on the Ancient and Historical Monuments of Scotland (including the National Monuments Record of Scotland)

Address   54 Melville Street
                 Edinburgh EH3 7HF

Telephone   (031) 225 5994

Enquiries to   Curator, Miss C.H. Cruft

Open   Mon–Fri: 9.30–5.00

Access   Generally open to the public.

Historical background   The amalgamation in 1966 of the Royal Commission on the Ancient and Historical Monuments of Scotland, founded in 1908 to make an inventory of all ancient and historical monuments in Scotland, and the Scottish National Buildings Record, set up in 1941 to make and preserve records of buildings in anticipation of their possible destruction by enemy action, enabled the two largest collections of photographs and drawings of ancient monuments and historic buildings in Scotland to be combined in a single archive known as the National Monuments Record of Scotland.

Acquisitions policy   To add to the existing collection of drawings, prints, photographs, slides and MSS by purchase, donation and deposit, and by making photographic copies of relevant material in other public and private muniments.

Major collections   Principally non-MS material (see below).
Society of Antiquaries of Scotland collection, MSS and drawings, 19th century.
Ordnance Survey record cards of archaeological sites.

Non-manuscript material   Burn Collection: office collection of architectural drawings from the London office of William Burn (1789–1879).
Lorimer Collection: office drawings of the architectural practice of Sir Robert Lorimer (1864–1929).
Erskine Beveridge collection of photographs of archaeological sites and buildings in the West Highlands and Fife.
Society of Antiquaries of Scotland Collection of aerial photographs of archaeological and architectural sites.
Library of over 8000 books and pamphlets.

Finding aids   Topographical and subject indexes to the National Monuments Record of Scotland (NMRS) collection. Alphabetical slip index to architects and their works. Summary guide slip index containing references to material in the NMRS, outside collections and published sources.

Facilities   Photocopying. Photography. Microfilm/fiche/reader printer.

Publications   Inventories of ancient and historical monuments, lists of archaeological sites and monuments, catalogues of aerial photographs, monographs etc. [A detailed list of publications is available from The Secretary, RCAM (Scotland), 54 Melville Street, Edinburgh EH3 7HF]

183   Royal Scottish Museum

Address   Chambers Street
                   Edinburgh EH1 1JF

Telephone   (031) 225 7534

Enquiries to   Librarian, Miss D.C.F. Smith

Open   By appointment
                   Mon–Thurs: 10.00–12.30; 2.00–5.00
                   Fri: 10.00–12.30; 2.00–4.30

Access   Generally open to the public.

Historical background   The Royal Scottish Museum was founded in 1854, originally as a museum of the arts and industry, later incorporating the Natural History Museum of Edinburgh University. It now consists of four departments: Art and Archaeology (which includes mainly the decorative arts and pre-1900 sculpture, ethnography, oriental art and world-wide archaeology, except Scotland); Natural History (zoology); Geology; Technology (history of sciences and technology). Each department keeps its own records relating to the acquisition of specimens, and there is no central archive record. In addition the Library has some MS material.

There are three out-stations: Museum of Flight, East Fortune Airfield, East Lothian; Shambellie House Museum of Costume, New Abbey, Dumfries (to open in 1982); Biggar Gasworks.

Acquisitions policy There is no acquisitions policy for MS material; most is obtained through donations, especially connected with specimens.

Major collections Archives are kept in each department and not recorded centrally. Library MSS: mainly natural historians' correspondence, including an 18th-century account of Orkney and Shetland; J.A. Harrie-Brown migration schedules from Scottish lighthouses, 1881–1904, with correspondence; material concerning William S. Bruce (1867–1921).
Natural History Department includes extensive correspondence of William Jardine (1800–74), with many eminent figures.

Non-manuscript material Technology Department: photography collection, including examples of early photographic techniques and photographs (e.g. Hill and Adamson); *c*300 technical drawings.
Large collection of natural history reprints and separates (some in library, some in departments; not catalogued).

Facilities Limited photocopying. Microfilm/fiche readers. (Photography temporarily unavailable.)

Publications J. Pitman: *Manuscripts in the Royal Scottish Museum, part 1*. William Jardine Papers, *Royal Scottish Museum Information Series: Natural History, 7* (1981) [Two further parts are projected, one on William S. Bruce papers and the other on J.A. Harvie-Brown correspondence]
Natural history collections are listed in Bridson *et al*: *Natural History Manuscript Resources of the British Isles* (1981), 87

184 The Royal Society of Edinburgh

Address   22 and 24 George Street
               Edinburgh EH2 2PQ

Telephone   (031) 225 6057

The library and the majority of the archives were transferred to the National Library of Scotland (*see* entry **177**). Archival material held consists of archives of the Society, 1783–; the MSS of Joseph Hume (1777–1855); and two volumes by James Hutton (1726–97) on agriculture.

185 Scottish Brewing Archive

Address c/o Heriot-Watt University Library
Chambers Street
Edinburgh EH1 1HX

Telephone (031) 225 8432 ext. 5/334

Enquiries to Director, Mr Alex Anderson (University Librarian, Heriot-Watt University)

Open Term: Mon—Fri: 9.00—9.00
Sat: morning, by appointment only
Vacation: Mon—Fri: 9.00—5.00

Access By application to the Director. Restricted access to some confidential records.

Historical background Heriot-Watt University (formerly the Heriot-Watt College) has taught and researched in brewing and related sciences since 1903, and its Library has extensive and established collections in these fields. The Scottish Brewing Archive was established in 1980 to act, by agreement with the Scottish Record Office, as a centre for the collection of records and other material relating to brewing and related industries (including malting but excluding distilling) in Scotland.

Acquisitions policy To receive on deposit, or by transfer, donation, purchase or otherwise, material, primarily MS but including printed and other material, relating to the brewing and related industries of Scotland.

Major collections Records (some include correspondence and brewing books) of the following: McEwans 1856— (c100 vols); Younger, c1805— (c20 vols and several hundred letters); Tennents, c1775— (c30 vols, plus correspondence and documents); Drybroughs, c1775— (c150 vols, plus documents); Ushers (Edinburgh) and associated companies, 1834— (c120 vols); Lorimer & Clark, 1910—(c100 vols); Belhaven, Dunbar, 1875—; Edinburgh United Breweries.
MS works on brewing; records of Brewers' Association of Scotland; notebooks of former brewing students.

Non-manuscript material Current books and periodicals in brewing and related subjects, e.g. biochemistry, brewery management and law (5500 vols, 40 periodical titles in brewing, c150 related subjects; housed in the University Library).
Historical Brewing Collection: older and historical books, periodicals, illustrations, labels on brewing; mainly British (especially Scottish), but including unusual foreign material, directories of breweries, annual reports and histories of firms, Acts of Parliament, xeroxes of rare material (c500 vols).
Department of Brewing and Biological Sciences: historical collection of brewing tools, equipment etc, including coopering and malting tools (plough, shoes, shovels), hydrometers, bottled and canned beer in original containers.

Finding aids   National Register of Archives (Scotland) lists cover collections as
follows: NRA(S) List 0274, McEwan, W. Younger; 944, Tennent; 1955, Drybrough;
2188, Usher etc. Other lists, indexes, guides in preparation include: Bibliography
of English-language material on brewing etc (*c*1000 titles); Union list of books on
brewing etc, in Edinburgh libraries; index to Younger correspondence, *c*1880–
1915.

Facilities   Photocopying. Microfilm/fiche readers. Audio-visual and TV equipment.

Publications   *Scottish Brewing Archive Newsletter* (1981–)

186   Scottish Catholic Archives

Address   Columba House
                   16 Drummond Place
                   Edinburgh EH3 6PL

Telephone   (031) 556 3661

Enquiries to   Keeper, Rev. Dr G.M. Dilworth

Open   By appointment only

Access   Access to almost all material, for purposes of scholarship.

Historical background   Material was collected from various sources at the seminary
of Aquhortics (Deeside), 1799–1829; Preshome (near Buckie), 1829–69; and
Blairs College (near Aberdeen), 1829–. The Blairs material was brought to
Edinburgh in 1958, the Preshome material in the 1970s.

Acquisitions policy   Each diocese or other body preserves its own modern records,
but they are encouraged to deposit their older records centrally.

Major collections   Scottish Catholic Mission correspondence, *c*1650–1878.
Muniments of Scots colleges on the Continent prior to the French Revolution.
Blairs Letters, *c*1600–1890 (*c*50,000 items).
Preshome Letters, *c*1750–1880 (*c*25,000 items).

Non-manuscript material   Printed books and pamphlets relevant to post-
Reformation Scottish Catholicism.

Finding aids   Blairs Letters indexed under writer and year. Some minor collections
listed or calendared. All holdings are being steadily calendared or listed. It is
intended to print a handlist.

Facilities   Photocopying. Photography.

Publications   D. McRoberts: 'The Scottish Catholic Archives 1560–1978', *The Innes
Review*, xxviii (1977), 59–128
M. Dilworth: 'The Scottish Catholic Archives', *Catholic Archives*, no.1 (1981), 10

187　Scottish National Portrait Gallery

Address　　　Reference Section
　　　　　　　1 Queen Street
　　　　　　　Edinburgh EH2 1JD

Telephone　　(031) 556 8921

Enquiries to　Assistant Keeper, Dr Rosalind K. Marshall

Open　　　　Mon–Fri: 10.00–12.30; 1.30–5.00

Access　　　Generally open to the public. For lengthy enquiries it is advisable
　　　　　　　to write in advance.

Historical background　Since the establishment of the Gallery in the late 19th
century, comprehensive records have been kept of Scottish portraits and portrait
painters.

Acquisitions policy　Engavings, drawings, early photographs and photographs of
portraits are acquired on a historical basis, for the importance of the sitter in
Scottish history, rather than for aesthetic merit. The Gallery does not collect MS
material.

Non-manuscript material　14,000 portrait engravings.
650 portrait drawings.
5000 Hill and Adamson calotypes.
25,000 photographs of portraits in other collections.
Biographical details of Scottish artists.
Analyses of information about costume, furniture and other aspects of social
history.

Finding aids　All materials are indexed by sitter, artist and for all social history
features.

Publications　R.K. Marshall: 'The Scottish National Portrait Gallery as a source for the
Local Historian', *The Local Historian*, ii (1975) 382
D. Thomson and S. Bruce Lockhart: *Concise Catalogue* (Edinburgh, 1977) [lists
portrait drawings as well as paintings in the collection]
R.K. Marshall: 'Scottish Portraits as a source for the Costume Historian', *Costume*,
xv (1981), 67
S. Stevenson: *David Octavius Hill and Robert Adamson* (National Galleries of
Scotland, 1981) [catalogue of holdings]

188　Scottish Record Office (SRO)

Address　　　HM General Register House
　　　　　　　Princes Street
　　　　　　　Edinburgh EH1 3YY

Telephone   (031) 556 6585

Enquiries to   The Keeper of the Records of Scotland

Open   Mon–Fri: 9.00–4.45

Access   Legal Search Room, HM General Register House: searches of a legal or commercial nature; a fee is charged.
Historical Search Room, HM General Register House, and West Search Room, West Register House: readers' tickets are issued on personal application (not by post).

Historical background   The Department originated in the office of the Clerk of the Rolls (13th century), who was responsible for the custody of the non-current records of government and whose successors, the Lord Clerk Register and Deputy-Clerk Register, were also responsible for supervising the framing of the public legal registers and their safe-keeping. The General Register House (founded in 1774) was designed by Robert Adam as the earliest purpose-built record repository in the British Isles, in order to centralize most of the public and legal records and facilitate access to them. In 1847 the Antiquarian Room, now the Historical Search Room, was opened to the public for the purposes of historical and literary research free of charge. The office of Keeper of the Records of Scotland and the modern development of the Scottish Record Office date from the Public Registers and Records (Scotland) Act, 1948. In 1971 the West Register House, an internal conversion of the former St George's Church, Charlotte Square (founded 1811), was opened as a branch repository, mainly for modern records.

Acquisitions policy   The SRO is the repository for the public (government and legal) records of Scotland and also assists in preserving Scotland's archival heritage by accepting custody of records for which it is the most suitable repository.

Major collections   The surviving legislative and administrative records of the kingdom of Scotland prior to the parliamentary union with England in 1707, thereafter the records of the various government agencies and departments in Scotland until the present, with regular transmissions of records from the departments of the Secretary of State for Scotland and nationalized industries.
Records of the Scottish central courts (Court of Session and High Court of Justiciary) and many local courts.
Public registers of sasines and deeds relating to property and private rights.
Records of local authorities and churches.
Over 300 separate collections of private archives, family papers, records of institutions, businesses and industrial firms.
Much of the material in private archives, and even in certain public record groups, relates to overseas. Details of records not in official custody are contained in surveys carried out by the national Register of Archives (Scotland) which is a branch of the SRO.

Non-manuscript material   Large collection of maps and plans, many of them hand-drawn, 18th century–.
Photographs in certain record groups; microfilm holdings both of records held

within and outside the SRO; modern records in microfiche (e.g. valuation rolls).
Early printed material, including books, in private archive deposits.
Printed books reference library (limited access), mainly legal, topographical,
biographical and general Scottish history, as well as many standard reference works
and historical clubs' publications.

Finding aids   Catalogue or Reference Rooms in both repositories (readers are
advised on how to use the repertories, inventories and handlists); indexes in the
Reference Rooms for some record groups. Source lists, prepared and distributed to
certain interested bodies and institutions, on major themes, e.g. overseas
countries, communications, industry, art and architecture (in preparation),
education, medicine, etc.

Facilities   Electrostatic copies. Photography and microfilming. Microfilm readers.
The West Search Room is also equipped for map and plan consultation, and the use
of tape-recorders and typewriters.

Publications   Full information on accessions and surveys in *Annual Report of the
Keeper of the Records of Scotland* [available from SRO and on microfiche from
Chadwyck-Healey Ltd, *Catalogue of British Official Publications not published by
HMSO*]
SRO record publications in print are listed in *British National Archives: Sectional
List 24* [published annually by HMSO]
Descriptive Lists of Plans and Gifts and Deposits (i.e. private archives) and *A List of
American Documents* [obtainable from HMSO and Government Bookshops]
A New Guide to the Scottish Record Office [in preparation]
A series of free information leaflets on the history, holdings and facilities of the
Office and an introductory leaflet for schools are available from the SRO.

189   The Theological College

Address   Rosebery Crescent
                 Edinburgh EH12 5JT

Telephone   Principal: (031) 337 3838
                 Vice-Principal and Chaplain/Librarian: (031) 337 4537

Enquiries to   The Principal
                 or
                 The Chaplain

Open   Normal office hours during term

Access   Approved readers, by appointment, after written application to the
                 Primus. Access to the Episcopal Safe is by arrangement between the
                 College and the NRA (Scotland) at West Register House, Edinburgh

Acquisitions policy   To strengthen the existing library, which is used chiefly by ordinands in training at the Theologial College, by purchase, donations, or deposits.

Major collections   Episcopal Safe, formerly 'the episcopal chest', papers relating to the Episcopal church in Scotland, 16th–19th centuries. The bulk is 18th-century and consists of proceedings of synods, deeds of consecration, letters of orders, institutions of clergy; also some papers relating to liturgical matters, to charity funds and to schools in the Highlands. Papers relating to the Seabury Consecration, 1784, including correspondence with Connecticut.

Correspondence, including that of the Duke and Duchess of Lauderdale and Archbishop Sharp, 1660–82.

Papers on the building of the College, 1810–96; other miscellanous papers, 17th–19th centuries.

Jolly Papers: an artificial collection formed by Bishop John Jolly (1756–1838) includes items from early 17th century.

Finding aids   A full inventory of the records of the Episcopal Safe is available in the Scottish Record Office (*see* entry **188**).

Facilities   Reading room.

190   Royal Holloway College Library
College Archives

Address   University of London
                   Egham Hill
                   Egham
                   Surrey TW20 0EX

Telephone   (87) 34455

Enquiries to   Librarian, Mr B.J.C. Wintour

Open   Mon–Fri: 10.00–4.00

Access   Approved researchers, on written application to the Librarian.

Historical background   The College, built in French Renaissance style to the design of the architect William Henry Crossland, was founded and endowed in 1883 by Thomas Holloway, the Victorian philanthropist who made a fortune from patent medicines. It was officially opened by Queen Victoria in 1886. Originally instituted as a women's college, it began admitting men in 1965. It has faculties of Arts, Music and Science.

Acquisitions policy   To collect official records of the College in all its aspects and to acquire miscellaneous material relating to the history of the Royal Holloway College, including its Picture Gallery.

Major collections   Board of Governors records, 1886–1949 and Council records, 1949–; records of the Academic Board, Academic Departments, Library,

Administrative and Residence Departments, Associations, Committees, Clubs, and Societies.

Non-manuscript material   A variety of miscellaneous material relating to Royal Holloway College, including photographs of the buildings and of members of the College and their activities; items relating to Thomas Holloway and his family; historical notes, newspaper articles and cuttings; reminiscences and memoirs of members of the College; verses and fiction, prints, drawings, and watercolours.

Facilities   Photocopying.

Publications   D. Paul: *Royal Holloway College Archives: a Guide* (1973)
J. Chapel: *Victorian Taste: the Complete Catalogue of Paintings in the Royal Holloway College* (due for publication in 1982) [of relevance to letters in the archives about the Picture Gallery and its paintings]

191   Gordonstoun

Address   Elgin
                   Moray
                   Grampian

Telephone   (0343) 830445

Enquiries to   School Archivist, Mr R.G. Waddell

Open   By appointment only

Access   Approved readers; very restricted, as much material has to be confidential.

Historical background   An ancient Scottish estate since the 13th century, Gordonstoun has been a public school since 1934.

Acquisitions policy   Any papers on the estate, past and present staff, old boys or past governors are most welcome.

Major collections   Minutes of boys', staff and Governors' meetings; material relating to the School's varied activities; letters to/from past Headmasters, Governors and Old Boys; general administrative papers.
Gordon Cumming private family papers (owners of Gordonstoun from 17th century to 1934) are deposited in the National Library of Scotland (*see* entry **177**).

Non-manuscript material   Pamphlets and photographs.

Finding aids   Various lists and indexes.

Facilities   Photocopying.

Publications   H.L. Brereton: *Gordonstoun* (Aberdeen, 1968, R/1981)
Various pamphlets

192   Devon Library Services

Address	Exeter Central Library
	Castle Street
	Exeter
	Devon EX4 3PQ
Telephone	(0392) 77977
Enquiries to	The Area Librarian
Open	Mon, Tues, Thurs, Fri: 9.30–8.00
	Wed: 9.30–6.00
	Sat: 9.30–4.00
Access	Generally open to the public. Prior enquiry advisable.

Historical background   Devon Library Services was formed out of a number of separate library authorities on local government reorganization in 1974. Two of these authorities, Exeter and Plymouth, were established in the 19th century and had considerable MS collections. They both suffered in World War II and their archives are now administered by Devon Record Office (*see* entry **193**). Any MSS in Devon Library Services are now non-archival in nature and relatively few in number. They are mainly to be found in the local studies collections in Exeter and Plymouth Central Library (*see* entry **587**). There are smaller collections at most service points throughout the county.

Acquisitions policy   To acquire non-archival MSS which reflect the development of Devon and the South West of England.

Major collections   Several hundred MSS and typescripts, mainly on local antiquarian topics, including the writings of historians such as Tristram Risdon (?1580–1640) and James Davidson (1793–1864), and several surveys of Devon churches.
A few literary MSS by R.D. Blackmore (1825–1900), John Galsworthy (1867–1933), Eden Phillpotts (1862–1960) and Sabine Baring-Gould (1834–1924).
Devon and Cornwall Record Society collection of transcripts of parish records (1200 vols; available to members only).

Non-manuscript material   Extensive collections of illustrations, newspaper cutting files, ephemera, maps.
Rare book collection including 2500 pre-1800 imprints.

Facilities   Photocopying. Microfilm/fiche reader/printers. Photography undertaken through the county's document reproduction unit.

Publications   Some material in A. Brodcett (comp.): *The Devon Union List* (Exeter University Library, 1977)

193   Devon Record Office

Address	Castle Street Exeter Devon EX4 3PQ
Telephone	(0392) 53509
Enquiries to	Head of Record Services, Mrs M.M. Rowe
Open	Mon–Thurs: 9.30–5.00 Fri: 9.30–4.30 Sat (1st and 3rd of each month): 9.30–12.00 There is a daily or annual charge.

Historical background   The old County Record Office was established in 1952 and the former Exeter City Record Office (originally Exeter MSS Department of the Library) was established in 1947. In 1974 the latter became the East Devon Office and amalgamated with the old County Office in 1977. The office also acts as the Diocesan Record Office for Exeter. There is a branch office at Plymouth (*see* entry **589**).

Major collections   Usual local authority record holdings and deposited collections including the following which have a wider significance:
Papers of: Henry Addington, first Viscount Sidmouth (1757–1844); Gen. John Graves Simcoe, relating to Canada and the campaign in the West Indies, 1776–97; William Buckland (1784–1856), geologist, and his son Frank Buckland (1809–91), naturalist.

Facilities   Photocopying. Photography and microfilming by arrangement. Microfilm reader.

Publications   *Devon Record Office, Brief Guide: Part 1 Official and Ecclesiastical*, (1969)

194   Exeter Cathedral Library and Archives

Address	Bishop's Palace Exeter Devon EX1 1HX
Telephone	(0392) 72894
Enquiries to	Mr Peter Thomas (Library) Mrs A.M. Erskine (Archives)
Open	Mon–Fri: 2.00–5.00 Closed: Christmas and Easter weeks

Appointment preferred; at least one day's notice for production of archives is essential.

Access   Generally open to the public. Some MSS on special application only. 100-year closure except in special circumstances.

Historical background   The library was founded by a gift of 66 MSS by Leofric, Bishop of Exeter (*d* 1072) and has had a continuous history since that date. A group of MSS including the Exeter Book of Poetry (10th century) and the Exon. Domesday (11th century) survive *in situ* from the medieval library; printed books, pamphlets etc, have accumulated since the post-medieval period. The library and archives are now administered together by the University of Exeter on behalf of the Dean and Chapter of Exeter Cathedral.

Acquisitions policy   Restricted to records directly relating to the Cathedral, its personnel and its present and former properties.

Major collections   Capitular archives: royal diplomas, 10th–11th centuries; charters, deeds, leases; lawsuits etc; chapter acts, late 14th century–; registers, cartularies etc; rentals, surveys, manorial records, maps, plans etc; accounts, 12th century –, including 18th–19th-century deeds, agreements and manorial records redeposited by the Church Commissioners.
Archives of Vicars Choral: 13th–20th centuries, of a similar nature to the Capitular archives.
Archives of Archdeaconry of Exeter: court records, visitations etc, 17th century–.

Non-manuscript material   Accumulating collection of photographs and coloured photographic slides, mainly of architectural and sculptural details of Exeter Cathedral, primarily to record the continuing conservation programme.

Finding aids   MS catalogue of part of capitular archives (compiled by A. Stuart Moore, 1873); gradually being superseded by numerous lists, card catalogues and indexes in progress. Complete summary class lists in typescript of records of the College of Vicars Choral and of the archdeaconry of Exeter.

Facilities   Photocopying and photography (in Exeter University reprographic department). Microfilm/fiche reader.

Publications   *Report on Manuscripts in Various Collections*, Historical Manuscripts Commission, iv (1907)
N.R. Ker: *Medieval Manuscripts in British Libraries*, ii: *Abbotsford to Keele* (1969), 800–46
L.J. Lloyd and A.M. Erskine: *The Library of Exeter Cathedral* (1974)
A.M. Erskine (ed.): *The Accounts of the Fabric of Exeter Cathedral, i: 1279–1326*, Devon and Cornwall Record Society, New Series, xxiv (1981)

195   Exeter University Library

Address	Prince of Wales Road Exeter Devon EX4 4PT
Telephone	(0392) 77911
Enquiries to	The Librarian
Open	Mon–Fri: 9.00–5.30
Access	By written application to The Librarian

Historical background   The University Library dates from 1955, when the University received its charter, but some of its stock dates back to the early years of the 20th century.

Acquisitions policy   Archives and MSS are occasionally purchased but the majority of items are gifts.

Major collections   University archives.
Literary: papers and MSS of R.D. Blackmore (1825–1900), Henry Williamson (1895–1977), Jack Clemo, Charles Causley (*b* 1917), Ted Hughes (*b* 1930).
Local history: local newspapers, prints and MSS.
Theatre: large collection of playbills of the Theatre Royal, Exeter, *c*1890 to early 1950s.
Autographs: small collection of 19th-century autographs and letters.
Astronomy: archives of Sir Norman Lockyer (1836–1920).
West Indies: collection of papers relating to estates and slavery in Jamaica.

Non-manuscript material   Early maps, mainly of Devon and Cornwall.
Photographs relating to former British colonies.
Very large collection of tapes, records, etc, of American blues music.

Finding aids   Lists.

Facilities   Photocopying. Photography. Microfiche.

196   Falkirk District Council

Address	Falkirk Museums 15 Orchard Street Falkirk FK1 1RE
Telephone	(0324) 24911 ext. 2202
Enquiries to	Curator, Mr J.M. Sanderson
Open	Mon–Sat: 10.00–5.00

Access   Generally open to the public.

Historical background   Founded in 1926 with a bequest by Mungo Buchanan, architect and antiquarian, and based on his collection of artefacts, MSS and photographic material, the collection was extended to form a local history archive for Falkirk town and, with local government reorganization in 1975, for Falkirk District.

Acquisitions policy   To strengthen existing primary and secondary collections in the local history and industrial history fields by purchase and donation.

Major collections   Burns Collection: diaries, MSS and ephemera, 1796–1860.
Kirklands diary, transcript and notes, 1722–6.
Love Collection: notebooks and MSS, 1877–1928.
Buchanan Collection: site plans, sketches.
Grangemouth Dockyard trial books and ship plans.
Forth and Clyde Canal: lock-keepers journals, reports, acts and various broadsheets.
Bo'ness Seabox Society (beneficent society), papers, 1634–(recent).

Non-manuscript material   Maps and plans, Falkirk District, 18th and 19th centuries.
Foundry catalogues, 1860–1960.
Photographic collection: townscapes, people, industries, archaeological excavations, 1860– (16,000 items).
Small collection of oral records on cassettes.

Finding aids   Classified index. Catalogued, 1926–74.

Facilities   Photocopying. Photography. Microfiche reader.

197   Kent Archives Office
South East Kent Branch

Address   Folkestone Central Library
Grace Hill
Folkestone
Kent CT20 1HD

Telephone   (0303) 57583

Enquiries to   Archivist-in-charge, Mrs Maureen Shaw

Open   Mon, Tues, Thurs, Fri: 9.00–7.00
Wed: 9.00–1.00
Sat: 9.00–5.00

Historical background   The office was established in 1976 following local government reorganization. The library had already accumulated a considerable collection of archives, the bulk pertaining to the Borough of Folkestone, and the office is now expanding its interest to cover the Shepway District.

Major collections   Usual local authority record holdings and deposited collections, primarily of local interest.

Facilities   Photocopying. Microfilm reader.

198   Angus District Council

Address	County Buildings
	Forfar
	Angus
Telephone	(0307) 65101
Enquiries to	Director of Administration, Mr John L. Richardson
Open	Mon–Fri: 9.00–5.00, by arrangement
Access	Generally open to the public.

Historical background   Angus District Council was set up by local government reorganization in 1975, taking over the functions of six burghs.

Acquisitions policy   Records of administration and constituent burghs.

Major collections   Angus District Council records 1975–.
  Records of former burghs: Arbroath, 1530–1975; Brechin, 1672–1975; Carnoustie, 1884–1975; Forfar, 1666–1975; Kirriemuir, 1834–1975; Montrose, 1458–1975.

Finding aids   Archive list.

Facilities   Photocopying.

199   Forfar Public Library
Meffan Institute

Address	West High Street
	Forfar
	Angus DD8 1BB
Telephone	(0307) 63468
Enquiries to	Librarian, Mr Ian Niel
Open	Mon–Weds, Fri, Sat: 9.30–7.00
	Thurs: 9.30–5.00
Access	Generally open to the public, on written application.

Historical background   The Library opened in 1870 and in 1898 moved to the

Meffan Institute, a free public library and museum. In 1975 it became part of the Angus District Libraries and Museums. The collection was built up by the librarian and by donations.

Acquisitions policy   Any local material.

Major collections   Glenprosen parish records 1794–1954.
Forfar Trades Incorporation records: Shoemakers, Tailors and Weavers, 17th–19th centuries.
Local voluntary society and business records, 18th–20th centuries.
Genealogical collections: families of Erskine, Ogilvie, Steele, Seton, Small, Gray, McLean, Duncan, Scrymgeour, Ducat, Whyte, Campbell, Adam, Ure, Skinner, McCombie, MacThomas, Thomas, Abercrombie, 15th–20th centuries.
Scottish and Continental music transcribed for the local Militia Fife Band, c1798–1816.

Non-manuscript material   Local maps and plans.
Local published monographs, periodicals, etc.

Finding aids   Archive list.

Facilities   Photocopying, by prior appointment.

200 Moray District Council
Department of Libraries, Museums and Art Galleries

Address   Record Office
                 The Tolbooth
                 Forres
                 Grampian

Telephone   (0309) 73617

Enquiries to   District Archivist, Dr David Iredale

Open   Mon–Fri: 9.00–12.30; 1.30–4.30

Access   Generally open to the public. Appointment advised for certain series of records. Restriction on access to documents less than 30 years old.

Historical background   The Department was established by Moray District Council in 1975.

Acquisitions policy   To collect and preserve official archives and private muniments referring to the Moray District.

Major collections   Local Government Archives: archives of pre-1975 authorities in Moray, including three royal and nine police burghs, county councils and commissioners of supply, schools, lunacy boards, parochial boards, district councils, water authorities etc, 1268–1975.

Gordon Papers: correspondence of Rev. George Gordon, minister of Birnie, naturalist and antiquarian, including letters from C.R. Darwin, T.H. Huxley and other scientists, *c*1830–*c*98. (2000 items).

Isaac Forsyth, bookseller, Elgin: correspondence with his brother Joseph, 1800–15, including the period when Joseph was a prisoner of war of the French, 1803–14 (100 items).

Paterson family: sermons of John, James, Robert and Alexander, with medical notes of R. Paterson and other miscellaneous papers, 1753–1820 (2000 items).

Non-manuscript material   Fowler photographic collection: 1000 glass negatives taken in Scottish borders and during tours of Europe *c*1900–*c*1930.

Photographs and maps are also housed at Elgin Public Library Local Studies Centre, Grant Lodge, Elgin.

Finding aids   Lists, calendars and card index of persons, places and subjects.

Facilities   Photocopying. Microfilm reader.

201   Gateshead Public Libraries
Local Studies Department

Address   Central Library
                   Prince Consort Road
                   Gateshead
                   Tyne and Wear

Telephone   (0632) 773478

Enquiries to   Borough Librarian, Mr D.W. Liddle

Open   Mon, Tues, Thurs, Fri: 9.30–7.30
                   Wed: 9.30–5.00
                   Sat: 9.30–1.00

Access   Generally open to the public.

Historical background   The Local History Collection has existed since the opening of the library in 1884. It became a separate local studies and archives department in 1974.

Acquisitions policy   Documents relating to the area covered by Gateshead Metropolitan Borough Council.

Major collections   The collections include the Cotesworth MSS: estate papers for the 17th and 18th centuries; important for the early history of coal mining in the Gateshead/North Durham area.

Non-manuscript material   Thomas Bell Estate Plans, *c*1780–1840 (*c*1000).

Finding aids   Calendars. MSS Accessions Book. Indexes.

Facilities   Photocopying. Photography. Microfilming. Microfilm reader.

Publications   F.W.D. Manders: *Gateshead Archives: a Guide* (1968)

202   Eastwood District Libraries
Local History Department

Address   Council Offices
                 Eastwood Park
                 Rouken Glen Road
                 Giffnock
                 Glasgow G46 6UG

Telephone   (041) 638 1101/6511

Enquiries to   Chief Librarian, Miss M. Ballantyne

Local History Collection of non-MS material; photographs especially have been actively acquired since 1975.

203   Gillingham Central Library

Address   High Street
                 Gillingham
                 Kent ME7 1BG

Telephone   (0634) 51066/7

Enquiries to   Divisional Librarian, Mr S.I. Robinson

Open   Mon, Tues, Thurs, Fri: 9.30–7.00
                 Wed, Sat: 9.30–1.00; 2.00–5.00

Access   Generally open to the public.

Historical background   The present Library was built and opened in 1937, but local collections predate this.

Acquisitions policy   To strengthen the existing collection of Gillingham material by purchase and donation.

Major collections   Special collections relating to Louis Brennan (1852–1932); J.B. McCudden, VC (1895–1918); and Will Adams (1564–1620), the first Englishman to settle in Japan (the Adams collection contains little original archival material). Methodist Church archives for the Medway and Gillingham areas.

Non-manuscript material   c800 photographs and prints; 250 slides. Oil paintings, mostly by Henry Hill.

Gramophone records of Kent folk music.
Microfilms of census returns for Gillingham, Rainham and parts of north east Kent, 1841–71.

Finding aids   Indexes and lists.

Facilities   Photocopying. Microfilm reader.

Publications   Local History Series: no. 1, *Archives Collection*; no. 2, *McCudden VC* [out of print]; no. 5/1 *Louis Brennan-Dirigible Torpedo*; no. 5/2, *Louis Brennan-Gyroscopic Monorail*; no. 6, *Chronology of Gillingham, 1860–1903*

204   Baillie Library

Address   69 Oakfield Avenue
                Glasgow G12 8LP

Telephone   (041) 339 9627

Enquiries to Librarian, Mrs M. Manchester

The Library was founded in 1863 and opened in 1887. Collections include autograph letters and theatre programmes, but details are not available.

205   British Steel Corporation
Records Services Section

Address   Scottish Regional Records Centre
                Tollcross Works
                Tollcross
                Glasgow G32 87P

Telephone   (041) 778555

Enquiries to Scottish Region Manager, Mr J.Y. Lancaster

The Centre covers Scotland and Cumbria. For enquiries covering more than one region write to The Director, Secretariat, at the Corporation's Head Office, 33 Grosvenor Place, London SW1.

For other information in common with each Records Centre, *see* East Midlands Regional Records Centre, Wellingborough (entry **687**).

206   Glasgow School of Art

Address   167 Renfrew Street
                 Glasgow G3 6RQ

Insubstantial archives are held, but press cuttings and bibliographical references to staff and students are collected.

207   Glasgow University Archives

Address   The University
                 Glasgow G12 8QQ

Telephone   (041) 339 8855 ext. 7516/7515/543

Enquiries to   Archivist, Mr M.S. Moss

Open   Mon–Fri: 9.15–4.45
                 Evenings and Sat by arrangement

Access   Generally open to the public, subject to normal confidentiality.

Historical background The Archives Department holds the records of the University since its foundation in 1451. In the last 20 years it has built up large collections of records relating to business and health care in the west of Scotland.

Acquisitions policy   To collect records relating to the University and to business and health care in the west of Scotland.

Major collections University records: relating to the administration, finance, students, staff and teaching of the University since 1451, together with papers from institutions such as the Queen Margaret College and the Veterinary School which now form part of the University (5000 feet).
Shipbuilding Records: administrative, financial and technical records relating to the development of shipbuilding in the Clyde, 1830s to late 1970s (3000 feet).
House of Fraser Archive: administrative, financial and promotional records relating to the stores that now form the House of Fraser Group (1000 feet).
Greater Glasgow Health Board Archive: administrative, financial and clinical records relating to the evolution of health care in the west of Scotland (2000 feet).

Non-manuscript material   *c*80,000 photographs relating to the University, local topography, building, locomotive and shipbuilding, engineering, machine tool making, health care and departmental stores.
*c*150,000 technical drawings of buildings, locomotives, cranes, and stationary steam engines.

Finding aids   Assorted computerized catalogues, hand lists and indexes. Summary guides to the business records collection and health care archives.

Facilities   Photography. Microfilming. Microfilm/fiche reader.

208   Glasgow University Library
Department of Special Collections

Address	Hillhead Street Glasgow G12 8QE
Telephone	(041) 334 2122
Enquiries to	Keeper of Special Collections, Mr J. Baldwin
Open	Term: Mon–Fri: 9.00 a.m.–9.30 p.m.; Sat: 9.00–12.30 Vacation: Mon–Fri: 9.00–5.00; Sat: 9.00–12.30 (not Christmas) Closed: Glasgow Fair Monday; 2 weeks at the end of Summer (Whitsun) term.
Access	Members of Glasgow University and all other bona fide researchers. Prior written application is desirable.

Historical background   Glasgow University was founded in 1451. A MS catalogue of 1691 shows the Library with a stock of 3300 volumes. From 1709 to 1836 the Library enjoyed the copyright privilege and by 1790 (the year of its first published catalogue) the Library's holdings had risen to 20,000 volumes. Vast collections were acquired by gift and bequest in the 19th and 20th centuries and by 1982 the Library's stock approached 1,300,000 volumes.

Acquisitions policy   To augment the following archival collections by purchase, gift and deposit:
18th-century medicine, with special emphasis on William Hunter and his work in anatomy and obstetrics.
Scottish theatre history in the 19th and 20th centuries.
History of art in the 19th and 20th centuries, with special emphasis on James McNeill Whistler and the painter-etchers of his period, and Scottish artists.
Papers of the physicist William Thomson, Lord Kelvin.
Alchemy and the early history of chemistry.

Major collections   316 medieval MSS.
*c*250 oriental MSS.
Post-medieval MSS, particularly covering the following subjects: 18th-century medicine and anatomy; alchemy and early chemistry; 19th and 20th-century art history; 19th and 20th-century Scottish theatre history; Gaelic literature (over 30,000 separate items).
Music: scores of several late 19th and early 20th-century Scottish composers.
Papers of individuals including: James Douglas (1675–1742); William Hunter (1718–83); William Cullen (1710–90); Theophilus Siegfried Bayer, early 18th century; William Thomson, Lord Kelvin (1824–1907); Adam Smith (1723–90); James McNeill Whistler (1834–1903); Dugald Sutherland Macoll (1859–1948); Harold James Lean Wright; Henry George Farmer (1882–1965); Edwin Morgan (*b* 1920).

Non-manuscript material   D.O. Hill Collection: early photographs, *c*1843–60. *c*3000 caricatures of the Franco-Prussian War and the Paris commune.

Finding aids   Main sheaf index (typescript) to the MS collections; access points include names of persons, institutions, and subjects. In addition, special typescript lists and abstracts of certain collections.

Facilities   Photocopying. Photography. Microfilm/fiche readers.

Publications   J. Young and P. Henderson Aitken: *A Catalogue of the Manuscripts in the Library of the Hunterian Museum in the University of Glasgow* (1908)

J. Mackechnie: *Catalogue of Gaelic Manuscripts in selected Libraries in Great Britain and Ireland*, i (1973), 365–454

N.R. Ker: *Medieval Manuscripts in British Libraries*, (1977), 871–933 [details of the non-Hunterian medieval MSS in Glasgow University Library]

J. Baldwin: 'Glasgow University Library's Manuscripts: the non-Hunterian Collections', *The Bibliotheck*, viii (1977), 127

Kelvin Papers: index (1977)

Whistler, MacColl, Wright: Art History Papers, 1850–1950, in Glasgow University (1979)

209   The Mitchell Library
Rare Books and Manuscripts Department

Address   North Street
Glasgow G3 7DN

Telephone   (041) 221 7030 ext. 139

Enquiries to   Departmental Librarian, Miss H. Wright

Open   Mon–Fri: 9.30–9.00
Sat: 9.30–5.00

Access   Generally open to the public. Prior notice to the Department is preferable.

Historical background   The Library was opened in 1877 as Glasgow's first free public reference library, following a bequest by Stephen Mitchell, a tobacco manufacturer in Glasgow, of £70,000 to the Town Council for that purpose. The Library was reorganized in June 1981 on a subject-departmentalized basis, Rare Books and Manuscripts being one of the new departments.

Acquisitions policy   Archives relating to Glasgow, and to the Library's major special collections (Scottish poetry, drama, family history and regimental history, and trade unions) are mainly sought. Business archives now normally go to the Regional Archives.

Major collections   Extensive MSS and archival holdings including estate and family papers, records of business, societies, schools, over 100 trade unions, etc, of which the following is a selection of those with wider significance:

Gaelic Society of London, 1871–1929.

Glasgow and West of Scotland Association for Women's Suffrage, 1902–19.

Alfred Morton diaries, 1887–1941.

Scottish Council for Community Service during Unemployment, 1935–51.

Non-manuscript material   North British Locomotive Company collection includes in addition to order books, weight diagram books, etc, 10,000 plate glass negatives. In other departments of the library:

Glasgow Collection: specialises in material relating to Glasgow; includes MSS, maps and illustrations.

History and Topography Department: Scottish local history, topography and genealogy; includes extensive collection of maps.

Finding aids   Interim catalogue of MSS (cards xeroxed in sheets and bound), gradually being superseded by detailed looseleaf catalogue with card index.

Facilities   Photocopying. Microfilm/fiche readers.

Publications   *The North British Locomotive Company Collection* (1974)
    The Mitchell Library, Glasgow; 1877–1977 (Glasgow, 1977)

210   Queen's College, Glasgow

Address   1 Park Drive
             Glasgow G3 6LP

No archives are held.

211   Royal College of Physicians and Surgeons of Glasgow

Address   234–242 St Vincent Street
                 Glasgow G2 5RJ

Telephone   (041) 221 2581

Enquiries to   Librarian, Mr A.M. Rodger

Open   Mon–Fri: 9.30–5.30

Access   Fellows and Members of the College; registered medical practitioners; College examination candidates and postgraduate students. Other approved readers, on written application to the Librarian.

Historical background   The College was established in 1599 by the grant of a Royal Charter from King James VI to Maister Peter Lowe and Professor Robert Hamilton, to regulate the practice of medicine in the west of Scotland. The original title of the College was the Faculty of Physicians and Surgeons of Glasgow. The Faculty's privileges were confirmed by Act of Parliament in 1672. It had the exclusive right to examine and license practitioners of surgery in the west of Scotland and no individual could practise medicine within its boundaries without its express permission. In 1909 the corporation became the Royal Faculty of Physicians and Surgeons of Glasgow, until the change to its present designation as a Royal College in 1962. Many outstanding individuals, such as Lister, Macewen, Livingstone and many names famous in the context of the Glasgow Medical School have been associated with the College.

Acquisitions policy   The College aims to supplement and improve in any way it can its archives and rare-book holdings. The recent completion of the setting up of an Archives section attached to the Library has expanded that area of interest in the College Library's remit.

Major collections   Sir William Macewen Collection: correspondence, lecture notes, private ward journals, photographs, memorabilia etc, relating to Macewen (1848–1924).
Sir Ronald Ross Collection: correspondence, private writings, pamphlets, memoirs etc, relating to Ross (1857–1932).
Lister Collection: correspondence, memorabilia etc relating to Lord Lister (1827–1912).
Strong collection of 19th-century lecture notes of students; records of seven major Glasgow Medical Societies.

Non-manuscript material   Strong collection of 15th–19th-century medical tracts and works by authors such as Boerhaave, Cullen, etc. The collection of early Latin and English medical books is very strong.

Facilities   Photocopying.

Publications   A. Duncan: *Memorials of the Faculty of Physicians and Surgeons of Glasgow* (1894)
A new history of the College, and a publication detailing the most important possessions of the College is in preparation. An Archives catalogue will also shortly be published.

212   Royal Faculty of Procurators' Library

Address   62 St George's Place
               Glasgow G2 1BT

Telephone   (041) 332 3593

Enquiries to Librarian, Mrs Ruth Ludlam

Open   Mon–Fri: 9.00–5.00

Access   Members of the Royal Faculty of Procurators of Glasgow; authorized
members of the legal profession (Sheriffs, Advocates); bona fide
research workers, on application to the Librarian.

Historical background   Although its existence dates from the latter part of the 18th
century, the Library was officially founded by the Faculty of Procurators in 1817
and has been housed in the present building since 1857. Its purpose was, and is, to
provide practising members of the legal profession in Glasgow with a specialized
law library where they can find all the legal information necessary for their daily
work and research.

Acquisitions policy   No policy of collecting MSS.

Major collections   Archives of the Royal Faculty of Procurators, 1668–.
Archives of the Hutcheson-Hill family, 16th century–.

Non-manuscript material   Maps of Glasgow, 18th century–.
Prints.
Rare books.
Hill Bequest: the Glasgow Library, a record of Glasgow in the 19th century (of
sociological interest).

Finding aids   Catalogue. Card index.

213   Royal Scottish Academy of Music and Drama

Address   58 St George's Place
Glasgow G2 1BS

Internal archives are held but are not yet catalogued or accessible.

214   Scottish Film Archive

Address   Dowanhill
74 Victoria Crescent Road
Glasgow G12 9JN

Telephone   (041) 334 9314

Enquiries to   Archivist, Ms Janet McBain

Open   Mon–Fri: 9.00–5.00

Access   Initial enquiries free. Researchers are advised to give prior notice of
their intention to visit. Viewings of film by appointment only, free to
academic and bona fide students; a fee is charged to commercial and
television users (rates available). Consultation on premises
preferred, although arrangements can be made to despatch available
viewing copies to an enquirer.

Historical background   The Scottish Film Archive was established in 1976 as a Job
   Creation Project with permanent status following in 1978. Active research into the
   sources of film and cinema history in Scotland has been undertaken since 1977,
   with a steadily growing collection of material.

Acquisitions policy   Actuality and non-fiction film relating to Scottish culture and
   history in the 20th century. Emphasis on local material.

Major collections   Principally non-MS material (see below), also Scottish film and
   cinema industry records.

Non-manuscript material   Locally produced cinema newsreels, comprising calendar
   customs, visits of celebrities, freedom of city ceremonies, etc.
   Upper Clyde Shipbuilders Limited: official films of launches and trials of vessels
   constructed by component companies, 1926–71.
   Educational and documentary films on Scotland, 1935–.
   Television news and documentaries, c1965–.
   Oral recordings: former cinema staff, film renters, exhibitors in Scotland.
   Photographs of cinemas.
   Cinema memorabilia and publicity.

Finding aids   Subject and personality index system. Alphabetical and chronological
   lists of titles. (Much of the collection still in process of being catalogued.)

Facilities   35mm and 16mm film viewing facilities.

Publications   *Scottish Archive Film for Education* [catalogue]

215   Strathclyde Regional Archives

Address   Correspondence:
                     PO Box 27
                     City Chambers
                     Glasgow G2 1DU
                   Visitors:
                     30 John Street
                     Glasgow

Telephone   (041) 221 9600 ext. 2021

Enquiries to   Principal Archivist, Mr Richard F. Dell

Open   Mon–Fri: 9.00–4.45

Historical background   The Glasgow City Archives department was established in
   1964 and following reorganization in 1975 became the Strathclyde Regional
   Archives. Ayrshire Sub-region Archives Office, Ayr, is a dependent repository.

Major collections   Usual local authority record holdings and deposited collections

including the following which have a wider significance:
Extensive shipbuilding and engineering records including: Upper Clyde
Shipbuilders, 1860–1973; G.L. Watson & Co., marine architects; Sir William Arrol
& Co. Ltd, bridge builders; W. Ralston Ltd, industrial photographers, c1925–.
Family records of the Stirling Maxwells of Nether Pollok, Keir and Cawder,
including correspondence of Sir William Stirling Maxwell (1818–78).

Facilities   Photocopying. Photography and microfilming by arrangement. Microfilm
readers.

216   University of Strathclyde
University Archives

Address   Livingstone Tower
                 Richmond Street
                 Glasgow G1 1XH

Telephone   (041) 552 4440 ext.2318

Enquiries to   Archivist, Mr James S. McGrath

Open   Mon–Fri: 9.00–5.00, by appointment

Access   Bona fide researchers. Recent official records, only by agreement
                 with the Registrar.

Historical background   The history of the University's development dates back to
   Anderson's Institution (later Anderson's University, then Anderson's College),
   founded by the will of John Anderson in 1796. In the course of time it took in
   Glasgow Mechanics' Institution, Atkinson's Institution and Allan Glen's Institution,
   and in 1887 became the Glasgow and West of Scotland Technical College, at which
   time it lost Anderson's Medical School which was finally absorbed into the Faculty
   of Medicine of Glasgow University in 1947. By 1956 the Glasgow and West of
   Scotland Technical College had become the Royal College of Science and
   Technology and in 1964 amalgamated with the Scottish College of Commerce,
   itself dating back to the 1840s, to become the University of Strathclyde.

Acquisitions policy   The University Archives concentrate on the records of the
   above bodies and the staff and students of these. There is no policy of seeking other
   accessions, although the University Archives inherited some deposited collections.

Major collections   Official records, of the University and its antecedents, including
   minutes, accounts, correspondence, student and staff records, administrative files
   and some departmental records.
   Deposited records include:
   Chemical Society of Glasgow, 1800–01; Scottish Association for Promotion of
   Technical and Secondary Education, 1891–1925; Glasgow Chemists and Druggists
   Association; Glasgow Dilettante Society, 1825–43; Glasgow Typographical
   Society, 1817–1960; Colin Garrett papers on bleaching, dyeing etc, 1862–1976;

Society of Chemical Industry (Glasgow and West of Scotland Section), 1884–1962. Papers of Sir Patrick Geddes, c1860–1930; Sir George Pepler, c1882–1959; James 'Paraffin' Young, c1845–1873.

Non-manuscript material   c700 photographs of campus, staff and students. Films relating to campus activities.

Finding aids   List available as completed. Catalogue of the Geddes Collection is in preparation.

Facilities   Photocopying. Photography.

217   Gloucester Cathedral Library

Address   6 College Green
                 Gloucester
                 Gloucestershire

Telephone   (0452) 21954

Enquiries to   Canon Librarian, Canon David Welander

Open   By appointment

Access   For research only.

Historical background   The room which houses the Library is late 15th-century and is approached by steep newel stairs from the cloisters. However, a library was in existence in the monastery of St Peter, Gloucester, c1390. The collection of books was made mainly during the late 18th and 19th centuries. There is a small collection of early printed books, and some MSS from the abbey period.

Acquisitions policy   Only modern works which relate to the history and architecture of the Cathedral. However, a watch is kept on the sale of MSS and a 15th-century MS written at Gloucester was recently acquired.

Major collections   Medieval MSS, including charters, leases and registers.
Post-medieval MSS including tithes and offerings of Trinity Parish, Gloucester, 1618–45.

Non-manuscript material   Collection of Hebrew books.

Finding aids   Card catalogue of music.

Facilities   No reading facilities in the Library: works are transferred to the County Record Office reading room for consultation (*see* entry **219**).

Publications   S.M. Eward and others: *Catalogue of Gloucester Cathedral Library* (1972)[available from the Canon Librarian]

218   Gloucestershire Collection

Address   Gloucester Library
                   Brunswick Road
                   Gloucester
                   Gloucestershire GL1 1HT

Telephone   (0452) 20020/20684

Enquiries to   Librarian, Mr G.R. Hiatt

Open   Mon, Tues, Thurs: 9.00–8.00
                   Wed, Fri, Sat: 9.00–5.00

Access   Generally open to the public.

Historical background   The nucleus of the Gloucestershire Collection was a bequest by J.J. Powell, QC, who left to the City of Gloucester several volumes of cuttings from Gloucestershire newspapers, with the understanding that should a public library be established they were to be kept there. On the death of Judge Powell in 1891 the bequest was added to by others and since the library opened in 1900 other gifts and bequests, coupled with a policy outlined below, has seen the Collection become a major one.

Acquisitions policy   All forms of material relating to the County, City, towns and villages of Gloucestershire, and items written by persons connected by birth or residence with the City or County.

Major collections   Hockaday MSS Collection: abstracts of ecclesiastical records relating to the diocese of Worcester and Gloucester, 1187– (compiled from diocesan records and other sources by F.S. Hockaday).
Ivor Gurney MSS Collection: material deposited by Mrs Joyce Finzi, comprising music, poems, correspondence, etc.
Smyth of Nibley Papers: c2000 papers, documents and letters concerning the business and personal affairs of John Smyth the elder, who was steward of the hundred of Berkeley.
The Dancey Gift: MSS, books, pamphlets and prints relating to the City and County of Gloucester (225 vols, 321 pamphlets, 282 prints and portraits); the Gift includes a series of MSS illustrating the histories of the Saxon churches of Gloucestershire which have been compiled from City records, parish registers and records and other sources; and Dancey's handbooks, which are full of matters relating to local history.
Many other small collections and individual MSS.

Non-manuscript material   Hitchings Collection of Bibles and New Testaments, 1540–1906.
Hannam-Clark Collection of books pertaining to the topography and history of Palestine.

Finding aids   Card catalogue.

Facilities   Photocopying. Photography. Microfilm/fiche readers.

Publications   *Catalogue of the Gloucester Collection* (1928) [out of print]
   Smyth of Nibley Papers, Local History Service Series, no.1, (1978)

219   Gloucestershire Record Office

Address   Worcester Street
               Gloucester
               Gloucestershire GL1 3DW

Telephone   (0452) 21444 ext. 227/228

Enquiries to County Archivist, Mr D.J.H. Smith

Open   Mon, Wed, Fri: 9.00–1.00; 2.00–5.00
               Thurs: 9.00–1.00; 2.00–8.00

Access   By reader's ticket, on application. A fee is charged.

Historical background   The County Record Office was founded in 1935, but there
   had been a previous tradition of collecting materials in the City Library (*see* entry
   218). Diocesan, probate records and other materials were amalgamated with the
   Office in 1974. The Office also acts as the Diocesan Record Office for Gloucester.
   Official records from the mid-19th century are available at the Shire Hall Search
   Room, Gloucester GL1 2TG (Mon–Fri: 9.00–5.00), by appointment. The County
   Archivist acts as Honorary Archivist to the Berkeley Trustees.

Major collections   Usual local authority records and deposited collections of which
   the following have a wider significance:
   British Waterways Board records, with material on many canals outside
   Gloucestershire.
   Belgian Refugees Committee minutes, 1914–19.
   Family and estate papers of Bathhurst of Lydney, including papers of Charles B.
   Bathhurst, MP, 1767–1828.
   Beaufort of Badminton: papers of Sir Richard Berkeley, early 17th century.
   Freeman-Mitford of Batsford: political papers of Mitford (Redesdale) family, 1754–
   1916.
   Hicks Beach of Coln St Aldwyn: political papers of the first Earl St Aldwyn relating
   to South Africa and Ireland, 1865–1938.
   Jenner-Fust of Hill: McLaire of Mull estate records, 18th and 19th centuries; Gaelic
   songs, 1689–c1810; Indian and Afghanistan records, 1803–82; Java business
   records, 1845–6.
   Lloyd-Baker of Hardwicke Court: papers of John Sharp, Archbishop of York (1645–
   1714), and Granville Sharp (1735–1813), philanthropist.
   Rooke of St Briavels: papers of Admiral Sir George Rooke, 1695–1703.
   Numerous engineering drawings.

Facilities   Photocopying. Photography. Microfilming.

Publications   Short Handlist of the Contents of Gloucestershire Record Office
(1979)
I.E. Gray and A.T. Gaydon: *Gloucestershire Quarter Session Archives 1660–1889
and the Official Records* (1958)
I.M. Kirby: *Catalogue of the Records of the Dean and Chapter* (1967) [Diocese of
Gloucester]
————: *Catalogue of the Records of the Bishop and Archdeacons* (1968)
[Diocese of Gloucester]

220   Charterhouse

Address   Godalming
                 Surrey GU7 2DX

Telephone   (04868) 6226

Enquiries to   Librarian, Mrs B. Freake

Open   By appointment

Access   Approved researchers on written application.

Historical background   Sutton's Hospital in the Charterhouse was founded in 1611
by Thomas Sutton to provide a home for 40 deserving men pensioners and to offer
board and education to 40 boys, nominated in turn by the Governors. These were
housed in London until 1872, when the school was moved to newly-built premises
in Godalming. In London the school always educated day boys, who lodged in
private boarding houses, though for many years these were not recorded as part of
the establishment.

Acquisitions policy   To add by purchase or donation books, photographs,
documents etc, by or about Old Carthusians. To house anything of interest to the
school, its history and pupils.

Major collections   School Registers.
Personal scrapbooks relating to the school, kept by Mrs Haig Brown, wife of the
Headmaster who moved the school from London and Mr Girdlestone, an assistant
master who founded the House which bears his name and was Housemaster of it
for many years, 1872–c1902.

Non-manuscript material   School photographs, 1870–.
Cartoons of John Leech and Max Beerbohm.
School magazines, 1872–.
Carthusian Collection: works by and about Old Carthusians, notably John Wesley,
Thackeray and Baden-Powell.
Daniel Wray Library: the remains of a collection of antiquarian books left to the
school in the 18th century, but subsequently partly disposed of.

Finding aids   Personal help is necessary and can usually be arranged, preferably in term time.

Facilities   Some photocopying and photography may be possible.

221   Kent County Library
Gravesham Division

Address   Central Library
Windmill Street
Gravesend
Kent DA12 1AQ

Telephone   (0474) 65600/52758

Enquiries to Area Librarian, Mr W.T.W. Woods

Open   Mon, Tues, Thurs: 9.30–6.00
Wed: 9.30–1.00
Fri: 9.30–6.30
Sat: 9.30–5.00
Advance notice required

Access   Generally open to the public.

Historical background   The Public Library was established in 1903 but was without proper premises until moving to the present building in 1905. It has a long tradition of collecting local material, starting with the deposit of a collection made by George Arnold. In 1926 it was described as the 'best local collection in the world'.

Major collections   Records of the former Gravesend Borough Council, 1568–.
Burmote or Town Minutes, complete, 1571–.
Chamberlain's accounts, early 17th century–.

Non-manuscript material   George Arnold Collection, including scrapbooks, printed material and artefacts, late 19th century.
c5000 engravings and photographs.

Finding aids   List for use in Library.

Facilities   Limited photocopying. Microfilm/fiche readers.

222   Inverclyde District Council

Address   Watt Library
9 Union Street
Greenock
Strathclyde

Telephone   (0475) 20186

Enquiries to   Mrs I. Couperwhite

Open   Mon, Thurs: 2.00–5.00; 6.00–8.00
                   Tues, Fri: 10.00–12.30; 2.00–5.00
                   Wed, Sat: 10.00–1.00

Access   Generally open to the public.

Historical background   Opened in 1837 as a memorial to James Watt, the Watt
   Library was originally a subscription library; it was taken over in 1974 by
   Inverclyde District Council and is used as a centre for the local archive material for
   the area.

Acquisitions policy   To collect material relating to the Inverclyde area by purchase,
   donations or deposits.

Major collections   Principally non-MS material (see below).
   Corporation minutes of Greenock, Gourock and Port Glasgow.

Non-manuscript material   Pamphlets; photographs; tapes, newspapers; rare books.

Finding aids   Indexes to newspapers, including ship-launches and births, marriages
   and deaths. Catalogue of main collections.

223   South Humberside Area Record Office

Address   Town Hall Square
                   Grimsby
                   South Humberside DN31 1HX

Telephone   (0472) 53481

Enquiries to   Archivist-in-charge, Mr J.A.S. Green

Open   Mon, Wed, Thurs: 9.30–5.00
                   Tues: 9.30–5.00; 5.00–9.00, by appointment only
                   Fri: 9.30–4.30
                   Appointment advisable

Historical background   The Office was established in 1976 following reorganization
   covering the administrative areas of Grimsby, Scunthorpe, Glanford and
   Cleethorpes.

Major collections   Usual local authority record holdings and deposited collections.

Facilities   Photocopying. Photography. Microfilming. Microfilm reader.

Publications   *South Humberside Area Record Office Summary Guide* (1977)

224   Surrey County Libraries
Local Studies

Address   Branch Library
             77 North Street
             Guildford
             Surrey GU1 4AL

Telephone   (0483) 34054

Enquiries to   Assistant Librarian, Mr D. Ryder

Open   Mon, Fri: 10.00–8.00
             Tues, Thurs: 10.00–5.00
             Wed: 10.00–1.00
             Sat: 9.30–4.00

Access   Generally open to the public.

Historical background   No tradition of collecting MS material.

Acquisitions policy   There is no settled policy for archive acquisition and it is
    unlikely that any recommendation would be made for one in view of the excellent
    working relationship with Surrey Record Office, Guildford Muniment Room (*see*
    entry **225**).

Major collections   MS diaries of Henry Peak, jobbing architect and mayor of
    Guildford, *c*1900.
    MS of Gertrude Jeykyll, *Old West Surrey*.

Non-manuscript material   Scrapbooks of the Guildford Theatre Group, 1940s and
    1950s.

225   Surrey Record Office
Guildford Muniment Room

Address   Castle Arch
             Guildford
             Surrey GU1 3SX

Telephone   (0483) 573942

Enquiries to   The Archivist-in-charge

Open   Tues–Thurs: 9.30–12.30; 1.45–4.45
             Sat (1st and 3rd of each month): 9.30–12.30, by appointment

Historical background   The Office was established in 1928 by the Surrey
    Archaeological Society and originally collected material from all over Surrey; it is

now mainly concerned with south-west Surrey. It also acts as the Diocesan Record Office for Guildford (parish records, excluding Emly and Epsom deaneries).

Major collections   Usual local authority record holdings and deposited collections of which the following have a wider significance:
Papers of More of Losely, including records of the office of the King's Tents, 1542–58, and of the Lieutenancy of the Tower of London, 1615–17.
Papers of Lewis Carroll (1832–98).

Facilities   Photocopying. Microfilm reader. Photography. Microfilming.

Publications   *Summary Guide to Guildford Muniment Room* (1967)

226   United Society for Christian Literature (USCL)

Address   Luke House
Farnham Road
Guildford
Surrey GU1 4XD

Records were transferred to the School of Oriental and African Studies (*see* entry 478) in 1982.

227   University of Surrey Library

Address   University of Surrey
Guildford
Surrey GU2 5XH

Telephone   (0483) 71281

Enquiries to   Librarian, Mr R.F. Eatwell

Open   Term: Mon–Fri: 9.00 a.m.–10.00 p.m.
Sat: 1.00–6.00 (Autumn and Spring); 9.00–6.00 (Summer)
Sun: 2.00–6.00

Access   Bona fide researchers.

Historical background   Battersea College of Technology, founded in 1894 as the Battersea Polytechnic, was awarded a charter as the University of Surrey in 1966. The Library supports the teaching and research of the University. The University archives are collected by the Library.

Acquisitions policy   The Library collects administrative and other documents from departments. No real policy, except to preserve items of historical interest about the institution and its courses.

Major collections   Administrative records of the University.

Non-manuscript material   Some tape recordings of older staff and others on the institution's history.

Finding aids   The collection will be indexed in the future.

Facilities   Photocopying. Photography. Microfilm/fiche reader/printer.

228   East Lothian District Council Library Headquarters

Address   Victoria Road
                Haddington
                East Lothian EH41 4DU

Local History Collection of non-MS material.

229   Royal Greenwich Observatory
Library and Archives

Address   Herstmonceux Castle
                    Hailsham
                    East Sussex BN27 1RP

Telephone   (0323) 833171

Enquiries to   Librarian and Archivist, Miss J. Dudley

Open   Mon–Fri: 9.00–5.30, by appointment only
                    Other hours by arrangement

Access   Written (preferably) or telephone application. All records over 30
                    years old and some more recent papers available.

Historical background   The Observatory is a place of deposit under Section 4 of the Public Record Act 1958 and is responsible for maintaining the records of the Royal Observatory, Greenwich (1675–1948), the Royal Greenwich Observatory (1948–), the Board of Longitude, the Royal Observatory, Cape of Good Hope, and various deposited collections. The Library collections cover the same period and were built up at the same time and so parallel, reflect and complement the archival papers.

Acquisitions policy   Records and papers produced by the Observatory and its staff, as prescribed by the Act. Papers of eminent men in the field of astronomy and astrophysical research, by donation or deposit.

Major collections   Papers of the Astronomers Royal from John Flamsteed (1646–

1719) to Sir Richard Woolley; and of the Directors of the Observatory from Margaret Burbidge to Professor F. Graham Smith.

Board of Longitude papers including those relating to various voyages of discovery, e.g. James Cook (1728–79), Matthew Flinders (1774–1814) and George Vancouver (1758–98); the development of the chronometer, e.g. John Harrison (1693–1776), Thomas Mudge (1717–94) and John Arnold (?1736–99); the administration of the £20,000 prize for finding an accurate method of measuring longitude at sea, offered by Act of Parliament in 1714.

Royal Observatory, Cape of Good Hope, records covering the establishment and development of a scientific community in a previously unsettled area, its administration from Greenwich and its place in the life of the Colony.

HM Nautical Almanac Office, records and papers, 1880– (many destroyed in 1930s).

Scientific papers of Professor R.O. Redman.

Non-manuscript material Airy Collection: c1000 rare books, maintained by the Library (printed catalogue in preparation, 1982).

Astronomical Tracts: large collection of mainly 18th and 19th-century papers on astronomical subjects (not yet properly indexed).

Photographic material: prints and negatives of astronomical subjects; photographs, postcards and other illustrations of the Castle.

Finding aids PRO class lists. Calendar and index of Flamsteed papers (in card form, to be published). Card index to the miscellaneous correspondence of G.B. Airy (to be published). Index to the correspondence in the Cape Observatory records (incomplete).

Facilities Photocopying. Photography. Microfilming. Microfilm/fiche readers/ printers.

Publications E.G. Forbes: 'Index of the Board of Longitude papers at the Royal Greenwich Observatory, parts 1–3', *Journal for the History of Astronomy*, i (1970), 169; ii (1971), 58; iii (1971), 133

'Maskelyne manuscripts at the Royal Greenwich Observatory', *Journal for the History of Astronomy*, v (1974), 67

230 Calderdale Metropolitan Borough Archives Department

Address Central Library
Lister Lane
Halifax
West Yorkshire HX1 5LA

Telephone (0422) 65105/60425

Enquiries to Borough Archivist, Dr A. Betteridge

Open	By appointment
	Original documents:
	Tues, Thurs, Fri: 10.00–5.30
	Wed, Sat: 10.00–12.00
	Documents on microfilm:
	Mon, Tues, Thurs, Fri: 10.00–8.00
	Wed: 10.00–12.00
	Sat: 10.00–5.00

Historical background The Calderdale Archives Service is very much a development of the Halifax Borough Archives Service, which was established in 1964 and which acquired the accumulations of the Halifax Museums Service and the Halifax Antiquarian Society. In 1974 the Archives Service took control of the archival records of the eight amalgamating local authorities and now holds approximately 850,000 original documents and over 400,000 frames of microfilm. It also acts as the Diocesan Record Office for Bradford (parish records).

Major collections Usual local authority record holdings and deposited collections, including significant textile, labour history and civil township administration records.

Facilities Photocopying. Photography by arrangement. Microfilm/fiche readers/ printers. Union catalogue of Calderdale archives held by other record offices.

Publications *Archives in Calderdale* (1976; annual Suppls, 1977–80)

231   Hamilton District Libraries

Address	98 Cadzow Street
	Hamilton
	Strathclyde ML3 6HQ
Telephone	(0698) 282323 ext. 143
Enquiries to	Chief Librarian, Mr C. Smith
Open	Mon, Tues, Thurs, Fri: 9.00–7.30
	Wed, Sat: 9.00–5.00
Access	Generally open to the public.

Historical background Hamilton District Libraries was formed in 1975. Hamilton Burgh Library joined with part of Lanark County Libraries to form the new authority.

Acquisitions policy To collect material relating to Hamilton and the surrounding area.

Major collections Burgh of Hamilton: Council minute books, 1701–1975; abstract of accounts, 1879–1939/40, 1941/2–1975; Register of Electors (incomplete),

1851–; Hamilton Police Commissioners minute books, 1857–1901; Hamilton Road Trustees minute books, 1808–65; Hamilton Combination Poor House (later Hamilton Home) minute books, 1864–1975.
Lanark County Council minute books, 1890–1975.
Small Collection of 18th- and 19th-century estate papers relating to the Duke of Hamilton's estates in Lanarkshire.

Non-manuscript material   Photographs and slides of Hamilton and district.
*c*1000 maps of Hamilton and the surrounding area.
Microfilm of census returns for the Hamilton area, 1841–81.
Local newspapers, 1862–.

Finding aids   Library catalogue.

Facilities   Photocopying.

232   Rothamsted Experimental Station

Address   Harpenden
                 Hertfordshire AL5 2JQ

Telephone   (05827) 63133

Enquiries to   The Librarian

Open   Mon–Thurs: 9.00–1.00; 2.00–5.30
                 Fri: 9.00–1.00; 2.00–5.00

Access   Bona fide enquirers, by prior arrangement.

Historical background   Rothamsted Experimental Station was founded in 1843 by Sir John Bennet Lawes and his co-worker Sir J.H. Gilbert, to study crop nutrition.

Acquisitions policy   No special policy for archives.

Major collections   Archival material of the history of the Station.
Results of field experiments.
MS estate books of the Marquis of Buckingham, 1717–1873.
Day book of Sir Richard Temple, 1677–80.
Farm diary of South Somerset, 1858.

Non-manuscript material   Old books on agriculture, 1480–1840.
Animal prints and paintings.
Maps.

Finding aids   Local catalogues.

Facilities   Photocopying. Microfilm/fiche reader.

233   Harrow School

Address	5 High Street Harrow-on-the-Hill Middlesex HA1 3HP
Telephone	(01) 422 1618 (Librarian, Mr J.H.W. Morwood) (01) 422 7811 (The Bursar) (01) 866 6722 (Assistant Archivist, Mr J.S. Golland)
Enquiries to	The Archivist
Open	By arrangement
Access	Approved students or researchers, on application to the Librarian.

Historical background   The School was founded in 1572 by John Lyon, a local landowner who left the rents from several estates to pay for it. Though intended to be a local Grammar School for parish children, a clause in the Statutes enabled boys from outside the parish to be taught and these soon outnumbered the local boys. It is an independent fee-paying school controlled by a Board of Governors. The School Archives have been collated in the last ten years and since 1981 have been housed in an Archives Room for the benefit of visiting students.

Acquisitions policy   To strengthen and add to the existing collection of material relating to the School and its history, or to the life and work of its Old Boys.

Major collections   Estate documents, 15th century–.
Governors' minutes and account books, 1615–1923; receipts and other vouchers, 1720–1880.
Correspondence of Head Masters, 1805–.
Latin orations by Heads of School; cricket score books, 1831–; school examination results, 1846–1940.
School lists, 1770–; apprenticeship indentures for local boys, 1648–1871; items relating to Silver Arrow Competition, 1689–1771.
Literary and other autographs; material relating to Byron (1788–1824) and Sheridan (1751–1816).
Transcriptions of some of the Harrow Manor Court Rolls in the Northwick Papers.

Non-manuscript material   Photographs of individuals, teams or buildings in the School, late 19th century–.
Map of London–Harrow Road, 1736; maps of John Lyon estates, 18th century–; architectural plans of School buildings by William Burges and C.R. Cockerell.
Photocopy of the School Charter of 1572 (the original is held at the Guildhall Library, *see* entry 349).

Finding aids   Card index in progress. Card index of photographs. Calendar of School Records made in 1886. Catalogue of Byroniana.

Facilities   Photocopying.

Publications   E.J.L. Scott: *Records of the Grammar School Founded by John Lyon at Harrow-on-the-Hill AD 1572* (Harrow, 1886)
   The Harrow Register 1571–1971
   The Harrovian (1888–)
   J.S. Golland: *The Harrow Apprentices* (Harrow, 1981)

234   Museum and Art Gallery

Address   Cambridge Road
                   Hastings
                   East Sussex TN34 1ET

Telephone   (0424) 435952

Enquiries to   Curator, Mr D.C. Devenish

Open   Museum opening hours:
                   Mon–Sat: 10.00–1.00; 2.00–5.00
                   Sun: 3.00–5.00
                   Access to records is strictly by appointment only.

Access   Generally open to the public.

Historical background   The Museum was founded in 1890 and moved to its present
   site in 1928. Originally only a Museum and Art Gallery, it gradually attracted
   records. In 1973 parish and other ecclesiastical records were transferred to the
   County Record Office at Lewes (*see* entry **290**).

Acquisitions policy   A small number of local MSS is accepted from time to time.

Major collections   Archives of Hastings and the Cinque Ports.
   Archives of local families, including the Ashburnhams and Milwards.

Non-manuscript material   Large collections of photographs, prints and ephemera
   (but these are reckoned as part of the Museum and Art Gallery).

Finding aids   Various registers and indexes.

Facilities   Normal archive office facilities cannot be provided. However, help will
   always be given to genuine researchers. Not suitable for student projects.

Publications   Various publications relating to Hastings, including *Museum and Art
   Gallery Guide*.

235   Hatfield House Library

Address   Hatfield House
                   Hatfield
                   Hertfordshire

Enquiries to   Librarian and Archivist to the Marquess of Salisbury, Mr R.H.
                    Harcourt Williams

Open   By arrangement with the Librarian

Access   Approved academic (normally postgraduate) researchers, on
                    written application.

Historical background   Hatfield House was built in 1612 by Robert Cecil, first Earl of
    Salisbury. It has remained in the possession of his direct descendants and is now
    the home of the sixth Marquess of Salisbury.

Major collections   Papers of William Cecil, first Baron Burghley (1520–98),
    Secretary of State and afterwards Lord Treasurer to Queen Elizabeth I.
    Papers of Robert Cecil, first Earl of Salisbury (1563–1612), Secretary of State and
    Lord Treasurer to King James I. (A microfilm copy of these papers may be
    consulted in the British Library, Department of Manuscripts, *see* entry **316**.)
    Papers of Robert Gascoyne-Cecil, third Marquess of Salisbury (1830–1903),
    Foreign Secretary and Prime Minister to Queen Victoria.

Non-manuscript material   Maps and architectural drawings.

Finding aids   Historical Manuscripts Commission *Calendar of the Salisbury (Cecil)
    Manuscripts*, vols i–xxiv (1883–1976), covers all papers up to 1668 (i.e. those of
    Lord Burghley and the first and second Earls of Salisbury).
    J.F.A. Mason: *Calendar of the private Foreign Office Correspondence of Robert,
    Third Marquess of Salisbury*, 2 vols (NRA typescript, 1963; available at the National
    Register of Archives). Card index at Hatfield House for remaining correspondence
    of the third Marquess.

Facilities   Photocopying (certain collections only).

Publications   Robert, fifth Marquess of Salisbury: 'The library at Hatfield House,
    Hertfordshire', *The Library*, 5th ser., xviii/2 (June 1963), 83
    R.A. Skelton and Sir J. Summerson: *A Description of Maps and Architectural
    Drawings in the Collection made by William Cecil, First Baron Burghley now at
    Hatfield House* (1971)

236   Hatfield Polytechnic Library

Address   PO Box 110
               Hatfield
               Hertfordshire AL10 9AD

No archives are held.

237 Dyfed Archives Service
Haverfordwest Office

Address The Castle
Haverfordwest
Dyfed

Telephone (0437) 3707/4591 ext. 5271

Enquiries to Archivist-in-charge, Mr J.R.H. Pepler

Open Mon–Thurs: 9.00–4.45
Fri: 9.00–4.15
Sat (1st and 3rd in each month, except Bank Holiday weekends):
9.30–12.30, by appointment

Historical background: The first County Archivist was appointed in 1963 and the office was established as Pembrokeshire Record Office in 1967. It also acts as the Diocesan Record Office for St David's (parish records). Administrative assistance is given to Tenby Museum.

Major collections: Usual local authority record holdings and deposited collections of which the following have a wider significance:
Deeds and documents of the Starbuck family of Sherborn, Nantucket Island, Massachusetts, 1660–1780.

Facilities: Photocopying. Photography. Microfilming. Microfilm reader.

238 Clwyd Record Office
Hawarden Branch

Address The Old Rectory
Hawarden
Deeside CH5 3NR

Telephone (0244) 532364

Enquiries to County Archivist, Mr A.G. Veysey

Open: Mon–Thurs: 9.00–4.45
Fri: 9.00–4.15
Two days' notice required for access to Glynne-Gladstone MSS

Historical background Flintshire Record Office was established in 1951 and was incorporated in Clwyd Record Office which was formed after local government reorganization in 1974, also taking in what was formerly Denbighshire and part of Merioneth. The County Archivist is Honorary Archivist to the St Deiniol's Library, Hawarden, whose archive collection (Glynne-Gladstone MSS) is made available for research at the Record Office. The Office also acts as the Diocesan Record Office for St Asaph parish records. There is a Branch Office at Ruthin.

Major collections   Usual local authority record holdings and deposited collections of which the following has a wider significance:
Glynne-Gladstone MSS, deposited in St Deiniol's Library by Sir William Gladstone in 1968, comprising family correspondence and papers of the Glynne and Gladstone families of Hawarden Castle, mostly c1800–1930; includes correspondence of W.E.G. Gladstone (1809–98), Herbert, Viscount Gladstone (1854–1930) and the fifth Duke of Newcastle (1811–64) (Detailed list in hand.)

Publications   A.G. Veysey: *Guide to the Flintshire Record Office* (1974) [includes St Deiniol's Library collections]
D. Pratt and A.G. Veysey: *Handlist of Topographical Prints of Clwyd* (1977)

239   St Deiniol's Library

Address   Hawarden
Deeside
Clwyd CH5 3DF

Telephone   (0244) 532350

Enquiries to   Warden and Chief Librarian, Rev P.J. Jagger

MS collections are produced for searchers in Clwyd Record Office, Hawarden (*see* entry **238**) and all enquiries should be addressed to the County Archivist there.

240   Hereford Cathedral Library

Address   The Cathedral
Hereford
Hereford and Worcester HR1 2NG

Telephone   (0432) 58403

Enquiries to   The Cathedral Librarian

Open   Tues, Wed, Thurs: 10.00–12.30
Other times by appointment

Access   Approved readers.

Historical background   The contents of the muniment room are formed by the natural accretion of records relating to the history and administration of the Cathedral of Hereford and of the affairs of the Dean and Chapter. The muniment room is closely associated with the Cathedral Library which acts as a repository for the Cathedral music and material relating to the Cathedral's function as a place of learning.

Acquisitions policy   The muniment room continues to take in material from the administrative and legal offices of the Dean and Chapter. Gifts and deposits are accepted of material relating to or associated with any aspect of the Cathedral's history.

Major collections   Acts of the Dean and Chapter; records of the Dean's Consistory court; manorial records; muniments of title and administrative papers of the Dean and Chapter and of the prebendaries. A subsidiary group is formed by the records of the now defunct Vicars Choral. The earliest deed is *c*840.
227 MS works, 8th–15th centuries.

Non-manuscript material   *c*1000 photographic negatives of the cathedral and contents.
Library includes *c*1500 early books, still chained, (from 1611).

Finding aids   Typescript and card indexes and calendars of muniments.

Facilities   Reference library equipped for students. Microfilm reader.

Publications   F.C. and P.E. Morgan: *Hereford Cathedral Libraries and Muniments* (2/ 1975) [illustrated]
A.T. Bannister: *A Descriptive Catalogue of the MSS in the Hereford Cathedral Library* (1927) [out of print; Sir Roger Mynors is working on a new catalogue of MSS]

241   Hereford Record Office

Address   The Old Barracks
                  Harold Street
                  Hereford
                  Hereford and Worcester HR1 2QX

Telephone   (0432) 65441

Enquiries to   Assistant County Archivist, Miss D.S. Hubbard

Open   Mon–Fri: 9.15–4.45

Historical background   Hereford County Record Office was established in 1959 and since 1974 has been a dependent repository of Hereford and Worcester Record Office (*see* entry **699**). It also acts as the Diocesan Record Office for Hereford.

Major collections   Usual local authority record holdings and deposited collections, some of national standing.

Facilities   Photocopying. Photography. Microfilming. Microfilm reader.

242   Hertfordshire Local Studies Collection

Address   Hertfordshire Library Service
             County Hall
             Hertford SG13 8EJ

Telephone   (0992) 54242 ext. 5486

Enquiries to   Librarian, Mrs S.R. Head

Local History Collection of non-MS material, including copy minutes of the North West Thames Regional Health Authority.

243   Hertfordshire Record Office

Address   County Hall
             Hertford SG13 8DE

Telephone   (0992) 54242

Enquiries to   County Archivist, Mr Peter Walne

Open   Mon–Thurs: 9.15–5.15
             Fri: 9.15–4.15

Historical background   A Records Committee was established in 1875 and the present premises opened in 1939. The office also acts as the Diocesan Record Office for St Albans.

Major collections   Usual local authority record holdings and deposited collections.

Facilities   Photocopying. Photography. Microfilm/fiche readers.

Publications   W. Le Hardy: *Guide to the Hertfordshire Record Office, Part 1: Quarter Sessions and other Records in the Custody of the Officials of the County* (1961)
Catalogue of Manuscript Maps (1969)
Genealogical Sources (rev. 1982)

244   Rochdale Libraries
Local Studies Collection

Address   Heywood Area Central Library
             Church Street
             Heywood
             Lancashire OL10 1LL

Telephone   (0706) 60947

Enquiries to	Assistant Librarian, Mrs J. Booth
	or
	Local Studies Librarian at Rochdale Library (*see* entry **608**)
Open	Mon, Thurs: 9.30–8.00
	Tues, Fri: 9.30–5.30
	Wed: 9.30–1.00
	Sat: 9.30–1.00; 2.00–4.00
Access	Generally open to the public.

Historical background   The dynamic growth of Rochdale, Middleton and Heywood during the 19th century produced a wealth of material relating to the area. In 1974 it was decided that the local collection should be retained at Heywood Area Central Library under the general supervision of the Local Studies Librarian at Rochdale Area Central Library (*see* entry **608**).

Acquisitions policy   The collection of documentary material relating to all aspects of life in the area of the Metropolitan Borough of Rochdale and its previously independent constituent authorities.

Major collections   Administrative material from the former Heywood Borough, including Council minutes and accounts; the Medical Officer of Health's reports; records of the Heywood and Middleton Water Board; electoral registers.

Non-manuscript material   Complete runs of local newspapers (original and microfilm copies).
Books; pamphlets; audio-visual material; photographs; maps; plans; broadsheets; political handbills; theatre posters.

Finding aids   Calendar of archival material.

Facilities   Photocopying. Microfilm/fiche readers.

Publications   *Introduction to Local Studies Collections* (1981)

245   Ulster Folk and Transport Museum

Address	Main Institution: Cultra Manor
	Holywood
	Co Down BT18 0EU
	Transport Museum: Witham Street
	Belfast BT4 1HP
Telephone	Cultra Manor: (02317) 5411
	Witham Street: (0232) 51519
Enquiries to	The Librarian, Cultra Manor
Open	Mon–Fri: 9.00–5.00, preferably by appointment

Access   Researchers seriously pursuing a specific enquiry.

Historical background   The Museum represents a merger of two institutions – the Ulster Folk Museum, established by Act of Parliament in 1958, and the Belfast Transport Museum, established by Belfast City Council and opened to the public in 1962. The merger occurred in 1967 to provide for the eventual transfer of the Transport Museum from Belfast to a new site adjoining the Folk Museum's premises. The Museum is administered by a statutory Board of Trustees representing central government, local government, Northern Ireland's two universities and the Ulster Polytechnic. It is funded by statutory grants from the Department of Education, Northern Ireland.

Acquisitions policy   The collection of information and material for purposes defined by Act of Parliament as 'illustrating the way of life, past and present and the traditions of the people of Northern Ireland'. Essentially small country-based industries and crafts.

Major collections   Professor K.H. Connell Collection: material covering Irish economic and social history, 18th–20th centuries.
Miscellaneous collections include old account books of farms or mills, recipe books.
Material generated by researchers, especially surveys.

Non-manuscript material   Ephemera; ballads; pamphlets.
Photographic collections, especially W.A. Green collection of several thousand photographs and glass plates.
Sound archive of folklore, oral history, folk music and song (c1200 items).

Finding aids   Various lists and indexes.

Facilities   Photocopying. Photography. Reference Library (consultation during office hours) and research assistance.

246   London Borough of Hounslow Local History Collection

Address   Hounslow Reference Library
Treaty Road
Hounslow
Middlesex TW3 1DR

Telephone   (01) 570 0622

Enquiries to   Local Studies Librarian, Miss A. Cameron

Open   Mon, Tues, Thurs: 9.00–8.00
Wed: 9.00–1.00
Fri, Sat: 9.00–5.00

Access   Generally open to the public.

Historical background   The collection for the Chiswick and Hounslow areas has been built up since the beginning of the 20th century, and contains all material relevant to the history of the individual parishes within the areas. The collection at Feltham has been in existence only since 1965, and is therefore smaller in extent, but still contains material on the history of the parishes within the area. The Chiswick Collection is housed in Chiswick Reference Library, Dukes Avenue, London W4. The Feltham Collection is housed at Feltham Reference Library, High Street, Feltham, Middlesex.

Acquisitions policy   All material on the history of the London Borough of Hounslow, or any of its constituent parts, by purchase, donation, or deposit.

Major collections   Local Authority archives: minutes, rate books, electoral registers etc, 1870–.
Parish records: All Saints Church, Isleworth 1564–c1900; St Lawrence's Church, Brentford, 18th-century only; St Mary the Virgin, East Bedfont, 17th century–.

Non-manuscript material   Several hundred large-scale maps covering most parts of the borough, 1635–.
Prints, paintings, photographs: 10,000 illustrations covering all parts of the borough, c1750–.
Local newspapers, c1870–.
Layton Collection: 1200 books, maps and prints of British topography, 16th–19th centuries (housed at Chiswick Town Hall, but access via Chiswick Library).

Facilities   Photocopying. Microfilm/fiche reader/printer.

247   East Sussex County Library, Hove Area
Wolseley Collection

Address   Church Road
               Hove
               East Sussex BN3 2EG

Telephone   (0273) 77042

Enquiries to Reference Librarian (for the County), Mr E.P. Scott, East Sussex County Library, St Anne's Crescent, Lewes BN7 1SQ

Open   Tues–Fri: 10.00–6.30
               Sat: 9.30–4.00
               Preferably by appointment

Access   Bona fide scholars.

Historical background   The library has not had a policy of collecting MSS and recently gave a small collection of deeds to the Record Office at Lewes (*see* entry **290**). The Wolseley Collection was offered to the Library in 1924 and an additional accession via Royal United Services Institute came in 1965. The collection was officially opened in 1970.

Acquisitions policy   Anything relating to Lord Wolseley and his family, by gift, purchase or deposit.

Major collections   Collection of Field Marshal Lord Wolseley (1833–1913): covers his career and campaigns and includes scrapbooks and autograph letters from leading figures in his day; also correspondence of his wife and with his family who lived in East Sussex (c8000 items).
Papers of Lord Wolseley's daughter, Lady Frances Garnet Wolseley, who was a pupil of Gertrude Jekyll and had a School of Gardening in Glynde.
Scrapbooks, pedigree notebooks and privately printed catalogue (biography) of Sir Walter Miéville (1855–1929) and his family.

Finding aids   Name index and rough lists.

Facilities   Photocopying. Photography by arrangement. Microfilm reader.

Publications   Duplicated Catalogue of Wolseley Collection
J. Dale: *All Sir Garnet* [catalogue of exhibition on Lord Wolseley, 1981]

248   Huddersfield Polytechnic Library

Address   Queensgate
                   Huddersfield
                   West Yorkshire HD1 3DH

Telephone   (0484) 22288 ext. 2041

Enquiries to   Dr D.M. Jones

Open   Term: Mon–Fri: 9.00–9.00
                   Vacation: Mon–Fri: 9.00–5.00

Access   Bona fide scholars.

Historical background   The Polytechnic has its origins in the Huddersfield Mechanics' Institute, founded in 1851. This was transformed into the Huddersfield Technical College in 1884, later Huddersfield College of Technology, which combined with the Oastler College of Education to form Huddersfield Polytechnic in June 1970.

Acquisitions policy   The Polytechnic has a flourishing Department of History and Politics in which there is considerable emphasis on teaching in the field of industrial history and in particular the history of the Labour movement. The library is concerned to support this teaching by the provision of such primary source material as is thought appropriate.

Major collections   Huddersfield Labour Party archives, 1918–25.
Colne Valley Labour Party archives, including minute books, 1891–1945.

Huddersfield Mechanics' Institute: a large collection of unsorted material, including attendance registers, minute books and other committee records, 1851–84.
Yorkshire Education Association for the Building Industry minute books, 1922–67.

Non-manuscript material G.H. Wood Collection: 5000 books, journals and pamphlets published *c*1850–1910 on economics, politics, social and industrial history. Wood was a professional statistician and social reformer ultimately employed as the Secretary of the Huddersfield Woollen Manufacturers' Association. The collection includes 300 pamphlets on the Labour Problem; other areas of special significance include trade unions, wage histories, bimetallism, free trade, early socialism, Fabianism, the textile and mining industries, and industrial health, safety and welfare; 20 vols of MS Wage Notes covering all industries, 1850–1910.

Finding aids Catalogue of the Wood Collection which lists material according to subject and also provides an author index.

Facilities Photocopying. Microfilm/fiche readers.

Publications Introduction to the Wood Collection and a Biography of Wood [copies available on request]
A note on the collection has been published in *Bulletin of the Society for the Study of Labour History*, no.40 (Spring 1980), 47

249 Kirklees Metropolitan Council Libraries and Arts Division
Local Studies and Archives Department

Address   Princess Alexandra Walk
Huddersfield
West Yorkshire HD1 2SU

Telephone   (0484) 21356 ext. 36

Enquiries to   The Archivist and Local Studies Officer

Open   Mon–Fri: 9.00–8.00
Sat: 9.00–4.00
Prior notice appreciated, but not obligatory

Access   Generally open to the public.

Historical background The local studies library developed from the general reference department. The post of Archivist was established in 1959.

Major collections Local authority records of all predecessor authorities.
Estate and family records of the Beaumonts of Whitley, 12th–19th centuries; Ramsdens of Longley and Huddersfield, 16th–20th centuries; Thornhills of Fixby,

18th–20th centuries; Saviles of Thornhill, 17th–18th centuries.

Parish and Nonconformist Church records.

Education records: school boards records, education departments log-books, minutes.

Societies' records: Co-operative, Chamber of Commerce, Thespians, Glee and Madrigal, Oddfellows.

Business records of firms of architects, joiners, accountants, engineers, woollen manufacturers.

Poor-law records.

Non-manuscript material   Pamphlets, photographs, maps, newspapers.

Finding aids   Calendars of archives. Catalogues for non-archive material.

Facilities   Photocopying. Photography. Microfilm/fiche readers.

250   Brynmor Jones Library

Address   University of Hull
Cottingham Road
Hull
Humberside HU6 7RX

Telephone   (0482) 46311

Enquiries to   University Librarian, Dr P.A. Larkin
or
University Archivist, Mr N. Higson

Open   Library:
Term: Mon–Fri: 9.00 a.m.–10.00 p.m.
Sat: 9.00–1.00
Vacation: Mon–Fri: 9.00–5.30
Sat: 9.00–1.00
MS material Mon–Fri: 9.00–1.00, 2.00–5.00, on application to the Archivist

Access   Extended consultation may require registration as an Associate Reader, for which a fee may be charged.

Historical background   Hull University College was incorporated in 1927 and received its charter as a University in 1954.

Acquisitions policy   To extend and strengthen existing collections by gift, purchase or deposit, particularly in the field of Labour history.

Major collections   Records of Co-operative Production Federation; National Council for Civil Liberties; Women's Co-operative Guild; Union of Democratic Control; Ellerman's Wilson Line; Socialist Medical Association.
Records of the families of Beaumont (Stapleton) of Carlton; Forbes-Adam (Beilby,

Lawley) of Escrick; Hortham of South Dalton; Lloyd-Greame of Sewerby; Maxwell-Constable of Everingham; Sykes of Sledmere; Wickham-Boynton of Burton Agnes.

Non-manuscript material   Pamphlets, play-bills and broadsides in general collection in library.

Finding aids   Calendars or initial lists of collections. Indexes of place and personal names.

Facilities   Photocopying. Photography. Microfilm/fiche readers.

251   Kingston upon Hull City Record Office

Address   79 Lowgate
                 Kingston-upon-Hull
                 Humberside HU1 2AA

Telephone   (0482) 222015/6

Enquiries to   City Archivist, Mr Geoffrey W. Oxley

Open   Mon–Fri: 8.30–5.00

Historical background   The Office was established in 1968 within the Town Clerk's Department and moved to specially converted premises in 1977.

Major collections   Usual local authority record holdings of purely local interest.

Facilities   Photocopying. Photography.

Publications   L.M. Stanewell: *City and County of Kingston upon Hull. Calendar of the ancient deeds, letters, miscellaneous old documents* (1951)
Guide, Part I
World War II

252   Cambridge County Record Office
Huntingdon Office

Address   Grammar School Walk
                 Huntingdon
                 Cambridgeshire PE18 6LF

Telephone   (0480) 52181 ext. 42

Enquiries to   Senior Archivist, Mr A.D. Hill

Open   Mon–Fri: 9.00–5.00
                 Sat: morning, by appointment

Historical background   The Huntingdon Office was established in 1949 and no accessions were received before that date. In 1975 it came under the administration of the enlarged Cambridge County Council. This office also acts as the Diocesan Record Office for Ely (archdeaconry of Huntingdon) and administers MSS of the adjacent Cromwell Museum (*see* entry **253**).

Major collections Usual local authority record holdings and deposited collections, including the following which have a wider significance:
MSS of the Earls and Dukes of Manchester.

Facilities Photocopying. Photography. Microfilming. Microfilm/reader.

Publications G.H. Findlay: *Guide to the Huntingdonshire Record Office* (1958)
P.G.M. Dickinson: *Maps in the County Record Office, Huntingdon* (1968)

253 Cromwell Museum

Address   Grammar School Walk
                  Huntingdon
                  Cambridgeshire PE18 6LF

The museum, opened in 1962, illustrates Oliver Cromwell's role in the Great Rebellion, 1640–60. With the exception of a few exhibition items all MS collections have been placed in the County Record Office, Huntingdon (*see* entry **252**).

254 London Borough of Redbridge
Libraries Department

Address   Central Reference Library
                  112b High Road
                  Ilford
                  Essex IG1 1BY

Telephone   (01) 478 4319

Enquiries to   The Reference Librarian

Open   Mon–Fri: 9.00–8.00
                  Sat: 9.00–5.00
                  Appointment preferred

Access   Generally open to the public.

Historical background Archival material was acquired haphazardly over a number of years from 1909, mainly by donations from local residents. Since 1965 a more definite policy has been pursued. The Reference Library has been designated as the repository for all Council archives, and to this end departments are transferring material to the Library.

Acquisitions policy   To acquire, by donation or purchase, when practicable, all documentary material relating to the Borough. The accession of archives from Council departments.

Major collections   Admission registers, reports, papers etc, relating to the former Infant Oprhans Asylum (later the Royal Infant Orphanage, later the Royal Wanstead School), Snaresbrook, Wanstead.

Sales reports, staff and work-force details, reports, maps, minutes of Board meetings etc, relating to the former chemical manufacturers, Howards of Ilford, Ltd. (The mass of this material has only just been acquired, and has not been calendared.)

Material relating to the activities and functions of the various departments of the Council of the London Borough of Redbridge.

Non-manuscript material   As part of the Local History Collection of the Reference Library: local maps and plans of Ilford, Wanstead and Woodford, mainly 19th and 20th centuries; *c*33,000 pamphlets and news-cuttings; 6000 photographs and 1200 slides; books dealing with the Borough and surrounding area.

Local newspapers, 1900– (earlier issues on microfilm).

Finding aids   The majority of archive material is as yet uncatalogued. Classified index for all illustrative material and pamphlet file material.

Facilities   Photocopying. Microfilm reader/printer.

Publications   *A Catalogue of Local History Documents* (September 1977) [Lists the majority of the archives held at that time, together with the holdings of various societies and organizations in the Borough]

255   Highland Regional Archive

Address   The Library
                  Farraline Park
                  Inverness IV1 1LS

Telephone   (0463) 36463

Enquiries to   Records Officer, Mr A.B. Lawson

Open   Mon–Fri: 9.30–5.30
                  Sat: 9.30–5.00

Access   Generally open to the public. Detailed guidance by arrangement. Records Officer available part-time only.

Historical background   The collection was formed in 1975 on the reorganization of local government and the creation of the Highland Region. It is basically a collection of the formal records of the former county authorities within the region.

Acquisitions policy   Acquisitions are by gift or loan. Only material of relevance to the Highlands is looked for. Documents and records relating to families, estates, industry and commerce are welcomed.

Major collections   Usual local authority record holdings together with the records of the parochial boards, parish councils and school boards within the region; a few deposited miscellaneous documents, very little of wider significance.
Records of the former burghs, except the former Royal Burgh of Inverness, are not held.

Finding aids   Catalogues and lists. Some MS documents not individually listed, but in bundle form only.

Facilities   Photocopying.

256   Suffolk County Library Headquarters

Address   County Hall
                 Ipswich
                 Suffolk IP4 2JS

Archives are neither held nor acquired.

257   Suffolk Record Office
Ipswich Branch

Address   County Hall
                 St Helen's Street
                 Ipswich
                 Suffolk IP4 2JS

Telephone   (0473) 55801 ext. 235

Enquiries to   County Archivist, Miss Amanda Arrowsmith

Open   Mon–Thurs: 9.00–5.00
                 Fri: 9.00–4.00
                 Sat: 9.00–1.00; 2.00–5.00
                 Material required on Sat must be ordered before 1.00 on Fri

Historical background   The Suffolk Record Offices at Ipswich and Bury St Edmunds (*see* entry **81**) were originally established in 1950 by the East and West Suffolk County Councils respectively, jointly with the County Borough of Ipswich and the Borough of Bury St Edmunds. In 1974 the two offices were amalgamated. The office also acts as the Diocesan Record Office for St Edmundsbury and Ipswich (archdeaconries of Suffolk and Ipswich).

Major collections   Usual local authority record holdings and deposited collections.

Facilities   Photocopying. Photography. Microfilming. Microfilm reader.

258   Salford City Archives

Address	Archives Centre
	658–662 Liverpool Road
	Irlam
	Manchester M30 5AD
Telephone	(061) 775 5643
Enquiries to	Archivist, Mr A.N. Cross
Open	Mon–Fri: 9.00–4.30, by arrangement
Access	Generally open to the public.

Historical background   The Archives Centre was established in 1974 with the reorganization of local government. Before then archives were kept by various libraries which have subsequently transferred some material.

Major collections   Usual local authority record holdings and deposited collections.

Publications   Information leaflets on genealogical sources and the history of houses [available on request]
Duplicated handlist 1978 [to be revised in 1982]

259   Ironbridge Gorge Museum Trust

Address	The Wharfage
	Ironbridge
	Telford
	Shropshire TF8 7AW
Telephone	(095245) 3522 ext.39
Enquiries to	Librarian, Mr John Powell
	or
	Curator of the Telford Collection, Mr Alastair Penfold
Open	Mon, Fri: 9.00–5.00
	Tues–Thurs: 9.00–5.30
Access	By prior appointment with the Librarian or the Curator of the Telford Collection.

Historical background   The Ironbridge Gorge Museum Trust was established in 1968 to conserve for posterity the unique industrial remains of the area's former period of greatness. It consists of the world's first iron bridge (1779), the furnace where coke smelting was first introduced in 1709, the Coalbrookdale Museum of Iron, the Severn Warehouse, Blists Hill Open Air Museum, Coalport China Works Museum and other sites within an area of 5 square miles. The Library and archive collections have been built up since 1968.

Acquisitions policy Material relevant to local industrial history; the majority of items received as donations.

Major collections Archives relating to the following companies: Coalbrookdale Company; Horsehay Company; Lilleshall Company; Maw & Co; Hathernware Company (of Loughborough, Leics).
Collection pertaining to the life and works of Thomas Telford (1757–1834): official correspondence, reports and accounts of the Gloucester and Berkeley Canal and his involvement in the Exchequer Loans Commission Board; draft versions of Telford's autobiography, with correspondence relating to its publication. (This collection is administered and financed by Telford Development Corporation.)

Non-manuscript material Illustrative material in the Telford Collection and xerox and microfilm copies of all known Telford MS material and printed Parliamentary reports containing Telford references.
Museum Library.
Elton Collection (material relating to the Industrial Revolution).

Finding aids Lists and indexes in the Library. Details of Telford Collection available on request.

Facilities Photocopying. Photography.

260   Renfrew District Libraries Archives Service

Address   Old Library
Collier Street
Johnstone
Renfrewshire PA5 8AR

Telephone   (0505) 20804

Enquiries to Archivist, Ms Fiona Watson
or
Local History Librarian, Mr Kenneth Hinshalwood, Central Library, High Street, Paisley, Renfrewshire PA1 2BB (telephone: (041) 889 2360)

Open   Tues, Thurs: 9.30–4.30
Other times by appointment

Access   Generally open to the public.

Historical background The Local History Department of Paisley's Central Library had amassed over the years a quantity of MS and other archival material. In 1975, as a result of the reorganization of Scottish local government, several town councils deposited their records with the department, adding considerably to its holdings. Some time later it was decided to separate the archives and local history stock, and in 1980 the post of Archivist was created under the Manpower Services Commission's STEP scheme.

Acquisitions policy To acquire by deposit, donation or puchase material relating to places, persons and companies within Renfrew District.

Major collections Burgh records of Renfrew, 1655–; Paisley, 1594–; Johnstone, 1857–; and Barrhead, 1894–.
Records of the co-operative movement in Paisley, late 19th and 20th centuries.

Non-manuscript material c4000 plans from Dean of Guild courts in Paisley and Johnstone, late 19th- and 20th centuries.

Finding aids List of local authority records to 1975. Indexes to plans. Catalogue of all other material in preparation.

Facilities Photocopying. Photography.

261 Air Photo Library

Address Department of Geography
University of Keele
Keele
Staffordshire ST5 5BG

Telephone (0782) 621111 ext.291

Enquiries to Curator, Mrs S. Walton

Open Mon–Thurs: 9.30–4.30, by appointment

Access Generally open to the public, on written application and subject to the provisions of the Official Secrets Act and the Public Record Act. Requests for access to photographs covering specific areas should state the name of the site and position to nearest latitude and longitude.

Historical background The Library is composed of a significant part of the air photo print library of the Allied Central Interpretation Unit from RAF Medmenham. The contents of the Library are the property of the Public Record Office and are on permanent loan.

Major collections Exclusively non-MS material (see below).

Non-manuscript material 5 million vertical air-photographs, Nov 1939–May 1945. (No coverage of any territory now belonging to member nations of the Warsaw Pact, countries neutral in World War II, or UK.)

Finding aids The collection is catalogued by latitude and longitude.

Facilities Copy-print service.

262   English Organ Archive

Address   Department of Education
                 University of Keele
                 Staffordshire ST5 5BG

Telephone   (0782) 621111

Enquiries to   Hon. Archivist, Dr Michael Sayer

Open   By appointment with the Hon. Archivist

Access   Bona fide scholars.

Historical background   The collection was begun in 1975 and aims to provide a research service to anyone engaged in the identification or restoration of historical musical instruments. Researchers can be directed to archives located elsewhere (no organ-makers' archives survive pre-1790s). The collection is financially independent of the University and of the British Institute of Organ Studies and depends on grants.

Acquisitions policy   To acquire MSS and printed records made or published by English instrument-makers, principally organ-builders.

Major collections   English musical instrument- makers' technical and business records: most major firms (some now out of business) have deposited their archives.

Publications   Publication of research by British Institute of Organ Studies.

263   Keele University Library

Address   Keele
                 Staffordshire ST5 5BG

Telephone   (0782) 621111 ext. 255

Enquiries to   Archivist, Dr I.H.C. Fraser

Open   Mon–Fri: 9.30–5.00
                 Sat: 9.30–12.00, by arrangement only

Access   Bona fide research workers, on written application.

Historical background   In 1957 the University College of North Staffordshire (later the University of Keele) purchased the papers of the Sneyds of Keele, which had by then become part of the collection of the late Raymond Richards MA, FSA, FRHistS, of Gawsworth, Cheshire. Most of the rest of this collection was purchased at the same time and became the nucleus of the MS holding. Subsequent deposits, gifts and some further purchases of mainly archive material have been added.

Acquisitions policy   To consolidate relevant holdings having regard to the interests of neighbouring repositories.

Major collections   Wedgwood MSS: *c*75,000 separate items, plus vols, reflecting the history of the family and the history of the firm; rich in material relating to the fine arts, the history of science and the development of humanitarian movements, as well as the history of the manufacture of ceramic products.
Raymond Richards Collection: Sneyd family papers and older collections such as the Hatton Wood MSS, a large proportion of which consists of medieval evidence of title, 12th century–.
Tamworth court rolls, comprising *c*250 items, 1289– (at least one earlier roll is believed to survive as a stray); the archive represents a unique record of the administration and eventual emergence of a medieval borough.
English Organ Archive (*see* entry **262**).

Non-manuscript material   Photographs; cartoons; drawings and paintings; music; printed ephemera.

Finding aids   Calendars, lists, indexes. Listing in progress.

Facilities   Photocopying. Photography. Microcard/fiche/film readers.

Publications   M.K. Dale: *Abstracts of Tamworth Court rolls* (1959)
I.H.C. Fraser: 'Sneyd MSS, University of Keele', *Bulletin of the National Register of Archives*, no.14 (1967)
————: 'Manuscripts in the Library of the University of Keele', *North Staffordshire Journal of Field Studies*, vii (1967)

264   Cumbria County Record Office
Kendal Office

Address   County Offices
Kendal
Cumbria LA9 4RQ

Telephone   (0539) 21000

Enquiries to   Archivist-in-charge, Miss Sheila J. MacPherson

Open   Mon–Fri: 9.00–5.00
Sat and evenings by arrangement

Historical background   The Office was established in 1962, originally with a Joint Archives Committee for Cumberland and Westmorland. Few archives other than local authority records had been acquired before that date. The Office also acts as the Diocesan Record Office for Carlisle (Bradford parish records) and gives administrative assistance to Levens Hall, Kendal.

Major collections   Usual local authority record holdings and deposited collections of which the following have a wider significance:

Fleming MSS of Rydal Hall: including correspondence of Sir Daniel Fleming, 17th century.
Hothfield papers: including Clifford family documents, particularly of Lady Anne Clifford, 17th century.

Facilities   Photocopying. Photography. Microfilming. Microfilm readers.

Publications   B.C. Jones: 'Cumberland, Westmorland and Carlisle Record Office, 1960–65' *Archives*, vii, 34 (1965), 80
———— 'Cumberland and Westmorland Record Offices, 1968', *Northern History* iii (1968), 162

265   Kidderminster Library

Address   Market Street
                 Kidderminster
                 Hereford and Worcester DY10 1AD

Telephone   (0562) 752832

Enquiries to   Assistant County Librarian, Mr Rex Clark

Open   Mon, Fri: 9.30–5.30
                 Tues, Thurs: 9.30–7.00
                 Sat: 9.30–4.00

Access   Generally open to the public, an advance notice in writing or by telephone.

Historical background   Kidderminster's first municipal library opened in 1855 in the new Town Hall in Vicar Street, all books being for reference only. In 1881 a lending library for home reading was begun. The present building in Market Street was opened in 1894 and in 1927 the organization became the Kidderminster Borough Library, Museum and Art Gallery. Later the special collections on local history and carpets and textiles were built up. Following the setting up of the National Register of Archives by the Historical Manuscripts Commission in 1945, the archive collection became established with a substantial deposit of the Knight Family MSS, followed by the Lea Family MSS and other donations of local documents.

Acquisitions policy   To add to the existing collection of primary source material on the history of Kidderminster and the surrounding area by donation, deposit or purchase.

Major collections   Charters and ancient documents, 12th–19th centuries (13 items).
Knight MSS: private papers and Iron Work account books of 18th-century ironmasters, 1726–78; also MSS relating to their Exmoor properties.
MSS of Henry Howard of Stone House.
Talbot MSS: including those of Kidderminster and Mid-Worcestershire

Parliamentary Election, 1892; Kidderminster Turnpike Trustees.

Maiden Bradley Priory registers.

Bewdley Charitable Donations MSS.

Baxter Church MSS (on permanent loan from Baxter Church Trustees).

Cookley new church and parsonage MSS.

Worcestershire Volunteer Rifle Corps records.

Kidderminster Borough records, including rate books and valuation lists, 19th century.

Minutes of Kidderminster Borough Council and its committees, 19th century.

Non-manuscript material Kidderminster Corporation yearbooks, 19th–20th centuries.

Finding aids The majority of the collection has been calendared and finding lists made for the remainder.

Facilities Photocopying. Microfilm/fiche reader.

266   Kilmarnock and Loudoun District Council Cultural Services
The Dick Institute

Address   14 Elmbank Avenue
Kilmarnock
Strathclyde KA1 3BU

Telephone   (0563) 26401

Enquiries to Curator, Mr James Hunter

Open   Mon, Tues, Thurs, Fri: 9.00–8.00
Weds, Sat: 9.00–5.00
(access to MSS by appointment)

Access   Generally open to the public.

Historical background The Foundation Stone of the Dick Institute was laid in 1898 by Mrs Dick, wife of the donor, and was formally opened in 1901. The museum owes its origin chiefly to James Thomson who gifted a rare and valuable collection of corals, fossils and minerals, to which extensive additions were made by Dr Hunter-Selkirk of Braidwood, and others.

Acquisitions policy MSS of local interest, or relating to museum subject areas.

Major collections Various collections including poems and letters of Robert Burns (1759–96); family papers of Boyds of Kilmarnock; records of local town councils, trade guilds and trade unions. A total of c5000 items, 14th–20th centuries.

Non-manuscript material Local maps.

Engineering and architectural plans and drawings.
*c*1500 paintings and prints.
*c*6000 photographs and slides.
Local newspapers.

Finding aids   Catalogues and indexes to most collections.

Facilities   Photocopying. Photography. Microfilming. Microfilm reader.

267   The Lynn Museum

Address   Old Market Street
King's Lynn
Norfolk PE30 1NL

Telephone   (0553) 5001

Enquiries to   Curator, Mr R. Trett

Open   Mon–Sat: 10.00–5.00, by appointment only

Access   Small admission charge to the museum, subject to seasonal alterations.

Historical background   The Museum was founded as a Society Museum in 1844 with a collection of natural history specimens and curiosities. The Museum received important gifts; it was taken over by King's Lynn Borough Council and the present building was opened in 1904. In 1973 a branch museum of social history was opened at 27 King Street, King's Lynn, and in 1974 both museums were included in the newly-formed Norfolk Museums Service.

Acquisitions policy   To collect material and information relating to King's Lynn and West Norfolk.

Major collections   Archaeological: records of excavations in King's Lynn etc.
Natural History: a few records relating to the Museum's collections.
Engineering: a vast collection of works' drawings and accompanying ledgers and papers from Dodman's of Lynn (founded *c*1850) relating to boilers, agricultural machinery, traction engines, marine equipment etc; works' drawings, ledgers etc relating to Savages of Lynn, who were important manufacturers of fairground machinery, traction engines etc.
Topographical: papers, MS letters etc, relating to the history of Lynn, including Museum records, 1844–, and some deeds and business records.
Miscellaneous MSS relating to Thomas Baines (1822–75) and Captain G.W. Manby (1765–1854).

Non-manuscript material   Pamphlets and broadsheets relating to Lynn.
Poster Collection: *c*6000 posters relating to the local theatres, politics, religion, sales and auctions etc, 18th century–.
Photographic collections relating to the Museum collections and to West Norfolk.

Local paintings, prints, sketches etc, including maritime subjects.

Finding aids   Various lists and indexes. A few select catalogues.

Facilities   Microfilm reader. No photocopier, but one available at the King's Lynn Library.

268   Kingston Polytechnic

Address   Penrhyn Road
Kingston upon Thames
Surrey KT1 2EE

Telephone   (01) 549 1366 ext. 400 (Chief Librarian)

Enquiries to   Mr Ian Beardwell (School of Business, Kingston Polytechnic, ext. 412)
or
The Centre Librarian, Gipsy Hill Centre, Kingston Hill, Kingston upon Thames, Surrey KT2 7LB
(telephone (01) 549 1141 ext. 233/267)

Open   Term: Mon–Fri: 9.00–9.00
Vacation: Mon–Fri: 9.00–5.30

Access   By appointment through the Centre Librarian at Gipsy Hill, where the collection is housed, or Mr Ian Beardwell.

Acquisitions policy   The Polytechnic acts as the archive repository for the Council of Civil Service Unions.

Major collections   The Polytechnic holds the archive maintained by the unions (now the Civil Service Unions) on the staff side of the Whitley Council, 1920–70; the archive consists of all major committee minutes and associated policy documents and correspondence. The Council of Civil Service Unions has agreed to release further documents as appropriate.

Finding aids   No organized finding aid exists; arranging and indexing will be the first aim of the research assistant (to be appointed).

Facilities   All the Library facilities at the Gipsy Hill Centre, including photocopying, are available.

Publications   The research assistant will initially organize the material and, it is hoped, subsequently produce publications.

269   Royal Borough of Kingston Archives

Address   c/o Surrey Record Office
County Hall
Kingston upon Thames
Surrey KT1 2DN

Telephone   (01) 546 1050 ext. 3557

Enquiries to   Archivist, Mrs M. Vaughan-Lewis
or
Honorary Borough Archivist, Dr D.B. Robinson

Open   By appointment only
Mon, Tues, Wed, Fri: 9.30–4.45
Sat (2nd and 4th of each month): 9.30–12.30
(Borough archives must be ordered at least two days in advance.)

Access   Generally open to the public. Council material restricted at least 30 years. Records are made available at Surrey County Record Office (*see* entry **270**).

Historical background   Archives are held under the various provisions of the 1882 Municipal Corporations Act, Local Government (Records) Act 1962, as modified by the London Government Act 1963, and the Public Records Acts 1958 and 1967. In 1965 the County Archivist of Surrey became the Honorary Borough Archivist and Kingston Corporation employed an assistant archivist. The present post is designated Archivist and is under the Heritage Officer in the Directorate of Education and Recreation for administrative and financial matters.

Acquisitions policy   Mainly the preservation of the Council's own records (including 20th-century accumulations). However, private deposits are accepted when related strictly to Kingston and where not to do so would be to break up a deposit containing material for the other Heritage Unit sections (i.e. the museum and the local history collections).

Major collections   Records of the Corporation of Kingston, including substantial deed groups for Corporation property, 13th–20th centuries. Very few private papers.

Non-manuscript material   Most of this material is placed in the Local History Collection, Heritage Centre, Fairfield West, Kingston upon Thames.

Finding aids   Lists and name and place index to deeds.

Facilities   Photocopying and microfilm readers (by courtesy of Surrey Record Office).

Publications   *Guide to the Borough Archives* (1971)
Archive Teaching Units: *Kingston Children*; *Kingston Market Place*; *Kingston in Maps*

270   Surrey Record Office

Address	County Hall Penrhyn Road Kingston-upon-Thames KT1 2DN
Telephone	(01) 546 1050 ext. 3561
Enquiries to	County Archivist, Dr D.B. Robinson
Open	Mon—Wed, Fri: 9.30—4.45 Sat (2nd and 4th of each month): 9.30—12.30 by appointment

Historical background   Records have been received since 1926. The first archivist was appointed in 1951. Administrative assistance is given to Royal Borough of Kingston Archive (*see* entry **269**). The office also acts as the Diocesan Record Office for Southwark, Canterbury (archdeaconry of Croydon) and Guildford (deaneries of Emly and Epsom).

Major collections   Usual local authority record holdings and deposited collections of which the following have a wider significance:
Papers of the Goulburn family of Betchworth relating to sugar estates in Jamaica, 1795—1858, and correspondence with Sir Robert Peel (1788—1850).
Records of the Royal Philanthropic Society's School, Redhill (founded in London for the reform of juveniles), 1788—.
Records of the Broadwood family of Lyne, including those of John Broadwood & Sons, piano manufacturers, 1800—.

Facilities   Photocopying. Photography. Microfilming. Microfilm reader.

271   Kirkcaldy District Libraries

Address	Central Library War Memorial Grounds Kirkcaldy Fife KY1 1YG
Telephone	(0592) 260707
Enquiries to	Librarian, Mrs Janet Klak
Open	Mon—Thurs: 10.00—7.00 Fri, Sat: 10.00—5.00 Preferably by prior appointment
Access	Generally open to the public.

Historical background   MS material has been acquired haphazardly over the years.

Acquisitions policy   Material of local interest is considered.

Major collections   Box of deeds and letters [listed by NRA Scotland].
MSS of Jessie Patrick Findlay, local author, 20th century.
Hutt–Proudfoot Collection, including letters and news-sheets relating to the
General Strike, 1921–26 [housed at Methil Library].

Non-manuscript material   Local History collection: books, maps, press cuttings and
photographs, covering Fife in general and Kirkcaldy District in particular.

Finding aids   Press cuttings index.

Facilities   Photocopying by arrangement. Microfilm/fiche reader.

272   Kirkcaldy Museum and Art Gallery

Address   War Memorial Gardens
                 Kirkcaldy
                 Fife KY1 1YG

Telephone   (0592) 260732

Enquiries to   The Curator

Open   Mon–Fri: 9.00–5.00, by appointment

Access   Generally open to the public.

Historical background   The Museum and Art Gallery was founded in 1925 as a
general museum for Kirkcaldy. In 1975 it became responsible for Kirkcaldy
District. The Archive is only part of the large general museum and art collections.
Much earlier local material is deposited with the Scottish Record Office (*see* entry
188). The bulk of the 19th and 20th-century government material is held by
Kirkcaldy District Council, Town House, Kirkcaldy.

Acquisitions policy   By donation and deposit, material relevant to the museum
collections and to the history of Kirkcaldy District.

Major collections   Records of the linoleum industry, including plans, buildings and
machinery, 1840–1940; Trade guilds, 1700–1850; Trade unions, local branches,
20th century; Local government, 19th–20th centuries; Friendly societies, 19th
century.
Rothes Papers: major collection of estate and personal papers of Earl of Rothes,
including mining operations, 1650–1820.
Other smaller collections, including local industry and ephemera.

Non-manuscript material   Photographic collections of the district.
Most non-MS material is held by Kirkcaldy District Libraries (*see* entry **271**).

Finding aids   Some indexing.

Facilities   Photocopying, by arrangement.

Publications Kirkcaldy Burgh Museum and Art Gallery, National Register of Archives (Scotland), no.744 (c1975)

273 Orkney Archives Office

Address	The Orkney Library Laing Street Kirkwall KW15 1NW
Telephone	(0856) 3166 ext. 4
Enquiries to	Archivist, Miss Alison Fraser
Open	Mon–Fri: 9.00–5.00

Historical background The Office was formally established in 1973, although the Librarian had collected archives previously.

Major collections Usual local authority record holdings including the following deposited collections which have a wider significance:
Balfour of Balfour and Trenabie collection of private papers, with considerable material relating to national events, politics, India etc, c1570–1880.
Business records: e.g. Highland Park Distillery; Orkney Islands Shipping Company etc.
6000 photographic glass negatives.
Sound archive, established in conjunction with local radio, 1981–.

Facilities Photocopying. Photography. Microfilm/fiche reader.

274 Saint David's University College

Address	Lampeter Dyfed SA48 7ED
Telephone	(0570) 422351 ext. 221
Enquiries to	Hon. Archivist, Rev. D.T.W. Price
Open	By appointment
Access	Generally open to the public.

Historical background The College opened in 1827 and for many years most of the graduates entered the ministry of the Anglican Church, although the College was never simply a theological college. In 1971 the College became a constituent institution of the University of Wales.

Acquisitions policy To retrieve and preserve all material concerned with the history of the College.

Major collections   Archives of the College including tutors' registers, which provide biographical material on all students of the College.

Non-manuscript material   College magazines; many photographs.

Finding aids   Various lists and indexes.

Facilities   Phototyping. Photocopying.

275   Clydesdale District Libraries

Address   Lindsay Institute
Hope Street
Lanark
Strathclyde ML11 7LZ

No archives are held.

276   Lancaster District Library
Local Studies Department

Address   Market Square
Lancaster
Lancashire LA1 1HY

Telephone   (0524) 63266/7

Enquiries to   District Librarian, Miss U.B. Murphy

Open   Mon, Thurs: 9.30–6.30
Tues: 9.30–5.00
Wed: 9.30–1.00
Fri: 9.30–7.00
Sat: 9.30–4.00

Access   Generally open to the public. A prior appointment will save time.

Historical background   Formerly Lancaster City Library, the library became part of the Lancashire Library in 1974. The City Library was formed in 1893, inheriting volumes from the Mechanics' Institute, Amicable Society, etc, which date to the late 18th century. Between World Wars I and II the library was designated an official repository of archives by the Master of the Rolls, prior to the creation of Lancashire Record Office (*see* entry **594**). Most archive material has been acquired since 1900.

Acquisitions policy   Material is acquired only by donation. In theory all types of MSS, maps, and unmounted illustrations etc, are accepted. Ephemera is collected.

Major collections   Local History Collection, for the area within 15 miles radius of

Lancaster, *c*9000 MSS including: Apprentice Registers; Methodist Circuit papers; Port Commissioners archives.
Cumbria, Lancashire and Yorkshire Collection: general interest material.

Non-manuscript material   Cumbria, Lancashire and Yorkshire map collections.
Local newspapers, 1801–.
Lancaster City Museum (Market Square, Lancaster) holds the Local Collection of pictures and objects, and houses the Regimental Museum.

Finding aids   Indexes to all local collections are sheaf catalogues with general subject lists as guides to the use of the catalogues. Newspapers are partly indexed, but quality of indexing varies.

Facilities   Photocopying (excluding bound newspapers). Microfilmed newspapers can be obtained by reader/printer. Photography (subject to conditions).

277   University of Lancaster

Address   University Library
Bailrigg
Lancaster
Lancashire LA1 4YH

No archives are held.

278   Lancing College Archives

Address   Lancing College
Lancing
West Sussex BN15 0RW

Telephone   (079 17) 2213

Enquiries to   Mr Basil W.T. Handford, 21 The Street, North Lancing, West Sussex BN15 0PN

Open   By appointment.

Access   Approved readers on written application.

Historical background   The College was founded by Nathaniel Woodard (1811–91) in 1848. A basic collection of Woodard Schools papers, made by Henry M. Gibbs during the 19th century, has been gradually added to since.

Acquisitions policy   To acquire further material relating to the past of Lancing College and the other 23 Woodard schools, and to preserve present material, including tape recordings.

Major collections   Woodard schools papers, 1848–.

c10,000 letters of Nathaniel Woodard, 1846–90.
Papers of Edmund Field.
Memoirs and other papers.

Non-manuscript material   Photographs and architectural drawings illustrating the architecture of Lancing College, in particular the construction of the Chapel, 1868–1979.
All pamphlets published by Nathaniel Woodard.

279   The Brotherton Collection

Address   University of Leeds
Leeds
West Yorkshire LS2 9JT

Telephone   (0532) 431751 ext. 6552

Enquiries to   The Keeper, Mr D. Cox
or
Sub-Librarian, Mr C.D.W. Sheppard

Open   Mon–Fri: 9.00–1.00; 2.15–5.00
Sat: 9.00–1.00 (9.00–12.30 in Long Vacation)

Access   Open to all at the discretion of the Keeper. Non-members of the University, other than casual visitors, should apply in advance to the Keeper and should provide a letter of introduction from a person of recognized status if so required.

Historical background   The basis of the Collection is the private library of Lord Brotherton of Wakefield (1856–1930), presented to the University 'for the Nation' shortly after his death. It is now greatly increased in size through subsequent purchases from endowed funds and through further gifts. It is part of the University (Brotherton) Library (*see* entry **280**), but physically and administratively distinct within it.

Acquisitions policy   Major current collecting fields are: English drama and poetry, 1600–1750, and material from this period relating to travel, science, language, translation, and political and economic thought; 19th- and 20th-century literary MSS and printed books; Romany subjects.

Major collections   Literary MSS, especially verse miscellanies, 17th and 18th centuries.
MSS of 19th-century writers including the Arnolds, the Brontes, A.C. Swinburne (1837–1909), George Borrow (1803–81).
Marrick Priory deeds and charters, 12th century–.
Archives of the Loder-Symonds family and Henry Marten (1602–80), regicide.
Papers of Thomas Townshend, first Viscount Sydney, (1733–1800); the Novello and Cowdon-Clarke families, 19th century.

MSS and correspondence of: Sir Edmund Gosse (1849–1928), P.H. Gosse (1810–88) and Dr Philip Gosse, 1867–1928; Edward Clodd (1840–1930); W.W. Gibson; Lascelles Abercrombie (1881–1938); John Drinkwater (1882–1937); W.R.M. Childe; Francis Berry and G. Wilson Knight.

Correspondence of: Bram Stoker and Sir Henry Irving (1838–1905); Henry Arthur Jones (1851–1929); G.A. Sala (1828–96).

Papers of Arthur Ransome (1884–1967).

Letters and MSS of Mendelssohn.

Archives of *The London Magazine*, 1972–.

Documents relating to the Chevalier D'Eon.

Papers of Alf Mattison relating to the development of socialism in Great Britain, late 19th and early 20th centuries.

Non-manuscript material Some paintings and other artefacts, particularly in Romany and Novello-Cowden Clarke sections.

*c*50,000 printed books in subjects similar to those of the MSS.

Finding aids Many lists and indexes.

Facilities Photocopying, photography and microfilming (all subject to copyright provisions and suitability of material). Microfilm/fiche reader.

Publications J.A. Symington: *The Brotherton Library: a Catalogue of ancient manuscripts and early printed works collected by Edward Allen Baron Brotherton of Wakefield* (Leeds, 1931)

Annual report of the Brotherton Collection Committee (1936–)

A Catalogue of the Gosse Correspondence in the Brotherton Collection . . . 1867 to 1928 (Leeds, 1950)

The Novello Cowden Clarke Collection (Leeds, 1955)

Catalogue of the Romany Collection formed by D.U. McGrigor Phillips LL.D and presented to the University of Leeds (Edinburgh, 1962)

D.I. Masson: 'The Brotherton Collection of rare books and manuscripts', *University of Leeds Review*, xxi (1978), 135

280 Brotherton Library
Department of Special Collections

Address	University of Leeds Leeds West Yorkshire LS2 9JT
Telephone	(0532) 431751 ext. 7278
Enquiries to	University Librarian, Mr D. Cox *or* Sub-Librarian, Mr P.S. Morrish

Open   Mon–Fri: 9.00–5.00, by appointment
              Closed: public and official holidays (see University Calendar)

Access   Bona fide researchers who are not current members of the
              University of Leeds may be admitted and should normally produce
              some means of identifying themselves and a recommendation from a
              responsible person on their first visit.

Historical background   The University Library, of which the Brotherton Library
   forms part, began as the library of the Yorkshire College in 1874.

Acquisitions policy   General, with bias towards the research interests of the
   University.

Major collections   Archives of West Riding wool textile manufacturers, mainly 18th
   century–; Dean and Chapter of Ripon, from middle ages; various Yorkshire Quaker
   meetings, 17th century–; Leeds Chamber of Commerce, 19th century–; Leeds
   Philosophical and Literary Society, 19th and 20th centuries; Association of
   Education Committees, 20th century.
   Woolley Hall estate papers, from middle ages.
   Roth MSS on Jewish history and culture, from middle ages.
   Papers and diaries of Herbert Thompson, music critic, 19th and 20th centuries.
   Correspondence of Jethro Bithell, mainly with mid-20th-century German writers.
   Papers of John Wilson of Broomhead, near Sheffield, antiquarian, 18th century.
   Russian papers, 20th century.
   Miscellaneous cookery and recipe books, 16th century–; medical treatises and
   papers, 18th century–.
   Diaries, letters and papers of various professors and other members of the
   University staff, 19th and 20th centuries.

Finding aids   Various handlists.

Facilities   Photocopying (limited in respect of MSS). Photography.

Publications   P. Hudson: *The West Riding Wool Textile Industry: a Catalogue of
   Business Records* (1975)
   C. Roth: 'Catalogue of Manuscripts in the Roth Collection', *Alexander Marx Jubilee
   Volume: English section* (1950), 503–535

281   Leeds Archives Department

Address   Chapeltown Road
               Sheepscar
               Leeds
               West Yorkshire LS7 3AP

Telephone   (0532) 628339

Enquiries to   Archivist, Mr J.M. Collinson

Open   Mon–Fri: 9.30–5.00 (limited service 12.00–2.00)
               Appointment always desirable and for some records essential

Historical background   MSS were acquired for the Reference Library from c1890,
   but the first archivist was appointed in 1938 (initially to care for private archives).
   The Archives Department is not incorporated with a printed Local History
   Collection. In the 1950s collecting from a wider area began; more recently
   business and parish records have been included. Following the 1974
   reorganization collection has been concentrated on the Metropolitan District area.
   Some local government records are available at the Civic Hall and where small
   collections of older local government records were placed in local libraries (e.g.
   Rothwell) they remain there, otherwise they are mostly centralized. The
   Department also acts as the Diocesan Record Office for Ripon and Bradford
   parishes.

Major collections   Local Government and related records.
   Family and estate archives, including Temple Newsom papers, 17th century–;
   Dartmouth Estate records 18th–19th centuries; Sir J.W. Ramsden's papers, late
   19th century; Lord Harewood (1767–1841) archives; papers of Samuel Smiles
   (1812–1904).
   Antiquarian collections; business records; solicitors and estate agents papers;
   ecclesiastical records.
   Records of societies include Arthington Trust; Yorkshire Ladies' Council of
   Education; Leeds Institute; Yorkshire Naturalists' Union; Conchological Society of
   Great Britain and Northern Ireland.

Facilities   Photocopying. Photography. Microfilm reader.

Publications   J.M. Collinson: 'The Leeds Archives Department', *Northern History*, xv
   (1979), 210
   Sources of Business and Industrial History [available from the Department]

282   Leeds Diocesan Archives

Address   Diocesan Curia
                13 North Grange Road
                Leeds
                West Yorkshire LS6 2BR

Telephone   (0532) 759232

Enquiries to   Diocesan Archivist, The Very Rev. Mgr G.T. Bradley

Open   Mon–Fri: 10.00–4.00, by appointment

Access   Bona fide students, by written application to the Archivist.

Historical background   The collection is part of the archives of the Vicars Apostolic
   of the Northern District (1688–1840); and the papers of the Vicar Apostolic of the

Yorkshire District (1840–50), the Bishops of Beverley (1850–78) and the Bishops of Leeds (1878–).

Acquisitions policy   The records of the Diocese of Leeds are all eventually passed to the Diocesan Archives, also any records of importance from parishes in the Diocese are deposited with the Diocesan Archives.

Major collections   Papers of the Roman Catholic Church in Yorkshire, 1688–; some papers for other parts of the North of England before 1840.
Hogarth MSS: 19th-century transcripts of the papers of the secular clergy in Yorkshire, 1660–.

Non-manuscript material   Printed Pastorals of Bishops.
Small collection of theological pamphlets for the period of the Archives.

Finding aids   Some lists and indexes (1821–61); other parts in process of being catalogued.

Facilities   Photocopying, by arrangement.

Publications   G.T. Bradley: 'Leeds Diocesan Archives – A Provisional Summary', *A Newsletter for Students of Recusant History*, no.4 (Nijmegen, 1962), 26

283   Leeds Polytechnic Library

Address   Leeds Polytechnic
Calverley Street
Leeds
West Yorkshire LS1 3HE

No archives are held.

284   Leeds University Archives

Address   Old Medical School
Thoresby Place
Leeds
West Yorkshire LS2 9JT

Telephone   (0532) 441199 ext.285/286

Enquiries to The University Archivist

Open   Mon and Wed, preferably by appointment

Access   Personal enquirers.

Historical background   The Yorkshire College of Science, precursor of the University of Leeds, was founded in 1874 and merged with the Leeds School of

Medicine (itself founded in 1831) in 1884 to become one of the constituent colleges of the Victoria University in 1887. The University of Leeds was created an independent institution in 1904. The University archives were established in 1977.

Acquisitions policy Administrative and teaching records and papers of the University of Leeds and such personal papers as may be appropriate.

Major collections Administrative records of the Leeds School of Medicine, Yorkshire College and the University of Leeds.
Some early departmental, teaching and student material and personal papers.

Non-manuscript material Photographs; building plans.

Finding aids Various lists and indexes in process of compilation.

Facilities Photocopying. Photography.

285   Leicestershire County Libraries and Information Service

Address First Floor
Thames Tower
2 Navigation Street
Leicester LE1 3T2

Archives are neither held nor collected.

286   Leicestershire Record Office

Address 57 New Walk
Leicester
Leicestershire LE1 7JB

Telephone (0533) 554100 ext. 238

Enquiries to County Archivist, Miss K. Thompson

Open Mon–Thurs: 9.15–5.00
Fri: 9.15–4.45
Sat: 9.15–12.15

Historical background Archives were collected by the City from 1849 and the City Museums Archives department was set up in 1930. The County Record Office was established in 1947. With reorganization in 1974 the Museum Archives department came under the County and was amalgamated with the County Record Office. The Office also acts as the Diocesan Record Office for Leicester (parish records), and Peterborough (Rutland parish records).

Major collections   Usual local authority record holdings and deposited collections, all of purely local interest.

Facilities   Photocopying. Photography. Microfilming. Microfilm reader.

Publications   *Brief Guide to the Muniment Room, City of Leicester Museum and Art Gallery* (1949)
   Handlist of the Records of the Leicester Archdeaconry (1954)
   A.M. Woodcock: *Records of the Corporation of Leicester* (1956)

287   University of Leicester Library

Address   University of Leicester
                University Road
                Leicester LE1 7RH

There are no significant holdings of archives.

288   Wigan Record Office

Address   Town Hall
                Leigh
                Greater Manchester WN7 2DY

Telephone   (0942) 672421 ext. 266

Enquiries to Archivist, Mr A.D. Gillies

Open   Mon–Fri: 10.00–4.00
                Appointment preferable

Access   Most records are generally open to the public, apart from a few more recent public records. Charges are not normally made.

Historical background   In 1968 Wigan Record Office began, in Wigan Library, to administer the records of Wigan Borough which were previously administered by the Library. In 1974 the Office moved to Leigh and extended its scope to cover the newly-created metropolitan borough of Wigan. It also acts as the Diocesan Record Office for Liverpool (parish records).

Acquisitions policy   All records relating to the locality, mainly by deposit or gift.

Major collections   Records of the ancient borough of Wigan, including charters, court leet, court of King's Pleas; Wigan Borough Quarter Sessions.
   Large family collections, including Anderton, Standish, Holt Leigh, Crawford, Scarisbrick.
   Edward Hall collection of diaries.
   Records of solicitors, businesses and societies.

Non-manuscript material   Large number of photographs of the locality.
   Printed records of predecessor local authorities.
   Miscellaneous pamphlets, broadsides etc.

Finding aids   Most collections have been listed and indexed.

Facilities   Photocopying. Photography. Microfilming. Microfilm reader.

Publications   *Guide to Wigan Record Office*
   Guide to Genealogical Sources in Wigan Record Office (1980)

289   Shetland Archives

Address   44 King Harald Street
                   Lerwick ZE1 0EQ

Telephone   (0595) 3535 ext. 286

Enquiries to   Archivist, Mr Brian Smith

Open   Mon–Fri: 9.00–4.00
                   Appointment preferable

Historical background   The Archives department was founded in 1976 and is now
   part of the Education Department.

Major collections   Usual local authority record holdings and deposited collections.
   Shetland Community History Project is collecting oral history reminiscences.

Facilities   Photocopying. Photography. Microfilm reader.

290   East Sussex Record Office

Address   The Maltings
                   Castle Precincts
                   Lewes
                   East Sussex BN7 1YT

Telephone   (07916) 5400

Enquiries to   County Records Officer, Mr C.R. Davey

Open   Mon–Thurs: 8.45–4.45
                   Fri: 8.45–4.15

Historical background   The office was established in 1949. It also acts as a Diocesan
   Record Office for Chichester (East Sussex parish records) and houses Sussex
   Archaeological Society records.

Major collections   Usual local authority record holdings and deposited collections

including the following which have a wider significance:
Sheffield Park archives concerning John Baker Holroyd, first Earl of Sheffield, politician and authority on commercial and agricultural topics, late 18th century.
Sussex Archaeological Society records, including papers of the Gage family (American material) and the Fuller family of Rosehill.

Facilities   Photocopying. Microfilming, by arrangement. Microfilm reader/printer.

Publications   *Descriptive Report on the Quarter Sessions, other Official, and Ecclesiastical Records in the Custody of the County Councils of West and East Sussex* (1954)
J.M. Coleman: *Sussex Poor Law Records: a Catalogue* (1960)
H.M. Warne: *Catalogue of the Frewen Archives*
F.W. Steer: *The Ashburnham Archives* [out of print]
R.F. Dell: *The Records of Rye Corporation: A Catalogue* [out of print]

291   Lichfield Joint Record Office

Address   Lichfield Library
Bird Street
Lichfield
Staffordshire WS13 6PN

Telephone   (054 32) 56787

Enquiries to   Archivist, Mrs J. Hampartumian
Genealogical enquiries:
Principal Librarian, Mr T.M. Rogers

Open   Mon, Tues, Thurs, Fri: 10.00–5.15
Wed: 10.00–4.45

Historical background   The office was established in 1959, when it was jointly administered by Lichfield City Council and Staffordshire County Council; it is now administered jointly with Staffordshire Record Office (*see* entry 648). It also acts as the Diocesan Record Office for Lichfield. Assistance is given to Burton on Trent Local History Library (*see* entry 79).

Major collections   Usual local authority record holdings and deposited collections

Facilities   Photocopying. Photography and microfilming by arrangement. Microfilm/fiche reader.

Publications   *Staffordshire Record Office Cumulative Hand List, Part 1: Lichfield Joint Record Office, Diocesan, Probate and Church Commissioners Records* (2/1978)

292   Lincolnshire Archives Office

Address   The Castle
                 Lincoln
                 Lincolnshire LN1 3AB

Telephone   (0522) 25158

Enquiries to   County Archivist, Mr C.M. Lloyd

Open   Mon–Fri: 9.30–4.45

Historical background   A Diocesan Record Office was established 1936 and Lincolnshire Archives Office was formally established in 1948. It also acts as the Diocesan Record Office for Lincoln and gives administrative assistance to Lincoln Cathedral Library and Lincoln Record Society.

Major collections   Usual local authority record holdings and deposited collections.

Facilities   Photocopying. Photography. Microfilming. Microfilm reader.

Publications   K. Major: *Handlist of the Records of the Bishop of Lincoln and of the Archdeacons of Lincoln and Stow* (1953)
D.M. Williamson: *Muniments of the Dean and Chapter of Lincoln* (1956)
Archivist's Reports (1948–77; with *Indexes*, 1948–68) [available from the Office]

293   Lincolnshire County Library

Address   Lincoln Central Library
                 Free School Lane
                 Lincoln
                 Lincolnshire LN2 1EL

Telephone   (0522) 33541

Enquiries to   The Senior Librarian, County Reference Service
                 or
                 The Local Studies Librarian

Open   Joseph Banks Collection: Mon–Fri: 9.00–7.00
                 Sat: 9.00–12.30
                 Tennyson Research Centre: Mon–Fri: 9.30–1.00; 2.30–5.00
                 By prior arrangement

Access   On application during normal library hours. A letter of authority is usually required for the Tennyson Research Centre.

Historical background   The Banks Collection was acquired by bequest and purchase. The Tennyson Research Centre was founded in 1964 following the deposit by the Tennyson Trustees.

Acquisitions policy   Any material relating to Sir Joseph Banks (1743–1820), or Alfred, Lord Tennyson (1809–92).

Major collections   Joseph Banks Collection: MS material covering a range of subjects relating to Lincolnshire, the militia etc, including many letters to and from Banks (21 boxes, *c*700 items).
Tennyson Centre: correspondence between Tennyson and members of his family, and letters from Browning, Gladstone, Lear, Sullivan, Fitzgerald etc (*c*8000 items); most complete MS of *In Memoriam*, plus MSS of Tennyson's plays, single poems, extracts from poems etc; various MS extracts (*c*50 items); miscellaneous material including day-books, diaries, journals, household account books etc.

Non-manuscript material   Joseph Banks Collection: topographical drawings of Lincolnshire by C. Nattes and others in the late 18th century, commissioned by Banks (4 folio vols, *c*770 sketches); biographies of Banks together with copies of his works.
Tennyson Centre: proofs and trial-books of Tennyson's poems (*c*220 items); illustrations, including *c*100 photographs by Julia Margaret Cameron; sound recordings and tapes of Tennyson's works; music based on Tennyson's poetry; biographical and critical material, mainly monographs and pamphlets (*c*1200 items); Tennyson family library and collection of his works.

Finding aids   Archive List giving brief details of the contents of each box.

Facilities   Photocopying. Photography. Microfilm/fiche reader/printer.

Publications   The letters in the Banks Collection are included in W.R. Dawson (ed.): *The Banks Letters* (1958)

294   Charity Commission for England and Wales

Address   Graeme House
Derby Square
Liverpool
Merseyside L2 7SB

Telephone   (051) 227 3191 ext.461 (Central Register of Charities), ext.439 (access to records)

Enquiries to   The Office Services Section

Open   Mon–Fri: 10.00–4.00, by appointment

Access   Central Register of Charities is open to the public; charity records over 30 years old are open to inspection on application.

Historical background   The Liverpool office covers Welsh charities and those in England north of the River Severn to the Wash. (*See* Charity Commission for England and Wales, London (entry **323**) for further details.)

295   Knowsley Library Information Services
Local Studies and Archives Collection

Address   Knowsley Central Library
                   Derby Road
                   Huyton
                   Liverpool
                   Merseyside L36 9UJ

Telephone   (051) 480 6126 ext.28

Enquiries to   Principal Librarian, Mr T.W. Scragg
                   or
                   Reference Librarian, Mr M.J. Sargant
                   or
                   Local Studies Librarian, Mrs G. Roberts-Tolen

Open   Mon—Wed, Fri: 10.00—7.00
                   Thurs: 10.00—1.00
                   Sat: 10.00—5.00

Access   Bona fide researchers.

Historical background   Knowsley Library Service came into being in April 1974 following local government reorganization. The area covers Cronton, Huyton, Kirkby, Knowsley, Prescot, Roby, Simonswood, Tarbock and Whiston. The Local Studies and Archives Collection was assembled during the first years of the library service, before the new Central Library was opened in Huyton in 1978.

Acquisitions policy   To strengthen existing collections regarding the history of areas presently incorporated in the Metropolitan Borough of Knowsley, by purchase, donation or deposit.

Major collections   Council minutes for Huyton-with-Roby, Kirkby and Prescot UDCs; Council minutes and Clerks' working papers for Whiston RDC, *c*1890–1974.
Molyneux-Seel papers relating to land in Huyton, 18th and 20th centuries.
Prescot Grammar School archives, 15th—19th centuries.
National Union of Mineworkers (Cronton Branch) minute books, 1952–71.
Huyton Cricket Club records, 1860–*c*1970.

Non-manuscript material   Earl of Derby's newscutting files (microfilm).
Knowsley Photographic Collection (*c*2500 photographs).
Election pamphlets, minutes and annual reports of Huyton Labour Party and Huyton Ratepayers' Association.
Parish registers (and Bishop's transcripts), tithe awards, census returns, directories relating to south-west Lancashire (microfilm or photocopy).
Sound archives of individuals connected with the Borough (*c*20 tapes).
Natural history reports, *c*1968–.
Newspaper cuttings, *c*1930–.

Finding aids   Photographic collection in process of being catalogued. Indexes to Local Studies collection.

Archival material in process of being catalogued. Census returns indexed by street and in part by name.

Facilities   Photocopying. Photography by arrangement. Microfilm/fiche readers/ printer.

Publications   W.L. French (ed.): *Registers of Kirkby St Chad's Chapelry,* i: *Baptisms 1610–1839* (1977); ii: *Marriages and Burials 1610–1839* (1979)
J. Knowles (ed.): *Prescot Records – The Court Rolls 1602–1648* (1980–81)
————: *Inns of Prescot and Whiston* (1981)

296   Liverpool City Libraries
Record Office and Local History Department

Address	William Brown Street Liverpool Merseyside L3 8EW
Telephone	(051) 207 2147 ext. 34
Enquiries to	Archivist, Miss J. Smith
Open	Mon–Fri: 9.00–9.00 Sat: 9.00–5.00 Prior appointment advisable
Access	Generally open to the public. Usually, 30-year closure on material. Some collections need permission of depositor.

Historical background   Local history material has been acquired continuously since 1852. The archive covers Liverpool, Merseyside and the surrounding county areas. The Office also acts as the Diocesan Record Office for Liverpool (parish records).

Acquisitions policy   Active policy pursued.

Major collections   Corporation archives including city charters, 1207–; minutes, 1550–.
Parish, ecclestical, non-conformist and Jewish records.
Family papers and deeds: Moore papers, 13th–18th centuries (especially relating to Civil War); Norris papers, 15th–18th centuries (especially re sailings to New World); manorial and estate records of Marquess of Salisbury, 15th–20th centuries. Papers of prominent Merseyside figures, including William Roscoe, poet and philanthropist, who corresponded with many eminent figures, early 19th century. Literary MSS; records of charities, societies, unions, etc.

Non-manuscript material   Census returns; slides; photographs (including Chambre Hardman Collection of over 14,000 negatives); newscuttings; tape recordings. Houses Library of the Historic Society of Lancashire and Cheshire.

Finding aids Catalogues for majority of collections. Index to unlisted accessions. General information sheets.

Facilities Photocopying. Microfilming. Microfilm reader.

297 Liverpool School of Tropical Medicine

Address Pembroke Place
Liverpool
Merseyside L3 5QA

The Archives are administered by the University Archives, University of Liverpool (*see* entry **300**).

298 Merseyside County Archives Service

Address Merseyside County Museums
RCA Building
64–6 Islington
Liverpool
Merseyside L3 8LG

Telephone (051) 207 3697/3698

Enquiries to County Archivist, Mr J.G. Read

Open Mon–Fri: 9.30–4.30
Appointment desirable

Access Bona fide researchers. Many collections require at least a week's notice. Modern business and charity records may include confidential material.

Historical background An Archivist was apppointed after the County of Merseyside came into existence in 1974, and the Museum archives collections (which had themselves developed from Liverpool City functions) were incorporated; they included valuable maritime archives, particularly in connection with the projected Maritime Museum.

Acquisitions policy To extend the holdings of the following categories of archives:
Archives of the County Council, its departments and associated organizations.
Maritime and business archives.
Archives of Merseyside relevance generally, especially charity and social agency archives.
Archives associated with Museum specialisms, especially natural history and the King's Regimental Museum.
Public records of local interest, principally Sefton Area Health Authority records and those of the Register of Shipping.

Major collections   Maritime archives: the largest being those of Mersey Docks and Harbour Company and its antecedents.

Business records: including extensive ship records and correspondence about American Civil War, trade abroad, slave trade, insurance, and H.A. Noel Woodall, architect, 1864–1970.

Charities: including records of the Society for Relief of Sick and Distressed Needlewomen, 1858–1927.

Military: records of King's (Liverpool) Regiment.

Natural History records: including thirteenth Earl of Derby's correspondence, 1799–1850.

Family papers: including those of Charles Blandell of Ince Blandell (with correspondence of Sir John Gladstone of Seaforth, 1833–7), and Danson family of Barnston and Birkenhead in Wirral, 19th and 20th centuries.

(No records of Metropolitan districts or Anglican or Roman Catholic diocesan records are held at present.)

Non-manuscript material   Stewart Bale photographic archive: glass negatives covering all aspects of business activity in the North West and elsewhere, c1910–1975.

Maritime history photographic and sound archives.

Horological material allied to horological collections, including the watch-tool maker's catalogue of John Wyke of Liverpool and Prescot, c1765.

Finding aids   Some 100 lists and indexes.

Facilities   Photocopying. Photography. Microfilm/fiche reader. Xerox banks, particularly on *Emigration and Children*.

Publications   *Merseyside County Archives – A Summary Guide* [updated yearly] Reproduction of posters and documents. Regular newsletters.

The Dockland Survey Team are producing definitive histories of the various dock systems based on the Dock Company Archives.

299   Sydney Jones Library

Address   University of Liverpool
PO Box 123
Liverpool
Merseyside L69 3DA

Telephone   (051) 709 6022

Enquiries to   Curator of Special Collections, Mr M.R. Perkin

Open   Mon–Fri: 9.00–5.00
Evenings and Sat mornings by arrangement

Access   Approved readers on written application. Restrictions on certain deposited archives.

Historical background   Collections were deposited in the Library, or given to it. The first important collection was that of Thomas Rylands (acquired in 1900), which reflects a wide range of interests, in particular the history of Lancashire and Cheshire.

Acquisitions policy   To strengthen existing holdings, especially in the following areas: Latin America, Spanish Africa, Liverpool shipping, trade and slave trade records, Cheshire, MS facsimiles (especially illuminated), selected contemporary British poets.

Major collections   MSS include: Oxyrhynchus papyri; collection of 56 medieval and Renaissance MSS; some Oriental MSS, mostly of late date and of no textual or artistic importance.

Mayer MSS, 126 items, of which over half are Oriental, the rest mainly medieval Western with a small group of Irish 18th-century items (on loan from Merseyside County Museums).

Modern papers, autograph letters and deeds, including those of José Blanco White (1775–1841); Sir John Tomlinson Brunner (1842–1919); Josephine Butler (1828–1906); John Bruce Glasier (1859–1920) and Katherine Glasier (1867–1950); Rathbone family of Greenbank, Liverpool, 18th–20th centuries; Sir Oliver Lodge (1851–1940); D.H. Lawrence (1885–1930); Cecil Day Lewis (1904–72). Merseyside Poets collection.

Records of Gypsy Lore Society, c1896–1974, and other gypsy and romany material in Scott Macfie collection; Liverpool Psychological Society, 1923–30; Liverpool Literary and Philosophical Society, 1812–27; Liverpool Royal Institution (incomplete), 1813–1942.

A few items relating to the history of the University.

The School of Education Library includes MS examples of school work.

Non-manuscript material   Maps; pamphlets and early printed books.

c5400 theses (Arts and Social Sciences), 1905–.

Microforms and slides; seals; prints and drawings; newscuttings; photographs; records and tapes.

Finding aids   Lists and indexes, including author index to MS collections. Detailed subject handlist. Detailed catalogues for most of larger collections. Guide to Special Collections (July 1978).

Facilities   Photocopying. Microfilm/fiche readers.

Publications   J. Sampson (comp.): *A Catalogue of the Books, Printed and in Manuscript, bequeathed by the late Thomas Glazebrook Rylands. . . to the Library . . .* (Liverpool, 1900)

Guide to the Manuscript Collections in Liverpool University Library (Liverpool, 1962)

300   University of Liverpool
University Archives

Address	PO Box 147 Liverpool Merseyside L69 3BX
Telephone	(051) 709 6022 ext. 2315
Enquiries to	The University Archivist
Open	Mon–Fri: 9.30–5.00, by prior appointment only
Access	Approved readers on written application. Restrictions on certain deposited archives.

Historical background The University of Liverpool was founded (as University College) in 1881, but its Medical School goes back to 1834 and there are certain other earlier constituent bodies. The University Archives were set up in 1968. The Liverpool School of Tropical Medicine is an associated archive. (*See also* Sydney Jones Library, entry **299**.)

Acquisitions policy To strengthen existing research resources, particularly in the fields of children and charitable bodies, complementary to the Barnardo archive; and town planning, complementary to the Holford, Reilly, Forshaw and Abercrombie archives. The Archives have a tradition of external surveys, especially in the field of medical archives, but does not seek to acquire original material where there are more natural repositories.

Major collections Archives of the University, its constituents and affiliated bodies.
Papers of certain members or former members of staff: principally those of Sir Cyril Burt (psychology); Lord Holford (town planning); Sir Charles Reilly (architecture).
Deposited archives: Cunard Steamship Company, 1878–c1950; Dr Barnardo's, 1867–c1970; Royal Society for the Prevention of Accidents, 1917–70.

Non-manuscript material Publications and prints emanating from the University, including student journals and publications of certain societies and clubs.
Recorded interviews with certain individuals.

Finding aids Holdings are fully listed in typescript. Printed catalogue of the Cunard archives in course of publication. A catalogue of the Holford archives is near completion. A general Guide is planned.

Facilities Photocopying and photography (central University facilities). Microfilm by arrangement.

Publications Annual reports in the annual *Reports to Court* of the University of Liverpool.
M. Cook: 'The Cunard Archives at Liverpool', *Business History*, xx (1978), 240
Reports on the Liverpool School of Tropical Medicine archives sent to National

Register of Archives (1976, 1978)
T. Kelly: *For Advancement of Learning: the University of Liverpool 1881–1981*
(Liverpool, 1981)
A.R. Allan and J.A. Carpenter (comp.): *Redbrick University: a Portrait of University
College Liverpool and the University of Liverpool 1881–1981* (Liverpool, 1981)

301 Powys County Council Libraries and Museums Department

Address Cefnllys Road
Llandrindod Wells
Powys LD1 5LD

Telephone (0597) 2212

Enquiries to Deputy County Librarian, Miss E.A. Ducker

Archives, including quarter sessions records for the historic counties now forming
Powys, passed to the National Library of Wales, Aberystwyth (*see* entry **10**). However,
in the Central Library of the Powys Library Service there is a muniment room
containing MS material relating to local history.

302 Llanelli Public Library

Address Vaughan Street
Llanelli
Dyfed SA15 3AS

Telephone (05542) 3538

Enquiries to The Borough Librarian

Open Mon–Fri: 9.30–7.00
Sat: 9.30–6.00

Access Generally open to the public.

Historical background The Public Library was established in 1892; it incorporated
the Mechanics' Institute which was established in 1847.

Acquisitions policy The Library is a general library which also has collections on all
aspects of local matters, with special emphasis on the coal industry, tinplate
making, ships and shipbuilding and local government. Material in any form in these
specialized areas is collected.

Major collections Llanelli Harbour Trust records.
Local Government records for Llanelli area.

Non-manuscript material   Coal-mining plans for Carmarthenshire.
*c*15,000 photographic prints, *c*2000 transparencies, and 16 mm cine-films, all devoted to local subjects (e.g. industry, town development, special events).
Tape interviews of local people.

Finding aids   Indexes, including local newspapers, 1863–.

Facilities   Photocopying. Microfilm/fiche readers. Cine-film and slide projectors.

Publications   Llanelli Public Library Local History Research Group Series [details on application]

303   Gwynedd Archives Service
Llangefni Area Record Office

Address   Shire Hall
                  Llangefni
                  Gwynedd LL77 7TW

Telephone   (0248) 723262

Enquiries to   Area Archivist, Miss Gwenith Parry

Open   Mon–Fri: 9.00–5.00
                  Other times by arrangement

Historical background   The Office was set up in 1974 following local government reorganization; prior to this Anglesey County Library did some collecting.

Major collections   Usual local authority record holdings and deposited collections.

Facilities   Photocopying. Photography.

304   Argyll and Bute District Council

Address   Kilmory
                  Lochgilphead
                  Argyll
                  Strathclyde PA31 8RT

Telephone   (0546) 2127

Enquiries to   Archivist, Mr Murdo MacDonald

Open   Mon–Fri: 9.00–5.15

Access   Generally open to the public

Historical background   The archives department was established in 1975 following the setting up of the District Council under local government reorganization. The

District Archives also acts on a local agency basis for Strathclyde Regional Archives.

Acquisitions policy   To encourage the deposit and donation of records relating to the District Council in general.

Major collections   Mainly local authority record holdings of local interest.

Finding aids   Lists.

Facilities   Photocopying.

305   Anglo-Jewish Archive

Address   University College London
                Gower Street
                London WC1E 6BT

Telephone   (01) 387 7050 ext. 778

Enquiries to Archivist, Mr J. Monck

A branch of the Jewish Historical Society, archives have been collected since *c*1968; before this time deposits had been made in the Mocatta Library (*see* entry **417**), housed next to the present Archive. (Access and facilities are as for the Mocatta Library.) The Archive consists of extensive material relating to Anglo–Jewish notables and institutions, mainly from the 19th century, and includes the records of the Anglo-Jewish Association and the papers of Cecil Roth, historian.

306   Archives of the English Province of the Society of Jesus

Address   114 Mount Street
                London W1Y 6AH

Telephone   (01) 493 7811

Enquiries to Rev. Francis Edwards, SJ
                or
                Rev. T.G. Holt, SJ

Open   Mon–Fri: 10.00–1.00, by appointment only
                (Arrangements may be made for longer daily periods where researchers come from a distance.)

Access   Bona fide students on written application.

Historical background   The Province archives supplement and continue the collection of MSS held at Stonyhurst which virtually began with the Jesuit mission to England, Scotland and Wales from 1580. Original papers at Farm Street begin c1623 and cover England and Wales, and Scotland from c1857.

Acquisitions policy   All kinds of archival material concerning the history of the Society of Jesus, especially in England, Scotland and Wales, is received. The main accessions come from Jesuit houses, especially those which close, and from the papers of deceased Jesuits.

Major collections   Official and private correspondence, registers and accounts of missions, c1623–.
Correspondence of John Morris, SJ (1826–93); John Hungerford Pollen, SJ (1820–1902); Joseph Stevenson, SJ (1806–95); Herbert Thurston, SJ (1856–1939).
Photocopies of significant early papers at Stonyhurst and relevant material in the General Archive in Rome.

Non-manuscript material   Circular letters from the general, English provincial and papal curia.
c500 printed books of politico-religious interest, 1525–.

Finding aids   Card index (not in general available, but cards of subjects of interest to researchers are shown them by an archivist or assistant).

Facilities   Limited photocopying and photography.

Publications   F. Edwards: 'The Archives of the English Province of the Society of Jesus', *Journal of the Society of Archivists*, iii (1966), 107

307   Bank of England

Address   Threadneedle Street
                   London EC2R 8AH

Telephone   (01) 601 4387

Enquiries to   The Museum and Historical Research Section

Open   By appointment only

Access   Permission to inspect records over 30 years old may be given for
                   specific and approved research; records relating to customers may
                   need to be withheld. Searchers are required to submit to the Bank
                   any text they propose to publish.

Historical background   The Bank of England was incorporated by Act of Parliament and Charter in 1694 and in return its proprietors subscribed funds to help finance the war being fought by William III against Louis XIV of France. The subscribers were granted a Royal Charter on 27 July 1694, under the title 'The Governor and Company of the Bank of England'. Of the original Charter, the only clauses now remaining unrevoked are those relating to the incorporation of the Bank, the Common Seal, legal suit and the holding of property. The Bank of England Act of

1946 brought the Bank into public ownership, but provided for the continued existence of 'The Governor and Company of the Bank of England' under Royal Charter.

Acquisitions policy   No external acquisitions.

Major collections   Records covering the principal activities of the Bank:
Advice to Government; market operations; management of Government, Bank and private accounts; management of Government and other stock issues; economic intelligence; relations with financial institutions abroad; industrial liaison; banknote printing; supervision of UK financial institutions; exchange control.

Finding aids   Not all the appropriate records have yet been transferred from their departments to the archive; descriptive lists can be seen of those that have. In other cases, it may be necessary for searchers to make fairly precise enquiries, which will be examined in the departments concerned.

308   Baptist Missionary Society

Address   93–7 Gloucester Place
London W1H 4AA

Telephone   (01) 935 1482

Enquiries to   Rev. Alan Easter (information and publicity)

Open   Mon–Fri: 9.00–4.45, by prior arrangement

Access   Bona fide students; reference required.

Historical background   The Society is the oldest Protestant missionary society; its foundation in 1792 was largely inspired by William Carey. The archives of the Society cover its work from that time, although some were destroyed in 1940 by bombing.

Acquisitions policy   No active policy of collecting.

Major collections   Committee minutes; candidates' papers; correspondence; Baptist Women's Missionary Association records; material relating to Cameroons, Congo, Angola, Sierra Leone, Canada, West Indies, Ceylon (Sri Lanka), China, India, Europe.
Other records include those of the Bible Translation Society (later a sub-committee of the Society).

Non-manuscript material   Very old books associated with mission work.

Finding aids   Most of the material is catalogued.

Publications   List of the archives, in R. Keen: *A Survey of the Archives of Selected Missionary Societies*, National Register of Archives Report (1968) [13pp, duplicated]

309 Baptist Union Library

Address	4 Southampton Row London WC1B 4AB
Telephone	(01) 405 9803
Enquiries to	The Librarian
Open	Mon–Fri: 9.30–4.30, by appointment only
Access	Approved readers on written application. Research students should produce a supervisor's letter of introduction.

Historical background The Library opened in the present building *c*1903; it includes the library of the Baptist Historical Society, with which it amalgamated.

Acquisitions policy Unpublished material and records of churches that are closing are accepted if offered.

Major collections Very limited collection of minute books of closed Baptist churches, 17th century–.

Non-manuscript material Baptist and local church histories.

Finding aids Catalogue and index.

Facilities Photocopying. Microfiche reader.

310 Bedford College

Address	University of London Regent's Park London NW1 4NS

There are no deposited collections. Internal records are held but not yet catalogued.

311 Birbeck College

Address	University of London Malet Street London WC1E 7HX
Telephone	(01) 580 6622

The papers of J.D. Bernal (1901–71), as well as other material including the archives of Birkbeck College and its predecessor the London Mechanics' Institution, amounting to over 10,000 items, have been deposited in Cambridge University Library (*see* entry **87**). A typescript of B. Swann's *Catalogue of the Papers of Professor J.D. Bernal* is available from the Librarian and from Cambridge University Library.

312   British and Foreign Bible Society

Address	146 Queen Victoria Street London EC4V 4BX
Telephone	(01) 248 4751
Enquiries to	Archivist, Miss Kathleen Cann
Open	Mon–Fri: 9.30–5.00, preferably by appointment.
Access	Generally open to the public. 50-year closure period.

Historical background   The British and Foreign Bible Society was formed in 1804 'to encourage a wider circulation of the Holy Scriptures'. It was a non-denominational, voluntary society, financed by the donations of its supporters, and involved in the translation, publication and distribution of the Bible throughout the world. It therefore had contacts with Churches, missionaries, linguists, printers, and many individuals who took an interest in the distribution of the Bible. It was incorporated by Royal Charter in 1948.

Acquisitions policy   To accept only material directly related to the work and staff of the Society.

Major collections   Archives of the Society; these have suffered severe losses, notably the original incoming correspondence, 1857–1900.

Non-manuscript material   Published Annual reports and magazines of the Society; pamphlet material on controversies in the Society's history; publicity leaflets etc.
The archives are a part of the Society's library services, which consist of a Bible library of *c*28,000 vols in more than 1800 languages, 1466–; collection of MSS of Bible versions in various languages (*c*700 items); information service.

Finding aids   Various lists and indexes.

Facilities   Photocopying.

Publications   T.H. Darlow and H.F. Moule (eds.): *Historical Catalogue of the printed editions of Holy Scripture* (1903–11); section revisions: English (1968), Africa (1966; supplement, 1975), China (1975), India (1977)
Historical Catalogue of MSS in Bible House Library (1982)

313   British Architectural Library

Address   Royal Institute of British Architects (RIBA)
                 66 Portland Place
                 London W1N 4AD
                 and
                 British Architectural Library Drawings Collection
                 21 Portman Square
                 London W1H 9HF

Telephone   (01) 580 5533

Enquiries to   Director of Library Services, Mr David Dean

Open   Mon: 10.00–5.00
                 Tues–Thurs: 10.00–8.00
                 Fri: 10.00–7.00
                 Sat: 10.00–1.30
                 Closed: August
                 (Drawings Collection and Photograph Collection by appointment
                 only)

Access   Generally open to the public.

Historical background   The RIBA was founded in 1834 for the general advancement
   of civil architecture and for promoting and facilitating knowledge of the various
   related arts and sciences. From the beginning, the British Architectural Library
   (BAL) has formed an important part of the Institute's activities and has always
   included special collections of drawings, MSS, photographs, pamphlets, and early
   printed works, in addition to its Reference and Loan libraries. There is a long
   tradition of members and well-wishers presenting material to the Library. The
   Library is funded by members of the RIBA and by a Trust Fund of donated money.

Acquisitions policy   To strengthen existing collections relating to the work of
   architecture, and in particular British architecture, by encouraging donations or
   deposits, and by purchase.

Major collections   BAL MSS Collection (occupying c100 metres of shelving): largest
   collection in Britain of the papers of architects, architectural organizations, and
   related groups (included MSS, typescripts and printed ephemera), 17th century–,
   but mainly British 19th- and 20th-century material.
   RIBA Archives (occupying c300 metres of shelving): administrative records of the
   Institute, documenting the affairs of the RIBA and the preoccupations of the
   architectural profession, and containing biographical information on its members,
   1834–; includes the archives of the Society of Architects (1884–1926) and the
   Architectural Union Company (1857–1916).

Non-manuscript material   BAL Drawings Collection (c250,000 drawings): largest
   collection in Britain of architectural drawings, mainly British, but including

important groups of foreign drawings, 16th century– (particularly rich in 19th-century material).

BAL Photographs Collection (*c*50,000 prints): several collections covering British and foreign architecture and topography of all periods; collection of photographic portraits of architects; particularly strong in work of the 1920s–.

Finding aids   Various lists and card indexes for use in the Library. The MSS Collection, the Photographs Collection and the RIBA Archives are in the process of being fully catalogued, and catalogues are being prepared for publication.

Facilities   Photocopies or photographs can sometimes be provided. Microfilm/fiche readers.

Publications   *Catalogues of the Drawings Collection of the Royal Institute of British Architects* (Amersham, 1969–) [8 alphabetical vols; 11 special vols (on Colen Campbell, Gentilhatre, Inigo Jones and John Webb, Lutyens, J.B. Papworth, the Pugin family, the Scott family, Alfred Stevens, Visentini, Voysey, the Wyatt family)]

314   British Film Institute (BFI)

Address	127 Charing Cross Road London WC2H 0EA
Telephone	(01) 437 4355
Enquiries to	Head of Library Services, Ms G. Hartnoll *or* Head of Stills, Posters and Designs, Ms M. Snapes

Open	Library Services:
	  Telephone enquiries
	  Mon–Fri: 9.30–6.00
	  Visitors
	  Tues, Wed: 11.00–9.00
	  Thurs, Fri: 11.00– ?.00
	
	Stills, Posters and Designs:
	  By appointment only
	  Tues–Fri: 11.00–5.30

Access	Generally open to the public, but regular users are expected to become members.

Historical background   The BFI was founded in 1933 'to encourage the development of the art of the film, to promote its use as a record of contemporary life and manners, and to foster public appreciation and study of it'. In 1961 the BFI's Memorandum of association was amended to include television. The Institute is financed primarily by an annual grant from the Department of Education and Science. The policy is controlled by a Board of Governors, appointed by the

Minister for the Arts. The National Film Archive (*see* entry **423**) is a division of the BFI.

Acquisitions policy   All types of material relating to film and television are acquired by purchase, donation and exchange.

Non-manuscript material   Library Services: 5,000 scripts, 40,000 newspaper clippings and 25,000 press books on microjackets.
Stills, Posters and Designs: more than 2 million black and white still photographs; 180,000 colour transparencies; 7,500 film posters; 800 original set and costume designs and animation cels.

Finding aids   Catalogues and indexes.

Facilities   Photocopying. Photography. Microfilm/fiche readers.

Publications   *British National Film Catalogue* [quarterly, with annual cumulations]
  British Film Industry (1981)
  Films on Artists (1982)
  Catalogue of Stills, Posters and Designs in the NFA (in preparation)
  Some special subject bibliographies [available free of charge]
  Full list of publications available.

315 British Institute of Recorded Sound and National Sound Archive of the United Kingdom

Address   29 Exhibition Road
  London SW7

Telephone   (01) 589 6603/4

Enquiries to   Information Officer, Mr E.A. Hughes
  or
  Playback Operator, Miss E. Wells

Open   Mon, Tues, Wed, Fri: 10.00–5.30
  Thurs: 10.00–9.00

Access   Generally open the the public, but it is advisable to make an appointment. Public playback service: most recordings in the National Sound Archive may be heard on the premises. Library: available for reference.

Historical background   The embryo Institute obtained its own premises in 1955 and is usually regarded as having started in that year. It first received government funding in 1961.

Acquisition policy   To add to the Archive holdings, in the following categories:

(*a*) Off-air recordings of radio broadcasts, live theatre recordings, poetry readings etc, made by the Institute.

(*b*) Private recordings made on behalf of the Institute or in the course of research.

(*c*) BBC recordings made for broadcasting.

(*d*) Commercially issued recordings.

The main emphasis is on British material, except in the case of IMC and BLOWS (*see* 'Major Collections' below).

The Reference Library concentrates on discographies, catalogues and release sheets issued by record companies and distributors, and books and periodicals concerned with records and recording.

Major collections   International Music Collection (IMC): commercially issued and privately made recordings of music outside the western concert tradition (administered separately within the Archive).

British Library or Wildlife Sounds (BLOWS): recordings (the majority privately made) of some of all kinds of animals, birds and fishes.

Other important collections (on tape unless otherwise specified) include: British in India oral archive (*c*150 hours);

Methodist Church sound archive (in progress);

Topic Records Ltd pre-production original recordings etc (*c*340 hours);

Poetry Society readings, etc (in progress);

British Jazz: live performances by numerous bands for broadcasting to France (acetate discs), late 1940s and early 1950s (*c*20 hours);

Interviews with Suffolk and Norfolk village residents by George Ewart Evans.

BBC Archive (discs; these are the only copies available to the public).

Other material   Small collection of archives of J.E. Hough and the Edison Bell Company.

Early recording documentation from EMI and their associated companies throughout the world (on microfilm).

The Bake, Grainger, Koch and British in India collections are among others accompanied by important written documentation.

Finding aids   Card catalogues for the main tape series and for Library holdings. Specialist catalogues for parts of the Archive, including IMC and BLOWS. Comprehensive computerised indexing system (in preparation).

Facilities   Photocopying. Microfilm reader/printer. Microfiche reader. Limited copying of recordings (subject to necessary clearances).

Publications   *Recorded Sound* [Journal of the Institute]; issues include numerous discographies and bibliographies relating to holdings.

A list is obtainable from the Institute.

316   British Library
Department of Manuscripts

Address   Great Russell Street
                London WC1B 3DG

Telephone	(01) 636 1544 ext. 579 (Students Room)
Enquiries to	The Keeper of Manuscripts (postal enquiries)
Open	Mon–Sat: 10.00–4.45
	Closed: last week in October; New Year's Day; Good Friday; first Monday in May; Dec 24–6
Access	By pass on application; applicants must be aged 21 or over.

Historical background The foundation collections (Sloane, Cotton, Harley) date back to the establishment of the British Museum in 1753. Material has been added constantly. The Archive passed to the British Library upon its formation in 1973.

Acquisitions policy Active policy of acquisitions by purchase and gift in the field of historical papers and in many others, literary, artistic, musical etc, of national interest.

Non-manuscript material Large collection of seals.
Some photographs and other miscellanea.
Good collection of facsimiles and microfilms of MSS not in the British Library.
MS maps (usually early, others in Map Department).
Lord Chamberlain's plays.

Finding aids Rough registers of acquisitions, 1955– (quinquennial vols; 1753–1955 published). Amalgamated index on cards (not subjects).

Facilities Photography. Microfilm readers. Video-spectral comparator. 'Visualtek' miniviewer.

Publications Many published catalogues, *see* M.A.E. Nickson: *The British Library: Guide to the Catalogues and Indexes of the Department of Manuscripts*
Rough Registers of Acquisitions, List and Index Society [quinquennial vols; last vol. published covers 1976–80]

317 British Library
Department of Oriental Manuscripts and Printed Books

Address	14 Store Street
	London WC1E 7DG
Telephone	(01) 636 1544 ext. 259 (Oriental Reading Room)
	ext. 342 (Administration)
Enquiries to	Director and Keeper Dr G.E. Marrison
Open	Mon–Fri: 10.00–5.00
	Sat: 10.00–1.00

Access All those with a serious interest in Asian studies. Readers' passes issued on a long-term or short-term basis, long-term passes require completion of an application form.

Historical background The foundation collections of MSS and printed books of the British Museum (1753) contained some material in the languages of Asia. A rapid increase in the quantity of this material during the 19th century led to the creation of an Oriental sub-department in the Department of Manuscripts in 1867. This was enlarged by taking over the collections of printed books in Asian languages from the Department of Printed Books to form a new Department of Oriental Printed Books and Manuscripts in 1892. On the inauguration of the British Library in 1973, incorporating the former library departments of the British Museum, it was renamed the Department of Oriental Manuscripts and Printed Books.

Acquisitions policy All significant material in the fields of the humanities and social sciences in the languages of Asia and of North-east Africa.

Major collections More than 45,000 oriental MSS: the largest collections are in Hebrew, Arabic, Persian, Turkish, Chinese, and the languages of South and South-East Asia; especially rich in illuminated and illustrated Islamic MSS, and Hebrew and Arabic religious and literary texts.
Stein Collection of Chinese fragments (c20,000 items).

Non-manuscript material Early blockprinted books from the Far East.
Over 500,000 printed books, serials and newspapers, representing all the literary languages and cultures of Asia and of North and North-east Africa.
Growing collections of microforms.
Large intake of official publications from Asian countries.

Finding aids Current catalogues in card form and in a computer-generated file supplement the printed catalogues.

Facilities Photocopying. Photography. Microfilm/fiche readers. Information is given to enquiries in person, by telephone and by post.

Publications *Guide to the Department of Oriental Manuscripts and Printed Books* (1977) [published catalogues (covering more than 100 languages) are listed and described]
Educational and popular booklets on various aspects of the collections.

318 British Library
Library Association Library

Address 7 Ridgmount Street
London WC1E 7AE

Telephone (01) 636 1544 ext. 202

Enquiries to   Deputy Librarian, Miss A.G. Polden

Open   Mon, Wed, Fri: 9.00–6.00
Tues, Thurs: 9.00–8.00 (mid-July–mid-Sept: 9.00–6.00)

Access   Library Association members. Others should give advance notice,
by letter or telephone, specifying what material they wish to use.

Historical background   The Library was founded by the Library Association *c*1900
and maintained as a service to the Association's members until 1974. In that year it
was transferred to the British Library, which wholly finances it as a service to the
UK library community. The Library now operates as a section of the Public Services
Branch in the British Library Reference Division.

Acquisitions policy   A representative collection of publications on library and
information science throughout the world.

Major collections   Archives have been deposited by the following organizations:
Association of Assistant Librarians; Library Association Cataloguing and Indexing
Group; Library Association London and Home Counties Branch; Art Libraries
Society; Association of Metropolitan Chief Librarians.
Papers of Anthony Thompson, first General Secretary of the International
Federation of Library Associations and Institutions.
H. Evelyn Bliss papers relating to the Bliss Classification.

Non-manuscript material   Collection of books and periodicals, including much that
is relevant to the history of libraries and librarianship.
Collections of illustrations and plans of library buildings; some photographs of
librarians.
Extensive collection of library annual reports, particularly strong in holdings of UK
public libraries' reports, is maintained.

Finding aids   Catalogues of the books and pamphlets. Index to part of the
illustrations collection. Other aids are planned.

Facilities   Photocopying. Microfilm/fiche readers.

319   British Library of Political and Economic Science
London School of Economics and Political Science (LSE)

Address   University of London
10 Portugal Street
London WC2A 2HD

Telephone   (01) 405 7686

Enquiries to   Archivist, Dr G.E.A. Raspin

Open   For current opening hours apply to the Archivist. It is advisable to make an appointment for the first visit.

Access   Approved readers undertaking original research. Students should produce letters of introduction from their supervisors or heads of departments.

Historical background   The Library of the London School of Economics was founded in 1896; it is not responsible for LSE archives.

Acquisitions policy   Modern British political, economic and social history, social anthropology (mainly post-1890); history of the London School of Economics.

Major collections   Papers of Beatrice Webb (1858–1943) and Sidney Webb (1859–1947); John Stuart Mill (1806–73); Hugh Dalton (1887–1962); Bronislaw Malinowski (1884–1942); George Lansbury (1859–1940); Walter Citrine.
Archives of National Institute of Industrial Psychology, 1919–74; Political and Economic Planning, c1931–73; Independent Labour Party National Administrative Council, minutes and other papers, c1893–1950.
Charles Booth Survey of London, 1885–1905 (426 vols).

Non-manuscript material   Webb Collection on Trade Unions.
Extensive collections of rare books on political, economic and social questions, 16th century, and on socialism.

Finding aids   Catalogues/handlists for most collections. General guide in preparation.

Facilities   Photocopying, microforms and photography by arrangement.

320   British Museum (Natural History)

Address   Cromwell Road
                 London SW7 5BD

Telephone   (01) 589 6323

Enquiries to   Museum Archivist, Mr R.E.R. Banks

Open   Mon–Fri: 10.00–4.30

Access   Approved readers, preferably by written application.

Historical background   The British Musuem (Natural History) was established at South Kensington in 1881, having separated from the British Museum, Bloomsbury, in that year. The natural history collections date from the time of Sir Hans Sloane (1660–1753) who bequeathed his vast private collection to the nation. This formed the nucleus of the British Museum. A few important MS collections were transferred to South Kensington in 1881, but the bulk of the Museum's holdings have been acquired since that date. The Museum Archives mostly comprise post-1881 documents, although some Departmental records go back to 1800 and a few are pre-1800.

Acquisitions policy   To obtain by purchase, gift or exchange all published and unpublished materials relevant to the work of the Museum.

Major collections   Large collections of MSS associated with the following scientists: Sir Joseph Banks (1743–1820) and his associates; Robert Brown (1773–1858); Albert C.L.G. Gunther (1830–1914); Sir John Murray (1841–1914); Sir Richard Owen (1804–92); Lionel Walter, second Baron Rothschild (1868–1937); Daniel Solander (1736–82); James Sowerby (1757–1822) and subsequent generations of the Sowerby family; Ernst J.O. Hartert (1859–1933); Edward C.S. Baker (1864–1944); George L. Bates (1863–1940); Claude B. Ticehurst (1881–1941); Hugh Whistler (1889–1943); Hubert Lynes (1874–1942); Richard Meinertzhagen (1878–1967); Miles J. Berkeley (1803–89); William Jardine (1800–74); David A. Bannermann (1886–1979); John Gould (1804–81); Philipp C. Zeller (1808–83); Arthur Russell (1878–1964); William Roxburgh (1759–1815); Henry T. Stainton (1822–92); Alfred Russel Wallace (1823–1913); Edward A. Wilson (1872–1912). Documents relating to Captain James Cook's three expeditions, 1768–71, 1772–5, 1776–80.

Non-manuscript material   Large collections of watercolour paintings, pencil sketches etc, of natural history subjects, including works by the following: Ferdinand Bauer (1760–1826); Franz Bauer (1758–1840); William Ellis (*d*1785); Johann Reinhold Forster (1729–98); Johann George Adam Forster (1754–94); Georg D. Ehret (1708–70); Thomas Hardwicke (1755–1835); Bryan H. Hodgson (1800–94); Sydney Parkinson (1745–71); John Reeves (1774–1856); John Russell Reeves (1804–77); John Latham (1740–1837); Alfred Waterhouse (1830–1905); William Jardine (1800–74); Richard Owen (1804–92); George E. Lodge (1860–1954); John Abbot (1751–*c*1842); Eugel Terzi (*d c*1944); Arthur Smith (1916–). *Challenger* voyage photographs; Indian botanical drawings; portraits of naturalists collection.

Finding aids   The main union catalogue of the Museum libraries contains catalogue entries for MSS and drawings; various more detailed lists are available. Summary list of Museum Archives; descriptive list of the same in preparation. Index of letters in course of compilation.

Facilities   Photocopying. Photography. Microform viewing and printing-out equipment.

Publications   *Catalogue of the Books, Manuscripts, Maps and Drawings in the British Museum (Natural History)* (London, 1903–40) [8 vols]
   The History of the collections, contained in the Natural History Departments of the British Museum (London, 1904–06) [2 vols]
   Bulletin of the British Museum (Natural History), Historical series, i (1953–)
   W.R. Dawson: *The Banks Letters. A calendar of the manuscript correspondence of Sir Joseph Banks preserved in the British Museum (Natural History) and other collections in Great Britain* (London, 1958)

F.C. Sawyer: 'A short history of the libraries and list of manuscripts and original drawings in the British Museum (Natural History)', *Bulletin of the British Museum (Natural History)*, Historical series, iv (1971), 77

J.B. Marshall: 'The handwriting of Sir Joseph Banks, his scientific staff and amanuenses', *Bulletin of the British Museum (Natural History)*, Botanical series, vi (1978), 1

W.T. Stearn: *The Natural History Museum at South Kensington* (London, 1981)

321   British Telecom Museum

Address   Baynard House
             135 Queen Victoria Street
             London EC4V 4AT

Telephone   (01) 248 7444

Enquiries to   The Assistant Curator

The Museum houses the Historical Telephone Directory Library, comprising London directories from 1880 and provincial directories from 1900. The Museum does not have the resources to undertake research but the directories may be consulted Mon–Fri: 9.30–12.30 and 2.00–4.00.

322   Charing Cross Hospital Medical School

Address   Reynolds Building
             St Dunstan's Road
             London W6 8RP.

Telephone   (01) 748 2040 ext. 2826

Enquiries to   Librarian, Mrs S. Godbolt
             or
             Archivist, Dr S.J.R. Reynolds

Open   Mon–Fri: 9.00–9.00, preferably by appointment

Access   Bona fide readers.

Historical background   The Hospital was founded in 1815 as the West London Infirmary, becoming the Charing Cross Hospital in 1827. The Medical School was founded in 1822.

Acquisitions policy   Material of relevance to the history of the Hospital and Medical School is accepted.

Major collections   Archives of School and Hospital including minutes from 1818, Finance Committee minutes from 1865, Medical Committee minutes from 1863,

nursing records, (c69ft, mostly bound vols).
Some items relating to Northwick Park and Fulham Hospital.

Non-manuscript material   Photographs, albums, newspaper cuttings.
   The Library includes a collection of articles and books relating to the Hospital.

Finding aids   Rough lists available.

Facilities   Photocopying. Photography. Microfilm reader.

323   Charity Commission for England and Wales

Address   14 Ryder Street
               London SW1Y 6AH

Telephone   (01) 214 8773/6075 (Central Register of Charities)
               (01) 214 8250 (access to records)

Enquiries to   The Office Services Section

Open   Mon–Fri: 10.00–4.00, by appointment

Access   Central Register of Charities is open to the public (at St Albans
               House, 57–60 Haymarket, London SW1Y 4QX); charity records over
               30 years old are open to inspection on application.

Historical background   The Charity Commission was established on a permanent
   basis by the Charitable Trusts Act, 1853, following the report of a Royal
   Commission set up in 1849. The Commissioners were given full powers of
   investigation and inquiry, including that of scrutiny of annual accounts, powers of
   advice, control over the institution of legal proceedings on behalf of charitable
   trusts and control over dealings with the real estate of charitable trusts in England
   and Wales. In 1860 the Commissioners were given important additional powers
   concurrent with those of the High Court to remove and appoint trustees; to vest
   property and to establish or to vary the purposes of a trust by means of a scheme,
   subject to appeal to the High Court. Their powers were confined to charity
   property which was permanent endowment or which the trustees wished to
   become subject to the Commissioners' jurisdiction. The Charities Act 1960, which
   followed upon the Nathan Committee's Report of 1952, consolidated the existing
   law of charity and to some extent extended its scope. It set out the position and
   functions of the Commissioners, extended its powers to all charities, established
   machinery to enable the needs of charities to be considered in relation to each
   other and to the statutory welfare services, provided for the registration of
   charities and widened the range of circumstances in which trust purposes could be
   revised. The London office covers national and overseas charities and those in
   England and south of the River Severn to the Wash (*see* entry **294** for Wales and the
   rest of England).

Major collections   Records relating to c136,000 charities.

Finding aids   The Central Register has four main indexes: by name (nominal index);
by object (classified index); by place (geographical index); by Diocese in respect
of Church of England charities.

Facilities   Photocopying.

324   Chelsea College Library

Address   University of London
                 Manresa Road
                 London SW3 6LX

Telephone   (01) 351 2488 ext. 2350

Enquiries to   The Librarian

Open   9.00–5.00

Access   Approved readers, on written application.

Historical background   The College was founded in 1891 as South Western
Polytechnic and from 1922 to 1966 was the Chelsea Polytechnic. It became a
School of the University of London in 1966.

Acquisitions policy   To support teaching and research activities in the College,
mainly in the sciences.

Major collections   College history documents, financial records etc.

Non-manuscript material   College history collection: annual reports, prospectuses,
pamphlets, press cuttings, etc, 1891–.

Facilities   Photocopying. Microfilm/microfiche readers.

325   Church Commissioners

Address   1, Millbank
                 London SW1P 3JZ

Telephone   (01) 222 7010

Enquiries to   Records Officer, Mr D.A. Armstrong

Open   Mon–Fri: 9.00–5.00, by appointment

Access   Bona fide enquirers. 30-year closure; closure also on other material
                 which has a direct bearing on current matters. All enquirers are
                 asked to write to the Records Officer in the first instance, giving as
                 much background information as possible, together with a plan
                 where relevant. Where possible a written answer will be given;

where more than routine research is involved the Records Officer will consider making the material available at the office.

Historical background   The material comprises the working papers of the Governors of Queen Annes Bounty, 1704–1948, the Church Building Commissioners, 1818–56, and the Ecclesiastical Commissioners, 1836–1948. The Ecclesiastical Commissioners took over the duties of the Church Building Commissioners in 1856, and the offices of the Governors of Queen Annes Bounty and the Ecclesiastical Commissioners amalgamated in 1948 to form the Church Commissioners. The bulk of the papers relate to the estates which the EcclesiasticaL Commissioners inherited from the Bishops and Deans and Chapters in the 19th century and the involvement of the Church Commissioners and their predecessors in a greaty variety of quite specific church matters as a result of various Acts and Measures over the years.

Major collections   Nearly all material is made up of the working papers of the Church Commissioners and their predecessors.

Facilities   Very limited photocopying and photography.

Publications   A. Savidge: *The Foundation and Early Days of Queen Annes Bounty*
G.F.A. Best: *Temporal Pillars* [history of Queen Annes Bounty and the Ecclesiastical Commissioners]
M.H. Port: *Six Hundred New Churches* [history of the Church Building Commissioners]
A. Savidge: *The Parsonages in England*

326   Church House Record Centre

Address   Church House
Dean's Yard, Westminster
London SW1P 3NZ

Telephone   (01) 222 9011

Enquiries to   The Archivist

Open   Mon–Fri: 10.00–5.00, by appointment

Access   Records are open to the public, except for 100-year closure on personal files, 30-year closure on certain administrative files.

Historical background   The Centre was set up in 1977 by the General Synod of the Church of England to provide for the records of the Synod, its predecessors and advisory bodies. The Centre also assists the voluntary organizations of the Church of England on request, and acts as a clearing-house for information on all Anglican records.

Acquisitions policy   Generally restricted to the records of the parent organization, but the papers of voluntary bodies are occasionally housed as an emergency measure, and there are papers of leading churchmen (normally with Church Assembly/General Synod connections). Only central Anglican records are accepted: parish and diocesan records are cared for by the Diocesan Record Office (normally the County Record Office).

Major collections   Mainly 20th-century departmental material, but inherited papers include those of the Church of England Purity Society, 1887–; the Church Defence Institution, 1859–; and the Church Reform League, 1895–.
The Colonial/Overseas Bishoprics Fund (founded 1841) is administered from Church House.
Personal papers include those of Dr Francis Eeles (1876–1954), former Secretary of the Central Council for the Care of Churches, and an authority on women's ministry; and certain correspondence of Lord Hugh Cecil (Lord Quickswood; 1869–1956), primarily on church affairs of the 1920s and 1930s.

Non-manuscript material   The reference library includes sets of published Church Assembly/General Synod debates and papers; the Church of England *Yearbook*, 1883–; Crockford/the Clergy List; and *Chronicles* of the Convocation of Canterbury.
Small photographic archive.

Finding aids   Listing and indexing in progress.

Facilities   Photocopying.

Publications   See C.J. Kitching: *The Central Records of the Church of England: A Report and Survey presented to the Pilgrim and Radcliffe Trustees* (1976)

327   Church Missionary Society (CMS)

Address   157 Waterloo Road
                  London SE1 8UU

Telephone   (01) 928 8681

Enquiries to   Archivist, Miss Rosemary Keen

Open   Mon–Fri: 9.30–5.00

Access   50-year closure period for official archives. Closure for unofficial deposited material varies according to the request of the depositor. Material available for research is being transferred gradually, on deposit, to Birmingham University Library (*see* entry **59**).

Historical background   The Church Missionary Society was founded in 1799. Its missionary activity is worldwide. The Society amalgamated with the Church of England Zenana Missionary Society (CEZMS) in 1957.

Acquisitions policy   Confined to records of former missionaries and staff and material relating specifically to CMS and CEZMS institutions.

Major collections   CMS archives, 1799–.
Church of England Zenana Missionary Society archives, 1880–1957.
Female Education Society archives, 1834–99.
Loochoo Naval Mission archives, 1842–57.
Eclectic Society of London notes, 1798–1814.
Venn MSS, 1679–1955.

Non-manuscript material   Photographs of missionaries and CMS institutions.

Finding aids   Catalogues and/or detailed lists of records of all CMS departments. Calendars of pre-1820 CMS mission series. Brief catalogues for Loochoo Mission and Female Education Society. Catalogues of c200 of the accessions of deposited unofficial material. Card indexes of names, places and subjects. Card index of some photographs.

Publications   *Catalogues of Africa (Group 3) Missions 1804–1934*: i, West Africa (Sierra Leone); ii, Nigeria; iii, South and East Africa (South Africa, Kenya and Tanzania); iv, East Africa (Nyanza, Uganda and Ruanda/Burundi); v, Egypt and Sudanese missions; vi, Mediterranean and Palestine; vii, New Zealand; viii, West Indies
Summary of archive holding, in R. Keen: *Survey of Archives of Selected Missionary Societies*, National Register of Archives Report (1968)

328   City and Hackney Health Authority

Address   St Bartholomew's Hospital
West Smithfield
London EC1A 7BE

Telephone   (01) 600 9000 ext 3478

Enquiries to   District Archivist, Ms Janet Foster

Open   Mon–Fri: 10.00–5.00, preferably by appointment

Access   Generally open to the public, but there is a 30-year closure on administrative records and 100-year closure on medical records.

Historical background   St Bartholomew's Hospital was founded, with a monastic priory, in 1123. It was re-established by Henry VIII in 1546 and thereafter controlled by a Board of Governors which continued after the Hospital joined the National Health Service in 1948 but was replaced with the reorganization of the NHS in 1974. St Bartholomew's then became part of the present Health Authority and assumed responsibility for the records of the other hospitals within the Authority: St Mark's, City Road (founded 1835); St Leonard's, Shoreditch (founded 1770); the German, Dalston (founded 1845); Hackney General (founded 1750); the Eastern, Homerton (founded 1871); the Mothers', Clapton (founded 1883); and the Metropolitan, Kingsland Road (1836–1976).

Acquisitions policy   Restricted to records produced by the hospitals or directly relating to any of them or to prominent members of staff.

Major collections   Records of all the hospitals that were previously voluntary hospitals, i.e. St Bartholomew's; St Mark's; the German and the Metropolitan, from date of foundation to present day or date of closure.
Records of Hospital Management Committee (Hackney Group), 1948–1974.
Records of the Alexandra Hospital for Children with Hip Disease, 1871–1958.
Records of the parish of St Bartholomew-the-Less, 1547–.
Some records of St Bartholomew's Hospital Medical College, c1800–1930s.

Non-manuscript material   Maps and plans of St Bartholomew's Hospital and its estates, 17th–20th centuries (c500 items).
Photographs of wards and members of medical and nursing staff, 19th and 20th centuries (10 albums and several hundred single items).
Portraits of eminent physicians, surgeons and benefactors of St Bartholomew's Hospital.

Finding aids   Index and calendar of medieval deeds of St Bartholomew's. Index to Governors' minutes, St Bartholomew's, 1549–1607 (subsequent minute books have contemporary indexes). Detailed list, on cards, of all holdings for each hospital.

Facilities   Photocopying. Photography.

Publications   N.J. Kerling: *Cartulary of St Bartholomew's, a Calendar* (London, 1973)
————: 'Archives', *The Royal Hospital of St Bartholomew, 1123–1973* V. Medvei and J.H. Thornton (eds): (London, 1974), 299
————: *Descriptive Catalogue of Archives in the Hospitals in the City and Hackney Health District from the beginning of each Hospital to 1974*, Historical Manuscripts Commission (1977) [includes records held by other repositories]

329   City of London Polytechnic
Fawcett Library

Address   Old Castle Street
                 London E1 7NT

Telephone   (01) 283 1030 ext. 570

Enquiries to   Fawcett Librarian, Miss Catherine Ireland

Open   Term: Mon: 1.00–8.30
                      Tues–Fri: 10.00–5.00
                 Vacation: Mon–Fri: 10.00–5.00
                 Preferably by appointment

Access   By subscription. Charges payable for day visit or at different rates per annum for individuals, undergraduates and registered post-graduates.

Historical background   The Library began as the Women's Service Library – the Library of the London and National Society for Women's Service (now the Fawcett Society), the direct descendant of the London Society for Women's Suffrage, founded in 1867. The Society was at the centre of the non-militant campaign for women's suffrage under the leadership of Millicent Garrett Fawcett, and accumulated a certain amount of material from the campaign and related issues. In the 1920s the Society decided to organize this material for the use of members and in 1926 the first Librarian was appointed. Over the years the Library acquired a number of other smaller collections, including the Cavendish-Bentinck and Edward Wright Libraries (originally suffrage collections with a high proportion of old and rare books), the Crosby Hall collection, the Sadd Brown Library (on women in the Commonwealth) and the Library of the Josephine Butler Society (formerly the Association for Moral and Social Hygiene). Gradually the Fawcett Library became a major national research resource. In March 1977, as the Society could no longer support the library, it was transferred to the City of London Polytechnic.

Acquisitions policy   Additions relating to suffrage. Papers relating to women's organizations and prominent women are considered.

Major collections   c400 boxes of archive material, mainly 19th and 20th centuries, including records of societies concerned with suffrage, especially the archive of the Fawcett Society; equal status; emigration; business and professional bodies, including trade unions; repeal of the Contagious Diseases Acts and other moral issues, including papers of feminists involved in the controversy of 1863–86; and records of the Association for Moral and Social Hygiene.
Papers of individuals, including Millicent Garrett Fawcett (1847–1929) and Dr Elizabeth Garrett Anderson (1836–1917).
40 folders of correspondence of Josephine Butler (1828–1906).
80 folders of miscellaneous letters and autograph letters.
Many more archives about to be listed.

Non-manuscript material   Photographs, many of individual women involved in suffrage movements; posters relating to suffrage campaign; newspaper cuttings on all aspects of women.
Special collections include: Josephine Butler Library (previously Library of the Association for Moral and Social Hygiene); Cavendish-Bentinck Collection (mainly rare and antiquarian works); Sadd Brown Collection, devoted to the role of women in the Commonwealth.

Finding aids   Typed index to major collections.

Facilities   Photocopying. Microfiche reader.

Publications   Holdings detailed in M. Barrow: *Women 1870–1928. A Select Guide to Printed and Archival Sources in the United Kingdom* (1981)

330   City of London School

Address   Victoria Embankment
London EC4Y 0DL

Telephone   (01) 353 0046

Most material relating to the foundation and history of the school, including minutes of the Governors' Meetings from 1837, is deposited in Guildhall Library (*see* entry 349).

331   The City University

Address   Skinner's Library
The City University
Northampton Square
London EC1V 0HB

There are no deposited collections. Internal records are held.

332   The Clothworkers' Company

Address   Clothworkers' Hall
Dunster Court
Mincing Lane
London EC3R 7AH

Telephone   (01) 623 7041

Enquiries to Archivist, Mr D.E. Wickham

Open   Mon–Fri: 9.30–4.30, by appointment only

Access   After acceptance of details of purpose and requirements of study. Suitable written reference required in advance. Problems of supervision and accommodation mean that random enquiries are not encouraged.

Historical background   The Company was incorporated by Royal Charter in 1528 and its records are practically complete to date. The Company's involvement with clothworking (i.e. cloth finishing) was always limited to London and the records are not normally of use for any aspect of the cloth trade of Kent, East Anglia, or the Cotswolds.

Acquisitions policy   Restricted to records relating directly to the Company, its prominent members, its history, and its post-industrial revolution status as a charitable organization. To a large extent these items are self-generating.

Major collections   All aspects of the history and modern work of this City of London
   livery company.

Finding aids   Some lists and indexes.

333   The College of Arms

Address   Queen Victoria Street
                   London EC4V 4BT

Telephone   (01) 248 2762

Enquiries to   The Officer in Waiting (heraldic and genealogical matters)
                   or
                   Archivist, Mr R.C. Yorke (academic matters)

Open   Mon–Fri: 10.00–4.00

Access   Through an Officer of Arms or the Archivist; prior contact by
                   academic enquirers recommended. A fee may be charged.

Historical background   The English heralds were made a body corporate in 1484.
   The College of Arms has been on its present site since 1555, being rebuilt after the
   Great Fire of 1666. The archives comprise both the official records of the College
   and the collections of many individual heralds, who have included well known
   antiquaries. There is medieval material dating from well before 1484.

Acquisitions policy   The archives are augmented by the generation of records within
   the College, and by the acquisition of collections from heralds. Relevant material
   may be purchased from, or given by, outside sources.

Major collections   Official records: these include visitations; grants of arms;
   enrolments of royal warrants, pedigrees, etc; royal and other ceremonials; records
   of Garter King of Arms; records of the Court of Chivalry; and the administrative
   records of the College.
   Semi-official and unofficial records include rolls of arms, armorials, pedigrees,
   painters' work-books, and papers relating to orders of chivalry.
   Some 50 collections of individual heralds and others.
   Other archives include the Arundel MSS; Talbot Papers; Combwell Priory and
   other charters; miscellaneous family and estate papers.

Non-manuscript material   Bookplate and seal collections.

Finding aids   Various lists and indexes.

Facilities   Photocopying. Photography and microfilming by arrangement. All
   reproduction is subject to permission; official records may not be copied.

Publications   W.H. Black: *Catalogue of the Arundel Manuscripts in the . . . College of
   Arms* (1829)
   A.R. Wagner: *The Records and Collections of the College of Arms* (1952)

F. Jones: *Report on the Welsh Manuscripts Contained in the Muniments of the College of Arms* (1957) [typescript]

G.R. Batho (ed.); *A Calendar of the Talbot Papers in the College of Arms* (Derbyshire Archaeological Society, 1968)

L.M. Midgley: *Report on Miscellaneous Deeds, including Charters relating to Combwell Priory, . . . in the Collections of the College of Arms* (1980) [typescript]

It is hoped that the first volume of a major catalogue of the College archives will be published in 1984.

334   Commonwealth Institute Library and Resource Centre

Address   Kensington High Street
                 London W8 6NQ

Telephone   (01) 602 3252 ext 242

Enquiries to   Librarian, Mr Michael Foster

Open   Mon–Sat: 10.00–5.30

Access   Serious users over the age of 14.

Historical background   The present Library and Resource Centre dates from 1962, when the new Institute building was opened in Kensington High Street. Before that, as the Imperial Institute at a site in South Kensington, there had existed a library, most of which was dispersed at the time of removal. It is believed that some archival materials, dealing with life in the colonial possessions and particularly a large collection of photographic slides, were destroyed before removal to the new premises. The Library in the new building was originally intended for use by teachers and collected materials mainly concerning contemporary life in Commonwealth countries. The Library was opened to the general public from *c*1972, and has gradually broadened its acquisitions policy to include historical and archival materials, though the holdings of these are still extremely modest. In 1977 most of the archives of the Imperial Institute, up to 1958, were deposited at the Public Record Office (*see* entry **441**), though there is still a small collection which has accumulated from donations or office turnouts since that date.

Acquisitions policy   There is no positive acquisitions policy, and no funding. Donations of materials which seem likely to explain and put into historical context the present state of Commonwealth countries excluding Britain are accepted.

Major collections   Garfield Todd (Zimbabwe) Archive: letters from Mrs G. Todd and her husband, ex-Prime Minister of Rhodesia, explaining conditions under detention, confinement and imprisonment during period of Unilateral Declaration of Independence, *c*1965–.

Harold Ingrams Archive: miscellaneous papers, articles and MS books covering his career as colonial administrator, journalist and writer, *c*1900–1970s.

Non-manuscript material   Small collection of 19th-century exploration literature. Some 19th- and early 20th-century exhibition catalogues.

Recordings of music on disc, cassette and reel-to-reel tape; much is traditional and ethnic, though modern music, popular and composed, is also collected. Because of the wide spread of Commonwealth countries, music from most of the main cultural and ethnic areas of the world is thus represented.

Special collection of Commonwealth literature (in English), consisting of published creative writing and critical responses from most Commonwealth countries.

Newscuttings and articles on writers; recordings of readings, dramatic productions and interviews.

Finding aids   Some lists of archival materials. The collection is uncatalogued at present.

Facilities   Photocopying. Photography. Microfilm/fiche reader. Large range of audio-visual hardware.

Publications   Printed and duplicated bibliographies; lists of some collections, including literature, recordings and audio-visual materials [list available on application].

335   Congregational Library

Address   15 Gordon Square
                   London WC1H 0AG

The records of the Congregational Library are now administered by Dr Williams's Library (*see* entry **340**).

336   Contemporary Medical Archives Centre

Address   Wellcome Institute for the History of Medicine
                   183 Euston Road
                   London NW1 2BP

Telephone   (01) 387 4477 ext. 3244/3350

Enquiries to   Archivist, Miss J.G.A. Sheppard

Open   Mon–Fri: 9.45–5.15, by appointment
                   Closed: additional days at Christmas

Access   Bona fide scholars, after signing readers' undertaking. Permission of owner may be needed for access. Up to 100-year closure on some material.

Historical background　The Centre was established in 1979 as a permanent unit within the Wellcome Institute for the History of Medicine (*see* entry **500**) to locate papers of 20th-century British medical practitioners and scientists working on medical and ancillary disciplines, covering all aspects of modern medicine and health care. Some collections were transferred to the Centre from the Western MSS Department of the Wellcome Institute. The Centre also maintains registers of information on the whereabouts of collections and records elsewhere, including institutions and hospitals.

Acquisitions policy　20th-century items or collections of members of the medical profession, or papers relevant to the study of health care in general, including records of societies, mainly by gift or donation.

Major collections　Papers of individuals including those of Sir Thomas Lewis, 1907–45; Sir George Pickering (1904–80); Sir E.A. Sharpey-Schäfer (1850–1935); Dr Marie Stopes, 1918–57; Sir Leonard Rogers (1868–1962).
Records and papers of general practitioners.
Records of societies and associations including Association of County Medical Officers of Health, 1902–74; British Pharmacological Society, 1931–79; Camberwell Council on Alcoholism, 1962–80; Eugenics Society, 1908–79.

Non-manuscript material　Some photographs and tape recordings.

Finding aids　Lists of nearly all collections.

Facilities　Photocopying. Photography. Microfilm/fiche reader.

Publications　*Consolidated Accessions List* (1982)

337　Corporation of London Records Office

Address　Guildhall
London EC2P 2EJ

Telephone　(01) 606 3030 ext. 2251

Enquiries to　Deputy Keeper of Records, Miss B.R. Masters

Open　Mon–Fri: 9.30–5.00
Sat: by arrangement

Historical background　Official record office for the archives of the Corporation of the City of London.

Major collections　Official archives of the Corporation, 11th–20th centuries; at many periods the principal classes include much of national interest.
Other classes of records reflect special responsibilities or associations of the Corporation and jurisdiction and property interests outside the City boundaries, these records include:
Southwark and Finsbury manor courts, 16th–19th centuries, and property records, 13th–19th centuries.

Emanuel Hospital, Tothill Hill Fields, records of administration of the charity and its estates, early 17th century–.

Bridge House Estates, deeds, rentals, accounts, minute books etc, relating to maintenance of London Bridge and later, other bridges within the City, 11th century–.

Royal Contract Estates, records of estates in many counties granted by the Crown in 1628 for sale to settle Crown debts, 17th century.

Thames Conservancy records, 17th–19th centuries.

Lieutenancy of the City of London, commissions, lists and minutes, 17th–19th centuries.

Irish Society records of the plantation of Ulster and management of estates there, 17th–19th centuries.

Facilities   Photocopying. Microfilm reader.

Publications   P.E. Jones and R. Smith: *Guide to the Records at Guildhall London, Part I, The Corporation of London Records Office* (1951)

338   Council for the Care of Churches

Address   83 London Wall
                 London EC2M 5NA

Telephone   (01) 638 0971/2

Enquiries to   Librarian, Mr David M. Williams

Open   Mon–Fri: 10.00–5.00, preferably by appointment

Access   Generally open to the public.

Historical background   The Council was established in 1921 as the central co-ordinating body for the Diocesan Advisory Committees for the Care of Churches. The library and National Survey of Churches were developed from the outset. The Council supplies photographic and documentary information on the work of contemporary artists and craftsmen who are interested in ecclesiastical commissions.

Acquisitions policy   To strengthen the National Survey of Churches, by donation and purchase; to acquire special collections through bequests and gifts; to augment records of contemporary craftsmanship and conservation, by donation from practitioners.

Major collections   National Survey of Churches survey files, many including photographs and guide books, on most of the 17,000 churches and chapels of the Church of England; the collection is particularly rich in postcards and photographs, c1900–50.

Canon B.F.L. Clarke collection of MS notes, covering c11,000 Anglican churches, with details of 18th- and 19th-century restorations; also photographs.

Canon P.B.G. Binnall's card index and MS notes on 19th-century stained glass.

Non-manuscript material   Canon B.F.L. Clarke collection of *c*20,000 postcards.
*c*12,000 printed items on ecclesiastical art and architecture, with special reference to Anglican churches and their furnishings.
5000 slides (available for loan).

Finding aids   Card catalogue. Duplicated typescript catalogue of slide lending library (available for purchase).

Facilities   Photocopying.

Publication   Information sheet [available from the Librarian]

339   Courtauld Institute of Art

Address   University of London
20 Portman Square
London W1H 0BE

Telephone   (01) 935 9292

Enquiries to   Librarian, Mr P.M. Doran

Open   Term: Mon–Fri: 9.30–7.00
Vacation: Mon–Fri: 10.00–6.00
Closed: August; 10 days at Christmas and at Easter

Access   Normally restricted to University staff and students, on the basis of satisfactory identification. Enquiries about archive material should be made well in advance of a visit.

Historical background   The Institute was founded in 1931 and moved to its present address in 1932. The Library (called the 'Book Library') was started in 1933.

Acquisitions policy   To provide books, periodicals, and other publications for the work of the Institute's undergraduates, research students, and teaching staff.

Major collections   Papers of Lord Lee of Fareham (1868–1947).
Correspondence of Philip Webb, architect (1831–1915).

Non-manuscript material   46,444 pamphlets.

Finding aids   Individual check-lists.

Facilities   Photocopying. Photography.

340   Dr Williams's Library

Address   14 Gordon Square
                London WC1H 0AG

Telephone   (01) 387 3727

Enquiries to Librarian, Mr John Creasey

Open   Mon, Wed, Fri: 10.00–5.00
                Tues, Thurs: 10.00–6.30
                Closed 24 Dec–2 Jan (incl.); Thurs before to Tues after Easter Day
                (incl.); first fortnight of Aug (exact dates printed in Annual Bulletin)

Access   Open to persons duly introduced and guaranteed in accordance
                with the regulations made by the Trustees. Regulations, membership
                forms etc, may be had on personal application or by post from the
                Librarian.

Historical background   The Library forms part of the charitable Trust established
under the will of Daniel Williams DD (*d* 1716), a Presbyterian minister; its nucleus
was the founder's personal library, principally of divinity. To this collection of
printed books, MSS, for the most part relating to English Nonconformity, began to
be added by purchase, gift or deposit, very soon after the Library opened in 1729/
30. The Library also administers the Congregational Library (*fd* 1831).

Acquisitions policy   Very little is added by purchase. Such MSS as are acquired are
given or, in some cases, deposited. Very little is added that is not related to English
Nonconformity or to material already here.

Major collections   Include Minutes of The Westminster Assembly, 1643–52, and the
Fourth London Classis, 1646–59; John Evans List of Dissenting Congregations,
1715–29, and similar lists of *c*1770 by Josiah Thompson; correspondence of
Joseph Priestley, Theophilus Lindsey and others associated with them;
correspondence and other papers of Richard Baxter (1615–91); collections made
by Roger Morrice, including the late 16th century *Second Parte of a Register* and
Morrice's political diary covering the years 1677–91; the collections for the
history of Dissenting Churches made by Walter Wilson (1781–1847); the
miscellaneous and largely personal collections of John Jones (1700–70) which
includes a MS of George Herbert's poems, English and Latin; the diary,
reminiscences and letters of Henry Crabb Robinson (1775–1867); items by
William Law and others in the collection of books and MSS deposited by
Christopher Walton (1809–77); the MSS from New College, London, including
much correspondence and papers of Philip Doddridge (1702–51).
The Congregational Library collection includes correspondence of Isaac Watts
(1674–1748), as well as letters and sermons of prominent Nonconformists.

Non-manuscript material   The MSS are really an adjunct to the printed books
(133,000), which are pre-eminent for the study of English Protestant Nonconformity.

Finding aids   Handlists of MSS and partial name index.

Facilities   Microfilm reader. Some items suitable for photocopying on premises.

Publications   *The Baxter Treatises; a catalogue of the Richard Baxter papers (other than the Letters) in Dr. Williams's Library* (1959)
I. Elliott: *Supplement* to E. Morley's Index in Edith Morley, *Henry Crabb Robinson on Books and their Writers* (1960).
J. Creasey: *Index to the John Evans List of Dissenting Congregations and Ministers, 1715–1729, in Dr Williams's Library* (1964)
K. Twinn: *Guide to the Manuscripts in Dr Williams's Library* (1969)
Nonconformist Congregations in Great Britain: a List of Histories and other Material in Dr Williams's Library (1974)
Thomas Jollie's papers: a list of the Papers in Dr Williams's Library, Manuscript no. 12.78 [Out of print]

341   Duchy of Cornwall Office

Address   10 Buckingham Gate
                 London SW1E 6LA

Telephone   (01) 834 7346

Enquiries to   The Secretary and Keeper of the Records

Open   Tues–Thurs: 10.00–5.00
                 other weekdays by arrangement

Access   On written application. In order to protect the privacy of lessees, material less than 100 years old is available for inspection only with the specific permission of the Keeper of the Records.

Historical background   The Duchy was created in 1337. It is the oldest of English Duchies, and, with the brief exception of the Interregnum, has existed continuously. The collection is concerned with the administration, revenues and agricultural history of the estate.

Acquisitions policy   All the records of the Duchy are maintained.

Major collections   Household Papers of Frederick, Prince of Wales: covering the life and activities of the Prince's household during the mid-18th century (55 vols).
Rolls series: 3500 paper and parchment rolls which are those of the receivers, ministers, particular ministers and manorial court officials.
Council Minutes: the minutes of the Duchy Council from 1611–45 and continuously from 1715 (150 vols).

Non-manuscript material   Vauxhall Gardens Prints: 300 items concerned with and depicting the famous 18th-century pleasure gardens.

Finding aids   Various lists and indexes available. Catalogues of all legal opinions, prints, and surveys exist. A catalogue of all photographic materials and another of the household papers of Prince Frederick is in preparation.

Facilities   Photocopying. Photography. Microfilm/fiche reader.

Publications   R.L. Clowes: 'On the Historical Documents in the Duchy of Cornwall Office', *Royal Cornwall Polytechnic Society Annual Report* (1930)

342 The Folklore Society

Address	University College London Gower Street London WC1E 6BT
Telephone	(01) 387 5894
Enquiries to	Hon. Archivist, Mr Paul Smith
Open	Strictly by appointment only.
Access	Although the Society was founded in 1878, no archivist was appointed until 1980. Consequently, little work has been undertaken on the collections and accordingly access is at present restricted and only by appointment.

Historical background   The Folklore Society was formed in 1878 and was the first organisation in the world to be devoted to the study of traditional culture. Since its formation the Society's interests have been world-wide, and its early publications contained numerous contributions from missionaries, colonial administrators and travellers in many lands. Today the Society continues to stimulate folklore studies throughout the world, and it provides a valuable point of contact for isolated collectors and scholars.

Acquisitions policy   No specific policy at present – most acquisitions are by donation from Society members.

Major collections   Over and above small single items the Archive houses c50 major collections deposited by past Society members.

Facilities   Photocopying and photgraphy by arrangement.

Publications   The Society publishes the journal *Folklore* in which reports of past donations to the Archive and a current annual report are included.

343 Foreign and Commonwealth Office (FCO)
Library and Records Department

Address	Sanctuary Buildings Great Smith Street London SW1P 2BZ

Telephone   (01) 212 0663

Enquiries to   The Librarian

Archives are regularly transferred to the Public Record Office (*see* entry **441**). The FCO holds no archival material that is available for public consultation. The libraries of the former Colonial Office and Foreign Office form the basis of the collection of books, which dates from *c*1782 and is available to researchers for reference.

344   Franciscan Archives English Province

Address   Franciscan Friary
              58 St Antony's Road
              Forest Gate
              London E7 9QB

Telephone   (01) 472 3900

Enquiries to   Fr Justin McLoughlin
                  The Friary, 160 The Grove, Stratford, London E15 1NS
                  Telephone (01) 534 1964

Open   By appointment

Access   Generally open to the public.

Historical background   The archive collection was begun in 1629.

Acquisitions policy   To acquire any material dealing with the English Franciscan Province.

Major collections   Chapter Registers, 1629–1838.
      Correspondence dealing with business of the Province.
      Deeds and wills connected with benefactors and relatives of Franciscans.
      Provincial Registers; procurators' account books; note-books of Franciscan provincials; notifications from Major Superiors in Rome and the Low Countries.

Facilities   Photocopying.

345   The Geological Society

Address   Burlington House
              London W1V 0JU

Telephone   (01) 734 2356

Enquiries to   The Librarian, or the Secretary (for official archives)

Open   Mon–Fri: 10.00–5.00

Access   Bona fide researchers.

Historical background   The Geological Society of London was founded in 1807. At present the conservationist and archivist posts are funded by the British Library.

Acquisitions policy   Any donations of geologically interesting MSS gratefully received.

Major collections   Administrative records: a full series of official records including Minutes from 1807, Fellowship and financial records, MSS relating to Society publications (*Journal* etc).
Acquired collections from Fellows and others, in particular Roderick I. Murchison (1792–1871) collection of notebooks, diaries and letters.

Non-manuscript material   Maps. Illustrations.

Finding aids   Internal MSS catalogue in preparation.

Facilities   Photocopying.

Publications   Various 19th-century catalogues of the library.

346   Goethe Institute Library

Address   Goethe Institute
            50 Princes Gate
            London SW7 2PG

Telephone   (01) 581 3344

No archives are held, but multi-media information on Germany, German literature and culture is collected.

347   Grange Museum of Local History

Address   Neasden Lane
            London NW10

Telephone   (01) 452 8311

Enquiries to   Librarian, Ms Judith Knight
            Museum keeper, Ms Valerie Bott

Open   Mon, Tues, Thurs, Fri: 12.00–5.00
            Wed: 12.00–8.00
            Sat: 10.00–5.00
            Those with complicated enquiries may find it useful to telephone in advance.

Access   Generally open to the public.

Historical background   The building was originally outbuildings to a farm, both of which were built c1700. It was converted into a 'gothick' dwelling house in about 1800, and remained in use as a house until c1970. Listed in 1950, the Grange remains isolated on a huge traffic island. It opened as a local history library and museum in 1977, and now houses material on the Borough of Brent and its predecessors, Wembley, Willesden and Kingsbury.

Aquisitions policy   The acquisition of printed and MS material, photographs, maps, prints and three-dimensional objects illustrating the life of the people of the area. Material is acquired by purchase, donation and deposit.

Major collections   Local government: minutes of the present Borough and its predecessors, with Medical Officer of Health reports, committee minutes etc.
Vestry minutes, overseers' and churchwardens' records for Willesden from the 17th century.
British Empire Exhibition: held at Wembley 1924–5; guides, maps, photographs, music, souvenirs, etc.
Collection belonging to Wembley History Society, including hundreds of mounted photographs.

Non-manuscript material   Photographs and postcards of the area, maps, paintings and prints.
Large map collection, especially strong on Willesden, including tithe and inclosure maps.
Collections of work by local authors, including Harrison Ainsworth, W.H.G. Kingston, Louis Wain, Gunby Hadath.

Finding aids   Index to the collection and to the local newspapers (*Willesden Chronicle* indexed 1880–; *Wembley Observer* indexed 1965–).

Facilities   Photocopying. Limited photographic service. Microfilm/fiche reader.

Publications   *Brent Streetnames* (1975)
   Brent Placenames (1977)
   A History of Wembley (1980)

348   Greater London Record Office

Address   40 Northampton Road
                   London EC1

Telephone   (01) 633 6851

Enquiries to   Head Archivist, Miss J. Coburn

Open   Tues: 10–7.30, from 4.45 by appointment only
                   Wed–Fri: 10–4.45
                   Closed 3rd & 4th weeks in October

Historical background The Greater London Record Office was formed in 1965 by the amalgamation of the London and Middlesex county record offices. The offices were physically amalgamated in 1980. Both these offices had their origins in the records inherited by their respective county councils in 1889. The Office is responsible for the official records of the Greater London Council, the London County Council, Middlesex County Council and their predecessors. It also holds rich and varied collections of deposited and non-official archives relating to the area of the former counties of London and Middlesex. The Office also acts as the Diocesan Record Office for London, Southwark and Guildford.

Major collections Usual local authority record holdings and deposited collections of which the following have a wider significance:
Records of the Middlesex Sessions, 1549–1971, together with the Gaol Delivery of Newgate for Middlesex, 1549–1834, and the Westminster Sessions records, 1620–1844.
Records of St Thomas' Hospital Group, 1556–1948, including records of the Nightingale School, 1860–1948.
Records of Guy's Hospital, 1725–1948, including personal records of Thomas Guy.
Records of the Westminster Hospital Group, 1715/16–1974.
Records of the Charity Organization Society (Family Welfare Association from 1946), excluding local area material outside London, 1869–1966.
Records of the Foundling Hospital (Thomas Coram Foundation for Children from 1954), 1739–1968.

Non-manuscript material Ancillary collections at Greater London History Library; Map Collection; Print Collection; Photographic Library.

Facilities Photocopying. Microfilm readers. Photography is undertaken by a commercial photographer.

Publications *Guide to the records in the London County Record Office, Part 1, Records of the Predecessors of the London County Council, except the Boards of Guardians* (1962)
Guide to the Middlesex Sessions Records, 1549–1889 (1965)
A Survey of the Parish Registers of the Diocese of London, Inner London Area [rev. ed in preparation]
A Survey of the Parish Registers of the Diocese of Southwark [Inner London Area] (1978)

349 Guildhall Library Manuscripts Department

Address Guildhall Library
Aldermanbury
London EC2P 2EJ

Telephone (01) 606 3030, ext. 2863

Enquiries to	The Keeper of Manuscripts
Open	Mon–Fri: 9.30–4.45
	Sat: 9.30–4.45 (but no delivery from strongrooms, 12.00–2.00)
Access	Generally open to the public, no appointment normally necessary. Access to some modern (mostly business) records dependent on depositor's permission.

Historical background   Guildhall Library was founded in 1824 and is primarily a library of London history, holding not only printed books but also prints, maps, drawings and paintings, and MSS. The Manuscripts Department is, in effect, the county record office for the City of London (excepting the archives of the Corporation of London). Because of the City's pre-eminence in commercial history, many of the Department's holdings are of national or international significance. Most City Livery Companies have deposited their records in Guildhall Library. The office also acts as Diocesan Record Office for London.

Acquisitions policy   Records relating to or emanating from the City of London (excepting the archives of the Corporation of London).

Finding aids   General catalogue, general subject, name and place indexes. Several specialized indexes, lists and guides.

Facilities   Photocopying. Microfilm/fiche readers.

Publications   *Vestry Minutes of Parishes within the City of London* (2/1964)
Churchwardens' Accounts of Parishes within the City of London (2/1969)
Guide to the London Collections (1978) [guide to collections of books, MSS, maps, paintings, etc in Guildhall Library relating to London].
Parish Registers at Guildhall Library [Part i contains Registers of Church of England Parishes within the City of London; Part ii contains Registers of Church of England Parishes outside the City of London, Non-Parochial Registers, and Registers of Foreign Denominations, Burial Grounds, and Marriage Documents; Part iii contains Registers and Register Transcripts of Anglican Communities Abroad] (2/1977).
A Guide to Genealogical Sources in Guildhall Library

350   Guy's Hospital Medical School

Address	The Will's Library
	Guy's Hospital Medical School
	London Bridge
	London SE1 9RT
Telephone	(01) 407 7600
Enquiries to	The Librarian

The bulk of the hospital records is held at the Greater London County Council Record

Office (*see* entry **348**). The minutes (incomplete) of Guy's Hospital Physical Society (1771–1852) are available to bona fide researchers on written application.

351 Heythrop College

Address   University of London
11–13 Cavendish Square
London W1M 0AN

No archives are maintained in the library. Relevant material is at the Society of Jesus (*see* entry **306**), or Westminster Diocesan Archive (*see* entry **503**).

352 HM Customs and Excise

Address   The Library
King's Beam House
Mark Lane
London EC3R 7HE

Telephone   (01) 626 1515, exts 2509, 3308, 2543

Enquiries to   Librarian and Archivist, Mr T.G. Smith

Open   Mon–Fri: 8.30–5.00 by appointment only

Access   100-year closure on Departmental Records.

Historical background   The Library dates from 1671 when the Board of Customs was established. Certain Excise records were deposited after amalgamation of HM Customs and Excise in 1909. There is also a museum showing historical traditions of the department and special displays on history of taxation of various commodities.

Acquisition policy   Directly relating to present functions of the department and to support historical collections.

Major collections   Current records of Department.
London Shipping Registers, 1818–95.
Bills of Entry (London, Liverpool, Clyde and Hull), c1830–1930.
Trade and shipping statistics (imports and exports).
Background material on taxation of goods, smuggling etc.
Books of Rates from 16th century.
Parliamentary Papers, 1820–.
Annual Register, 1756–.

Non-manuscript material   Small collection of prints and photographs on subjects relating to work of department.
Some 18th-century maps and charts of British coast.

Finding aids Index.

Facilities Limited photocopying.

Publications E. Carson: 'Customs Records as a Source for Historical Research', *Archives*, xviii (1977), 74
Handouts on various historical subjects.

353 HM Land Registry

Address Lincoln's Inn Fields
London WC2A 3PH

Telephone (01) 405 3488

The Land Registry does not, as a rule, retain the deeds of title which are submitted for registration. The records kept by the Registry are retained only for the periods required by the Public Records Act 1958, except in the case of permanently retained documents still under the provisions of the Land Registration Acts 1925–71, and Rules. The register of title itself is strictly private and not open to public inspection.

354 House of Lords Record Office

Address House of Lords
London SW1A 0PW

Telephone (01) 219 3074

Enquiries to Clerk of the Records, Mr H.S. Cobb

Open Mon–Fri: 9.30–5.30, preferably by appointment

Access Generally open to the public. There is a 30-year closure period on administrative and certain committee records and longer closure periods on a few classes (e.g. post-1946 public petitions).

Historical background The records of the House of Lords have been kept at Westminster since 1497 (earlier records are to be found among the Chancery and Exchequer records in the Public Record Office). The House of Lords records escaped the fire of 1834 which gutted most of the medieval Palace of Westminster but the House of Commons records were destroyed, with the exception of the original Journals dating from 1547. In 1864 the Lords records were moved into the Victoria Tower of the new Palace of Westminster where they are still housed. The Record Office was established in 1946 and now has custody both of the House of Lords records and of the House of Commons Journals and post-1834 records and certain deposited private papers.

Acquisition policy To acquire records relating to proceedings in either House of

Parliament; the history, architecture and decoration of the Palace of Westminster; Peers, MPs and Officials particularly concerned with the running of Parliament.

Major collections   c100,000 Acts of Parliament, 1497–.
   Papers laid before the House of Lords, 1531–.
   House of Lords Journals, 1510–.
   House of Commons Journals, 1547–.
   Committee Proceedings, 1610–.
   Plans of canals, railways, roads and other works, 1794–.
   Peerage Claims, 1604–.
   Historical Collections: Parliamentary Diaries, Clerks' Papers etc, 1545–.
   Private Political Papers, 1712–, including the papers of Lord Beaverbrook (1879–1964), David Lloyd George (1863–1945) and Andrew Bonar Law (1858–1923).

Non-manuscript material   Plans and drawings of the Palace of Westminster including drawings by Barry and Pugin, c1840–60; photographs of the Palace of Westminster and of Peers and MPs, 1892–.
   Sound archives: Proceedings in both Houses and certain other political recordings, 1978– (not open to the public).

Finding aids   Various typescript and MS lists and indexes.

Facilities   Photocopying. Photography. Microfilm/fiche reader.

Publications   M.F. Bond: *Guide to the Records of Parliament* (1971)
   ————*A Short Guide to the Records of Parliament* (3/1980)
   Reports of the Historical Manuscripts Commission Reports 1–14 include lists of House of Lords MSS, 1498–1693
   The Manuscripts of the House of Lords, 1693–1718 [12 vols]
   A Guide to Historical Collections of the Nineteenth and Twentieth Centuries Preserved in the House of Lords Record Office, House of Lords Record Office *Memorandum*, no. 60 (1978)
   The Annual Reports (including accessions) and reports on various collections are to be found in HLRO *Memoranda* nos. 1–66 (1950–81)

355   Hudson's Bay Company

Address   Beaver House
                 Great Trinity Lane
                 London EC4

The Hudson's Bay Company was founded in 1670 to exploit the fur trade of the region which is now Canada. A number of the archives have been published by the Hudson's Bay Board Society (32 vols, 1938–79) and The Champlain Society.
The archives, which had been housed in London, were moved to Canada in 1974. Enquiries should be made to The Keeper, Hudson's Bay Company Archives, Manitoba Department of Cultural Affairs and Historical Resources, Provincial Archives, 200 Vaughan Street, Winnipeg, Manitoba R3C OV8, Canada.

356   The Huguenot Library

Address   c/o University College Library
                   Gower Street
                   London WC1E 6BT

Telephone   (01) 387 7050 ext. 249

Enquiries to   The Hon. Librarian

Open   Strictly by appointment only with member of Huguenot Library.

Access   Fellows of the Huguenot Society of London and current members of
                   University College London; other accredited persons engaged on
                   academic or official research may be admitted after due application.

Historical background   The Huguenot Library is the joint library of the French
    Protestant Hospital founded by royal charter in 1718 (now at Rochester) and of
    the Huguenot Society of London founded in 1885. It was housed at the Hospital
    until its transfer on deposit to University College in 1957, but is not administered
    by the College archivists.

Acquisitions policy   The collection of books and archives relating to the Huguenots,
    in particular those who came to Britain, and their descendants.

Major collections   'Royal Bounty' MSS
    French Hospital archives, with some associated Huguenot philanthropic bodies.
    Collection of Huguenot pedigrees and other genealogical material made by the
    late Henry Wagner.

Finding aids   Dictionary catalogue on cards.

Facilities   Genealogical enquiries from non-members are dealt with by the Society's
    Research Assistant, Mrs C. Hickey, 19 Lloyd Square, London WC1X 9AJ (details on
    application).

Publications   55 vols (1885–) in the Society's Quarto Series, including all surviving
    registers of the Huguenot churches in England and Ireland; lists of denizations and
    naturalizations; the 'Royal Bounty' papers by Raymond Smith (vol. 51); and all
    remaining archives by Irvine Gray (vol. 56, in press). Also annual Proceedings
    (1885–).

357   Imperial College Archives

Address   University of London
                   Room 455
                   Sherfield Building
                   Imperial College
                   London SW7 2AZ

Telephone	(01) 589 5111, exts 2039/2096
Enquiries to	College Archivist, Mrs J. Pingree
Open	Mon–Fri: 10.00–5.30, by appointment
Access	Open to bona fide scholars who produce evidence of their identity. There is a 25-year closure on administrative records. There is a longer period for some records and some material is not available for consultation (e.g. students' files).

Historical background   Imperial College was established by Royal Charter in 1907 and was a federation of the Royal School of Mines and Royal College of Science and the City and Guilds College.

Acquisition policy   Material collected is directly related to the college or any of its past or present staff and students.

Major collections   Records of the Royal College of Chemistry, 1845–53; the Royal School of Mines, 1851–; the Royal College of Science, 1881–; the City and Guilds College, 1884–; Imperial College, 1907–.
MS Collections: the largest is that of T.H. Huxley (1825–95), who was a member of staff, 1854–95.

Non-manuscript material   Photographs, maps, plans and models of college buildings; photographs of staff and students; records, and videotape interviews; microfilms of financial records; scientific drawings and teaching apparatus; medals etc.

Finding aids   Card index and shelf list for the archival material. Student records are indexed by computer and listed on microfiche.

Facilities   Limited photocopying. Photography by arrangement. There are no central facilities for these and the work is carried out on a departmental basis.

Publications   W.R. Dawson: *The Huxley Papers* (London, 1946)
Handlists for most collections.

358   Imperial War Museum
Department of Documents

Address	Lambeth Road London SE1 6HZ
Telephone	(01) 735 8922 ext. 253/255
Enquiries to	Department of Documents
Open	Mon–Fri: 10.00–5.00, preferably by appointment Closed: New Year's day; Good Friday; May Day bank holiday; Dec 24–6; last two full weeks in Oct.

Access   Bona fide readers over the age of 15. Some collections are governed
                        by special access conditions.

Historical background   Although the Museum has been collecting MSS relating to
    20th-century warfare since its formation in 1917, the Department of Documents
    has its origins in the Foreign Documents Centre, which was set up in the Museum
    and supported by a grant from the Leverhulme Trust from 1964 to 1969. On the
    expiry of the grant the Centre was incorporated into the Museum as the
    Department of Documents and assumed responsibility for the acquisition and
    administration of collections of British private papers while continuing in its role
    of custodian of major series of foreign records for the period 1933 to 1945.

Acquisitions policy   To expand the Museum's holdings of unpublished records
    written by officers and other ranks of all three services and by civilians where they
    relate to their experiences in World Wars I and II.

Major collections   Foreign documents:
    Copies of papers relating to the following areas: the German military high
    command and the conduct of land campaigns of World War II; Luftwaffe planning
    and supply, 1939–45; German aerial, armaments, industrial and technical research
    during the period of the Third Reich; the Nuremberg and Tokyo War Crimes Trials.
    British Private Papers:
    Notable collections include the papers of Field Marshals Sir John French (1852–
    1925) and Sir Henry Wilson (1864–1922); Sir Henry Tizard, Scientist (1885–
    1959); Isaac Rosenberg, war poet (1890–1918).
    Several thousand collections of unpublished diaries, letters and memoirs written
    by officers and other ranks, many of them civilians in uniform (i.e. not regulars),
    during and between World Wars I and II.

Non-manuscript material   Department of Art: unique collection of correspondence
    with artists who were commissioned under the war artist schemes in World Wars
    I and II.
    Department of Films: more than 40 million feet of film, including films sponsored
    by the service ministries and the Ministry of Information, films obtained from other
    Allied and enemy sources, and television compilations and feature films.
    Department of Photographs: some 5 million photographs, including those taken by
    official war photographers and others acquired from private sources.
    Department of Sound: some 6 thousand hours of recorded material, including
    interviews conducted by Museum staff since 1962, broadcast recordings acquired
    from radio and television sources, and sound effects and music.

Finding aids   In-house lists and indexes.

Facilities   Photocopying and microfilm services. Special room for readers wishing to
    use typewriters or dictaphones.

Publications   Leaflet outlining the holdings of the Department
    *A Catalogue of the Records of the Reichsministerium Für Rüstung Und
    Kriegsproduktion*, part 1 (1969)
    For further information about individual collections of British private papers in the

Museum, readers should consult C. Cook: *Sources in British Political History 1900–1951* (especially vol. ii) and S. L. Mayer and W.J. Koenig: *The Two World Wars: a Guide to Manuscript Collections in the United Kingdom*

359 India Office Library and Records

Address   197 Blackfriars Road
London SE1 8NG

Telephone   (01) 928 9531

Enquiries to   Director, Mr B.C. Bloomfield

Open   Mon–Fri: 9.30–6.00
Sat: 9.30–1.00

Access   Approved readers.

Historical background   Archives of the East India Company from its formation in 1600 to 1858; of the Board of Control, 1784–1858; the India Office, 1858–1947; and the Burma Office, 1937–48. MSS collected by the Library (fd1801) of the East India Company and the India Office.

Acquisition policy   Following the independence of India and Burma in 1947–8, the official India Office archive is closed. Papers of individuals, ranging from Viceroys to private soldiers, are still being acquired, together with relevant oriental MSS.

Major collections   India Office Records: c200,000 vols and files which form the official archive; while concentrating upon South Asia, the archive also covers the general history of the British penetration of Asia, ranging at different periods from St Helena, via South and East Africa, the Middle East, Malaysia, Indonesia and China, to Japan; includes maps (c20,000 items).
Oriental MSS: (c20,500); major collections in Persian and Arabic, many illuminated and illustrated.
European MSS: over 11,000 vols and boxes; private papers of such individuals as Robert, 1st Baron Clive and his son, 1733–1832; Robert Orme (1728–1801); Sir Stamford Raffles and family, 1799–1957. Viceregal collections include 1st Viscount Chelmsford, 1916–21; 1st Marquess of Curzon, 1899–1905; 1st Marquess of Dufferin and Ava, 1884–88; 1st Earl of Halifax, 1926–31; 5th Marquess of Lansdowne, 1888–94; 1st Baron Lawrence, 1841–79; 1st Earl of Northbrook, 1872–90; 1st Marquess of Reading, 1898–1935.

Non-manuscript material   India Office Records: c110,000 volumes of official publications.
India Office Library: c100,000 European printed books.
c200,000 vols of Oriental printed books.
c60,000 prints, drawings, paintings and photographs.

Finding aids   A large number of lists and indexes are available, including many contemporary finding aids. A general guide is in preparation.

Facilities   Photocopying. Photography. Microfilm/fiche reader.

Publications   A list of publications, giving details of earlier catalogues of the official archive (many of which are gradually being superseded) together with catalogues of the European MSS, Oriental MSS, European and Oriental printed books, and prints and drawings, is available upon request. The *Annual Report* lists MSS accessions and contains articles on all aspects of the collections.
W. Foster: *A Guide to the India Office Records 1600–1858* (London, 1919)
S.C. Hill: *Catalogue of the Home Miscellaneous Series of the India Office Records* (London, 1927)
J.C. Lancaster: 'The India Office Records', *Archives* ix (1970), 130
A. Farrington: *The Records of the East India College Haileybury and other Institutions* (London, 1976)
R. Seton: *Accessions of Private Collections 1937–1977* (1978)
I.A. Baxter: *A brief Guide to Biographical Sources* (London, 1979)
A. Griffin: *A brief Guide to Sources for the study of Burma in the India Office Records* (London, 1979)
P. Tuson: *The Records of the British Residency and Agencies in the Persian Gulf* (London, 1979)
A.K. Jasbir Singh: *Gandhi and Civil Disobedience: Documents in the India Office Records 1922–1946* (London, 1980)
L.A. Hall: *A brief Guide to Sources for the Study of Afghanistan in the India Office Records* (London, 1981)
J. Sims: *A List and Index of Parliamentary Papers relating to India 1908–1947* (London, 1981)
A. Farrington: *A Guide to the Records of the India Office Military Department* (in preparation)

360   Inner Temple Library

Address   Inner Temple
                 London EC4Y 7DA

Telephone   (01) 353 2959

Enquiries to   Librarian and Keeper of Manuscripts, Mr W.W.S. Breem

Open   Mon–Fri: 10.00–1.00

Access   Members of the Inner Temple; other members of the legal profession, by application to the Librarian; bona fide research scholars upon application in writing only.

Historical background   A private library, established c1507 by the Honourable Society of the Inner Temple. Its primary function is to provide legal materials for the professional activities of its members. Its general collection of literature reflects the non-professional interests of its members. This general collection is now no longer added to.

Acquisition policy   Acquisitions are restricted to legal materials relevant to the profession of barrister.

Major collections   The MS Collection comprises five groups:
The Petyt Collection (386 vols); the Barrington Collection (57 vols); the Records of the Inner Temple (39 vols); the Mitford Collection of Legal Manuscripts (79 vols); miscellaneous MSS (211 vols).
The collective material totals 9048 separate MSS of mainly historical, legal and literary interest. The Records of the Inner Temple (1546 items) consist of miscellaneous loose records of the Inn of the 16th to 18th centuries, and are not to be confused with the official records of the Inn under care of the Treasurer's Office which are kept elsewhere.

Non-manuscript material   Printed material relevant to the law of the UK and the Commonwealth.

Facilities   Photocopying of MS material is not permitted. Photography is permitted, subject to approval, through the agency of a professional photographic firm.

Publications   F.A. Inderwick and R.A. Roberts (eds.): *Calendar of Inner Temple Records* (1896–1937) [5 vols, privately printed, covering the period 1505–1800; these relate to the records of the Inn under care of the Treasurer's Office]
J.C. Davies (ed.): *Catalogue of Manuscripts in the Library of the Honourable Society of the Inner Temple* (1972) [3 vols; sets available for sale on application to the Librarian]

361   Institute of Advanced Legal Studies Library

Address   University of London
17 Russell Square
London W1H 0BE

Telephone   (01) 637 1731

No archives are held.

362   Institute of Archaeology

Address   University of London
31–4 Gordon Square
London WC1H 0PY

Telephone   (01) 387 6052

Enquiries to   Librarian, Miss H.M. Bell

Open   Term: Mon–Fri: 10.00–8.00

                         Sat: 10.00–4.30
                Vacation: Mon–Fri: 10.00–5.30
                         Sat: 10.00–4.30 (closed during Summer vacation)

Access   Members of London University and bona fide researchers on
                  application.

Historical background   The Institute of Archaeology was founded in 1937 by Dr
    (later Sir) Mortimer Wheeler as a 'laboratory of archaeological science' where 'the
    archaeologist of the future may learn his business'. Originally a postgraduate
    Institute only, in 1968 it began to take undergraduate students and at present it is
    by far the largest archaeological teaching and research institute in the country,
    with more students than any other department of archaeology in Britain.

Acquisitions policy   The library acquires books by purchase, exchange and
    donation, but has no deliberate policy in acquiring archival material, all of which
    has come by unsolicited gift.

Major collections   Excavation records: field note-books, photographs, maps, indexes
    of finds etc, predominantly of Western Asiatic sites. (The large collection relating
    to the excavations at Lachish (Tell Duweir) is being sold and transferred to the
    British Museum.)
    Working note-books of Professor Gordon Childe, former Director of the Institute.
    Some letters, newspaper cuttings etc, deposited by individuals.

Non-manuscript material   Negatives and prints of air-photographs of the Middle East
    taken by the RAF after World War I.
    Various collections of photographs of general archaeological interest (largely
    uncatalogued).

Finding aids   Brief lists of the excavation material. Detailed finding lists for the air-
    photographs.

Facilities   Photocopying. Photography. Microfilm/fiche reader.

363   Institute of Commonwealth Studies

Address   University of London
                   27 Russell Square
                   London WC1B 5DS

Telephone   (01) 580 5876

Enquiries to   Librarian, Mrs P.M. Larby

Open   Term: Mon–Wed: 9.30–7.00
                        Thurs–Fri: 9.30–6.00
                   Vacation: Mon–Fri: 9.30–5.30

Access   Postgraduate and other bona fide research students on production
                   of identification.

Historical background   The Institute was founded in 1949 to promote advanced study of the Commonwealth and Empire and to provide facilities for postgraduate students and academic staff engaged in research on the Commonwealth in the fields of social study and recent history.

Acquisitions policy   Advanced level monographs, research papers, official and other primary documents on and from countries of the Commonwealth are collected. Archival collections are normally built up by donation rather than purchase.

Major collections   Southern Africa collection: MS and cyclostyled material, much of political interest relating to countries of Southern Africa south of the Zambezi, collected under the Southern Africa Materials Project, 1973–6.

Non-manuscript material   Political parties collection of materials issued by political parties in the Commonwealth: 6000 items, including conference proceedings, posters, car stickers, constitutions, manifestos and campaign literature. Some microfilms.

Finding aids   Accession list: political parties supplement (annual). List of holdings.

Facilities   Photocopying. Microfilm/fiche reader.

Publications   V.J. Bloomfield: 'African ephemera', *Proceedings of the International Conference on African Bibliography, Nairobi, 1967*, (ed. J.D. Pearson) (London, 1969) [on political party collection]
B. Willan: *The Southern African Materials Project, University of London, 1973–76* (London, 1980)

364   Institute of Education Library

Address	University of London 11–13 Ridgmount Street London WC1E 7AH
Telephone	(01) 637 0846
Enquiries to	Librarian, Dr N.W. Beswick
Open	Term: Mon–Thurs: 9.30–8.00 Fri: 9.30–7.00 Sat: 9.30–12.30 Vacation (Christmas and Easter): Mon–Fri: 9.30–7.00, Sat: 9.30–12.30 (Summer): Mon–Fri: 9.30–6.00
Access	Generally open to the public, but written application should be made to the Librarian by those wishing to consult archives.

Historical background   The University of London Institute of Education came into existence in 1902 as the London Day Training College, financed and controlled by the London County Council with the academic support of the University of London. In 1932 it was agreed that the College should be transferred wholly to the control of the University of London with the title Institute of Education.

Acquisitions policy   Archives of organizations concerned with education are accepted, if sufficient storage space is available.

Major collections   German archive: papers relating to German educational reconstruction after World War II (mainly microfiche).
Incorporated Association of Assistant Masters in Secondary Schools papers, c1899–c1960.
National Union of Women Teachers minute books and other administrative papers.
World Education Fellowship (formerly the New Education Fellowship) papers, c1936–c1972 (further papers may be deposited at a later date).
The Library does not hold the Institute's own archives.

Non-manuscript material   World Education Fellowship: tape recordings of conference speeches and Mrs Ensor's reminiscences.

Facilities   Photocopying. Microfilm/fiche readers.

Publications   *World Education Fellowship*, Royal Commission on Historical Manuscripts Report no.74/1 (1974)
Incorporated Association of Assistant Masters in Secondary Schools, Royal Commission on Historical Manuscripts Report no.75/12 (1975)

365   Institute of Geological Sciences

Address   Exhibition Road
London SW7 2DE

Telephone   (01) 589 3444

Enquiries to   Chief Librarian and Archivist, Mr K.J. Spencer

Open   Mon–Fri: 10.00–4.30, appointment preferred.

Access   Generally open to the public. Two weeks' notice is needed before material from series IGS 3 and 4 can be consulted.

Historical background   The collection and organization of the Institute's archives began in 1967 in order to bring together and preserve manuscript, graphic, photographic and ephemeral printed material of all kinds relating to the history of British geological sciences, and in particular to the history of the Institute of Geological Sciences and its forerunners, the Geological Survey, the Museum of Practical Geology, and Overseas Geological Surveys. In 1971 a major conservation programme was undertaken using the services of the Public Record Office. This is now completed. The scope of the collection, over 30,000 items, has been widened to include material about geology on an international basis; the overall aim being to provide a national geological archive available for public reference.

Acquisitions policy   To add to the existing collection in pursuance of the Institute's role as a repository for national geological archives.

Major collections   Arranged on a system originally laid down by the Public Record Office, in four series:
IGS 1: correspondence and papers, paintings, drawings, photographs.
IGS 2: registered files.
IGS 3: official field notebooks of Geological Survey staff.
IGS 4: original 'fieldslips' of published Geographical Survey maps.
[prior to July 1973 the series bore the prefix GSM]
Apart from the Institute's own archives [which include constituent bodies, the Geological Survey, Museum of Practical Geology, Royal School of Mines and Mining Record Office] a wide range of other collections includes the records of the Palaeontographical Society, 1847–1950.
Correspondence and notes of celebrated geologists in many varied collections, much of which has been donated during the last 15 years.

Non-manuscript material   25,000 photographs (survey and geology).
Drawings and ephemera.
MS maps of British geology produced by the Geographical Survey [now part of the Institute] and many unpublished maps, mostly produced in the 19th century.

Finding aids   Typescript guide to the archives. Typescript registers to the whole collection are available at the Institute's libraries at Leeds and Edinburgh, and at the Public Record Office. The collection is currently being indexed in detail and a card index is maintained in each library.

Facilities   Microfilm. Photocopying.

366   Institute of Germanic Studies

Address   University of London
29 Russell Square
London WC1B 5DP

Telephone   (01) 580 2711/3480

Enquiries to   Librarian, Mr W. Abbey (general archive queries)
Dr J.L. Flood (History of German studies in Great Britain)
The Hon. Secretary (English Goethe Society papers)
Professor C.V. Bock (Dept of German, Westfield College, London NW3 7JT, for Gundolf Archive)

Open   Mon–Fri: 9.30–6.00; Wed in term: 9.30–7.00

Access   Staff and postgraduates of Departments of Germanic Languages and Literature in the University of London; all others on written application.

Historical background The Institute was founded in 1950 as an independent institute of the University of London. It is sponsored by the Senate of the University. The objects of the Institute are to promote the advancement of the study of Germanic languages and literature and to provide facilities for research and opportunities for contacts between scholars, the former through its library which concentrates its resources mainly on primary texts and journals, the latter through regular seminars and lectures. The initiator of the Institute and its first Honorary Director (1950–53) was Professor L.A. Willoughby.

Acquisitions policy To strengthen existing archive collections by encouraging donations or deposits, and, if necessary, by purchase.

Major collections Majut Correspondence: letters to Dr R. Majut (formerly of Leicester University) from German scholars in Berlin, 1920s–1930s; letters from Jethro Bithell, 1940s–1950s.
Bithell Correspondence: letters to Jethro Bithell from various correspondents.
Breul Correspondence: letters to Karl Breul, first Schröder Professor of German at Cambridge, from various correspondents, c1900–32.
Correspondence of German writers and scholars with Professor E.M. Butler, Professor W. Rose, Professor L.W. Forster and others.
Gundolf Archive: letters to and from Professor Friedrich Gundolf of Heidelberg, with typescripts and MSS of lectures, poems, publications, etc, c1900–31 (c1000 items).
History of German studies in Great Britain: records collected on behalf of the Conference of University Teachers of German in Great Britain and Ireland (on deposit).
English Goethe Society: records and papers (on deposit).

Non-manuscript material Photographs; printed material such as offprints, newspaper articles, theatre programmes, invitation cards etc.
Large collection of pamphlets and cuttings, as well as books on German languages and literature, many of which complement the MSS collection.

Finding aids Gundolf Archive: typed handlist. Card index in progress for all other material.

Facilities Self-service photocopying. Microfilm/microfiche reader.

Publications C.V. Bock: 'First Report on the Gundolf Papers at the Institute of Germanic Languages and Literature in the University of London', *German Life and Letters*, New series no.15 (1961/2), 16
C. Neutjens: *Friedrich Gundolf: ein bibliographischer Apparat* (Bonn, 1969) [includes almost complete list of the Gundolf Archive]

367   Institute of Historical Research

Address   University of London
                   Senate House
                   London WC1E 7HU

Telephone   (01) 636 0272

Enquiries to   Secretary and Librarian, Mr W. Kellaway

With the exception of the Institute's own records all archival material is deposited in the University of London Library (*see* entry **495**).

368   Institute of Latin American Studies Library

Address   University of London
                   31 Tavistock Square
                   London WC1H 9HA

No archives are held.

369   Institute of United States Studies Library

Address   University of London
                   31 Tavistock Square
                   London WC1H 9HA

No archives are held.

370   Institution of Civil Engineers (ICE)

Address   1–7 Great George Street
                   Westminster
                   London SW1P 3AA

Telephone   (01) 222 7722

Enquiries to   The Archivist
                   or
                   The Librarian

Open   Mon–Fri: 9.15–5.30

Access   Items can be consulted in the Library by members of the Institution
                   and by approved readers by prior arrangement.

Historical background   The Institution was founded in 1818, absorbing the Smeatonian Civil Engineers which continues as a dining club. The first Royal Charter was received in 1828. The Institution is the learned society and qualifying body for the civil engineering profession. The Library has as its nucleus the gifts of Thomas Telford (1757–1834), who became the Institution's first President in 1820. The archive collections consist of records relating to the Institution and to the civil engineering profession.

Acquisitions policy   All important ICE records. Select civil engineering archives, usually acquired by the Library by gift, very occasionally by purchase.

Major collections   ICE archives: records of meetings, membership, accounts; Council and committees' minutes; MSS of early papers; minute books of the Society of Civil Engineers, 1771–92, and the Society of Smeatonian Civil Engineers, 1793–. Civil engineering archives: MS records relating to the work of Telford; the Rennie family – John Rennie (1761–1821), George Rennie (1791–1866) and Sir John Rennie (1794–1874); John Smeaton (1724–92); the Thames Tunnel.

Non-manuscript material   Engineering drawings and plans; prints; paintings; portraits; slides; photographs.
Medals; various artefacts, e.g. drawings and instruments belonging to Telford.

Finding aids   Various indexes and lists, including 'Archives of the ICE provisional list' (1979).

Facilities   Microform reader/printer. Photocopying.

Publications   *Collection of prints and drawings* (1978) [duplicated typescript]
Save Engineering Records (1979) [pamphlet]

371   Institution of Electrical Engineers

Address   Archives Department
Savoy Place
London WC2R 0BL

Telephone   (01) 240 1871

Enquiries to   Archivist, Mrs E.D.P. Symons

Open   Mon–Fri: 10.00–5.00, by appointment

Access   Bona fide researchers.

Historical background   The Institution was founded in 1871 as the Society of Telegraph Engineers, taking its present name in 1888. A Royal Charter granted in 1921 recognized it as the representative body of electrical engineers in the United Kingdom. The Institution houses a Library (formed in 1880) and an Archives Department (formed in 1975), which holds manuscript material relating to the history and development of magnetism and electricity from medieval times to the present, and modern papers relating to the development of telegraphy, the submarine cable, electrical engineering and physics.

Acquisition policy   To acquire by donation, deposit or purchase, material relevant to the history and development of electrical engineering and electronics, and allied fields including modern industrial records.

Major collections   Archives of the Institution: official records and working papers of the Institution, 1871–.
Special Collection Manuscripts: material deposited in or acquired by the Institution; including medieval MSS; the scientific papers of Michael Faraday (1791–1867), Sir Francis Ronalds (1788–1873), Oliver Heaviside (1850–1925); Sir William Fothergil Cooke (1806–79) including letters from Sir Charles Wheatstone (1802–75); several 19th- and 20th-century engineers and academics.
National Archive for Electrical Science and Technology: modern technical and manufacturing records and engineering drawings.

Non-manuscript material   Portraits (mainly photographs and engravings) of eminent scientists and electrical engineers, Presidents of the Institution, 18th–20th centuries.
Photographs of electrical equipment and Institution events.
Silvanus Phillips Thompson Collection of 1000 rare books relating to magnetism and electricity, 15th–19th centuries.
Sir Francis Ronalds Collection of 2000 rare books and 3000 pamphlets relating to magnetism and electricity and the development of the telegraph, 17th–19th centuries.

Finding aids   General index to all collections. Handlists for most collections. Index to photograph collections.

Facilities   Photocopying. Photography by arrangement.

Publications   Catalogues to rare book collections:
F. Ronalds: *Catalogue of Books and Papers relating to Electricity, Magnetism, the Electric Telegraph* (1880)
S.P. Thompson: *Handlist of Magnetic and Electrical Books* (1914)

372   Institution of Mechanical Engineers

Address   1 Birdcage Walk
                   Westminster
                   London SW1H 9JJ

Telephone   (01) 222 7899

Enquiries to   Librarian, Mr S.G. Morrison
                   or
                   Information Officer, Mr John Devine

Open	Mon–Fri: 9.30–5.30
Access	Bona fide researchers.

Historical background   The Institution was formed in 1847 and moved into its current premises in 1899; the library was purpose-built at that time. The library contains some 150,000 publications covering all aspects of mechanical engineering and fringe engineering subjects.

Acquisitions policy   To maintain the collection on mechanical engineering by purchase, donation or presentation.

Major collections   Many original letters to and from famous engineers, including an extensive collection from George Stephenson (1781–1848), first President of the Institution.

Non-manuscript material   10,000 pamphlets.
Drawings, paintings and prints.

Facilities   Photocopying. Microfilm reader/printer.

Publications   R.H. Parsons: *A History of the Institution of Mechanical Engineers 1847–1947* (1947) [centenary vol.]

373   Institution of Mining and Metallurgy

Address	44 Portland Place London W1N 4BR
Telephone	(01) 580 3802
Enquiries to	Head of Library and Information Service, Mr M. McGarr

A library was started in 1894 soon after the founding of the Institution. Internal administrative archives are held; there is also an extensive map collection and a small group of unpublished articles dating from the 1900s and 1940s.

374   Islington Libraries Archives and Local History Collections

Address	Islington Central Library 2 Fieldway Crescent London N5 1PF
Telephone	(01) 609 3051 ext. 31/33
Enquiries to	The Principal Reference Librarian
Open	Mon–Fri: 9.00–8.00 Sat: 9.00–5.00

Access Generally open to the public.

Historical background Founded in 1887 when Clerkenwell adopted the Public Libraries Acts and in being from 1890 – Islington since 1906.

Acquisitions policy To acquire all possible material, in any format, by gift or purchase.

Major collections Extensive records, including deeds, rate books etc, relating to Islington, Highbury, Holloway, Tufnell Park and all parts of Islington; Vestry minutes, 1662–.

Non-manuscript material Special collections relating to W.R. Sickert (1860–1942) and pictures of G.S. Fletcher.
Maps and plans.

Finding aids Catalogues arranged by class and subject, finding word, authors etc.

Facilities Photocopying. Microfilm reader/printer.

375 Islington Libraries Archives and Local History Collections

Address Finsbury Library
245 St John Street
London EC1 4NB

Telephone (01) 609 3051 ext. 66

Enquiries to Finsbury Reference Librarian, Mr J. Metcalfe

Open Mon, Tues, Thurs: 9.00–8.00
Wed, Fri: 9.00–1.00
Sat: 9.00–5.00

Access Generally open to the public. Appointment necessary.

Historical background Founded in 1887 when Clerkenwell adopted the Public Libraries Acts and in being from 1890.

Acquisitions policy To acquire all possible material, in any format, by gift or purchase.

Major collections Papers and special collections relating to Finsbury, Clerkenwell, St Luke's and Sadler's Wells.
Finsbury Dispensary records, 1790–; Penton Estate records.

Non-manuscript material Special collections include iconographic material.

Finding aids Catalogues arranged by class and subject, finding word, authors etc.

Facilities Photocopying. Microfilm readers.

376 The Jewish Museum

Address   Woburn House
             Upper Woburn Place
             London WC1H 5EP

Telephone   (01) 387 3081/2

Enquiries to   The Curator

The Museum was founded in 1932. Its collections, including the Fergusson Collection, with papers of many eminent figures, was transferred to the Anglo-Jewish Archive (*see* entry **305**) in 1979. It retains only marriage certificates, press-cuttings, photographs and engravings of Jewish interest.

377 Jews' College Library

Address   Finchley Synagogue
             Kinloss Gardens
             London N3 3DU

Telephone   (01) 346 7647

Enquiries to   Librarian, Mr Ezra Kahn
             or
             Catalogue Librarian, Mr Aron Prys

Open   Term: Mon, Tues, Thurs: 10.00–4.45
                 Wed: 10.00–6.00
                 Fri: 10.00–1.00
             Vacation: Mon–Thurs: 10.00–4.45
                 Wed: 10.00–6.00
                 Fri: 10.00–1.00
             Closed: all Jewish Holy-days and public holidays.

Access   Open to those who are interested in Hebrew and Jewish Studies. Students, scholars and other enquirers who need guidance should telephone prior to a visit and produce a letter of introduction.

Historical background   The Library was founded in 1860. It is part of Jews' College which trains students to become rabbis, cantors, and teachers; it is also used for general Jewish studies.

Acquisition policy   Acquisition is dependent on the amount of donations received. Financial assistance is welcomed as well as donations, from individual books to entire collections.

Major collections   Jews' College Collection of MSS (*c*150 vols).
    Montefiore Collection of MSS (*c*600 vols).

Non-manuscript material Jews' College Collection of printed books and pamphlets (*c*55,000 vols).
Montefiore Collection of printed books (*c*3000 vols).
Hebrew and Jewish Periodicals Collection.

Finding aids Lists and indexes.

Facilities Photocopying. Microfilm reader.

Publications H. Hirschfield: *Descriptive Catalogue of the Hebrew MSS of the Montefiore Library* (London, 1904) 1969)

378 Keats House

Address	Wentworth Place
	Keats Grove
	Hampstead
	London NW3 2RR
Telephone	(01) 435 2062
Enquiries to	Assistant Curator, Mrs C.M. Gee
Open	Mon–Sat: 10.00–1.00; 2.00–6.00
	Sun: 2.00–5.00
Access	Approved readers on written request.

Historical background The Keats Collection was begun in 1897 by Hampstead Public Library and transferred to Keats House, when the house was acquired in 1921. It was opened to the public in 1925. The London Borough of Camden continues to maintain the Collection and the house as part of the Libraries and Arts Department.

Acquisitions policy To add to the collections on Keats, Shelley, Byron, Leigh Hunt and their circles and to maintain the collection on general Romantic literature. To add, where possible, to the relics of the poets.

Major collections Dilke Collection (presented 1911): contains MSS, books, paintings, relics of Keats.
Leigh-Browne Lockyer Collection: contains 20 commonplace books relating to friends of Keats.

Non-manuscript material Kate Greenaway Collection: original drawings, proofs, Christmas cards and books.
Charles Lamb Collection: *c*1000 books on Lamb.
Maurice Buxton Forman Collection: *c*2500 books on Keats and his circle.
Smaller collections from the families of Fanny Brawne, Charles Brown, Joseph Severn and Fanny Keats.

Finding aids Old catalogue of MSS and Relics (1966). Card catalogue of pamphlets and ephemera. Re-cataloguing in progress.

Facilities   Photocopying in adjacent Branch Library. Microfilm reader.

Publications   *Guide to Keats House* (8/1980)

379   Kensington and Chelsea Borough Libraries

Address   Central Library
                     Hornton Street
                     London W8 7RX

Telephone   (01) 937 2542 ext. 38

Enquiries to   Local Studies Librarian, Mr B.R. Curle

Open   Mon, Tues, Thurs: 10.00–8.00
                     Wed, Sat: 10.00–5.00
                     Previous notice advisable, and essential for Chelsea Library MSS

Access   Generally open to the public.

Historical background   The local history department operates on behalf of Kensington Council under the Local Government (Records) Act 1962, although no formal records management scheme is in operation yet. Collections are based on pre-1965 boundaries but include material common to both libraries.

Acquisitions policy   To acquire by donation, deposit or purchase material of relevance to the history of the boroughs.

Major collections   Usual local authority record holdings and deposited collections including the following which have a wider significance:
Records of Chelsea Literary and Scientific Institution, 1846–79; and Chelsea Arts Club, 1890–1974.
Correspondence of Frederick, Lord Leighton (1830–96) with G.F. Watts and others (c350 letters).

Non-manuscript material   Extensive collections of illustrations, photographs, newspaper cuttings and maps.

Finding aids   Some card catalogues and indexes. Brief list of Alexander family MSS. Transcript of Leighton collection.

Publications   A number of publications, including *Historic Kensington in Maps 1741–1894* and *Historical Chelsea in Maps 1700–1894* [list of publications available at the Central Library]

380 King's College Hospital Medical School Library

Address   Denmark Hill
                 London SE5 8RX

Telephone   (01) 274 6222 ext. 2069

Enquiries to   Chief Librarian, Miss G.M. Penelow

The Library holds Hospital and Medical School minute books from the mid-19th century; some of Lord Lister's case records; a few volumes of workhouse records; and a small number of personal papers. No catalogue or list is available.

381 King's College London Archives

Address   King's College London
                 Strand
                 London WC2R 2LS

Telephone   (01) 836 5454 ext. 2187

Enquiries to   College Archivist, Miss Patricia Methven

Open   By appointment
                 Term: Mon–Fri: 9.30–5.30
                 Vacation: Mon–Fri: 9.30–4.30
                 Closed last fortnight in August

Access   Researchers who can demonstrate their bona fides. 30-year closure on records pertaining to College business. Personal records are closed for 80 years but may be consulted under special conditions.

Historical background   King's College London was founded in 1828. Archives were collected from that date, and have been considerably enriched by a succession of benefactors to the library.

Acquisitions policy   Internal records and personal papers of staff and students.

Major collections   Records created by the College, 1828–, and including King's College for Women, the Strand School and records relating to King's College School; many eminent members of staff have deposited substantial collections of papers from the College's foundation to the present day.
Other collections: P.H. Leathes, especially 18th-century antiquarian and topographical literature, c1650–1844; William Marsden, especially Oriental MSS and records relating to Portuguese missionaries, 1580–1780; Frida Mond collection, including Goethe and Schiller papers, 1794–1831; King George III Museum collection, especially Richmond Observatory records, 1769–1929.

Non-manuscript material Daguerreotypes, salt prints and waxed paper negatives including a number of stereoscopes (currently closed for conservation).

Finding aids Handlists (a certain number may be found in the National Register of Archives).

Facilities Restricted photocopying and photography. Photocopies will only exceptionally be supplied to enquirers who have not consulted the papers in person.

Publications Published lists include those prepared for the Hanson and McClare papers by the Contemporary Scientific Archives Centre (*see* 'List of Useful Addresses').

382 Labour Party Archives

Address   150 Walworth Road
London SE17 1JT

Telephone   (01) 703 0833 ext. 292

Enquiries to   Archivist, Mr Stephen Bird

Open   Mon–Fri: 10.00–5.00

Access   Labour Party members. Other users pay a research fee. 15-year restriction on all primary material.

Historical background The Labour Representation Committee, the forerunner of the Labour Party, was founded in February 1900 and the records go back to that date. Whilst a large collection accumulated in the basement of Transport House, the Party's third home, no archival policy was adopted until 1971, when the sorting and listing of the records began under the auspices of the Historical Manuscripts Commission. When the Party moved its headquarters to its present address, the archives were greatly expanded, owing to the various departments clearing out their offices. A number of other collections pre-dating the Labour Party, such as the Miniken/Vincent papers, have been added and some Party members have donated their personal collections. Recently the correspondence of the Parliamentary Labour Party has been added.

Acquisitions policy To conserve all Labour Party primary material at the Party headquarters and to make it available for research. To encourage local Labour parties to preserve their records.

Major collections National Executive Committee minutes from the first in February 1900 to date.
Correspondence from the foundation of the Labour Representation Committee in 1900 to 1907, after which there is subject-filed correspondence to the 1950s.
Papers and correspondence of the War Emergency Workers National Committee.
Miniken/Vincent papers: letters from the Chartist Henry Vincent to his cousin John

Miniken, with copies of his journal *The Western Vindicator*, 1837–41.
Papers relating to the Labour and Socialist International Congresses, 1917–63.
Correspondence of the General Secretaries Jim Middleton and Morgan Phillips and the International Secretaries, Willie Gillies and Denis Healey.

Non-manuscript material   The Labour Party Library holds volumes of a number of Labour Party and Socialist journals and newspapers, including the following: *The Daily Herald*, 1911–30; *Tribune*, 1937–; *The Clarion*, 1891–1932; *Commonweal*, 1885–89; the *New Leader*, 1922–46.
Collection of election addresses of Labour candidates, 1900–79.
Labour Party and ILP pamphlets and leaflets, 1893–.
Photographs of Labour Party personalities and events, 1900–.
ILP records on microfilm.

Finding aids   Lists and indexes of much of the material.

Facilities   Photocopying. Microfilm/fiche reader.

Publications   *Guide to the Labour Party Archives* [in preparation]

383   Lambeth Archives Department

Address   Minet Library
                  52 Knatchbull Road
                  London SE5 9QY

Telephone   (01) 733 3279

Enquiries to   The Archivist

Open   Mon, Tues, Thurs, 9.30–1.00; 2.00–5.00, preferably by
                  appointment
                  Some Sats, by appointment

Access   Generally open to the public. Restrictions on certain deposited and
                  Council Records.

Historical background   William Minet donated the library to the vestries of Lambeth and Camberwell in 1890, together with his local history collection, which related to the whole of Surrey before 1888. The library continued to be administered jointly until 1956, when the Borough of Lambeth took over sole responsibility.

Acquisitions policy   In addition to the records of the London Borough of Lambeth and its predecessors, the department seeks to acquire by purchase, donation or deposit material relating to the present county of Surrey and to those parts of the historic county now administered by the Greater London Council.

Major collections   Records of the London Borough of Lambeth and its predecessors. Manorial, parochial, charity, poor law and non-conformist records.
*c*13,000 deeds.

Special collections including:

Magdalen Hospital Trust, 1757–1975.

Theobald Papers (papers of an 18th-century steward of the Dukes of Bedford at Streatham).

Papers of the Graham and Polhill families of Clapham, including letters and diaries, 1803–55.

Thornton Papers (Thorntons of Clapham); mainly 19th century.

Correspondence of Henry Beaufoy, mostly relating to the setting up of Ragged Schools, 1847–51.

Artagen records (Artisans, Labourers and General Dwellings Company), 1867–1975.

Non-manuscript material   10,000 illustrations including 'extra-illustrated' vols (e.g. Manning and Bray's *Surrey*); 4 vols of Phillips watercolours; Petrie watercolours.
Photographic survey of the Borough of Lambeth.
Playbills and theatre programmes.
Vauxhall Gardens song books, playbills, newscuttings etc.
Printed books, guides, pamphlets and newscuttings relating to the Crystal Palace.
Cuttings collection (includes ephemera), mainly post-1956.
Maps and plans (printed and MS), from the 17th century.
Periodicals, newspapers, directories, pamphlets, including all standard printed material as well as rarer items.

Finding aids   Person, place and subject indexes to deeds and special collections. Catalogue of deeds and special collections. Street index to census returns (on microfilm) and trade index to 1841 census. Vauxhall songs index. Rate books name index, 1729–73. Lambeth Vestry minutes subject index, 1652–1858. *South London Press* index, 1909–14.

Facilities   Limited photocopying. Microfilm/fiche reader.

Publications   *Catalogue of Works Relating to the County of Surrey* (1900 suppl. 1923)
M.Y. Williams: *A Short Guide to the Surrey Collection* (1965)

384   Lambeth Palace Library

Address   London SE1 7JU

Telephone   (01) 928 6222

Enquiries to   Librarian, Mr E.G.W. Bill

Open   Mon–Fri: 10.00–5.00

Access   Bona fide students, at the discretion of the Library Committee; new readers are required to provide a letter of introduction from a person or institution of recognized standing. Special permission is needed for access to some categories of MSS (e.g. illuminated MSS).

Historical background Lambeth Palace Library is the historic library of the Archbishops of Canterbury. It was founded as a public library by Archbishop Bancroft in 1610. Its original endowment included a celebrated collection of medieval MSS and a large quantity of English and foreign printed books, to which considerable additions have been made over the past 350 years. The Church Commissioners are now responsible for the maintenance of the Library.

Acquisitions policy Records of the Archbishops of Canterbury. Historical records of the central institutions of the Church of England, with the exception of records of the General Synod and its associated bodies. Papers of ecclesiastics of national distinction and of statesmen where these fall within the Library's general area of interest.

Major collections Registers of the Archbishops of Canterbury, 13th century–.
Correspondence and papers of the Archbishops of Canterbury, 16th century–.
Archives of the Province of Canterbury, including those of the Court of Arches, the Faculty Office, the Vicar-General and Convocation.
Records of Lambeth Conferences, 1867–.
Papers of societies etc within the Church of England.
Registers of foreign churches, e.g. Basra and Khartoum.
Papers of bishops and statesmen.
Papers of the Bishops of London, including extensive collections concerning colonial America, 17th century–.

Non-manuscript material c150,000 printed books, particularly strong in English and foreign books published from the invention of printing to 1800.
Large collection of pamphlets.

Finding aids Catalogues and indexes.

Facilities Photocopying. Photography and microfilming by arrangement. Colour slides available for loan.

Publications *The Resources and Facilities of Lambeth Palace Library* (1981) [includes list of 30 published catalogues and indexes to the archives and MS collections; available from the Library]
E.G.W. Bill: *Unexpected Collections at Lambeth Palace Library*, LRCC Occasional Publication, no. 2 (London, 1982)

385   Leo Baeck College

Address   The Manor House
East End Road
Finchley
London N3

Telephone   (01) 346 0029

Enquiries to   Librarian, Mr H. Maccoby

Founded in 1956 as an institution of higher Jewish learning, it is now a Progressive Seminary training rabbis. There are no MSS apart from unpublished sermons and thesis. The large library includes pamphlets.

386   Lewisham Library Service
Archives and Local History Department

Address	The Manor House Old Road Lee London SE13 5SY
Telephone	(01) 852 5050
Enquiries to	Archivist, Mr C.W. Harrison
Open	Mon, Fri, Sat: 9.30–5.00 Tues, Thurs: 9.30–8.00
Access	Generally open to the public. Restrictions on a few official and deposited collections.

Historical background   The Archives and Local History Department for the Metropolitan Borough of Lewisham was opened at The Manor House in 1960. Since 1965 it has acted as the archive repository and local history library for the London Borough of Lewisham, including the former Metropolitan Borough of Deptford. It holds official records of the Council and its predecessor authorities, and deposited records relating to Lewisham. The Department is appointed as a place of deposit for parish, manorial and tithe records. It also has large collections of non-MS material, including museum objects. The Department also acts as the Diocesan Record Office for Southwark (Lewisham parish records).

Acquisitions policy   To collect, preserve and make available all types of archive and local history materials relating to the London Borough of Lewisham, within the terms of the relevant Local Government Acts and the Department's formal appointments.

Major collections   Local government records: Metropolitan Boroughs of Lewisham and Deptford, Lewisham Board of Works, Lee and Plumstead Board of Works, Greenwich Board of Works St Paul's Deptford Committee, parishes of Lewisham, Lee and St Paul's Deptford, 18th–20th centuries.
Anglican parish records: parishes within the deaneries of East and West Lewisham, 16th–20th centuries.
Nonconformist records: Lewisham and Peckham Methodist Circuit and constituent churches, 19th–20th centuries; Deptford Wesleyan Mission, 19th–20th centuries; Deptford and Brockley Congregational churches, 18th–20th centuries.
Family and estate records: Baring Estate, Lee, including manorial records, 16th–

19th centuries; Mayow Estate, Sydenham, 17th–20th centuries; Evelyn Estate, Deptford, 19th–20th centuries; other lesser estates and miscellaneous deeds, 16th–20th centuries.

Charity records: Deptford Fund (Albany Institute), 19th–20th centuries; Parochial and other charities and voluntary bodies, 17th–20th centuries.

Business records: Chiltonian Ltd, biscuit manufacturers, 20th century; Cobbs of Sydenham, department store, 19th–20th centuries; Stone's foundry, Deptford, 19th–20th centuries (restricted access.)

Education records: Blackheath Proprietary School, 19th–20th centuries; St Dunstan's College, Catford, 19th–20th centuries.

Clubs and societies records: Bellingham Bowling Club, 20th century; Catford Cycling Club, 19th–20th centuries.

Non-manuscript material Prints of Lewisham, London and Kent, 18th–20th centuries (1400 items).

Art collection: mainly Lewisham topography and local artists, 19th–20th centuries (500 items).

Photographic prints, postcards, negatives and transparencies: almost entirely Lewisham; includes current photographic survey, *c*1857–. (*c*30,000 items).

Printed maps and plans: Lewisham, London, Kent, Ordnance Survey etc, (16th)–20th centuries.

Local newspapers, 1834– (originals and microfilm).

Local Census returns, 1841–71 (microfilm copies).

Audio-visual materials: 53 miscellaneous local films (mainly home movies); tape recordings of local events and 'oral history' reminiscences (22 items).

Printed books and pamphlets: Lewisham, London and Kent, local history topics, works by local authors (e.g. John Evelyn, Edgar Wallace, Henry Williamson), 16th–20th centuries.

Finding aids Various card indexes. Lists of archive collections.

Facilities Photocopying. Photography. Microfilm readers.

387   Liberal Jewish Synagogue (LJS)

Address   28 St John's Wood Road
London NW8 7HA

Telephone   (01) 286 5181

Enquiries to   Archivist, Mr M.D. Brown

Open   Mon–Thurs: 9.45–5.15
Fri: 9.45–3.00

Access   Approved readers on written application.

Historical background   The LJS was founded in 1911, as an offshoot of the Jewish Religious Union formed in 1902 by the Hon. Lily Montagu (1873–1963) and

Claude Goldsmid Montefiore. Archives were transferred to the present building in 1925.

Acquisition policy Acquisitions are normally restricted to records directly related to the LJS and its ministers.

Major collections Administrative records from date of formation to the present. Miscellaneous sermons.
Personal correspondence of the Hon. Lily Montagu (1873–1963); Claude Montefiore (1858–1938); and Rabbis I.I. Mattuck (1883–1954) and L. Edgar (1905–).

Non-manuscript material Portraits of council presidents and senior ministers.

Finding aids Typescript check-lists. Ministerial correspondence is in process of being catalogued.

388   Library of the Hellenic and Roman Societies and the Institute of Classical Studies

Address University of London
31–4 Gordon Square
London WC1H 0PP

Telephone (01) 387 7697

Enquiries to The Librarian

Open Mon–Fri: 9.30–6.00
Sat: 10.00–5.00 (except August)

Access Open to members of the Hellenic Society and the Roman Society (subscription and sponsor required) and of the Institute of Classical Studies (university teachers, museum staff and registered postgraduate students are eligible for membership if working on subjects within the scope of the Institute). Postal and telephone enquiries accepted from the general public.

Historical background The Hellenic Society was founded in 1879 and the Library was begun in 1880; the Roman Society was formed in 1910 and the Library became a Joint Library. The Institute of Classical Studies (University of London) was founded 1953. The Societies then handed over primary published material to the Institute, which took responsibility for the primary (reference) library; they kept responsibility for the secondary (lending) library and slides collection. The two libraries are housed and run as one unit, but separate ownership is maintained.

Acquisitions policy MSS: to accept donations where appropriate. Printed material and slides: to maintain and improve the coverage of all aspects of classical antiquity, in close co-operation with other libraries whose interests overlap.

Major collections Wood donation (property of the Hellenic Society): 27 items including diaries and sketchbooks relating to Robert 'Palmyra' Wood (?1717–71) and his travels.

Bent diaries and notebooks (property of Hellenic Society): 25 items mainly diaries of Mabel Bent (*d*1929) with notebooks of Theodore Bent, covering travels from 1883 to 1898.

Non-manuscript material Unpublished University of London theses on classical subjects, mainly from 1954 (240 vols).

Library covering all aspects of classical antiquity: *c*55,000 books, pamphlets and bound periodicals; *c*1100 sheets of maps, (*c*60 items on microfilm or microfiche); 20,000 3¼" black and white slides; 5000 2" coloured slides.

Finding aids Wood donation list in Suppl. 3 (1926) to the Joint Library's published catalogue. List of the Bent papers. Card catalogue of unpublished theses, which are listed in University of London and Aslib lists.

Non-manuscript material Catalogues, including catalogue off colour slides (pub 1977, addenda 1978).

Facilities Photocopying and photography by courtesy of neighbouring libraries. Microfilm/fiche reader.

Publications Annual Report of the Hellenic Society (1926), xxii [on the Wood donation]

C.A. Hutton: 'The travels of "Palmyra" Wood in 1750–51', *Journal of Hellenic studies*, xlvii (1927), 102

University of London Bulletin, xiv (1974), 5

P.T. Stevens: *The Society for the Promotion of Hellenic Studies 1879–1979: a historical sketch* (London, 1979)

389   Library of the Religious Society of Friends

Address	Friends House Euston Road London NW1 2BJ
Telephone	(01) 387 3601
Enquiries to	Librarian, Mr Edward H. Milligan
Open	Mon–Fri: 10.00–5.00 Closed: week preceding Spring Bank Holiday and one week in August (variable year to year)
Access	Open to members of the Society of Friends, and to bona fide researchers, who are asked to provide advance introductions or letters of recommendation on arrival. There is an hourly fee for genealogical research. Documents less than 50 years old are not normally available.

Historical background   The Library was founded in 1673 and serves as the main reference library and central archive repository of the Religious Society of Friends in Great Britain. It moved from Devonshire House, Bishopsgate, London EC2, in 1962 to the present location.

Acquisition policy   Society archives; to strengthen MS collections of Quaker private and family papers and archives of bodies with Quaker associations, by donation, deposit and (occasionally) purchase.

Major collections   The Central Archives of the yearly meetings, including digest registers of births, marriages and burials, mid-17th century onwards.
Archives of London and Middlesex Area Meetings. (Other local Quaker records are deposited in the appropriate local Record Office.)
Swarthmore MSS: *c*1400 letters and transcripts relating to the early history of Quakerism, 17th century.
A.R. Barclay MSS: 250 letters of early Friends, 1654–88.
Gurney MSS: *c*1900 letters, mainly written by or to members of the Gurney family of Norfolk (including Joseph John Gurney and Elizabeth Fry), *c*1750–1850.
Wilkinson MSS: *c*500 letters, mainly written to Thomas Wilkinson (1751–1836) of Yanwath, Westmorland.
Lloyd MSS: *c*800 letters and papers relating to the Lloyd family of Dolobran, Montgomeryshire, and Birmingham, *c*1680–1850.
Barclay (Bury Hill) MSS: letters and papers relating to the Barclay family of Urie, Aberdeenshire, London and Bury Hill, Surrey, *c*1650–1850.

Non-manuscript material   Picture collections including some oil paintings and watercolours; engravings, etchings and lithographs; a sizeable collection of photographs of friends, meeting houses, and Quaker work.
Most British printed Quaker works since 1650, listed in J. Smith: *Descriptive Catalogue of Friends' Books* (2 vols, London, 1867; suppl., 1893); a substantial proportion of other Quaker printed works.
Printed works relating to peace, slavery, conscientious objection and relief work.
Quaker periodicals, from the early 19th century.

Finding aids   Some lists and indexes available in the Library, both to MS and printed collections.

Facilities   Photocopying. Photography. Microfilm reader.

Publications   *Journal of Friends Historical Society* (1903–) [includes numerous references to material in the Library; now published annually c/o the Library]
A typescript dictionary of Quaker biography (currently 20,000 entries) in collaboration with Haverford College, Pennsylvania, is in preparation.

390 Liddell Hart Centre for Military Archives

Address   King's College London
Strand
London WC2R 2LS

Telephone   (01) 836 5454 ext. 2187

Enquiries to   Archivist in the Liddell Hart Centre for Military Archives,
Miss Patricia Methven

Open   By appointment
Term: Mon–Fri: 9.30–5.30
Vacation: Mon–Fri: 9.30–4.30
Closed last fortnight in August

Access   Readers who can demonstrate their bona fides. Readers will also be required to undertake to submit all MSS for publication to the Trustees of the Centre prior to publication. Restricted access to some collections.

Historical background   The Centre was founded in 1964 to meet the then evident need for a depository to which owners of documents bearing on the military affairs of the 20th century could send them in the knowledge that they would be preserved under conditions which would respect their confidential nature. The Centre was named after Captain Sir Basil Liddell Hart (1895–1970) in 1978 to mark the acquisition of his papers and library.

Acquisition policy   Personal papers of higher commanders of the armed services of the 20th century.

Major collections   c200 collections of personal papers.

Non-manuscript material   Numerous photographs illustrating the life and work of the armed services from the Boer War onwards; especially important are those relating to the development of photographic reconnaissance at the turn of the century.

Finding aids   Handlists are available in the reading room and a certain number may be found in the National Register of Archives and the copyright libraries.

Facilities   Restricted photocopying and photography. Photocopies will only exceptionally be supplied to enquirers who have not consulted the papers in person.

Publications   *Consolidated List of Accessions* (October 1981)

391 Lincoln's Inn Library

Address   Holborn
               London WC2A 3TN

Telephone   (01) 242 4371

Enquiries to   The Librarian

Open   Mon–Fri: 9.30–7.00

Access   Members of Lincoln's Inn and bona fide enquirers bringing a letter
               of recommendation.

Historical background   The Library was established c1475.

Major collections   Black Books: minutes of the governing body, 1422–.
   Red Books: finance and building [7 vols], 1614–1877.
   Account Books Vacation Commons, 1629–35, 1649–58, 1660–80.
   Treasurers' Accounts, 1672–81, 1713–22.
   Works Department Accounts, 1779–84.
   Cook's Accounts, 1806–32.

392 Linnean Society of London

Address   The Library
               Burlington House
               Piccadilly
               London W1V 0LQ

Telephone   (01) 734 1040

Enquiries to   Librarian and Archivist, Miss G. Douglas

Open   By written appointment
               Mon, Tues, Thurs, Fri: 10.00–1.00; 2.00–5.00
               Wed: 2.00–5.00

Access   Bona fide scholars.

Historical background   The Society was founded in 1788. Linnaeus's MSS were
   acquired in 1828 and other MSS have been acquired by bequest or gift.

Major collections   Linnean Society Archives, including charters, minute books,
   accounts, records relating to collections of specimens, correspondence,
   ephemera, etc, from 1788.
   Zoological Club of the Linnean Society, minutes and papers, 1822–9.
   Papers read at Society meetings; most published in Society *Transactions*.
   Carolus Linnaeus MSS, 18th century.
   General collections, including archives of Society for Promoting Natural History,

1782–1822; Sir James E. Smith correspondence, 1780–1828 (c3000 letters).
Animal and Plant Sciences collections.

Non-manuscript material   Prints, watercolours and sketches included in collections.

Finding aids   Internal catalogue and various individual handlists.

Facilities   Photocopying. Photography. Microfiche reader.

Publications   *Catalogue of the Manuscripts in the Library of the Linnean Society of London* (1934–)
Natural History Manuscript Resources in the British Isles (1981), 213 [list of collections]

393   Barnet Public Libraries

Address   Local History Library
                 Hendon Catholic Social Centre
                 Egerton Gardens
                 Hendon
                 London NW4 4BE

Telephone   (01) 202 5625 ext. 27/28/55

Enquiries to   Archivist, Mrs J.M. Corden
                 Ravensfield House
                 The Burrows
                 Hendon
                 London NW4 4BE

Open   Mon–Fri: 9.30–5.30, preferably by appointment
                 Every other Sat: 9.00–4.00
                 Other times by appointment

Access   Generally open to the public.

Historical background   Archives have been collected by the Library since 1932.
   Administrative assistance is given to Barnet Local History Society.

Acquisitions policy   Material of relevance relating to the London Borough of Barnet
   (former Boroughs of Hendon and Finchley and Urban districts of Barnet, East
   Barnet and Friern Barnet). There is no modern records management programme.

Major collections   Usual local authority record holdings and deposited records of
   local interest.

Non-manuscript material   Maps, newspaper cuttings, photographs, iconographic
   material.

Publications   J. Hopkins: *A History of Hendon*, Barnet Libraries Local History
   Publications (1964)

394   London Borough of Camden
Local History Library

Address	Holborn Library 32–38 Theobalds Road London WC1X 8PA
Telephone	(01) 405 2706
Enquiries to	Librarian-in-charge, Mr R.G. Knight
Open	Mon–Thurs: 9.30–8.00 Fri: 9.30–6.00 Sat: 9.30–5.00
Access	Generally open to the public, except for certain administrative records for which there is a minimum 30-year closure.

Historical background   Holborn Library should be consulted for enquiries relating to the area of the former Holborn Borough, for all Camden rate-book searches and for the majority of other Council archives. (*See* London Borough of Camden, Swiss Cottage Library (entry **395**) for further details.)

395   London Borough of Camden
Local History Library

Address	Swiss Cottage Library 88 Avenue Road London NW3 3HA
Telephone	(01) 278 4444 ext. 3007/3001
Enquiries to	Local History Librarian, Mr M.J. Holmes
Open	Mon–Thurs: 9.30–8.00 Fri: 9.30–6.00 Sat: 9.30–5.00
Access	Generally open to the public, except for certain administrative records for which there is a minimum 30-year closure.

Historical background   In April 1965 the London Borough of Camden was formed by the amalgamation of the former Metropolitan boroughs of Hampstead, Holborn and St Pancras. Each library system had a collection of archive and local history material which had been gathered continuously since the first of the library services was established in 1896. The Local History Library acts as a repository for many archives of the London Borough of Camden and its predecessors, and many local organizations have deposited their records. Swiss Cottage Library should be consulted for general Camden enquiries and those relating to the areas covered by the former Boroughs of Hampstead and St Pancras, and all census enquiries. See also Holborn Library (entry **394**) and Keats House (entry **378**).

Acquisitions policy   The aim of the Local History Library is to record life in Camden: its people, buildings and institutions. Any material which helps to record this is acquired: museum objects, printed matter, illustrations, ephemera, tape recordings, maps and a wide variety of archives.

Major collections   The following list covers holdings in both Swiss Cottage and Holborn Libraries:

London Borough of Camden: archives of Camden and the various vestries and boards forming the present Borough, earliest minutes, 1617–; rate-books, 1726–1958 (c9000 vols).

Highgate Cemetery: registers of burials and other records, 1839–1968.

Hampstead Manor: minute books, 1742–1843, plus many papers concerning disputes and court cases, particularly concerning Hampstead Heath.

Original census returns for Hampstead, 1801 and 1811.

Transcriptions of tombstone inscriptions covering most burial grounds, 1860s–1880s; by F.T. Cansick for St Pancras and Holborn and R. Milward for Hampstead.

Heal Collection: rich collection of MSS, maps, drawings, paintings, playbills ephemera etc.

Heath and Old Hampstead Society records, 1897–.

c13,000 deeds (c3000 are catalogued and indexed).

Non-manuscript material · 4000 slides.

Paintings, drawings, prints, photographs (c30,000 items).

2800 maps (plus many uncatalogued).

Bellmore Collection: material collected by Thomas J. Barratt, mainly printed or illustrated items (21 vols).

G.B. Shaw Collection: biographies, his works (many first editions), pamphlets by him and on him, newscuttings, playbills, ephemera, records, photographs, original letters.

Dalziel Collection: c250 proof copies of engravings, the work of the Dalziel brothers who lived and worked in Hampstead and Camden Town.

Census returns for Camden area, 1841–81 (microfilm).

Finding aids   Card catalogues. Various lists and indexes.

Facilities   Photocopying. Microfilm/fiche readers/printers (both libraries). Photography by arrangement.

Publications   C. Lavell: *Beginning in Local History* (1972); *Guide to the Local History library* (1982), available on request

Guide to London Local History Resources – London Borough of Camden (1982)

396   London Borough of Enfield Libraries Department
Local History Section

Address	Southgate Town Hall Green Lanes Palmers Green London N13
Telephone	(01) 886 6555 ext. 15
Enquiries to	Local History and Museums Officer, Mr D.O. Pam or Local History Officer, Mr G.C. Dalling
Open	Mon–Sat: 9.00–5.00, preferably by appointment
Access	Generally open to the public.

Historical background   The former boroughs of Enfield and Edmonton each had a local collection, and there was also a collection of books, pamphlets, photographs and drawings at Broomfield Museum in Southgate.

Acquisition policy   To obtain by donation, purchase or photocopy material on the area of the London Borough of Enfield. To acquire non-current documents by transfer from other local authority departments.

Major collections   Local History and topography collections relating to Edmonton, Enfield and Southgate, including those of the former local government authorities in the area, the Edmonton and Enfield school boards, Edmonton and Enfield Local Boards of Health and Edmonton and Enfield vestries.

Non-manuscript material   500 paintings, drawings and prints.
20,000 photographs and 1500 transparencies.
14,000 newspaper cuttings.
All non-current maps of the area.

Finding aids   General index on cards. Detailed classified catalogue: books, pamphlets and printed ephemera. Name indexes to census records, World War II civilian casualties etc.

Facilities   Photocopying. Microfilm reader.

397   London Borough of Greenwich Libraries Department
Local History and Archives Library

Address	'Woodlands' 90 Mycenae Road Blackheath London SE3 7SE
Telephone	(01) 858 4631
Enquiries to	Local History Librarian, Mr Julian Watson
Open	Mon, Tues, Thurs: 9.00–8.00 Sat: 9.00–5.00

Historical background   The Department opened as a Local Library and Art Gallery in 1970, enabling the separate collections of the former metropolitan boroughs to be amalgamated. There is no systematic records programme yet. The department also acts as the Diocesan Record Office for Southwark (Greenwich parish records).

Major collections   Official records of the Borough and the former Civil parishes.
Deeds, 16th–20th centuries
Family and estate papers relating to Martin, Newton and Fuller families.
Records of Christchurch School, East Greenwich, 1870–1950.
Business records, including Woolwich Ferry Company.
Records of Greenwich and Lewisham Antiquarian Society; West Kent Natural History Society.

Non-manuscript materials   MS plans and surveys.
Extensive picture and photographic collections.

Facilities   Photocopying. Photography. Microfilm/fiche reader.

398   London Borough of Hackney
Archives Department

Address	Rose Lipman Library De Beauvoir Road London N1 5SQ
Telephone	(01) 241 2886
Enquiries to	Archivist
Open	Mon: 10.00–8.00 Tues–Fri: 10.00–5.30 Sat: 10.00–1.00; 2.00–5.00

Access   Generally open to the public. 30-year closure on official records. Restricted access to Bryant & May archive.

Historical background   The Department was established in 1965 and administers the official and inherited records of the former metropolitan boroughs of Hackney, Shoreditch and Stoke Newington and their predecessors, as well as the local history collections of the former authorities. Deposited records are also held.

Acquisitions policy   To preserve by departmental transfer, on a systematic basis, the non-current administrative records of the authority and to acquire by deposit, gift and purchase records which bear on the social and economic history of the community.

Major collections   Records of Hackney Borough and its predecessors.
Records of Bryant & May, matchmakers, and subsidiaries, c1850–c1965.
Other business and non-conformist records, 19th–20th centuries.
Tyssen Collection: a considerable collection of MSS, many of which are mid-19th century transcripts of records formerly in the Tower of London, including Close and Patent Rolls, 1291–1597; fines, 1189–1730; Commissary Court wills, 1374–1692; and Manorial records, 1327–1857; also books, maps and plans, drawings and paintings.

Non-manuscript material   John Dawson Collection: 600 books printed before 1767, believed to be the only surviving Parochial Library in London; MS notebooks and a diary.
Theatre Collection: includes 1000 playbills of four Shoreditch theatres, c1831–90; cuttings; illustrations; some MSS.
Maps and plans; paintings and drawings; pamphlets; several thousand photographs, mainly topographical.

Finding aids   Various lists and indexes.

Facilities   Photocopying. Microfilm/fiche readers. Photography by arrangement.

399   London Borough of Hammersmith Public Libraries
Archives Department

Address   Shepherd's Bush Library
7 Uxbridge Road
London W12 8LJ

Telephone   (01) 743 0910

Enquiries to   Borough Archivist, Mr C. Jeens

Open   By appointment only
Mon, Thurs, Fri: 9.15–5.00
Tues: 9.15–8.00

Access   Generally open to the public.

Historical background   Hammersmith and Fulham libraries accumulated material from the late 19th century. In 1955 the Metropolitan Borough of Hammersmith appointed an archivist and on the amalgamation of the borough with Fulham in 1965 appropriate material was also transferred to the archives. Local history collections at Hammersmith and Fulham libraries are under the direction of the Borough Archivist.

Acquisition policy   Deposits are accepted and in some cases purchases made of material of relevance to the history of the London Borough of Hammersmith.

Major collections   Usual local authority records and deposited collections including the following which have a wider significance:
Fulham Pottery records, 1865–1968.
Hammersmith Bridge Company records, 1824–80.
Sir William Bull's antiquarian and other papers of local interest, 1882–1930.
William Morris (1834–96) and Burne-Jones (1833–98): miscellaneous papers.

Non-manuscript material   Mostly housed at Fulham and Hammersmith Libraries, it includes:
Extensive photographic collections, drawings and prints.
Printed ephemera, theatre programmes.
Newspapers, including *West London Observer*, 1856–; newspaper cuttings.
Microfilm census returns, 1841–81.

Finding aids   Name and place index. Catalogues of deposited collections.

Facilities   Photography and photocopying by arrangement. Microfilm reader.

Publications   See contribution to *Guide to London History Resources* [available at the National Register of Archives]

400   London Borough of Haringey, Libraries, Museum and Arts Service
Bruce Castle Museum

Address   Lordship Lane
                   London N17 8NU

Telephone   (01) 808 8772

Enquiries to   Archivist, Mr I.G. Murray

Open   Tues–Fri: 10.00–5.00
                   Sat: 10.00–12.30; 1.30–5.00

Access   Generally open to the public. Notification of a visit preferred.

Historical background   Bruce Castle was opened as a world history museum in 1926 and subsequently acquired an important collection of material on the history of the British Post Office. It is now a museum of local and postal history, containing also the museum of the Middlesex Regimental Association. The collection of archival material relating to Tottenham commenced early; since the formation of the London Borough of Haringey in 1964, Hornsey and Wood Green material has been added.

Acquisitions policy   Limited to public and private records relating to the Haringey area.

Major collections   Court Rolls of the Manor of Tottenham, 1318–1732.
Records of the parishes of Tottenham and Hornsey, 15th century–.
Records of the former boroughs of Tottenham, Hornsey and Wood Green, 1850–1964.
Administrative records of the Alexandra Park and Palace, 1866–1966.

Non-manuscript material   The museum contains also a collection of local history material consisting of printed books and pamphlets, maps and plans (*c*1000); newspapers; *c*10,000 photographs; prints and paintings; census returns; other material relating to the area.

Finding aids   Lists of parochial and manorial holdings and indexes by person and place to the archive collections in general. Translations of manorial court rolls fully indexed. Census material and newspapers in process of indexing.

Facilities   Photocopying. Photography. Microfilm reader.

Publications   *Guide to London Local Studies Resources* [includes details of archive holdings and local history material in the Haringey return]
Handlist no. 1 – Deposited Parish Records [Tottenham and Hornsey]
Court Rolls of the Manor of Tottenham [translations appearing so far (6 vols): 1318–99 and 1510–82]
Illustrated exhibition catalogues covering education, leisure activities, housing, the Middlesex Regiment and transport.

401   London Borough of Merton Library

Address   Merton Cottage
                 Church Path
                 Merton Park
                 London SW19 3HH

Archives are neither held nor acquired.

402

London Borough of Newham
Local Studies Library

Address Stratford Reference Library
Water Lane
London E15 4NJ

Telephone (01) 534 4545 ext. 309/334

Enquiries to Assistant Borough Librarian, Reference and Local Studies, Miss M. Lister
or
Local Studies Librarian, Mr H. Bloch

Open Mon, Tues, Thurs, Fri: 9.30–7.00
Wed, Sat: 9.30–5.00
Intending readers should telephone first to ensure that the Local Studies Librarian will be on duty. Appointment preferred, especially for access on Sats.

Access Generally open to the public.

Historical background The Local Studies Library forms part of the Stratford Reference Library, but is housed in a separate room. The collection contains material on Essex, London and the former County Boroughs of East and West Ham. The Local Studies room was opened in 1978. Large amount of pre-20th century material, especially official records, is in Essex Record Office (*see* entry 117).

Acquisition policy To collect materials directly related to the London Borough of Newham, the former County Boroughs of East and West Ham, and Essex and London materials where relevant.

Major collections Archives of Newham Borough and its former constituent authorities.
West Ham Quarter Sessions rolls, 1894–1965; manorial rolls and books, 1603–24 and 1736–1922.
Parochial and religious records: East Ham, 1809–1965; Little Ilford, 1887–1900; West Ham, 1646–1965; Newham, 1964–.
Minute and rate books of Stratford Abbey Landowners, 1715–1874.
Records of local charities, 17th–19th centuries.
Deeds and family papers: Rawstorne of Plaistow, 17th–19th centuries; Henniker of Stratford and East Ham, 17th–19th centuries.
Non-conformist records, 19th and 20th centuries.
Air Raid Precaution files relating to East and West Ham, 1939–1945.

Non-manuscript material Newspapers and journals; newspaper cuttings, 18th–20th centuries (systematic for Newham, 1964–).
Maps and surveys of East and West Ham, 1741–.

Finding aids Catalogue. Various indexes.

Facilities   Photocopying. Microfilm reader/printer.

Publications   *Guide to the Local Studies Library*
  Background to the Borough [folder of illustrations, maps and facsimiles with notes]

403   London Borough of Tower Hamlets
Local History Library

Address   Tower Hamlets Central Library
                  277 Bancroft Road
                  London E1 4DB

Telephone   (01) 980 4366 ext. 47

Enquiries to   The Chief Librarian

Open   Mon, Tues, Thurs, Fri: 9.00–8.00
                  Wed, Sat: 9.00–5.00

Access   Generally open to the public.

Historical background   The Library is based on the local collections of the former Metropolitan Boroughs of Stepney, Poplar and Bethnal Green.

Acquisitions policy   To collect and make available material in whatever form illustrating the past, present and future of Tower Hamlets.

Major collections   Merchant Shipping Collection: books, pamphlets, illustrations, MS ship indexes especially relating to the period 1850–1920.
  *c*3500 MS vols and files, especially World War II records.
  *c*15,000 Title Deeds.
  Census returns, 1821–81 [1841–81 on microfilm].

Non-manuscript material   *c*20,000 photographs and prints.
  *c*13,000 books, pamphlets and theses.
  *c*400 boxes of cuttings.
  *c*1600 maps.
  *c*5000 transparencies.
  Microfilm files of local newspapers.
  London and local directories, from *c*1800.

Finding aids   Several catalogues and indexes to the different sections of the collection.

Facilities   Photocopying. Photography by arrangement. Microfilm/fiche readers/ printer.

Publications   C. Kerrigan: *History of Tower Hamlets* [in preparation]
  Leaflet on family history resources in the collection.

404 London Festival Ballet
Festival Ballet Archives

Address	Festival Ballet House 39 Jay Mews London SW7 2ES
Telephone	(01) 581 1245
Enquiries to	Archivist, Mr John Travis
Open	By appointment only
Access	Bona fide research students, on written application.

Historical background   The archive was established in 1975 to maintain the records of London Festival Ballet, which was founded in 1950.

Acquisitions policy   Primary and secondary material relating to the history of London Festival Ballet. Also material relating to the history of ballets in the company's repertoire and to the careers of artists who have worked with the company. Emphasis is on 20th-century ballet. Material is acquired by donation, purchase and deposit.

Major collections   Primarily records of the London Festival Ballet Company; also particularly good records of the careers of Dame Alicia Markova (1910–) and Sir Anton Dolin (1904–).
Other material relating to British and foreign dance.

Non-manuscript material   Photographic collection.
Video library, including tapes of productions and classes; some films.
Audio recordings.
Designs for Festival Ballet productions.

Finding aids   At present the archive is not catalogued.

405 London Hospital Medical College Library

Address	University of London Turner Street London E1 2AD
Telephone	(01) 377 8800 ext. 17
Enquiries to	Librarian, Mr Paul Hockney

The Library has no responsibility for archives and the College's extensive but scattered collection is uncatalogued.

406   The London Library

Address	St James's Square London SW1Y 4LG
Telephone	(01) 930 7705/6
Enquiries to	Librarian, Mr Douglas Matthews

Established in 1841 as a subscription circulating and reference library, it is one of the major independent collections in the country. The Library holds virtually no archival material apart from internal records and files relating to the Library and a few items of literary interest, for example, the notebooks of Charles Reade (1814–84).

407   London School of Hygiene and Tropical Medicine

Address	University of London Keppel Street London WC1E 7HT
Telephone	(01) 636 8636
Enquiries to	Librarian, Mr R. Brian Furner

Open	Term: Mon–Fri: 9.00–7.30
	    Sat: 9.30–12.00
	Vacation: Mon–Fri: 9.30–5.00
	    Sat: 9.30–12.00 (except August)

Access	Bona fide researchers.

Historical background   The School was opened in 1899 and the Library has existed since that date. It is the largest medical library in the University of London. There is a broad coverage of all aspects of exotic diseases and public health as well as the history of both subjects.

Acquisitions policy   To maintain the collection up to date and, where possible, acquire material relating to the history of the areas of special interest by purchase or, more usually, by donation or deposit.

Major collections   Ross Archives: c20,000 items consisting of MSS, correspondence and reprints relating to the life and work of Sir Ronald Ross (1857–1932).
Manson Collection: diaries and artefacts of Sir Patrick Manson (1844–1922).
Leiper Collection: material relating to the family of Professor Robert Thomson Leiper (1881–1969).

Daley Papers: papers relevant to the life and work of Sir (William) Allen Daley (1887–1969).

Architect's drawings for the building in Keppel Street and documents relating to the development of the London School of Hygiene and Tropical Medicine.

Non-manuscript material A small collection of photographs of personalities connected with the history of the School and Ross Institute.

Finding aids Catalogue of the Ross Archives.

Facilities Photocopying. Microfilm/fiche reader.

Publications G.K. Hall: *Dictionary Catalogue of the London School of Hygiene and Tropical Medicine* (Boston, 1965; suppl. 1970) [7 vols]
M.E. Gibson: *Catalogue of the Ross Archives* (London, 1982) [microfiche]

408 Mark Longman Library
National Book League

Address	Book House
	45 East Hill
	Wandsworth
	London SW18 2QZ
Telephone	(01) 870 9055
Enquiries to	Librarian, Ms Linda Holman
Open	Mon–Fri: 9.00–5.00, by appointment
Access	Generally open to the public; all special collections can be viewed by appointment with the Librarian.

Historical background The Mark Longman Library was founded in 1929 by the presentation of 200 books by the Secretary of the then National Book Council, Maurice Marston. The Library has since increased steadily, and now contains c8,000 books, as well as subscribing to some 50 journals. Following an appeal launched in 1973 to raise money to re-equip and fund the Library, it was renamed the Mark Longman Library in July 1975 in memory of one of its major benefactors, the late Chairman of Longmans and Chairman of the National Book League.

Acquisitions policy The Mark Longman Library is one of the country's main collections of books about books, a specialist collection of interest to bibliographers, book collectors, students and researchers in the fields of book production, librarianship, book trade history and current practice. The collection is important because of its broad scope, preserving items of historical interest alongside the latest publications.

Major collections Principally non-MSS material (*see* below).
18th- and 19th-century Book Trade: a collection of letters and business papers

signed by early British booksellers, printers and publishers.

May Lamberton Becker (1873–1958) and Arnrid Johnston collections containing correspondence.

Non-manuscript material Children's illustrators: original artwork by the animal artist Arnrid Johnston, and Diana Stanley, original illustrator of *Worzel Gummidge* and Mary Norton *The Borrowers*.

Linder Collection: *c*300 original watercolour drawings and sketches by Beatrix Potter, and first editions of many of her books, collected by the late Leslie Linder.

Perez Collection: 12,000 British bookplates, presented to the National Book League by the collector Luis Marino Perez in 1965, early 17th century to the early 1900s.

20th-century Engravers Collection: a recently-formed collection of the work of modern artists who have specialized in the use of woodcuts and etchings for book illustration and artwork, including examples of the work of Leo Wyatt, Joan Hassall and Reynolds Stone.

Facilities Photocopying. Microfiche reader.

Publications *The Linder Collection of Beatrix Potter* (1971) [illustrated catalogue]

409   Marx Memorial Library

Address	37a Clerkenwell Green London EC1R 0DU
Telephone	(01) 253 1485
Enquiries to	The Librarian
Open	Mon, Fri: 2.00–6.30 Tues–Thurs: 2.00–9.00 Sat: 11.00–1.00
Access	Library members. An annual subscription is charged. Enquiries welcomed.

Historical background The Library was started in 1933 as a response to Hitler's Fascism and the burning of Marxist and progressive books, and to commemorate the fiftieth anniversary of Karl Marx's death.

Acquisitions policy To build and maintain a library relating to all aspects of Marxism, the history of Socialism and the working-class movement.

Major collections Spanish International Brigade Archives, including letters, cuttings, pamphlets and books.

Non-manuscript material Books, pamphlets and periodicals on all aspects of Marxism and the Labour movements, with particular reference to Great Britain, including:

John Williamson Collection of the American Communist and Labour Movement.
James Klugmann Collection of Chartist and early radical literature, 1649–.
J.D. Bernal Peace Collection

Finding aids   Author and subject catalogues.

Publications   A. Rothstein: *The House on Clerkenwell Green*
Marx Memorial Library Bulletin

410   Marylebone Cricket Club Library (MCC)

Address   Lord's Cricket Ground
St John's Wood
London NW8 8QN

Telephone   (01) 289 1611

Enquiries to   Curator, Mr Stephen E.A. Green

Open   Mon–Fri: 9.30–5.30, by appointment
Most Sats in the cricket season

Access   Approved readers on written application.

Historical background   Lord's was founded in 1787 and has a historical collection of
paintings since 1864. The MCC library dates from 1893.

Acquisition policy   To build up a representative body of material on the history of
cricket.

Major collections   Domestic archives of the MCC, 1787–.
MS collections concerning other cricket clubs and famous players.

Non-manuscript material   Books, photographs and films concerning cricket.

Finding aids   Catalogues to much of the collection.

Facilities   Photocopying. Photography.

Publications   Many publications relating to Lord's but none specifically to the MS
collection.

411   Merchant Taylors' Company

Address   Merchant Taylors' Hall
30 Threadneedle Street
London EC2R 8AY

Telephone   (01) 588 1091

Enquiries to   The Clerk of the Company

Microfilm copies of all records are available at Guildhall Library (*see* entry 349). Any request for research at the Hall will be dealt with only by letter, and charitable contribution may be requested. Records are also held by the Merchant Taylors' School (*see* entry 553).

412   Methodist Missionary Society
Methodist Church Overseas Division (MCOD)

Address	25 Marylebone Road London NW1 5JR
Telephone	(01) 935 2541
Enquiries to	Assistant Archivist/Secretary, Mrs Ina Ellis
Open	Mon–Thurs: 9.00–4.30
Access	Approved readers on written application, subject to 30-year rule.

All archival material up to 1945 is now at the School of Oriental and African Studies (*see* entry 478). There will be a further move of material every five years. The MOCD still deals with written requests and will also help anyone wanting information on post-1945 material.

413   The Middlesex Hospital

Address	Mortimer Street London W1N SAA
Telephone	(01) 636 8333 ext. 7422
Enquiries to	Honorary Archivist, Mr W.R. Winterton
Open	By arrangement.
Access	By written application.

Historical background   The Middlesex Hospital was founded in 1745. The Hospital for Women, Soho Square, was founded in 1842. St Luke's Woodside, Psychiatric Hospital, was founded in 1751 and houses its own records. The other collections were brought together in 1971.

Acquisition policy   To strengthen by purchase, donation or deposit the existing collection of written, printed and photographic records relating to The Middlesex Hospital and illustrating its work and organization since its foundation in 1745.

Major collections   Middlesex Hospital: Board of Governors minutes, 1747–1974; Medical Committee minutes, 1851–; admissions registers, 1747–; lying-in registers, 1747–1829; case notes 1855–; register of surgeons' pupils and house surgeons, 1763–; physicians' pupils, 1766–; register of refugee French clergy, 1789–1814; Hospital Reports, 1820–1940 (incomplete); register of nurses, 1867–; The Hospital for Women: Reports, 1843–1940; Committee of Management minutes, 1843–1939.

Non-manuscript material   Pamphlets. Photographs.

Finding aids   Card indexes.

Facilities   Photocopying by arrangement.

414   Middlesex Polytechnic
Silver Studio Collection

Address	Bounds Green Road
	London N11 2NQ
Telephone	(01) 368 1299
Enquiries to	Keeper, Mr Mark Turner
Open	Mon–Fri: 10.00–5.00, by appointment
Access	Generally open to scholars.

Historical background   The Polytechnic was founded in 1979, on the amalgamation of several institutions. There is no centralized systematic storage of records, but some minutes of constituent bodies survive in the Education Offices etc. The Silver Studio Collection was acquired in 1967.

Acquisitions policy   Examples of Silver Studio designs are added as discovered, but the main effort is concentrated on the conservation, cataloguing and exhibiting of the existing collection.

Major collections   Records of Arthur Silver (1852–96) and Rex Silver (1879–1965), wallpaper and textile designers of London, including business and personal correspondence from manufacturers and others, e.g. Walter Crane (1845–1915), c2000 letters; day books, diaries (30 vols), 1880–1960.

Non-manuscript material   60 photographic record albums; c25,000 designs for textiles and wallpapers; c5000 textile samples; c3000 wallpaper samples; c5000 postcards.
Newspaper cuttings, scrapbooks, ephemera.
Large library.
Design objects.

Finding aids   Letters preliminarily sorted but not fully catalogued.

Facilities   Typed catalogue.

Publications   Lund Humphries: *Catalogue of Museum of London Exhibition of Silver Studio Work* (1980)

415   Ministry of Agriculture, Fisheries and Food

Address   Whitehall Place
London SW1A 2HH

Telephone   (01) 233 8544

All records are regularly transferred to the Public Record Office (*see* entry **441**), where they are made available after 30 years.

416   Ministry of Defence (MOD)
Library Services

Address   Old War Office Building
Whitehall
London SW1A 2EU

Telephone   (01) 218 9000 ext.0266

Enquiries to   Chief Librarian, Mr J.C. Andrews

The Library is strictly a printed library supplying information to the Ministry and holds no MS material: all surviving Departmental papers are held by the Public Record Office (*see* entry **441**).

417   Mocatta Library

Address   University College London
Gower Street
London WC1E 6BT

Telephone   (01) 387 7050 ext. 778

Enquiries to   Librarian, Mr Robert Kirby (Tues–Thurs: 2.00–4.00)
or
Mrs Trude Levi (Mon and Fri: 9.00–5.00)

Open   Mon–Fri: 2.00–4.00; Mon and Fri morning by arrangement
(Gaster papers open mornings, but arrangement only)

Access   Members of the Jewish Historical Society of England (JHSE) and members of University College London. Also open to the public, but if use of library is more than occasional, permission is required, and usually obtained, from the Librarian of University College.

Historical background   The Mocatta Library is the library of the Jewish Historical Society of England. Founded upon the library of Frederic David Mocatta, the library became part of University College London in 1905. The library was largely destroyed in 1940. It was reformed by the JHSE after World War II and reopened in 1954; material was added by gift, purchase or deposit. The Gaster collection was donated to University College Library after Moses Gaster's death in 1939 and is not strictly part of the Mocatta Library.

Acquisitions policy   Mainly material of Anglo-Jewish interest; however, MS material now mainly goes to the Anglo-Jewish Archive (*see* entry **305**).

Major collections   Extensive collections and papers of Jewish persons and relating to Jewish history (a number of papers in Hebrew), including:
Lucien Wolff (*d* 1930) Collection: MSS of Anglo-Jewish interest.
Löwy family papers, early 18th century, including a history of the Jews in Moravia, 1722.
Diaries, account books and letters of Sir Moses Montefiore, 1827–c1874.
Letters of George Gawler and Henry Gawler concerning agricultural and industrial training and Russian influence in Palestine, 1848–53; 1874.
Gaster Papers: correspondence, MSS, photographs and ephemera of Dr Moses Gaster, 1870–1939 (c170,000 items).

Non-manuscript material   Microfilms of the Collyer-Ferguson collection (genealogical material).
Iconographic collection, including portraits and caricatures of Anglo-Jewish persons.
Newspaper cuttings.

Finding aids   Card index catalogue of Mocatta Library.

Facilities   Photocopying. Microfilm reader by arrangement.

Publications   *Guide to the Gaster papers* (1973)
The Gaster Papers, Occasional Papers no. 2, Library of University College London (1976)

418   Morden College Archives

Address	19 St Germans Place
	London SE3
Telephone	(01) 858 3365
Enquiries to	Archivist, Miss I. Dyer
Open	Tues and Thurs only, by appointment

The Archives department holds administrative records from the foundation of the charity in 1695 and other documents relating to its endowment, the Manor of Old Court.

419 Museum of London

Address   London Wall
              London EC2Y 5HN

Telephone   (01) 600 3699

Enquiries to   Head of Library and Documentation, Ms Joanna Clark

Open   Mon–Fri office hours, by appointment only
              (The exhibition galleries of the Museum are closed on Monday.)

Access   Generally open to the public.

Historical background   The Museum of London was opened in 1976, created by the amalgamation of two major collections, the Guildhall Museum of the City of London (1826–1975) and the London Museum (1911–75).

Acquisitions policy   The Museum collects, conserves and records evidence relating to the development of London and to life in London from earliest times. Documentary evidence is excluded unless it falls within one of the following categories:
Records created by the Museum or by others (individuals or societies) in the course of research on London.
Material relating to or illuminating aspects of the existing object-collections.
Archives which form an integral part of an object-collection acquired.

Major collections   Archives of the Guildhall and London Museums, c1908–75.
Site records of archaeological excavations in the City, 1930s–; miscellaneous other site records from other parts of Greater London.
The Young MSS: commonplace books, household accounts and letters of the Young family of Limehouse (family of G.F. Young, shipbuilder), 1736–1862.
Port of London Authority archives, 1911–.
Whitefriars Glass Company archives, 1680–1980 (recently acquired, not catalogued).
Suffragette Collection, 1800–: includes Women's Social and Political Union Archive and the research papers of David Mitchell, author of *The Fighting Pankhursts*.
Miscellaneous deeds, letters, etc, 15th century–.

Non-manuscript material   Printed ephemera collection: includes trade cards, 16th century–; valentines, 19th century; material from London pleasure-gardens, 18th century, and theatres, 18th–20th centuries.
Historic photograph collection, 1840s–.
Maps and plans of London, 1553–1981.

The Library (London Collection): includes the Tangye Collection (contemporary printed works and some MSS of the Civil War/Commonwealth period, collected by Sir H. Lincoln Tangye); W.G. Bell Collection (similar, concerning the Great Fire and Plague of London); newspaper cuttings, 20th century; London Guide Books, 19th century–.

The Museum also possesses a large number of prints, drawings and oil paintings of London (please consult Dr Celina Fox, Curator of Prints, Drawings and Paintings).

Finding aids   Indexes and catalogues to the collections.

Facilities   Photocopying. Photography.

420   National Army Museum

Address   Royal Hospital Road
London SW3 4HT

Telephone   (01) 730 0717 ext. 24

Enquiries to   The Keeper of Records

Open   Tues–Sat: 10.00–4.30

Access   By reader's ticket, available on application to the Director.

Historical background   Formed in 1950 as the Indian Army Museum, it became the National Army Museum in 1959. The Museum moved to London in 1971 and a new reading room was opened in 1980.

Acquisitions policy   Printed books, MSS, photographs, prints and drawings relating to the British Army and auxiliary forces, 1485–; the Indian Army from the establishment of the East India Company to 1947; Commonwealth forces to their date of independence.

Major collections   Substantial collections of private papers, letters, journals and diaries of soldiers, giving their view of warfare, from 18th century (c1000 ft), including:
Papers of Lord Raglan (1788–1855); Sir William John Codrington (1804–1884); Field Marshal Earl Roberts (1832–1914); and Sir Henry Rawlinson (1864–1925).

Non-manuscript material   Prints and drawings including the Crookshank Collection of British military campaigns and the Cambridge Collection of British military costumes (c25,000).
c1000 albums and c100,000 loose items of photographs.
c35,000 printed books.

Finding aids   Card index by subject.

Facilities   Photography. Photocopying. Microfilming. Microfiche/film reader.

Publications   Articles on the collections in the archives appear in the *Annual Report*.

421

National Council for Voluntary Organizations (NCVO)

Address	26 Bedford Square London WC1B 3HU
Telephone	(01) 636 4066 ext. 61
Enquiries to	Head of Central Registry, Ms Irene Storer
Open	Mon–Fri: 9.00–5.00, by prior arrangement
Access	Bona fide researchers. Not all material is available.

Historical background   The National Council of Social Service (NCSS) was founded in 1919 to promote the systematic organization of voluntary social work, both nationally and locally. In 1980 it became the NCVO, with aims of encouraging and supporting voluntary organizations.

Acquisitions policy   Retains own working papers only. In certain circumstances these have been handed over to repositories (*see* 'Major collections').

Major collections   Correspondence, minutes and other papers dating back to NCVO's foundation: documents cover the development of the Welfare State, the NHS, unemployment in the 1930s, the formation of Councils for Voluntary Service and Rural Community Councils, and specific projects such as International Year of the Disabled. (Some parts have been deposited elsewhere: Standing Conference of Women's Organizations and Women's Group (Fawcett Library; *see* entry **329**); Goodman Committee (House of Lords; *see* entry **354**); material relating to Village Halls, including architects' drawings (to be transferred to local Rural Community Councils).)

Non-manuscript material   Some maps and photographs (mostly uncatalogued). Newspaper cuttings kept by Information Department.

Finding aids   Still in process of being catalogued. Typescript lists available.

Facilities   Photocopying.

Publications   M. Brasnett: *Voluntary Social Action* (1969) [history of the NCSS]

422

The National Farmers' Union

Address	Agriculture House 25–31 Knightsbridge London SW1X 7NJ
Telephone	(01) 235 5077
Enquiries to	Librarian, Mrs V. Beale

Records of the Union, 1909–1943, are housed with the Institute of Agricultural History, (*see* entry **601**).

423   National Film Archive

Address   81 Dean Street
London W1V 6AA

Telephone   (01) 437 4355

Enquiries to   Curator, Mr David Francis

Open   Mon–Fri: 10.00–5.30, by appointment

Access   Bona fide researchers may consult the Catalogue of film and TV collection, a research fee may be charged. The film and TV collection is not available for loan or hire.

Historical background   The Archive was founded in 1935, 'to maintain a national repository of films of permanent value'. Its brief was extended in the 1950s to include television programmes. There has been complementary development of a stills, posters and designs collection. The Archive is a founder-member of FIAF (International Federation of Film Archives). The National Film Archive is a Division of the British Film Institute (*see* entry **314**).

Acquisitions policy   The main aim of the Archive is to select, acquire, preserve, document and make permanently available for research and study a national collection of films and television programmes of all kinds exhibited or transmitted in the UK, from any source and of any nationality, which have lasting value as works of art, or are examples of cinema and television history, historical or scientific records, portraiture, or records of contemporary life and behaviour.

Non-manuscript material   The film and TV collection currently amounts to around 50,000 titles, ranging in period from 1895 to the present and comprising feature and fiction films, shorts, documentaries and newsreels.

Finding aids   On-site catalogues of all films and television programmes in preservation, consisting of complete alphabetical title list, subject index of non-fiction and newsfilm classified by UDC, biographical index and cast index.

Facilities   Microfilm/reader-printer. 35mm and 16mm table viewers for film study. Video players and monitors for video-cassette viewings. Stills copying service.

Publications   *National Film Archive Cataloguing Rules* (1960)
National Film Archive Catalogue (1965–80) [part i: Silent News Films; part ii: Silent Fiction Films; vol i: Non-fiction Films]
Catalogue of Viewing Copies [rev. annually]
Keeping Television Alive: The Television Work of the National Film Archive

424   National Gallery

Address	Trafalgar Square London WC2N 5DN
Telephone	(01) 839 3321
Enquiries to	Research Assistant, Mrs A.M. Bacon
Open	Mon—Fri: 10.00—6.00, by appointment
Access	Approved readers on written application only.

Historical background   The National Gallery was founded in 1824 and houses the National Gallery collection, which comprises old master pictures, mid-13th—early 20th centuries.

Acquisition policy   To strengthen by purchase or donation existing records directly related to the National Gallery, its history and formation, and to its benefactors, trustees and staff.

Major collections   A limited collection of archives concerned with the history of the picture collection.

Finding aids   Various indexes and lists.

425   National Maritime Museum

Address	Romney Road Greenwich London SE10 9NF
Telephone	(01) 858 4422
Enquiries to	Readers' Service Section
Open	Mon—Fri: 10.00—5.00 Sat: 10.00—1.00; 2.00—5.00, prior arrangement necessary. (In 1981 financial constraints led to a restricted service on Mondays, similar to that provided on Saturdays; this is likely to continue.)
Access	By reader's ticket issued to prospective readers who can prove their identity. Access to certain items is restricted. A large amount of material is housed away from the Museum; prior arrangement may therefore be necessary.

Historical background   The Museum was formally established by Act of Parliament in 1934 for the instruction and study of the maritime history of Great Britain; it opened in 1937. The MS collections began to be assembled before this date. The

Museum is a recognized repository for Public Records. The Manuscript Section is now part of the Department of Printed Books and Manuscripts; other departments in the Museum include Pictures, Weapons and Antiquities, Ships, Navigation and Astronomy and the Archaeological Research Centre.

Acquisition policy To collect by purchase, gift or deposit MSS relating to all aspects of maritime affairs.

Major collections Public records, including Admiralty, Navy Board and dockyard records, 17th–19th centuries.
Business records, including P&O and subsidiary companies; Lloyds Register Surveys, c1833–c1964; Shipbuilders and Repairers National Association.
Personal papers: c300 collections, including papers of Edward Hawke (1705–81); Lord Hood (1724–1816); Viscount Nelson (1758–1805); Matthew Flinders (1774–1814); Lord Beatty (d 1936); Baron Chatfield (1873–1967).
Artificial collections, including the maritime papers collected by Sir Thomas Phillips
Items acquired singly by the Museum, e.g. atlases, logs, signal books, letter- and order-books; tapes relating to seamen and shipboard life.

Non-manuscript material Library: c50,000 books and pamphlets.
Ships' Draught collection (Department of Ships, including the Admiralty Draught collection).
Chart collection (Department of Navigation).
Historic photographs (Department of Pictures; Photo Records).

Finding aids Lists are available for most of the collection. Index of people, places, ships and subjects.

Facilities Photocopying. Photography. Microfilming. Microfilm/fiche reader.

Publications R.J.B. Knight (ed.): *Guide to the Manuscripts in the National Maritime Museum*: i, *The Personal Collections* (1977);ii, *Public Records, Business Records and Artificial Collections* (1980; suppl. in preparation)

426 National Monuments Record

Address   Fortress House
                     23 Savile Row
                     London W1X 1AB

Telephone   (01) 734 6010 ext. 328 (architecture) ext. 355 (archaeology) ext. 337 (air photography)

Enquiries to   The Secretary

Open   Mon–Fri: 10.00–5.30

Access   Generally open to the public.

Historical background   Founded in 1941 as the National Buildings Record, it was formed to be a systematic photographic record of English architecture. In 1963 the Record became part of the Royal Commission on Historic Monuments (RCHM *fd* 1908) and the name was changed to the National Monuments Record when its work was extended into the fields of archaeology and air photography.

Major collections   Record cards of published and unpublished RCHM(E) inventory work, 1908–.
400,000 Ordnance Survey record cards of archaeological sites and excavation records on microfiche.

Non-manuscript material   2,000,000 photographs, measured drawings and written reports of historic buildings and archaeological sites in England.
800,000 photographic negatives.
Small collection of reference books.

Finding aids   Various lists and indexes.

Facilities   Photocopying. Photography. Microfilm/fiche readers/printers.

Publications   Five-yearly Report
Annual accessions list
National Monuments Record Photographic Archives (1981–) [series designed to publicize the collection]

427   National Museum of Labour History

Address   Limehouse Town Hall
Commercial Road
London E14

Telephone   (01) 515 3229

Enquiries to   Curator, Mr T.J. McCarthy

Open   Tues–Fri: 9.30–5.00

Access   Generally open to the public.

Historical background   To obtain records from individuals and organizations who have played a part in the evolution of the social history of the people.

Major collections   Extensive collections of records and papers covering radical movements from the Industrial Revolution onwards, including minute books of the Labour Party, Social Democratic Federation, Independent Labour Party.
Various trade unions' archives, (e.g. Agricultural Workers).
Numerous collections of papers of individuals including eminent radical supporters.

Non-manuscript material   Photographs, photographic slides and negatives.
Recordings on subjects related to the nature of the Museum.

Early newspapers, ephemera and posters.
Extensive Reference Library.

Finding aids   Record cards. Indexes.

Facilities   Photocopying. Photography. Microfilm reader.

428   National Portrait Gallery Archive and Library

Address   15 Carlton House Terrace
London SW1Y 5AH

Telephone   (01) 930 1552

Enquiries to   Head of Archive and Library, Mr Malcolm Rogers

Open   Mon–Fri: 10.00–5.00, by appointment

Access   Bona fide researchers.

Historical background   The National Portrait Gallery was founded in 1856. The Archive and Library were originally built up to aid staff in the acquisition of portraits, in the compiling of catalogues of the collection, and to help answer general enquiries. The Archive and Library moved from the main Gallery building to Carlton House Terrace in 1980 to provide room for expansion.

Acquisition policy   Photographs, engravings, drawings and MSS which extend the collection of information on British portraiture are acquired by purchase and donation.

Major collections   Principally non-MSS material (*see* below).
Sketchbooks and diaries of Sir George Scharf (1820–95).
Artists' sitters' books, account books, letters, etc.
Collection of MSS on the history of the National Portrait Gallery and the building.

Non-manuscript material   Extensive collection of reference photographs and other reference material on portraits in collections other than the Gallery's.
Portrait engravings.
Original portrait photographs.
Original drawings which are not considered suitable for the Gallery's primary collection.

Finding aids   Card catalogue to Library and MSS. Card index of portraits.

Facilities   Limited photocopying. Photography.

Publications   A. Davies and E. Kilmurray: *Dictionary of British Portraiture* (1979–81) [4 vols; based on information in the Archive]

429 National Trust

Address 42 Queen Anne's Gate
London SW1H 9AS

The Trust was established in 1895. Internal archives only are held; any papers acquired with properties are deposited at the appropriate local record office.

430 Naval Historical Library
Ministry of Defence (MOD)

Address Empress State Building
Lillie Road
London SW6 IT2

Telephone (01) 385 1244

Enquiries to The Head of Naval Historical Library (postal enquiries)

Open Mon–Fri: 10.00–5.00, prior notification of visit preferred but not essential

Access Bona fide researchers.

Historical background The Library was founded early in the 19th century and estalished in 1862 by Order in Council. It is scheduled for amalgamation with the MOD (central) Library early in 1985.

Acquisitions policy To update the maritime history, technology and policy collections.

Major collections Fisher (of Kilvestone) papers, 1900–10.

Non-manuscript material Charts and atlases (printed), 16th century–.
Admiralty (public) publications.
Pamphlets.

Finding aids Unique cataloguing/indexing system.

Facilities Photocopying (subject to staff availability).

431 Office of Population Censuses and Surveys (OPCS)

Address General Register Office
St Catherine's House
10 Kingsway
London WC2B 6JP

Telephone	(01) 242 0262
Enquiries to	The Registrar General (postal enquiries)
Open	Mon–Fri: 8.30–4.30
Access	The search rooms are open to the public. (Birth and marriage indexes are housed at the Public Search Room, St Catherine's House. Death indexes are housed at Alexandra House, 31 Kingsway, London WC2B 6TR.) 100-year closure on census returns; some other papers have an extended closure beyond the normal 30-year period.

Historical background   The General Register Office was founded in 1837 when a service was created for the state registration of births and deaths and the solemnization and registration of marriages in England and Wales; registration commenced from 1 July 1837. On 11 May 1970 the General Register Office merged with the Government Social Survey to form the Office of Population Censuses and Surveys. The General Register Office still exists as a statutory body under the direction of the Registrar General who is also Director of OPCS. The decennial census returns and departmental papers worthy of preservation are transferred to the Public Record Office under the provisions of the Public Records Acts, 1958 and 1967.

Acquisitions policy   The records accumulate as registration proceeds.

Major collections   Birth, death and marriage registers, 1 July 1837–.
Records kept by British Consuls and High Commissioners in respect of British subjects abroad, 1849–.
Army records (personnel and families), some of which date back to 1761.
Royal Air Force returns, 1920–.
Births and deaths on board British registered vessels, 1894–.

Finding aids   Indexes to Birth, Death and Marriage Registers.

Publications   Information leaflets [available on request]

432   Order of St John
Library and Museum

Address	St John's Gate Clerkenwell London EC1M 4DA
Telephone	(01) 253 6644
Enquiries to	The Curator
Open	Mon–Fri: 10.00–5.00, by appointment
Access	Bona fide researchers.

Historical background The collection was started after the establishment of the Venerable Order of St John in 1831 and more particularly after the acquisition of St John's Gate in 1874, where the collection is housed. St John's Gate and Priory Church are the remains of the Priory of the Medieval Order of St John, dissolved in 1540. The Museum was opened to the public on a regular basis in 1978.

Acquisitions policy To build up a representative collection relating to the Order of St John and its foundations, and to St John Ambulance and the Ophthalmic Hospital, Jerusalem, by purchase and donation.

Major collections c5000 MS records of the Order of St John, including documents relating to British properties, and estates in France, Malta and Rhodes, 1140–.
Records relating to the foundation of St John Ambulance and its activities in various wars including Zulu, Boer and both World Wars, 1860s–.

Non-manuscript material Prints and drawings collection.
Photographs and glass negatives.
Pamphlets and books relating to the Order of St John, 15th–20th centuries.
Coins: Crusader and Order of St John (including the King, Wilkinson and Sprawson collections).
St John Ambulance Collections.

Finding aids Card index. Some typescript catalogues.

Facilities Photocopying. Photography.

Publications *The Early Statutes of the Knights Hospitallers* (1932)
The Thirteenth-Century Statutes of the Knights Hospitallers (1933)
Six Documents relating to Queen Mary's Restoration of the Grand Priories of England and Ireland (1935)
Notes on the History of the Library and Museum (1945)

433 Overseas Development Institute Library

Address 10–11 Percy Street
London W1P 0JB

No archives are held.

434 Pharmaceutical Society

Address 1 Lambeth High Street
London SE1 7JN

Telephone (01) 735 9141

Enquiries to Librarian, Miss P.M. North

Open   By appointment

Access   Bona fide researchers.

Historical background   The Society was founded in 1841 and material was acquired over the years.

Acquisitions policy   Material relating to the profession of pharmacy, by donation or purchase.

Major collections   Archives of the Society [some were destroyed during World War II].
Not particularly strong on MSS, but small collection of letters and recipe books.

Non-manuscript material   Early printed works including herbals and prints. Photographs.

Finding aids   MSS are described in the main catalogue; specialist staff will need to be consulted.

Facilities   Photocopying.

435   The Polish Library

Address   238–46 King Street
London W6 0RF

Telephone   (01) 741 0474

Enquiries to   Librarian, Dr Z. Jagodziński

Open   Mon, Wed: 10.00–8.00
Tues, Fri: 10.00–5.00
Thurs, Sat: 10.00–1.00
(July, Aug, Sept: Mon–Wed, Fri: 10.00–5.00; Thurs, Sat: as above)

Access   Scholars and researchers, subject to Library rules and reservations of depositors, which in some cases means closure until the end of the 20th century.

Historical background   The Polish Library was established in 1942 by the Ministry of Education of the Polish Government in Exile. Between 1948 and 1953 it became part of the Polish University College in London; later it was taken over by the Committee for the Education of Poles in the United Kingdom. Since 1967 the Polish Social and Cultural Association has accepted full responsibility for the Library as its legal owner on behalf of the Polish community in Great Britain.

Acquisitions policy   To collect and preserve records of cultural, social, political, literary etc, activities and life of Poles abroad, especially in the UK since 1939.

Major collections   Private archive of Jozef Retinger (1888–1960).

Archives of Polish war-time or post-war periodicals in the UK and some Polish émigré organizations.

MSS, private papers, diaries, memoirs, biographical materials, literary works etc, of Polish writers, scholars, politicians, artists and other members of Polish communities abroad.

Non-manuscript material   Large collections of periodicals (*c*3300 titles), bookplates, photographs, maps and engravings.

Books, pamphlets etc, including special collections of Conradiana (in co-operation with the Joseph Conrad Society), and works on Anglo-Polish relations.

Finding aids   Inventory books. Card catalogues.

Facilities   Photocopying.

436   Polytechnic of Central London

Address   309 Regent Street
               London W1R 8AL

Telephone   (01) 580 2020 ext. 106/54

Enquiries to The Assistant Librarian, Archives

Open   By appointment

Access   To any person with a relevant enquiry.

Historical background   The Polytechnic of Central London was so designated on 1 May 1970. It was formed by the amalgamation of The Polytechnic, Regent Street and the Holborn College of Law, Language and Commerce, and its roots lie in the educational and religious work of Quintin Hogg among the poorer classes of young people in central London in the 1860s. In order to extend his work Hogg purchased in 1881 the building in Regent Street which had formerly housed the Royal Polytechnic Institution. At Regent Street were developed the schemes of practical technical education which resulted in the foundation of other polytechnics moulded on Quintin Hogg's Institution. The variety of educational activities was matched by the provision of a large number of social, religious and recreational opportunities, since it was always Hogg's intention to develop the whole man—body, mind and soul.

Acquisitions policy   To collect material relating to the Royal Polytechnic Institution and to the Polytechnic of Central London (with emphasis on the period up to 1970).

Major collections   The material available is mostly connected with the Regent Street Polytechnic and the Royal Polytechnic Institution which preceded it on the Regent Street site.

Royal Polytechnic Institution: a limited amount of legal and other material regarding the founding of the Institution; bound volumes of programmes of activities at the Institution, 1873–8; newspaper cuttings, extracts from journals etc.

The Polytechnic: minutes of the Governing Body, 1891–; *Polytechnic Magazine*, June 1879–Aug 1971; prospectuses (bound vols), 1888–1965; membership records, educational records and governing body correspondence for various periods; records of some clubs and societies; some material related to the Sidney Webb College of Education, and particular Schools of the Polytechnic; volumes of press cuttings, mainly pre-1950.

Non-manuscript material   A collection of photographs: buildings; educational and recreational activities; personalities (students, members, governors etc); events. A few tapes of speeches on particular occasions.

Finding aids   A list of material and an information index on cards is in preparation.

Facilities   Photocopying. Photography.

437   Polytechnic of North London Archive

Address   Holloway Road
               London N7 8DB

Telephone   (01) 607 2789 ext. 2451

Enquiries to Ms Angela Taylor

Open   By appointment

Access   Open to students studying the history of education.

Historical background   The Polytechnic of North London was formed by the amalgamation of the Northern Polytechnic (founded 1896) and North Western Polytechnic (founded 1929).

Acquisitions policy   Active collection of relevant material. Everything welcome.

Major collections   Archives date from the 1890s and include internal and external correspondence.
Receipts and invoices relating to the supplies bought by the Polytechnics.
Student record cards.

Non-manuscript material   Departmental and committee papers and reports.
Polytechnic anniversary documents.
Prospectuses, annual reports, governors minutes, student union publications, arts societies programmes, annual accounts, course leaflets, house journals.
Files of press cuttings, relating to the Polytechnic.
Large collection of photographs of buildings and classrooms.
Oral history collection [in process].

Finding aids   Card index in preparation.

Facilities   Photocopying. Photography.

Publications   An illustrated history of Northern and North-Western Polytechnics will be published in 1982.

438   Polytechnic of the South Bank

Address   Library Services
                   Borough Road
                   London SE1 0AA

No archives are held.

439   Port of London Authority (PLA)

Address   London Dock House
                   1 Thomas More Street
                   London E1 9AZ
                   (PLA are considering moving their library in 1982 and it would be advisable to check the address before visiting the Library.)

Telephone   (01) 476 6900

Enquiries to   Mr S.A. Miller

Open   Mon–Fri: 9.00–5.00, by appointment

Access   Students and researchers, by arrangement. Not all of the material is housed in the Library itself and potential users should explain their needs at the time of making an appointment.

Major collections   Minute books of the London Dock companies and the Thames navigation authorities from 1770.
Craft registers.
Some PLA archives from 1911 are at the Museum of London (*see* entry **419**).

Non-manuscript material   A selection of books on London and riverside areas.

440   Post Office Archives

Address   Post Office Headquarters Building
                   St Martin's-le-Grand
                   London EC1A 1HQ

Telephone   (01) 432 4521

Enquiries to   Departmental Record Officer and Archivist, Mrs Jean Farrugia

Open   Mon–Fri: 9.00–4.40

Access   Generally open to the public.

Historical background   The Archives Unit holds all the archives of the Post Office, including those of British Telecommunications and the National Savings Bank up to 1969. The National Postal Museum is part of the same administrative department; it was established on the initiative of R.M. Phillips, who donated his collection to the Post Office in 1965. British Telecom is now a separate organization (*see* entry **321**).

Acquisitions policy   The National Postal Museum occasionally purchases philatelic material to enhance its official philatelic collections.

Major collections   Archives Unit: administrative records reflecting all aspects of Post Office operations, late 17th century–.
National Postal Museum: correspondence of the De La Rue Company, stamp printers for the Post Office, 1855–1955.
R.M. Phillips Collection of material relating to British stamps, 1837–.

Non-manuscript material   National Postal Museum: Post Office Collection of artists' designs, stamp assays, die proofs and registration sheets from the mid-19th century. Berne (Universal Postal Union) Collection: stamps from other countries sharing common postal arrangements with the UK, acquired by exchange, 1878–.

Finding aids   Catalogues for records held in both the Archives Unit and the National Postal Muscum (although for the latter much of the material is permanently on public display).

Facilities   Photocopying. Photography.

Publications   Research articles and notes on material in the R.M. Phillips and other Museum collections are published in the monthly *Philatelic Bulletin* [these and a list of Museum publications are available from the Museum]

441   Public Record Office (PRO)

Address   Chancery Lane
London WC2 1AH
and
Ruskin Avenue
Kew, Richmond
Surrey TW9 4DU

Telephone   (01) 405 0741 (Chancery Lane)
(01) 876 3444 (Kew)

Enquiries to   The Keeper (postal enquiries)
or
Enquiries (telephone)

Open   Mon–Fri: 9.30–5.00
Closed: public and privilege holidays and usually the first fortnight of each October (for stock-taking)

Access   On production of form of identity; in the case of non-nationals a passport is required.

Historical background   The Chancery Lane building was constructed, following the Public Records Act 1838, between 1851 and 1899. By the 1960s overcrowding caused the need for a new building at Kew (where modern records are now kept), which was opened in 1977. Medieval and early modern records are retained at Chancery Lane.

Acquisitions policy   All government archives selected for permanent preservation are transferred to the PRO for the use of the public 30 years after their creation, unless retained for a longer period by the Department concerned under statute or on application to the Lord Chancellor.

Non-manuscript material   Proportionately little, but including the following:
Official printed material.
Extensive photograph holdings (mostly scattered among administrative archives).
Some film, sound and machine-readable material (no facilities for use).
Staff library, very strong on English topograpy; administrative, legal and archival history; and inland transport.

Finding aids   MS, typescript and card lists, indexes and calendars.

Facilities   Photocopying. Photography. Microfilming. Microfilm/fiche reader/printer.

Publications   *Guide* (1963–8)
Current Guide [in preparation]
Lists, indexes, calendars, handbooks, museum catalogue and pamphlets [listed in HMSO sectional list no. 24]
Lists and indexes published by List and Index Society

442   Queen Elizabeth College Library

Address   University of London
Campden Hill Road
Kensington
London W8 7AH

No archives are held.

443   Queen Mary College

Address   University of London
                   Mile End Road
                   London E1 4NS

Telephone   (01) 980 4811

Enquiries to   Librarian, Mr T.H. Bowyer

Open   Term and Easter Vacation: Mon–Fri: 9.15–9.00
                   Christmas and Summer Vacation: Mon–Fri: 9.15–5.00

Access   On written application to the Librarian.

Historical background   The People's Palace in the East End was founded in 1884, following a fund-raising occasion at the Mansion House. Educational aspects were dealt with by the People's Palace Technical Schools, founded in 1887. The latter expanded from part-time evening classes to the status of a full school of the University of London, shown in its changes of name first to the East London Technical College in 1892, then to East London College and finally to Queen Mary College in 1934. Cultural activities at the People's Palace continued but dwindled and the College bought the building in 1954. Queen Mary College is a multi-faculty college covering Arts, Laws, Social Studies, Science and Engineering.

Acquisitions policy   To reflect the teaching and research needs of the staff and students in the College.

Major collections   Archives of the People's Palace, including press cuttings, minutes of meetings and correspondence, 1884–c1920.

Non-manuscript material   Palace *Journal*.

Finding aids   Chronological index on cards. Handlist.

Facilities   Photocopying.

444   Royal Agricultural Society

Address   35 Belgrave Square
                   London SW1X 8QN

Telephone   (01) 235 5323

Most of the official administrative records, including the old Board of Agriculture records, have been transferred to the Institute of Agricultural History (*see* entry **601**).

445 Royal Air Force Museum

Address	Department of Aviation Records Aerodrome Road Hendon London NW9 5LL
Telephone	(01) 205 2266 ext. 41/42
Enquiries to	Mr R.F. Barker
Open	Reading room: Mon–Fri: 10.00–4.30, by appointment
Access	Bona fide researchers.

Historical background   The museum was set up in 1968 and has acquired individual documents and collections of papers since its opening at Hendon in 1972. While the emphasis is predominantly on British military aviation, a substantial collection on civil aviation has also been deposited at the museum.

Acquisitions policy   Additions are constantly made to the collection, primarily by donation, but there is also an active microfilming programme.

Major collections   Imperial Airways and British Overseas Airways Corporation Archives.
Supermarine Spitfire drawings.
Papers including those of the following: Lord Brabazon of Tara (1884–1964); ACM Lord Dowding (1882–1970); MRAF Lord Newall (1886–1963); ACM Sir James Robb (1895–1968); Lt. Col. V.C. Richmond (designer of R 101); Handley Page Company.

Non-manuscript material   Large photograph, art and book collections.

Finding aids   Card catalogues for all collections.

Facilities   Photocopying. Photography. Reproduction of microforms.

446 Royal Anthropological Institute of Great Britain and Ireland
Manuscript and Archive Collection

Address	56 Queen Anne Street London W1M 9LA
Enquiries to	Mr K. Forrest, c/o Museum of Mankind, 6 Burlington Gardens, London W1X 2EX
Telephone	(01) 437 2224 ext.31
Open	Mon–Fri: 10.00–5.00, appointment preferred

Access   Accredited scholars after written application.

Historical background   The Institute was founded in 1871, incorporating the Ethnological Society and the Anthropological Society of London. It is recognized internationally as the representative body in the UK for the whole field of the study of Man. In 1976 the Library was donated to the British Museum and merged with the Departmental Library of the Museum of Mankind, where the Manuscript and Archive Collection is now also stored.

Acquisitions policy   There have been no major additions in recent years.

Major collections   Domestic archives of the Institute, consisting of minute books, committee reports and other documents relating to its administrative history, mid-19th century–.
MSS of fieldwork and papers of the following: E.H. Man, 1875–1920; Sir Everard im Thurn, 1887–1923; H.B.T. Somerville, 1889–1900; M.E. Durham, 1900–36; M.W. Hilton-Simpson, 1906–9; R.S. Rattray, 1919–27; J.D. Unwin, 1919–34; Marian W. Smith, 1945.

Non-manuscript material   See entry **447**.
Film library of *c*80 films is managed by the Scottish Film Archive, Glasgow (*see* entry **214**).

Finding aids   Typescript catalogue, entry by author with author/subject index (3 vols, compiled by B.J. Kirkpatrick).

447   Royal Anthropological Institute of Great Britain and Ireland
Photographic Collection

Address   56 Queen Anne Street
London W1M 9LA

Telephone   (01) 486 6832

Enquiries to   Photo Librarian, Ms Linda Hunt
or
Chairperson, Photographic Committee, Mrs Roslyn Poignant

Open   By appointment, preferably on written application because of limited staff.

Access   Consultation of the illustrated catalogue is open to all. Access to the original photographs is restricted and by written application only.

Historical background   The photographic collection predates the Institute (founded in 1871), some of the photographs having come from one or other of the parent societies – the Ethnological Society and the Anthropological Society of London. Few photographs in the collection can be dated earlier than the 1860s. The taking of photographs was actively encouraged by the Institute in *Notes and Queries on Anthropology* (first published in 1874). The photographs taken by these early 'travellers and anthropological observers', as well as those by some of the pioneers of modern anthropological fieldwork, were lodged with the Institute. Attempts to classify the photographs began in 1899, at first independently, and then in conjunction with the British Association. This scheme was abandoned by 1911. After a period of inactivity work began again on the collection in 1974 and this has led to more recent acquisitions.

Acquisitions policy   To encourage the deposit or donation of photographs relating to the study of anthropology, including early photographs with anthropological content, and recent or present-day fieldwork photographs with associated documentation. Very limited resources for purchase.

Non-manuscript material   Two sets of photographs of 'The natives of Greater Russia', organized by Professor A. Bogdanov for the Moscow Ethnographic Exhibition in 1867.
Prince Roland Bonaparte's Portraits of the Lapps, 1884.
Album of *c*700 photographs selected from the Collection of Portraits of North American Indians made by the US Geological Survey in the 1870s, and presented by F.V. Hayden, geologist in charge of the survey.
Other collections:
E.H. Man (Andaman and Nicobar Islands), Sir Everard im Thurn (Indians of Guyana), P.A. Johnston and T. Hoffman (Sikkim, Nepal and Tibet), Vice-Admiral H.B.T. Somerville (Solomon Islands and New Hebrides), all 19th century.
R.W. Williamson (Melanesia), C.G. Seligman (Vedda of Sri Lanka, Sudan, New Guinea), Emil Torday (Congo), Mary Edith Durham (Bosnia, Serbia and Albania), Professor I. Schapera (Southern Africa), M.W. Hilton-Simpson (Algeria), all early 20th century.
E.E. Evans-Pritchard (Africa), Sir Max Gluckman (Southern Africa), 1930s and 1940s.
Dr Audrey Richards (East Africa).

Finding aids   Illustrated catalogue cards for three-quarters of the prints and some of the negatives. Various lists.

Facilities   Photocopying. Photography. Copy prints may be supplied on loan to general users (publishers etc), as well as to specialists and students. Loan and reproduction fees charged are available on application.

Publications   R. Poignant: *Observers of Man. A catalogue of an exhibition of a selection of photographs from the collection of the Royal Anthropological Institute* (1980)

448   Royal Army Medical College Muniment Room

Address	Millbank London SW1P 4RJ
Telephone	(01) 834 9060 ext. 220
Enquiries to	Curator, Colonel (retd) A.V. Tennuci RAM Corps Historical Museum, Keogh Barracks, Ash Vale, Aldershot, Hampshire GU12 5RQ
Open	By appointment with the Curator
Access	Approved persons on application to the Curator.

Historical background   Originally the Army Medical School, Fort Pitt, Chatham, in the mid-19th century, it later moved to Netley and finally to Millbank, London, as the RAM College where the muniments are housed, although administered via the Curator, RAM Corps Historical Museum.

Acquisitions policy   To acquire items of military medical interest by donation and purchase with assistance from grants.

Major collections   MSS and records of medical persons throughout military medical history.
Records of the official history of the two World Wars in the Army Medical Services.

Non-manuscript material   17 original paintings by Sir Charles Bell (1774–1842) of wounds at the Battle of Waterloo.

Finding aids   Catalogues. Index cards. Acquisition Books are held at both the Museum and the Muniment Room.

Facilities   Photocopying.

Publications   *Muniment Room RAMC* (1973)

449   Royal Artillery Institution

Address	Old Royal Military Academy Woolwich Common London SE18 4JJ
Telephone	(01) 856 5533 ext. 2523
Enquiries to	The Assistant Secretary (Historical)
Open	Mon–Fri: 10.00–12.00; 2.00–4.00, by appointment
Access	By written appointment only to bona fide historians and researchers

who hold recongized readers' tickets and who are approved by the Royal Artillery Historical Affairs Committee.

Historical background   The Royal Artillery Library and Archives were founded in 1778. The Library is a private Reference Library relating to the tactics, technology, application and history of both British and foreign artillery.

Acquisitions policy   Only books and papers directly concerned with artillery are sought. The majority of acquisitions are donated to the Institution, few are purchased.

Major collections   RA Unit War Diaries, World Wars I and II.
c1500 military documents covering a variety of artillery topics, 1716–.

Non-manuscript material   Photographs.
2 portfolios of 19th-century military sketches and caricatures by Colonel L.G. Fawkes, RA.
Royal Carriage Dept, Woolwich, 19th-century lithographed general assembly plates of artillery equipment.
Rare books.

Finding aids   Cross-referenced lists.

Facilities   Photocopying. Microfilm/fiche reader.

Publications   *Battery Records of The Royal Artillery 1716–1877* [2 vols]
Proceedings of The Royal Artillery Historical Society

450   Royal Asiatic Society Library

Address   56 Queen Anne Street
                   London W1M 9LA

Telephone   (01) 935 8944

Enquiries to   The Librarian, Dr R. Pankhurst

Open   Mon–Fri: 11.00–5.00
                   Closed: August

Access   Fellows, and approved bona fide scholars on written application.

Historical background   The Society was founded by Henry Thomas Colebrooke in 1823 and received its first Royal Charter that year for 'the investigation of subjects connected with and for the encouragement of science, literature and the arts in relation to Asia'. Many distinguished scholars have been associated with the Society and their work has been presented at its meetings.

Acquisitions policy   Material in the field of Oriental Studies, mainly by donation, but some limited purchases.

Major collections   The collection is devoted to the history, culture and languages of Asia and North Africa:
Large collections of Oriental MSS, including Arabic, Persian and Urdu MSS given by the late Professor C.A. Storey in 1967.
Eckstein Collection, includes letters by and about Sir Richard Burton (1821–90).

Non-manuscript material   Drawings and engravings.
c100,000 vols of books and periodicals.

Facilities   Reading room.

451   Royal Astronomical Society

Address   The Library
Burlington House
Piccadilly
London W1V 0NL

Telephone   (01) 734 3307/4582

Enquiries to   The Librarian, Mrs E. Lake
(from end of 1982: Mr P.H. Hingley)

Open   Mon–Fri: 10.00–5.00

Access   Private library, but access may be granted on application in writing to the Librarian.

Historical background   The astronomical library has been accumulated by the Royal Astronomical Society since its foundation in 1820. The founder President was William Herschel and through the benefactions of his family and others associated with it, the Society has become the owner and guardian of many MSS and archives of value. The archives were temporarily stored at Churchill College, Cambridge, and the collection was catalogued by a temporary archivist (appointed by the Council of the Society), 1974–76.

Acquisitions policy   Gifts of astronomically significant archives and books are considered on their merits.

Major collections   The archive comprises c500 boxes:
The Society's general correspondence, 1820–.
Papers generated by the Society: minutes, register books, papers relating to expeditions etc.
MSS, mainly 35 named collections.
Herschel Archive: papers of Sir William Herschel (1738–1822), Sir John Herschel (1792–1871) and Caroline Herschel (1750–1848) (housed at Churchill College, Cambridge (*see* entry **90**) and not available for study, but microfilm copy at Burlington House).

Non-manuscript material   Astronomical drawings.
   Extensive library of astronomical and some other scientific works.

Finding aids   Guide to Library (in preparation).

Facilities   Photocopying. Microfilm/fiche reader.

Publications   J.A. Bennett: 'Catalogue of the Archives of the Royal Astronomical Society', *Memoirs of the RAS*, lxxxv (1978)

452   Royal College of Art

Address   College Library
   Kensington Gore
   London SW7 2EU

There are no deposited collections. Some internal records are held but are not open to the public.

453   Royal College of Music

Address   Parry Room Library
   Prince Consort Road
   London SW7 2BS

Telephone   (01) 589 3643

Enquiries to   Reference Librarian, Mr Christopher Bornet
   or
   Keeper of Portraits, Mr Oliver Davies

Open   Mon–Fri: 10.00–5.00
   Specialized enquiries preferably by appointment

Access   Generally open to the public, but reading room space is extremely limited during term.

Historical background   The Royal College of Music was founded by the Prince of Wales, later King Edward VII, in 1883. The important library of the Sacred Harmonic Society was bought for it by public subscription in that year, and very large collections of MSS and early printed music, musical instruments, and portraits have accumulated since, mainly by gift. The Department of Portraits opened in 1971.

Acquisitions policy   To extend all classes of material held by purchase as well as gift.

Major collections   MSS, much of English origin, 16th century–.
   MSS of people connected with the College, e.g. Hubert Parry (1848–1918), Herbert Howells (*b* 1892).

Full scores of British choral music, mainly autograph, from Novello's publishing house, 19th century.
Sir Henry Walford Davies (1869–1941) and Frank Bridge (1879–1941) Trust MSS [housed on loan].

Non-manuscript material   Antiquarian books and special collections.
Department of Portraits: many thousands of prints, photographs and original portraits.
*c*75,000 concert programmes.
Reference library on musical iconography.

Finding aids   Author-title index to MSS and published books. Handlist of portraits.

Facilities   Microfilm reader. Photocopying of approved material. Photography.

454   Royal College of Physicians of London (RCP)

Address   11 St Andrew's Place
                London NW1 4LE

Telephone   (01) 935 1174

Enquiries to   Librarian, Mr D.N. Cole

Open   Mon–Fri: 10.00–5.00

Access   Bona fide researchers. Special permission is required for access to certain College records of the last 50 years.

Historical background   The RCP was granted its first Charter in 1518 by Henry VIII. Thomas Linacre gave some of his own books to form the basis of the original library, most of which perished in the Great Fire of London (1666). In 1680 the Marquis of Dorchester made the College a gift of his own library. Since the 19th century, following the donation of Matthew Baillie's chemical, anatomical and medical books, the College has added to the library, with growing emphasis on the history of medicine. The MSS in the library evolved largely as a record of College activities, with the addition of donations of private collections and autograph letters.

Acquisitions policy   To add to existing collections by purchase, donations and deposits, with special emphasis on individual items, e.g. autograph letters relating to medical biography and history.

Major collections   Internal records of the College, including typescripts of College lectures and addresses, 16th–20th centuries.
Western MSS: several thousand, including collections of papers relating to individual doctors, e.g. C.E. Brown-Séquard (1817–94); Samuel Gee (1839–1911); Sir Robert Arthur Young (1871–1959); Lord Rosenheim (1908–72).

Autograph letter collection, mainly 19th and 20th centuries.
Oriental MSS: c66 vols, representing six languages, mostly Arabic.

Non-manuscript material Collections of prints, photographs and slides; plans; medical book-plate collection.
Microfilm/fiche of the College Annals.
c48,000 printed books and pamphlets, including journals.

Finding aids Card indexes to autograph letters and general archives.

Facilities Photocopying. Microfilming of material not suitable for photocopying, and the making of photographs and slides, can be arranged.

Publications *Catalogue of Legal Documents* (1924)
Catalogue of Oriental MSS (1951)
N.R. Ker: *Medieval Manuscripts in British Libraries* (1969), 196.

455 Royal College of Surgeons of England (RCS)

Address   35–43 Lincoln's Inn Fields
                   London WC2A 3PN

Telephone   (01) 405 3474

Enquiries to   Librarian, Mr E.H. Cornelius

Open   Mon–Fri: 10.00–6.00
                   Closed: August

Access   Approved readers on written application. New readers should enclose with their application a letter of introduction from a Fellow of the College, the Dean of a Medical School, or a Medical Librarian.

Historical background The College was founded in 1800, as successor to the Surgeons Company which broke away from the Barber Surgeons Company in 1745. The Library, opened in 1828, maintains a reference collection of monographs and journals in surgery and its specialities as well as historical collections.

Acquisitions policy To improve existing collections in the history of surgery and its specialities by gifts, deposits or purchase.

Major collections Records of the College and of the Surgeons Company, 1745–.
Hunter-Baillie Collection: papers and letters to, or collected by, members of the Hunter, Baillie and Denman families, 18th and 19th centuries.
Papers and letters of Matthew Baillie (1761–1823); Thomas Denman (1733–1815); John Hunter (1728–93); William Hunter (1718–83); Edward Jenner (1749–1823); Sir Arthur Keith (1866–1955); Lord Lister (1827–1912); Sir Richard Owen (1804–92); Sir James Paget (1814–99).

Non-manuscript material 3000 engraved portraits.
2000 book-plates.

Finding aids Various lists and indexes.

Facilities Photocopying. Microfiche reader.

456 Royal College of Veterinary Surgeons' Wellcome Library

Address 32 Belgrave Square
London SW1X 8QP

Telephone (01) 235 6568

Enquiries to Librarian, Miss B. Horder

Open Mon–Fri: 10.00–5.00

Access All those on the Statutory Register of the College. Others on introduction by a member of the College or a Librarian.

Historical background The College was incorporated by Royal Charter in 1844 and members immediately offered to present books to form the nucleus of a library. Several important collections have been acquired by bequest.

Acquisitions policy To strengthen existing collections by purchase, exchange and donation.

Major collections Minute books of the College, 1844–; other records of the College. Papers of Sir Frederick Smith (1857–1929) concerning veterinary history, veterinary physiology, army history (particularly South African Wars).

Non-manuscript material Portraits of presidents of the College. A few drawings and prints; small collection of photographs.

Finding aids Individual MSS indexed in main library catalogue. Contemporary indexes to some minute books.

Facilities Photocopying.

457 Royal Commonwealth Society

Address 18 Northumberland Avenue
London WC2N 5BJ

Telephone (01) 930 6733

Enquiries to Librarian and Director of Studies, Mr D.H. Simpson

Open   Mon–Fri: 10.00–5.30

Access   Members of the Society and approved readers.

Historical background   The Society, founded as the Colonial Society in 1868, has built up a library since its earliest days. The Society has been in Northumberland Avenue since 1885, but its headquarters was completely rebuilt in 1936. Despite severe damage from bombing in 1941, the library remains a comprehensive collection on the Commonwealth and its members past and present, and a wide range of subjects including art and literature is covered.

Acquisitions policy   To acquire new books bearing on the historical aspect of the collection as well as the contemporary Commonwealth. Donations of relevant MSS and photographs are welcome but the Society's finances do not permit purchases in these fields.

Major collections   Archives of the Royal Commonwealth Society: substantial collection of minute books of the Council of the Society and varied committees; correspondence; memoranda; miscellaneous items.
Papers of Sir George Arthur (1784–1854) as Superintendent of British Honduras, 1814–24.
Some official correspondence and private papers of Hugh Childers (1827–96), Cabinet Minister.
Diaries and notebooks of Cuthbert Christy (1863–1932), doctor and traveller.
Correspondence and diaries of Sir John Glover (1829–85), administrator in West Africa.
Papers of Colonel Henry Burney (1792–1845), diplomat in Siam and Burma.
British Association of Malaya: diaries, letters, reminiscences, 20 boxes.
Collection of Oriental MSS.

Non-manuscript material   A substantial collection of photographs estimated at well over 40,000 prints is being catalogued with the aid of a British Library grant. There is a much smaller collection of negatives and some slides. The collection of photographs of members of the Society totals about 3000 and covers 1880–1925.

Finding aids   New additions to the MS collection are included in *Library Notes*, published every other month.

Facilities   Photocopying on premises. Photography by arrangement. Microfilm reader.

Publications   D.H. Simpson: *Manuscript Catalogue of the Royal Commonwealth Society* (1975)

458   Royal Free Hospital School of Medicine

Address   Medical Library
                 Royal Free Hospital
                 Hampstead
                 London NW3 2QG

Telephone   (01) 794 0500 ext. 3201

Enquiries to   Librarian, Ms Patricia Fear

Open   Mon–Fri: 9.00–7.00, by appointment

Access   Bona fide readers on written application or telephone call.

Historical background   The history of the Medical School is closely bound up with
    the entry of women into the medical profession. It was founded in 1874 as the
    London School of Medicine for Women in order to enable women to qualify. In
    1877 the Royal Free Hospital agreed to admit clinical students to its wards and 20
    years later the name of the school was changed to London (Royal Free Hospital)
    School of Medicine for Women. In 1947 when the School became coeducational it
    acquired the title of Royal Free Hospital School of Medicine.

Acquisitions policy   By donation.

Major collections   MSS and documents relating to the background and development
    of medical education for women and biographical information on the women
    pioneers of the 19th century.
    Records relating to the founding of the School and its subsequent history.

Non-manuscript material   Portraits, photographs, press cuttings, 1874–.

Finding aids   Card index.

Facilities   Photocopying. Photography. Microfiche reader.

459   Royal Geographical Society

Address   1 Kensington Gore
                 London SW7 2AR

Telephone   (01) 589 5466

Enquiries to   Archivist, Mrs. Christine Kelly

Open   Mon–Fri: 10.00–5.00

Access   Normally restricted to Fellows of the Society. Applications from non-
                 Fellows should be addressed to the Director and Secretary.

Historical background   The Society was founded in 1830 to encourage exploration
    and geographical research. From the time of its foundation the Society collected

books, maps, pictures, MSS, and museum items relevant to the Society's interests.

Acquisitions policy   To accept gifts of MSS relevant to the history of exploration and travel or relevant to notable Fellows of the Society.

Major collections   Minute books, administrative records, correspondence and working papers of the Society.
Special collections of the papers of Dixon Denham (1786–1828); Ney Elias (1844–97); David Livingstone (1813–73); Sir Clements Markham (1830–1916); F.W.H. Migeod; Sir Henry C. Rawlinson (1810–95); Henry M. Stanley (1841–1904); Captain R.F. Scott's *Discovery* expedition, 1901–04.
Files of worldwide astronomical observations (to fix positions) and meteorological and topographical observations.

Finding aids   Author and geographical card indexes. Typewritten catalogues.

Facilities   Photocopying. Microfilming and other photography by arrangement.

Publications   C. Kelly (comp.): *The RGS Archives: a Handlist* (1977)

460   Royal Historical Society

Address   University College London
Gower Street
London WC1E 6BT

Telephone   (01) 387 7532

Enquiries to The Executive Secretary

Open   Mon–Fri: 10.00–5.00

Access   Fellows and Associates, staff and graduate students of University College London; others at the discretion of the Hon. Secretary.

Historical background   The Historical Society was founded in 1868 and became the Royal Historical Society in 1887. In 1897 the Camden Society was amalgamated with the Royal Historical Society.

Acquisitions policy   No intention of acquiring MSS.

Major collections   Archives of the Society and the Camden Society: minute books, accounts, correspondence, etc, 1867–.
Papers of Sir George Prothero (1848–1922) including diaries, letters, notebooks, newspaper cuttings, printed pamphlets and proofs.
Solly Flood Manuscript (a history of the writ of Habeas Corpus by Solly Flood, HM Attorney General in Gibraltar).

Non-manuscript material   The library consists mainly of printed primary sources of British history.

Finding aids Duplicated list and supplementary handwritten list of the Prothero papers.

Publications *Report on the archives of the Camden Society and the Royal Historical Society 1867–97*, Royal Commission on Historical Manuscripts (1977).
Transactions; Camden Series; Guides and Handbooks series; Guides and Handbooks supplementary series.

461 Royal Horticultural Society

Address Lindley Library
Vincent Square
London SW1P 2PE

Telephone (01) 834 4333

Enquiries to The Librarian

The archives, MSS and drawings collection were auctioned in 1859, but a number of items has since been re-acquired by the Society. A selective list appears in G. Bridson et al: *Natural History Manuscripts Resources in the British Isles* (1981), 273.

462 Royal Institute of International Affairs

Address Chatham House
10 St James's Square
London SW1Y 4LE

Telephone (01) 930 2233

Enquiries to Honorary Archivist, Ms Dorothy Hamerton

Open Mon–Wed: 10.00–6.00
Thurs: 10.00–7.00, by written request

Access Bona fide researchers with suitable references. A fee may be charged. 30-year closure on all archives (archives dealing with purely internal Chatham House affairs are closed indefinitely).

Historical background The Institute was established in 1920 as a result of discussions between British and US delegates to the Paris Peace Conference of 1919. Its Royal Charter, granted in 1926, precludes it from expressing opinions of its own, so opinions expressed in its publications or at meetings are the responsibility of the authors and speakers. Its aim is to advance the objective study and understanding of all aspects of international affairs from 1920 to date.

Acquisitions policy Acquisitions are restricted to unpublished material emanating from the Institute.

Major collections   Records of Chatham House from its foundation, including correspondence and texts of off-the-record meetings held at the Institute [speakers include many of international repute]; unpublished material from the research and meetings departments of the Institute.

Non-manuscript material   An important press cuttings library.

Finding aids   Typed lists of contents of each section.

Facilities   Photocopying.

463   The Royal Institution of Great Britain

Address   21 Albemarle Street
                   London W1X 4BS

Telephone   (01) 409 2992 ext. 4

Enquiries to   Librarian, Mrs I.M. McCabe

Open   Mon–Fri: 10.00–5.30 (closed Fri during the academic term)

Access   Approved readers on written application.

Historical background   Founded in 1799 by Benjamin Thompson, Count Rumford, to promote the study and advancement of science, for over 180 years the Institution has occupied the same premises where many major scientific discoveries have been made. Apart from specific research project grants the Royal Institution receives no financial support from Government and activities are funded by income from property endowments, donations and subscriptions from members.

Acquisitions policy   Donations and deposits.

Major collections   Royal Institution archives.
MSS including correspondence, research notes, etc of eminent scientists of the 19th and 20th centuries associated with the Royal Institution, including Sir Humphry Davy (1778–1829); Michael Faraday (1791–1867); Sir William Grove (1811–96); John Tyndall (1820–93); Sir William H. Bragg (1862–1942); William Lawrence Bragg (1890–1971).
Journals of Thomas Archer Hirst (1830–92).

Non-manuscript material   Pictures and busts.
Prospectuses and lecture lists.

Finding aids   Lists and indexes.

Facilities   Photocopying. Photography. Microfilm/fiche reader.

Publications   *Proceedings of the Royal Institution; Manager's Minutes 1799–1903* (1971)
T. Martin (ed.): *Faraday's Diary 1820–1862* (London, 1932) [out of print]

J.R. Friday, R.M. MacLeod and P. Shepherd: *John Tyndall: Natural Philosopher: 1820–1893. Catalogue of correspondence, journals and collected papers* (1974) [microfiche]
W.H. Brock and R.M. MacLeod: *The Journals of Thomas Archer Hirst, FRS* (1980) [microfiche]

464   Royal Opera House Archives

Address	The Archives Royal Opera House Covent Garden London WC2E 7QA
Telephone	(01) 240 1200 ext. 235
Enquiries to	Mr Ken Davison *or* Miss Francesca Franchi
Open	Mon–Fri: 10.00–1.00; 2.00–6.00, preferably by appointment
Access	Approved readers. Some administrative records are confidential; some only available following written application.

Historical background   The Royal Opera House is the third theatre to have been built on the Covent Garden site and was opened in 1858. The first two theatres opened in 1732 and 1809. Due to the fires that destroyed these two buildings in 1808 and 1856, relatively little material remains relating to their history. There have been various museums and archives at Covent Garden over the years and when the Royal Opera House reopened after World War II, the Archives were re-established in the 1950s. The collection concentrates on performances that have taken place at Covent Garden, with biographical information on the people involved and related general information where possible (e.g. prints/photos of world premières of operas/ballets not at Covent Garden). There has been a full-time archivist since 1969, when the present cataloguing system was introduced.

Acquisitions policy   Material mainly from within the Opera House and from donations. Acquisitions are restricted to items necessary to consolidate the collection and provide general reference material.

Major collections   Principally non-MS material (see below).
Correspondence and administrative papers.

Non-manuscript material   c5000 playbills, 1750s–1840s.
Programmes, 1850s–1980s [complete from 1946].
Prints and photographs of singers, dancers, composers, choreographers, designers, producers, productions, Royal Opera House personnel.
Prints, plans and photographs of the three theatres.

*c*1000 costume designs by Attilio Comelli; some other costume and set designs, stage plans etc.

Small reference library of books and periodicals.

Press-cutting library.

Finding aids　Various lists and statistics available. Opera and theatre collection almost completely catalogued; ballet catalogue in the process of being fully completed. Archive staff always present.

Facilities　Photocopying. Photography.

465　The Royal Society of London

Address　　　　6 Carlton House Terrace
　　　　　　　　London SW1Y 5AG

Telephone　　　(01) 839 5561

Enquiries to　　Librarian, Mr N.H. Robinson

Open　　　　　Mon–Fri: 10.00–5.00

Access　　　　Fellows of the Royal Society and those introduced by Fellows. Bona fide scholars of the history of science on written application.

Historical background　The Royal Society was founded in 1660 and has been in continuous existence since that date. One of its earliest activities was to collect scientific books and MSS to form a library.

Acquisitions policy　Original papers and correspondence of past Presidents and Officers of the Society.

Major collections　Royal Society Archives: Journal books (of meetings), 1660–; Register books, 1661–1738 (21 vols); Letter Books, 1661–1740 (31 vols); Classified Papers, 1660–1740 (39 vols); early letters, 1660–1740 (38 vols); letters and papers, 1741–1806 (70 vols); referees' reports, 1832–.
MSS collections: Robert Boyle (1627–91), letters and papers (53 vols); Charles Blagden (1748–1820), letters and papers, diary (25 vols); Sir John Herschel (1792–1871), scientific correspondence (35 vols).
Papers of Sir Henry Dale (1875–1968); Lord Florey (1898–1968); Lord Blackett (1897–1974).

Non-manuscript material　Tape recordings of some Fellows, including the Society's named lectures since 1974.

Finding aids　General card catalogue in the Library.

Facilities　Microfilming. Microfilm/fiche reader/printer.

Publications　J.O. Halliwell: *A catalogue of the Miscellaneous Manuscripts, preserved in the Library of the Royal Society* (London, 1840)

W.E. Shuckard: *Catalogue of the Manuscript Letters in the possession of the Royal Society* (London, 1840)

A.H. Church: *Some account of the 'Classified Papers' in the Archives* (Oxford, 1907)

————: *Some account of the 'Letters and Papers' in the Archives* (Oxford, 1908)

R.K. Bluhm: 'A Guide to the Archives of the Royal Society and to other Manuscripts in its possession', *Notes and Records of the Royal Society, London*, xii (1956), 21

466 Royal Society for the encouragement of Arts, Manufactures and Commerce (RSA)

Address 6–8 John Adam Street
London WC2N 6EZ

Telephone (01) 839 2366

Enquiries to Curator-Librarian, Dr D.G.C. Allan

Open Mon–Wed: 9.30–12.30; 1.30–5.30
Thurs–Fri: 9.30–5.30

Access Fellows of the Society and bona fide research students.

Historical background The Society was founded in 1754 as the Society for the encouragement of Arts, Manufactures and Commerce. Its present headquarters is the house in the Adelphi built for it by the Adam brothers in 1772–4. It was incorporated by Royal Charter in 1847 and granted the title 'Royal' in 1908.

Acquisitions policy Fugitive items and other material relevant to the Society's history.

Major collections The Society's records: minutes, 1754–; *c*10,000 items of correspondence, *c*1755–1851.
John Scott Russell collection on the Great Exhibition of 1851 [5 vols].

Non-manuscript material *c*400 pamphlets and tracts forming part of the Society's Library, all pre-1830.

Finding aids Card catalogue for MS correspondence.

Facilities Photocopying of unbound MS items only.

Publications Series of studies in the Society's history and archives, published in *Journal of the Royal Society of Arts* (1958–)

467 Royal Society of Chemistry

Address   Burlington House
             Piccadilly
             London W1V 0BN

The Society has very little archive material and no details are available.

468 Royal Society of Medicine (RSM)

Address   1 Wimpole Street
             London W1M 8AE

Telephone   (01) 580 2070

Enquiries to   Librarian, Mr D.W.C. Stewart

Open   Mon–Fri: 9.30–9.30
             Sat: 9.30–5.30
             Archives available only when the Librarian is in attendance

Access   By arrangement with the Librarian and at the discretion of the
             Executive Director following written application.

Historical background   The Society was formed in 1907 by the amalgamation of a
   number of specialist societies, but its origins go back to 1805.

Acquisitions policy   Papers and minute books relating to the work of the Society
   and its sections.

Major collections   The papers of 17 predecessor societies including:
   Royal Medical and Chirurgical Society, 1805–1907.
   Pathological Society of London, 1846–1907.
   Epidemiological Society of London, 1850–1907.
   Odontological Society of Great Britain, 1856–1907.
   Obstetrical Society of London, 1858–1907.
   Society of Anaesthetists, 1893–1908.
   Considerable collection of lecture notes and some correspondence of eminent
   medical and surgical practitioners, 18th–19th centuries.

Finding aids   Preliminary short title list in typescript.

Facilities   Photocopying. Photography. Microfilm/fiche reader.

Publications   *Report on the Records of the Royal Society of Medicine 1805–1968*,
   Royal Commission on Historical Manuscripts no. 75/42 (London, 1975)

469 Royal United Service Institute for Defence Studies

Address	Ministry of Defence Library Whitehall London SW1A 2ET
Telephone	(01) 218 4714/5062
Enquiries to	Librarian, Mr R. Tubb

All the Institute's MS material was deposited in other libraries in 1969 as follows:
Naval and chart collections to the National Maritime Museum (*see* entry **425**).
Military collection, with some exceptions, to the National Army Museum (*see* entry **420**).
Harper papers and sheet map collection to the British Library (*see* entry **316**).

470 Royal Veterinary College

Address	University of London Royal College Street London NW1 0TU
Telephone	(01) 387 2898

The College was founded in 1791. Apart from Council minutes from the late 19th century, a register of students from the 19th century, and some lecture notes, it mostly has books rather than archives. The College would not refuse personal papers if offered.

471 St George's Hospital
Archives Department

Address	Room 60, Grosvenor Wing St George's Hospital Blackshaw Road Tooting London SW17
Telephone	(01) 672 1255 ext. 4954
Enquiries to	Honorary Archivist, Mr Hugh Anderson
Open	Mon–Fri: 10.00–5.00, by appointment
Access	Accredited researchers and interested persons.

Historical background   St George's Hospital was founded in 1733. It was controlled by a Board of Governors which continued after the hospital joined the National Health Service in 1948. The Board was replaced by a Health District Authority when the NHS was reorganized in 1974. The Atkinson Morley Hospital at Wimbledon was built (1867–9) originally for convalescents, but is now the neurological, neurosurgical and psychiatric department of St George's. The Hospital assumed the management of the Victoria Hospital for Children, Tite Street, in 1948 until its closure in 1964. In 1954 St George's began to refurbish derelict wards at the Grove Fever Hospital, Tooting, and in 1968 building of the new St George's began on the sites of The Grove and Fountain Hospitals. The original St George's at Hyde Park Corner was closed in 1980 and the new hospital at Tooting was formally opened by the Queen on 6 November 1980.

Acquisitions policy   Acquisitions are restricted to records relating to St George's, the Atkinson Morley and Tite Street Hospitals.

Major collections   Records of weekly Boards of St George's Hospital, 1733–1948.
Records of Tite Street and Atkinson Morley Hospitals.
Pathological Reports of St George's Hospital, 1844–1946.

Non-manuscript material   Photographs, pictures, plans.

Finding aids   List of main material.

Facilities   Photocopying.

472   St George's Hospital Medical School
St George's Library

Address   Hunter Wing
                 St George's Hospital Medical School
                 Cranmer Terrace
                 London SW17 0RE

Telephone   (01) 672 1255 ext. 4855

Enquiries to   Librarian, Mr J.A. McGuirk

Open   Mon–Fri: 9.00–5.00, preferably by appointment

Access   Accredited researchers and interested persons.

Historical background   St George's Hospital has been associated with the teaching of medicine since 1733 when the Hospital was founded. From the beginning the Physicians and Surgeons of the hospital were permitted to have a limited number of pupils and the register of these past students is still preserved in the Medical School. A number of celebrated men has been associated with the School including John Hunter, the founder of modern surgery, and his brother William Hunter; Edward Jenner, the discoverer of vaccination; Sir Benjamin Brodie, first President of the General Medical Council; Henry Gray, the anatomist; and Edward Wilson, the deputy leader of the last Scott Antarctic Expedition. The Medical School at St George's was built in 1834 and in 1901 the School was incorporated as a clinical school within the University of London. In 1976 pre-clinical teaching began at the Tooting site. All clinical teaching ended at Hyde Park Corner in 1980 when the Medical School was transferred to the South London site.

Acquisitions policy   Acquisitions are restricted to material directly related to the existing collections, the history of the Medical School and prominent members of staff, preferably by donation.

Major collections   MSS of or relating to Sir Benjamin Collins Brodie (1783–1862).
MSS of lectures delivered at St George's Hospital.
MSS of Hyde Park Corner Whist Club.
MSS of St George's Hospital Medical and Surgical Society (later Hunterian Society).
MSS of St George's Hospital Medical School Library.

Non-manuscript material   Photographs, pictures, plans.

Finding aids   List of principal items of interest.

Facilities   Photocopying.

473   St Mary's Hospital Medical School Library

Address   Paddington
                 London W2 1PG

No archives are held.

474   St Paul's Cathedral

Address   London EC4

Enquiries to   Librarian, Mr F. Atkinson

The cathedral archives have been transferred to Guildhall Library (*see* entry 349).

475   St Paul's School Archives

Address   Lonsdale Road
                 London SW13 9JT

Telephone   (01) 748 9162

Enquiries to   The Archivist

Open   Mon–Fri: 9.30–4.30 during term, by appointment

Access   Open for research on written application.

Historical background   St Paul's School was founded by Dean Colet, probably in 1509. The School and most of its records were destroyed in the Great Fire of London (1666); any surviving early records are held by the Mercers' Company (*see* entry **511**). The Library and Archives both have items connected with the history of the School and its pupils.

Acquisitions policy   The Library purchases books and MSS by Old Paulines. The Archives have no funds but actively encourage donations and deposits by the School, old boys and masters.

Major collections   School Archives: Apposition lists, 1749–; Governors' minutes, 1876–1959; boys' reports, 1877–1917, 1934–1957.
Correspondence of Duke of Marlborough (1650–1722); William Camden (1551–1623); Judge Jeffreys (1648–89); Benjamin Jowett (1817–93); Thomas Clarkson (1760–1846); Ernest Raymond (1888–1974); Viscount Montgomery (1887–1976).
Literary MSS of Rev. R.H. Barham (1788–1845); Laurence Binyon (1869–1943); G.K. Chesterton (1874–1936); E.C. Bentley (1875–1956).

Non-manuscript material   School magazines, 1831–; Calendars, 1881–; Club lists of masters and boys, 1918–; Examination papers; Team photographs; Engravings of the School.
Newspapers cuttings collection.
Naimaster Collection of engravings of Old Paulines and High Masters.
Books by and about Edward Thomas (1878–1917).
Books relating to the early history of the School, including grammars from 1575, preces from 1644 and sermons from 1674.
School copy books, 17th and 18th centuries.

Finding aids   Card indexes of authors, subjects, masters and boys.

Facilities   Photocopying.

476   St Thomas's Hospital Medical School

Address   The Library
                   St Thomas's Hospital
                   London SE1 7EH

Telephone   (01) 928 9292 ext. 2367

Enquiries to   The Librarian

Open   Mon–Fri: 9.00–9.00
                   Summer vacation: Mon–Fri: 9.30–6.00

Access   On application to the Librarian.

Historical background   St Thomas's Hospital Medical School as an organization dates from the early 18th century. The first purpose-built accommodation was provided between 1813 and 1815 and in 1844 a Medical School Committee was established. By 1860 the School was self-sufficient and it was reconstituted with management vested in the teachers who were to elect a dean annually. The School was established in new buildings at Lambeth in 1871. The records of the Hospital have been transferred to Greater London Record Office (*see* entry **348**).

Acquisitions policy   Restricted to records of the Medical School.

Major collections   Registers of students and records of their fees, 1724–.
Minute books of various School committees, c1880–.
A few case notes and lecture notes, 18th and 19th centuries.
A small number of autograph letters.

Non-manuscript material   Prints, 18th and 19th century.
Photographs relating to people and places associated with the Medical School, 1859–.

Finding aids   Card catalogues (in preparation). Name indexes to the registers of students.

Facilities   Photocopying. Photography.

477   Salters' Company

Address   The Salters' Hall
                     4 Fore Street
                     London EC2Y 5DE

Telephone   (01) 588 5216

Enquiries to   The Clerk of the Salters' Company

Open   By appointment only

Access   Bona fide researchers, by arrangement. Access is restricted.

Historical background   The Company had its origins in a religious fraternity founded in 1394 and received Charters of Incorporation as a Livery Company in 1559 and 1607.

Acquisitions policy   Continuous policy of incorporating current material in Company Archives and of acquiring relevant material for Company and other (e.g. Almshouses) archives as they become available.

Major collections   Charters and other constitutional documents.
Court minutes, 1627–.
Reports of other committees.
Documents on charitable matters (e.g. Almshouses and Salters' Institute of Industrial Chemistry).

Documents relating to the Company's English and Irish estates.
Records relating to the admission to the Freedom, 1716–; apprenticeship, 1678–; and livery, 1714–.

Non-manuscript material Photographs, drawings and plans.

Finding aids Check list, Calendar.

Publications J. Steven Watson: *History of the Salters' Company* (1963)

478   School of Oriental and African Studies (SOAS)

Address   University of London
Malet Street
London WC1 7HP

Telephone   (01) 637 2388

Enquiries to   Archivist, Mrs R.E. Seton

Open   Term and Easter vacation: Mon–Fri: 9.00–8.30
                              Sat: 9.30–12.30
Christmas and Summer vacation: Mon–Fri: 9.00–5.00
                              Sat: 9.30–12.30

Access: Persons wishing to consult the archives and MS collections are usually required to become reference members of the Library. Day tickets can be issued to those with an approved letter of introduction.

Historical background The School, founded in 1916 as the School of Oriental Studies, provides courses for the study of the languages and literature of, and ancient and modern society in, Africa, Asia and Oceania. It also acts as a centre of research in those areas. The Library holds some 500,000 volumes, serves the needs of staff and students of the School and also acts as a national library. The archives and MSS section of the Library has grown rapidly since the Library moved into its new accommodation in 1973.

Acquisitions policy To acquire materials, by gift, deposit and purchase, relating to the areas of the School's teaching and research interests. Recently, policy has been to concentrate on papers of missionary interest and materials relating to the Far East.

Major collections Missionary Archives: includes the archives of the London Missionary Society, the Methodist Missionary Society and the Presbyterian Church of England.
Business and Trade: includes the archives of John Swire & Sons, the China Association, the Imperial British East Africa Company, and the British India Steam

Navigation Company (in the papers of Sir William Mackinnon); papers of members of the Chinese Maritime Customs.

Private Paper Collections: travellers, linguists, educationists, anthropologists, administrators and diplomats.

Oriental MSS: *c*2000 MSS representing 107 languages; many of these were formerly part of the collection of William Marsden (1754–1836).

Non-manuscript material *c*300 cassettes (with transcripts) containing the reminiscences of men and women who experienced the closing years of British rule in India.

Several of the missionary archives deposited in the Library have been filmed (microfiche copies are held by the Library).

Collections of photographs deposited with the Missionary Archives.

Finding aids   Various lists and inventories. Card-index to MSS, arranged by language. Work on a catalogue of MS collections is in progress.

Facilities   Photocopying. Photography and microfilming (small orders only). Microfilm/fiche readers.

Publications   Sectional guide to the archives and MS collections in the *Library Guide* (1980)

Published guides to the archives of the London Missionary Society, the Methodist Missionary Society, John Swire & Sons, the papers of Sir William Mackinnon and the collection of Arabic MSS in the School's Library.

479   School of Pharmacy Library

Address   University of London
                 29–39 Brunswick Square
                 London WC1N 1AX

No archives are held.

480   School of Slavonic and East European Studies

Address   University of London
                 Senate House
                 London WC1E 7HU

Telephone   (01) 637 4934

Enquiries to   Librarian, Mr J.E.O. Screen

Open   Term, Christmas and Easter Vacations: Mon–Fri: 10.00–7.00
                 Long Vacation: Mon–Fri: 10.00–6.00

Access   Approved readers, following written application.

Historical background   The School was founded at King's College London in 1915 and became an Institute of the University of London in 1932.

Acquisitions policy   The Library accepts donations and deposits of MS material relating to its areas of interest: Russia, the countries of Eastern and South-Eastern Europe (excluding Greece), and Finland.

Major collections   Papers of Manó Kónyi (1842–1917) and Count Menyhért Lónyay relating to Hungarian politics and the constitutional settlement of 1867.
Correspondence, notes and papers of Sir Bernard Pares (1867–1949) relating to Russia and Russian history.
Photograph albums depicting the life of Countess Natalia Sergeevna Brasova (1880–1952) between 1909 and 1913 with the Grand Duke Mikhail Aleksandrovich.

Non-manuscript material   The Library is primarily a collection of printed books with *c*220,000 items and 1200 current periodicals.

Finding aids   Some lists.

Facilities   Photocopying. Photography and microfilming by arrangement. Microfilm/fiche readers.

481   Science Museum Library

Address   Exhibition Road
                   London SW7 5NH

Telephone   (01) 589 3456

Enquiries to   Keeper of the Library, Mr. L.R. Day

Open   Mon–Fri: 10.00–5.30
                   Appointments with archives staff not usually possible on Saturday

Access   For collections housed in the Library, most MS material is available without an appointment on production of a reader's ticket; an appointment is, however, advisable on a first visit, and is essential for those consulting pictorial material. Collections housed in other Museum departments (*see* 'Historical background') are accessible at the discretion of the Keeper of the department concerned, to whom application should be made in writing. The Library can advise on the location of individual collections.

Historical background   The Science Museum evolved from the science-based collections of the South Kensington Museum (founded 1857) and from the Patent Office Museum (merged 1883–7), and became administratively separate from the Victoria and Albert Museum in 1909. Both the Museum and its Library (which is housed in a separate building) have acquired MS material, including large archival collections, throughout their history. An Archives Collection was set up within the Library in 1979, to co-ordinate future acquisitions and to centralize and catalogue existing MS collections.

Acquisitions policy Records relating to the Museum's fields of interest as the National Museum of Science and Industry, with particular reference to museum collections; records in the general field of physical science and technology for which there is no suitable local or specialist repository.

Major collections Museum records not transferred to the Public Record Office are the responsibility of the Museum Superintendent. Some early records have, however, now been deposited with the Archives Collection in the Library.
Major MS collections of individuals include:
Charles Babbage, mathematician, notes and drawings relating to calculating engines, 1832–71.
Papers of Stanley Gill, computer scientist, 1947–75.
Papers and drawings of Simon Goodrich, engineer to the Navy, 1770–1850.
Notes and correspondence of W.H. Fox Talbot, pioneer of photography, 1837–76.
Major collections of industrial records include:
Maudslay, Sons & Field, engineers, 1800–92; Alexander Morton & Co. and Morton Sundour Fabrics Ltd (Edinburgh Weavers), textile manufacturers, 1862–1963; North British Locomotive Co. and its predecessors, 1842–1909; S. Pearson & Son Ltd, contractors with major subsidiary oil interests, 1876–1960; Robert Stephenson & Co. Ltd, locomotive manufacturers, 1825–1901.

Non-manuscript material Extensive collections of portraits, photographs, prints, technical drawings and ephemera (within the Library's Pictorial and Archives Collection).
Map collection, including early railway maps (in Library).
The following types of material are divided between the Library and Museum curatorial departments:
Trade literature, chiefly 19th and 20th centuries.
Newspaper cuttings collections.
Transport ephemera.
Ships' plans.

Finding aids Various lists and indexes to major collections. It is hoped to make a catalogue available on microfiche early in 1983 and to issue updated versions thereafter at regular intervals.

Facilities Photocopying. Photography. Microfilming. Beta-radiography for the identification and recording of watermarks.

482 Sir John Soane's Museum

Address   13 Lincolns Inn Fields
           London WC2A 3BP

Telephone	(01) 405 2107
Enquiries to	Curator, Sir John Summerson
Open	Tues–Sat: 10.00–5.00
	Research Room: 10.00–1.00 and 2.00–5.00
Access	Generally open to the public.

Historical background   Founded by Sir John Soane R.A. (1753–1837), architect who obtained an Act of Parliament in 1833 which vested the property in trustees. On his death in 1837 the trustees were placed under obligation to maintain the house and collections as they then stood (from funds left by Soane). The Act remained in force till 1969 when a scheme was made under the Charities Act, but the character of the Museum remains unchanged. No 12 Lincolns Inn Fields was added to the Museum in 1970.

Acquisitions policy   The collection being personal and static, there is no provision for acquisitions. Gifts and objects having a close association with Soane are sometimes accepted.

Major collections   The Soane Archive: personal and professional papers of Sir John Soane.

Non-manuscript material   c30,000 architectural drawings of which 20,000 are British. Models of Soane's works.
Pamphlets, sale catalogues.
7783 volumes, more than half of which are books on art, architecture, topography etc.

Finding aids   Lists and indexes (MS or typescript) are available for every part of the collection.

Facilities   Photography by accredited photographer can be arranged. Large collection of negatives.

Publications   *A New Description of Sir John Soane's Museum* (1955, 5/1981)

483   The Skinners' Company

Address	Skinners' Hall
	8 Dowgate Hill
	London EC4R 2SP
Telephone	(01) 236 5629
Enquiries to	The Clerk
Open	By appointment only
Access	Bona fide researchers

Historical background   The Skinners, the guild of furriers, had their first Hall during Henry III's reign. The first charter was granted in 1327 and the final charter by James I. The present Hall was built in 1668–9 following the destruction of the first, Copped Hall, in the Great Fire. The Company funds four schools (Tonbridge School, *fd* 1553; Judd School, Tonbridge, *fd* 1888; School for Boys, Tonbridge, *fd* 1886; School for Girls, North London, *fd* 1889) and has almshouses at Palmers Green, which were established in 1894.

Major collections   Records of Apprentices and Freemen admitted from 1496.
Court books from 1551.
Account books from 1491.
Title deeds from 1249.

Non-manuscript material   Collection by paintings by Sir Frank Brangwyn, RA.
Portraits of past Masters.

Finding aids   Lists and indexes

Publications   J. Lambert: *Records of Skinners of London Edward I to James I*
J.F. Wadmore: *Some Account of the Skinners' Company*

484   Society for Promoting Christian Knowledge (SPCK)

Address   Holy Trinity Church
                   Marylebone Road
                   London NW1 4DU

Telephone   (01) 387 5282

Enquiries to   The Archivist/Librarian

Open   By appointment

Access   By written application except in cases of genuine urgency.

Historical background   In March 1698/9 Dr Thomas Bray, a priest of the Church of England, together with four distinguished laymen, founded the Society, now generally known as the SPCK 'to meet and consult upon the best means of promoting religion and learning in any part of His Majesty's plantations abroad and to propagate Christian knowledge at home', this last by the provision of libraries and schools. For nearly three centuries the SPCK has performed its vocation of upholding Christian belief and values through educational work and literature. It ranks as the oldest Anglican missionary society and, while it has never sent out missionaries in the accepted sense, it has been able to support a wide range of missionary enterprises. It is now chiefly known for its publishing and bookselling activities at home and its assistance through grant aid to the local agencies responsible for production and distribution of Christian literature in the Third World, where it has special links with the autonomous Churches of the Anglican Communion.

Acquisitions policy Acquisitions are confined to material bearing directly on the Society's history and activities.

Major collections Minute Books of the Society and its Committees, 1699–1970.
Letter Books of Henry Newman, Secretary, 1708–43.
Abstract Letter Books, Correspondence received, 1699–1771.
East India Mission records, 1710–1825.
Pitcairn Island, community of *Bounty* mutineers, Register, Committee minutes, Correspondence books, 1790–1854.
Salzburg Emigration and French Protestant Relief records, 18th century.
Many volumes of financial transactions, 1699–.

Non-manuscript material Printed Annual Reports of SPCK to date.
Printed Monthly Reports of SPCK, 1838–1917.
Pamphlets, memorials and pronouncements, illustrating controversies and historical turning-points in the life of the Society.
Collection of c20,000 File Copies of books, tracts, prints and pamphlets published by the SPCK, including those destined for overseas readers in 207 foreign languages and dialects, among which translations of the Book of Common Prayer are the most prominent.

Finding aids Card indexes of classified records, by name and subject. Volume indexes.
Catalogues of all past publications. File Copy list.

Facilities Photocopying.

Publications *S.P.C.K. Early 18th Century Archives* (World Microfilm Publications)
McClure (ed.): *A Chapter in English Church History: Being the Minutes of the S.P.C.K. for 1698–1704, together with Abstracts of Correspondents Letters* (London, 1888)
Allen and McClure: *Histories of the Society* (1898; later edn by W.K. Lowther Clarke, 1959)
M. Clement (ed.): *Correspondence and Minutes of the S.P.C.K. relating to Wales, 1699–1740* (Cardiff, 1952)
W.E. Tate: 'S.P.C.K. Archives, with special reference to their value for the history of education (mainly 1699–c1740)', *Archives* iii/18 (1957)
The Charity Sermons 1699–1732 as a Source of Educational History
Some Yorkshire Charity School References in the Archives of S.P.C.K., 1700–74

485 Society of Antiquaries

Address Burlington House
Piccadilly
London W1V 0HS

Telephone (01) 734 0193; (01) 437 9954

Enquiries to   Librarian, Mr J.H. Hopkins

Open   Mon–Fri: 10.00–5.00

Access   Fellows and approved readers on request.

Historical background The present Society was founded in 1707 by Humphrey Wanley and has had a continuous existence from 1717. There was no connection with the Elizabethan Society of Antiquaries. A Royal Charter was granted in 1751, commanding the Society to devote itself 'to the study of antiquity and history of former times'. The Society moved to the present premises in 1875 having previously occupied premises in Chancery Lane (1753–80) and Somerset House (1780–1875).

Acquisitions policy To acquire material by purchase, donation, deposit etc.

Major collections 800 MSS, dating from 1100, reflecting the interests of past and present Fellows covering every branch of antiquarian studies.
Society's Minutes, 1707/8, 1717–.
Correspondence of Fellows, c1700–.

Non-manuscript material c20,000 prints and drawings of topographical nature.
3000 broadsides from 1400.
Lowther Collection: 200 printed books and 1500 tracts largely relating to the Civil War period.
10,000 casts of seals.

Finding aids Topographical and subject catalogue.
Catalogues of MSS and of broadsides.

Facilities Photocopying. Photography. Microfilm reader.

486   Southwark Local Studies Library

Address   211 Borough High Street
London SE1 1JA

Telephone   (01) 403 3507

Enquiries to   Local Studies Librarian, Mr E.B. Nurse

Open   Mon–Thurs: 9.30–12.30; 1.30–8.00
Tues, Fri: 9.30–12.30; 1.30–5.00
Sat: 9.30–1.00, by appointment

Access   Generally open to the public, except in the case of some categories of modern Council records, to which restrictions of varying duration apply.

Historical background The London Borough of Southwark was formed in 1965 by the merger of the Metropolitan Boroughs of Southwark, Bermondsey and

Camberwell. These Metropolitan Boroughs in their turn were formed in 1900 from ten vestries which had governed their parishes from Tudor times.

Acquisitions policy   Acquisitions comprise records which are transferred from the custody of departments of the London Borough of Southwark, and various private deposits which relate to institutions and individuals within the borough or its predecessors.

Major collections   Records of the Civil Parishes up to 1900: vestry minutes, rate books, Poor Law records, churchwardens' accounts, highway records and other series of the parishes of St Saviour, St Olave, St Mary Magdalen (Bermondsey), St Mary (Rotherhithe), St Mary (Newington), St Giles (Camberwell), St John Horselydown, St Thomas, St George and Christ Church; the earliest item dates from 1546 (the collection is strong in Poor Law records of the late 18th and early 19th centuries and in the records of the vestries from 1856 to 1900, which operated under the Metropolis Local Management Act of 1855).
Records of the Boroughs, 1900–.
Deposited private records, including about 15,000 local deeds and a large collection of local Methodist records.

Non-manuscript material   Printed books, pamphlets, press cuttings and other ephemera; microfilms (of local newspapers, census returns and directories); photographs and prints; maps; gramophone records and tape recordings of older residents' memories.

Finding aids   Calendar of the deeds, with indexes by name and place; more detailed aids in progress. Author and subject card catalogue of the non-MS items.

Facilities   Photocopying. Microfilm/fiche reader/printer.

Publications   Duplicated summary list of archives is available on request.

487   Tate Gallery Archive

Address   Tate Gallery
                 Millbank
                 London SW1 3RG

Telephone   (01) 821 1313

Enquiries to   Curator, Ms Sarah Fox-Pitt

Open   Thurs and Fri: 10.00–1.00; 2.00–5.30, by appointment only

Access   Postgraduates and approved readers by written application with two letters of reference.

Historical background   The Archive was established in 1970. It is the national archive of 20th-century British art with responsibility to the Public Record Office for the Tate Gallery's public records.

Acquisitions policy   Funded acquisition is of papers relating to 20-century British art but material related to the main collections of the Tate Gallery is acquired by gift or loan.

Major collections   Artists International Association: official records and correspondence, 1933–71.
Charleston Trust: correspondence of Vanessa Bell, Clive Bell, Roger Fry, Duncan Grant and others, 1902–60.
George Frederick Watts (1817–1904) correspondence, 1846–1904.
Alan Durst (1883–1970) correspondence, drawings and photographs, 1924–70.
Paul Nash (1889–1946) correspondence and papers, 1908–46.
David Bomberg (1890–1957) correspondence and papers, 1917–57.
Stanley Spencer (1891–1959) correspondence and papers, 1910–59.

Non-manuscript material   Auction records of MSS sales relevant to the Archive's own collections.
*c*300 interviews with artists and personalities in the art world.
Drawings and prints, usually part of the MSS collections.
Microform; more than 60 collections of loan material.
Photographs of British and 20th-century art and artists including installation photographs of exhibitions, photographs of artists, their work and their studios.
*c*600 artist-designed posters.
A large collection of press cuttings covering a wide field relating to British and 20th-century art.
Private view cards of exhibitions, mainly from 1970 onwards.

Finding aids   Lists and indexes.

Facilities   Photocopying. Photography. Microfilm/fiche reader.

Publications   A. Causey: *Paul Nash's Photographs: Document and Image* (1973)
The Tate Gallery Biennial Report (1974–6; subsequent issues 1978, 1980)
S. Fox-Pitt: 'The National Archive of 20th Century British Art and Artists at the Tate Gallery', *Art Libraries Journal*, iii/4 (1978), 39

488   Thames Water Authority

Address   New River Head
               Rosebery Avenue
               Clerkenwell
               London EC1R 4TP

Telephone   (01) 837 3300

Enquiries to Manager, Headquarters Administration, Mr J. Le Patourel (general enquiries)
               The Administration Manager, North London Division (Metropolitan

Water Board and predecessor companies; telephone (01) 837
3300)
Mr E.H.M. Wakefield, South London Division (Greater London
sewerage; telephone (01) 222 7788)
Mr M.R.L. Hall, Directorate of Scientific Services, Reading (Thames
Conservancy; telephone (0734) 593333)

Open   Mon–Fri: 9.30–4.30

Access   By written application. Restrictions may apply to legal and other
records.

Historical background   The Thames Water Authority covers c5000 square miles. It
was established in 1974 and based on the Metropolitan Water Board (1904–74),
which itself was formed from the merger of eight water companies, mostly dating
from the 19th century. Although some centralization of legal documents is taking
place at Reading, most of the records are scattered in different sections and there is
no full-time archivist.

Acquisitions policy   Records received for protection within limits of
accommodation.

Major collections   Records of predecessor water companies and boards, local
authorities' river and sewerage boards, especially metropolitan water companies,
including minutes, accounts, legal documents, letter-books, and letters, late 18th
century–.

Non-manuscript material   Plans and drawings of predecessor undertakings; plans of
London drainage.
Library of historic books concerning the River Thames (on loan to Reading
Museum).

Finding aids   Some lists and indexes. Some indexing of Metropolitan Water
Companies minutes.

Facilities   Photocopying.

Publications   Metropolitan Water Board: Fifty Years' Review, 1903–1953 (1953)

489   Theatre Museum

Address   Victoria and Albert Museum
South Kensington
London SW7 2RL

Telephone   (01) 589 6371

Enquiries to   Curator, Mr Alexander Schouvaloff

Open   Archives open by prior appointment
Tues–Thurs: 10.00–1.00; 2.00–4.30

The Museum is closed to the public until it opens in its permanent home in the Old Flower Market building in Covent Garden in 1984.

Access　　Readers with specific enquiries who should write in advance.

Historical background　　The Gabrielle Enthoven Theatre Collection which was given to the Victoria and Albert Museum in 1925 formed the basis of the Museum, with later additions from the British Theatre Museum Association and the Friends of the Museum of Performing Arts. The Theatre Museum was finally established in 1974.

Acquisitions policy　　To collect material on all aspects of the performing arts, while strengthening the existing collections.

Major collections　　Gabrielle Enthoven Theatre Collection: comprehensive archive on the history of the theatre, opera, ballet, pantomime, circus, etc, in Britain.
British Theatre Museum Association Collection: extensive collection on the London theatre.
London Archives of the Dance and Cyril Beaumont Collections: material relating to the history of dance.

Non-manuscript material　　Harry R. Beard Collection: playbills, programmes, etc recording particularly the history of opera.
Gift of Dame Bridget D'Oyly Carte: designs for Gilbert and Sullivan operas.
Antony Hippisley Coxe Circus Collection.
Friends of the Museum of Performing Arts Collection: costumes, backcloths, designs and other material relating to Diagilev and the Ballets Russes.
Arts Council Collection: modern theatre designs.
British Council Collection: post-war theatre design.
Guy Little Collection of historic photographs.
Houston Rogers Collection of theatre photographs.
Baron Nicholas de Rakoczy circus photographs.

Finding aids　　Various lists and indexes, but no comprehensive catalogue for the entire collection. Catalogues of finite collections are in course of preparation for the Museum's opening in 1984.

Publications　　*Spotlight* (1981) [exhibition catalogue]
Show Business (in preparation)

490　Times Newspapers Ltd
Archives of *The Times* (and its Supplements)

Address　　PO Box 7
Gray's Inn Road
London WC1X 8EZ

Telephone　　(01) 837 1234 ext.7298 (after 10.00)

Enquiries to　　Archivist

Open Strictly by arrangement only; normally from 11.00 onwards

Access Editorial staff of Times Newspapers Limited and accredited researchers, generally limited to postgraduates. Historians should be familiar with the *History of The Times* (*see* 'Historical background'), so as to be in a position to know both the strengths and limitations of holdings. A 30-year closure rule is in operation.

Historical background The Archives department was originally set up for the compilation of the official *History of The Times* (4 vols [5th in preparation], 1935–52); its usage was originally kept confidential to senior members of staff. It was opened to wider scholarship by the then Editor, Sir William Rees-Mogg, in 1967.

Acquisitions policy The collection and preservation of all material relevant to *The Times* and its commercial operations (and latterly Times Newspapers Limited), other than press clippings, which are the exclusive preserve of the Library. A Records Manager, appointed in late-1981, has initiated a company-wide records management scheme, aimed at a regular transfusion of non-current material for retention by the Archives, after review and selection.

Major collections Managerial letter-books, 1847–1910, with subsequent business and commercial records.
Correspondence of Proprietors, 1788–.
Private editorial correspondence, memoranda, background briefings, cablegrams, diaries, notebooks, and other papers, 1830s–, most notably: Walter Papers, 1778–; J.T. Delane Correspondence, 1841–77; Northcliffe Papers, 1908–22; Sir William Howard Russell diaries, 1857–1904.
Also large collections of other papers of Editors, foreign editors, foreign correspondents etc, 1850s–, are maintained.

Non-manuscript material c2000 books and pamphlets by *The Times*, about *The Times*, or written by staff correspondents, plus some items of museum or picturesque interest.

Finding aids Internal card-index system, arranged by biography, subject or country.

Facilities Photocopying. Very limited seating.

Publications See C. Cook: *Sources in British Political History 1900–1951*, i (1975)
Business Archives (Jan 1976)

491 United Kingdom Atomic Energy Authority

Address 11 Charles II Street
London SW1Y 4QP

Telephone (01) 930 5454

Enquiries to Authority Record Officer, Miss J.A. Robertson

The Authority's records are deposited in the Public Record Office (*see* entry **441**).

492   United Reformed Church History Society

Address	86 Tavistock Place London WC1H 9RT
Telephone	(01) 837 7661
Enquiries to	The Hon. Secretary
Open	Mon–Fri, by appointment only
Access	Members of the Society, the United Reformed Church and other enquirers by arrangement.

Historical background   The largest part of the collection was assembled by the Presbyterian Historical Society and the collection is strongest in the history of English Presbyterianism. Since 1972 it has been acquiring some Congregational material.

Acquisitions policy   Although a limited amount of archive material is still accepted from former Presbyterian churches which already have deposited at the Library, recent policy has been to encourage former Congregational churches to deposit archives locally. The Library concentrates on acquiring books and archive material to add to its Presbyterian collection and establish basic reference material concerning the Congregational Churches of Christ and other denominations.

Major collections   United Reformed Church archives.
Records of some closed Presbyterian churches, including baptismal registers.
Biographical information about former Presbyterian, Congregational and United Reformed Church ministers.

Non-manuscript material   Collection of 17th-century pamphlets and books.

Finding aids   Author index for books and pamphlets and some MSS. Lists of other items.

Facilities   Limited photocopying service.

Publications   *United Reformed Church History Society Journal*
The Transactions of the Congregational Historical Society

493   United Society for the Propagation of the Gospel (USPG)

Address	15 Tufton Street London SW1P 3QQ
Telephone	(01) 222 4222
Enquiries to	The Archivist

Open   Mon–Thurs, 10.00–5.00, by appointment

Access   Generally open to the public.

Historical background   USPG is an amalgamation of the Society for the Propagation of the Gospel (*fd*1701), Universities Mission to Central Africa (*fd*1858) and the Cambridge Mission to Delhi (*fd*1877).

Acquisitions policy   Acquisitions are limited to the records of the Society and its missionaries.

Major collections   The records of the Society, central administration and home organization, and correspondence and reports from the following areas: USA, Canada, West Indies; Central and South America; Europe; West, Central and Southern Africa; India; Pakistan; Bangladesh, Burma; Malaysia, China, Japan, Korea; Australasia and the Pacific, 1701–.

Non-manuscript material   Large photograph collection
c25,000 books, including a collection of USPG publications; many books on area studies (history, biography, topography etc).
Colonial diocesan magazines and pamphlets, 19th century onwards.

Finding aids   Various lists and indexes. Some material not yet listed.

Facilities   Photocopying. Photography. Microfilming by arrangement with outside agency. Much early material is not now photocopied.

494   University College London Library

Address   University of London
                  Gower Street
                  London WC1E 6BT

Telephone   (01) 387 7050, ext. 249

Enquiries to   Archivists, Ms Gillian Furlong and Mrs Janet Percival

Open   Mon–Fri: 10.00–5.00, preferably by appointment
                  At other times by appointment only

Access   Open to bona fide scholars on application to the Librarian or to the Archivist, preferably giving prior notice.

Historical background   The Library was opened in 1829, a year after the University of London first admitted students. The first acquisitions of MS material were donations or bequests, the most notable being the Bentham MSS (1849), the Society for the Diffusion of Useful Knowledge (SDUK) Papers (1848), the Chadwick papers (1898), and the Graves Library (1870). Major purchases included the Brougham papers and a collection of very interesting MSS which came with the Ogden Library (1953) and a succession of purchases of early manuscripts in 1911, 1921 and 1927. The large collection of Latin American business archives was transferred to the Library from firms going into liquidation in the 1960s as a result of a survey undertaken on behalf of the *Guide to MS Sources for the History of Latin America and the Caribbean in the British Isles* (ed. P. Walne, 1973).

Acquisitions policy To strengthen existing collections by gift, loan, deposit or purchase and to encourage the deposit of archival material relating to College history, including professorial papers.

Major collections 19th and 20th centuries: Correspondence and papers of eminent political, literary and scientific figures including Lord Brougham (1778–1868) (c60,000 MSS); Jeremy Bentham (1748–1832) (c75,000 MSS); Sir Edwin Chadwick (1800–90); Karl Pearson (1857–1936); Sir Francis Galton (1822–1911); Lionel Penrose (1878–1972); George Orwell (1911–50).

Publishing archives of Routledge & Kegan Paul Ltd, 1853–1973, and the Society for the Diffusion of Useful Knowledge, 1824–48.

Papers of former UCL Professors including Sir William Ramsay (1852–1916); A.F Murison (1847–1934); W.P. Ker (1855–1923); Sir J. Ambrose Fleming (1849–1945); R.W. Chambers (1874–1942).

College Archives: including correspondence (1825–1905); Professorship applications, (1827–1920); Professors' Fee Books, (1833–80); and Committee papers (1836–1918).

Other records are held by the College Records Office.

Latin American Business Archives. The largest collection outside South America covering in particular banking, trade, railways and shipping, mainly 19th century.

Smaller collections include 99 medieval MSS in 9 different languages; 40 Phillips MSS relating to Swiss towns; 40 Graves MSS relating to the history of mathematics and science; and 102 Ogden MSS covering a wide range of subjects.

Departments in the College also hold papers, in particular the Zoology Department (contact Mrs. R. Down) and the Egyptology Department (contact Ms Barbara Adams).

Non-manuscript material Over 250 photographs covering UCL history – members of staff, buildings etc. Several MS collections contain photographs which are variously listed.

Finding aids Handlists and/or card indexes to most collections.

Facilities Photocopying. Photography. Microfilming. Microfilm/fiche reader.

Publications D.K. Coveney: *Descriptive catalogue of manuscripts in the Library of University College* (London, 1935)
A. Taylor Milne: *Catalogue of the manuscripts of Jeremy Bentham in the library of UCL* (1937)
N.R. Ker: *Medieval Manuscripts in British Libraries*, i, *London* (1969)
J. Percival: *Manuscript Collections in the Library of University College London* Occasional Publications of UCL Library no.1 (London, 2/1978)
Occasional Publications of UCL Library nos. 3–7 [handlists to the Chadwick, Chambers and SDUK papers and to the archives of Routledge and Kegan Paul and of the Peruvian Corporation]

M. Merrington and J. Golden: *A List of the Papers and Correspondence of Sir Francis Galton (1822–1911)* (London, 2/1978)

M. Merrington, and others: *A List of the Papers and Correspondence of Lionel Sharples Penrose (1898–1972)* (London, 1979)

J. Golden: *A List of the Papers and Correspondence of George Bellas Greenough (1778–1855)* (London, 1981)

A List of the Papers and Correspondence of Karl Pearson (in preparation)

495　University of London Library

Address　Palaeography Room
Senate House
Malet Street
London WC1E 7HU

Telephone　(01) 636 4514 ext. 910

Enquiries to　Archivist, Miss Joan Gibbs

Open　Mon–Fri: 9.30–5.30

Access　By letter of recommendation. Restrictions on certain collections. Much of the University Archives material has restricted access and permission to consult any part should be sought in the first instance from the Director of the University of London Library.

Historical background　The Library at Senate House is the central library of the University of London. The Library itself dates from 1838 and since 1936 it has been housed with the chief administrative departments of the University of London. The Palaeography Room contains a library of printed materials on MS studies and archives, and its staff are responsible for administering the Library's holdings of MSS and deposited archives. In 1901 Herbert S. Foxwell (1849–1936) sold his collection of books, pamphlets and MSS relating to economic history to the Worshipful Company of Goldsmiths and in 1903 the Company gave this collection to the University. This subject interest has influenced the acquisition policy for MS material since then, especially for the period covering the 15th century to the 19th century.

Acquisition policy　Economic and social history up to 1850 (excluding topographical material), papers of university figures, writers, etc, especially building on collections already in the Library. Acquisition is by gift, purchase and deposit.

Major collections　Individual historical and literary MSS and 'autograph letters', 12th–20th centuries; includes the foundation collection of MSS acquired with the Goldsmiths Library of Economic Literature.

Collections of papers of individuals and institutions including the following: papers of Charles Booth (1840–1916), Professor Augustus De Morgan (1806–71),

(Henry) Austin Dobson (1840–1921), Duckworth Publishers, c1936–56; Captain A.W. Fuller's collection of documents and seals, 13th–20th centuries; MSS transferred from the Institute of Historical Research; papers of Harry Price (1881–1988), including correspondence of Sir A. Conan Doyle; papers of Herbert Spencer (1820–1903); literary MSS collected by Sir Louis Sterling (d 1958); papers of Thomas Sturge Moore (1870–1944); University of London Collection (historical material relating to the history of the University).

Archives: includes the records created by the central administrative offices of the University in Senate House (other bodies in the University have their own administration and their own archives), and minutes of Boards of Studies.

Non-manuscript material Considerable quantity of microfilm copies of MS material held elsewhere.

Detached seals, proofs and casts, University of London collection.

Finding aids Card index to holdings. Typescript catalogue to post-1930 MS acquisitions. Handlists to many collections. Typescript lists.

Facilities Full range of photographic services. Microfilm/fiche reader/printer.

Publications R.A. Rye: *Catatlogue of Manuscripts and Autograph Letters in the University Library* (London, 1921; Supplement, 1921–30 (London, 1930)
P. Kelly: *Modern Historical Manuscripts in the University of London Library: a Subject Guide* (London, 1972)
J. Gibbs and P. Kelly: 'Manuscripts and Archives in the University of London Library', *Archives*, xi/51 (1974), 161
H. Young: *Guide to Literary Manuscripts*
Catalogue of the Goldsmiths' Library of Economic Literature, iii [including MSS; in preparation for 1982]

496 Upper Norwood Public Library

Address Westow Hill
Upper Norwood
London SE19 1TJ

Telephone (01) 670 2551

Enquiries to Reference Librarian, Mr J.G. Savage

Open Mon: 10.00–7.00
Tues–Fri: 9.00–7.00
Sat: 9.00–5.00

Access Generally open to the public.

Historical background The Library is situated by the borough border between Lambeth and Croydon. It opened in 1900 and has been run since then as an independent public library financed jointly by Croydon and Lambeth.

Acquisitions policy　To supplement the local history collection with any materials of interest concerning the Upper Norwood area that come to the Library's notice.

Major collections　Principally non-MS material (*see* below).

Non-manuscript material Local history collection, including pamphlets, programmes and handbills, newspapers, press cuttings, maps, slides and books, covering Upper Norwood area and to a lesser extent the surrounding localities of Croydon, Dulwich, Camberwell, Sydenham, Southwark, Anerley and Penge. There is a considerable amount on the Crystal Palace which stood nearby until 1936.

Finding aids　Card indexes of subjects, individuals and buildings.

Facilities　Photocopying.

Publications　Fact-sheets on early history of Norwood and the Crystal Palace.

497　Victoria and Albert Museum Archive of Art and Design
National Art Library

Address　　Cromwell Road
　　　　　　South Kensington
　　　　　　London SW7 2RL

Telephone　(01) 589 6371

Enquiries to　The Keeper of the Library
　　　　　　or
　　　　　　Deputy Keeper of the Library

Open　　　By appointment only. A minimum of three working days' notice is required.

Access　　Shortage of staff may at times severely restrict access. Applicants must either hold a Victoria and Albert Museum Library endorsed reader's ticket or provide a letter of recommendation and proof of the serious nature of their research.

Historical background　The archive was set up in 1978 to preserve material which formerly would have been dividend between different departments of the museum, but whose real value lies in being kept together.

Acquisitions policy　To complement by purchase and donation existing primary collections in the National Art Library and the Archive of Art and Design, with special reference to the fields covered by the departments of the Victoria and Albert Museum.

Major collections　Separate archives relating to firms, societies or individuals in the fields of art and design, with particular emphasis on 20th-century material.

Non-manuscript material   Glass negatives relating to several different archives; photographs; films; finished artwork.
Printed matter; brochures; books.

Finding aids   The handlist of the Archive of Art and Design may be consulted in the Victoria and Albert Museum Library.

Facilities   Photography and photocopying of some material.

Publications   I. Whalley: 'Manuscripts and archives at the V & A', *Art Libraries Journal*, iii/4 (1978), 33

498   Waltham Forest Libraries and Arts Department
Vestry House Museum

Address   Vestry Road
                   Walthamstow
                   London E17 9NH

Telephone   (01) 527 5544 ext. 391

Enquiries to   Archivist

Open   By appointment
                   Tues–Fri: 10.30–1.00; 2.00–5.30
                   Sat: 10.30–1.00; 2.00–5.00

Access   Generally open to the public.

Historical background   Vestry House Museum was opened by the Walthamstow Antiquarian Society, with recognition from the Master of the Rolls that it was a suitable repository for manorial material. Vestry House is a museum of local history of the Waltham Forest area, and now houses the archive collections built up by Leyton Libraries, Walthamstow Libraries and the collection of the Chingford Historical Society. It also acts as the Diocesan Record Office for Waltham Forest parish records.

Acquisitions policy   To hold the records of the former boroughs of Chingford, Leyton and Walthamstow, and to hold and continue to acquire public and private records relating to the Waltham Forest area. To maintain the printed collection records relating to the Waltham Forest area. Also maintains the printed collection relating to the Borough and to Essex. A modern records management project for Waltham Forest Council records is under consideration.

Major collections   Civil parish records for Leyton amd Walthamstow, including two sets of pre-Poor Law Union workhouse records.
Local government records, including school and education records.
Manorial records for the five Walthamstow manors.

Deed series relating to Leyton and Walthamstow.
Records of local societies.

Non-manuscript material   Maps and plans, including a large collection from a local estate agent.
Large collections of books, pamphlets and ephemera relating to Waltham Forest and Essex; photographs, prints, drawings etc; collection of oral history tapes (transcribed).

Finding aids   Catalogue of the published, archival and map collections; indexes of names for Chingford, Leyton and Walthamstow. Calendars of deeds with indexes for Leyton and Walthamstow. Various archive lists.

Facilities   Photocopying. Photography. Microform reader/printer. Copies from aperture cards can be made full size from a CAPPS machine.

Publications   *Survey of Local History Resources in London* [Waltham Forest edn]

499   Warburg Institute

Address   University of London
                 Woburn Square
                 London WC1H 0AB

Telephone   (01) 580 9663

Enquiries to   Librarian, Dr W.F. Ryan

Open   Mon–Fri: 10.00–6.00
                 Sat: 10.00–1.00 (except Aug and Sept)

Access   By reader's ticket to suitably qualified persons on application to the Director.

Historical background   The Institute is named after its founder Aby Warburg (1866–1929), historian of Renaissance art and civilization. In 1913 Warburg was joined by Fritz Saxl (1890–1948) who in 1921 turned the library in Hamburg into a research institute. After the rise of the Nazi regime it was transferred to London where in 1934 it was housed at Thames House, moving in 1937 to the Imperial Institute, South Kensington. In 1944 it was incorporated into the University of London and moved to its permanent home in Woburn Square in 1958. The Institute is concerned with the study of the Classical tradition, i.e. those elements of European thought, literature, art and institutions which derive from the ancient world.

Major collections   Working papers inherited from private scholars including Aby Warburg; Fritz Sazl; Henri Frankfurt (1897–1954); Robert Eisler (1882–1949); Roberto Weiss (1906–69); Evelyn Jamison (1877–1972); A.A. Barb (1901–79); F.A. Yates (*b* 1899).

Non-manuscript material   Photographic collection, primarily designed for the study of iconography relating to the areas of scholarship represented in the library. 190,000 books and offprints; 1000 runs of periodicals.

Finding aids Photographic collection arranged by subject; card index supplies cross-references.

Facilities MSS are not photocopied.

Publications Annual Report.

500 Wellcome Institute for the History of Medicine (WIHM)

Address 183 Euston Road
London NW1 2BP

Telephone (01) 387 4477

Enquiries to Librarian, Mr E.J. Freeman

Open Mon–Fri: 9.45–5.15
Closed: additional days at Christmas

Access Approved readers on written application.

Historical background The WIHM is owned and maintained by the Wellcome Trust, a charity set up under the will of Sir Henry Wellcome (1853–1936). He built up a historical medical museum and library, the latter being opened to the public in 1949. The museum was transferred on indefinite loan to the Science Museum in 1976 and the Institute (so called since 1968) houses the library (with MSS and iconographic collections) and academic research centre. Wellcome amassed a vast amount of material covering the whole history of man, with medicine as a central core. Although a great deal of irrelevant material was dispersed by gift or sale in 1938 and subsequently, the collections have a wide scope. (*See also* Contemporary Medical Archives Centre, entry **336**).

Acquisitions policy To strengthen existing primary and secondary collections in the history of medicine and allied sciences by purchase, donations or deposits.

Major collections Oriental MSS: c9000 MSS representing 37 languages [one of the major collections of Oriental material in the UK]; rich in Indian material (especially Sanskrit and Hindi); c400 Singhalese palm-leaf MSS; 24 Batak MSS.
American Collection: covering North, South and Central America and the Caribbean (150 MSS), particularly about plant remedies and the ethnology of the American Indian.
Western MSS: c5000 MSS and c100,000 autograph letters, including 15th-century Apocalypse MS; herbals; letters, papers, and MSS of many eminent in medicine including John Hunter (1728–93), William Cullen (1710–90), Joseph Lister (1827–1912), Marie Curie (1867–1934), Louis Pasteur (1822–95), etc.

Non-manuscript material   c50,000 printed ephemera, pamphlets and tracts [most form part of general collection in library].
Iconographic collections: Drawings, paintings and extensive print collection (c100,000).
Many photographs including Röntgen's first nine radiographs, 1895; clinical photographs, from 1860s; John Thompson's photographs of Hong Kong, Saigon etc, 1860s.
Sound Archives: c300 tapes comprising a miscellaneous collection of recordings, mainly of eminent medical figures including Florence Nightingale (1820–1910), Sir Alexander Fleming (1881–1955), also lectures and symposium meetings.

Finding aids   Various lists and indexes. Much of the Oriental collection is in the process of being catalogued. An annotated catalogue of Latin American and Caribbean collection, to be published soon.

Facilities   Photocopying. Photography. Microfilm/fiche reader.

Publications   S.A.J. Moorat: *Catalogue of Western Manuscripts on medicine and science in the Wellcome Historical Medical Library* (1962, 1973) [3 vols]
A.Z. Iskandar: *A Catalogue of Arabic Manuscripts on medicine and science in the Wellcome Historical Medical Library* (1967)
N. Allan: 'The Oriental collections in the Wellcome Institute', *Journal of the Asiatic Society* i (1981) 10

501   Westfield College

Address   University of London
Kidderpore Avenue
London NW3 7ST

Telephone   (01) 435 7141

Enquiries to   Librarian, Dr P. Revell

Open   Term: Mon–Fri: 9.00–9.00
Sat: 9.00–5.00
Vacation: Mon–Fri: 9.00–5.00

Access   Approved readers on written application.

Historical background   The College was founded 1882 as a residential college for women students preparing for University of London degrees; it has been co-educational since 1964. The library serves the needs of staff and students, including postgraduates, for teaching and research. The MS collection has been built up from donations and occasional purchases.

Acquisitions policy   To acquire materials relevant to subjects taught, primarily in literature, history and history of art.

Major collections   c3000 letters of the Lyttelton family, with relevance to British and

South African history, late 19th to early 20th centuries.
Small collections on 19th-century British art, especially Benjamin Robert Haydon, John Martin and James Smetham.

Finding aids   Typed draft of catalogue of all MSS, except Lyttelton papers, available for consultation.

Facilities   Photocopying. Photography. Microfilm/fiche readers and dual reader-printer.

502   Westminster City Libraries Archives Department

Address   Victoria Library
Buckingham Palace Road
London SW1W 9UD
and
Marylebone Library
Marylebone Road
London NW1 5PS

Telephone   Victoria Library: (01) 730 7371
Marylebone Library: (01) 828 8070 ext. 4030

Enquiries to   Chief Archivist, Miss M.J. Swarbrick (Victoria Library)
Archivist, Mr R.A. Bowden (Marylebone Library)

Open   Mon–Fri: 9.30–7.00
Sat: 9.30–1.00; 2.00–5.00

Access   Generally open to the public.

Historical background   Westminster became a city on the foundation of the episcopal see in 1540. From the 16th century local government was by parishes and by the Court of Burgesses, the Court gradually losing most of its powers to the parishes and being abolished in 1900. The ten Westminster parishes were united in 1900 to form the City of Westminster. In 1965 the boroughs of Paddington and St Marylebone, which had each been a single civil parish before 1900, and the City of Westminster formed the present city. The Libraries Archives Department also acts as the Diocesan Record Office for London (South Westminster parish records). Most Westminster City Council records are held at Westminster City Hall.

Acquisitions policy   Records relating to Westminster are acquired.

Major collections   Records of the parishes which constitute Westminster.
Grosvenor estate archives, c1700–1960.
Howard de Walden, formerly Portland, estate archives, 18th–20th centuries.
Royal Botanic Society archives, 1838–1931.
St Marylebone Charity School for Girls archives, 1750–1932.

Gillow archives, 1731–1932.
Liberty archives, 1883–1979.
Westminster Fire Office archives, 1717–1943.
Royal Institute of Chartered Surveyors records, 1868–1956.

Non-manuscript material 28,000 prints and photographs; 21,900 theatre programmes; 47,000 cuttings; 1400 microfilms; 3350 slides; 1560 maps; 18,000 books.

Finding aids Lists and indexes. The Grosvenor Estate archives are in the process of being catalogued.

Facilities Photocopying. Photography by arrangement. Microfilm readers.

Publications *Guide to Local History Resources* [available from both libraries; duplicated]

503 Westminster Diocesan Archives (Roman Catholic)

Address	Archbishop's House
	Ambrosden Avenue
	London SW1P 1QJ
Telephone	(01) 834 1964
Enquiries to	Archivist, Miss Elizabeth Poyser
Open	Mon–Fri: 10.00–5.00 (with lunch break), appointment preferred
Access	Generally open to the public. 30-year closure rule as far as possible.

Historical background After the Elizabethan Reformation settlement in 1559, Roman Catholic life was initially organized from centres abroad such as the seminary college at Douai. From 1623, however, a rudimentary national network, known as the Old Chapter, was created for secular priests, though it lacked papal recognition and ecclesiastical authority, especially *vis-à-vis* the Religious Orders. In 1688 England and Wales were divided into four Districts under bishops, known as Vicars Apostolic, who enjoyed ecclesiastical jurisdiction of a limited nature (albeit under penal laws and some persecution) until 1850; the number of Districts was doubled in 1840. In 1850 a normal diocesan jurisdiction was restored, though with the reservation of certain powers to Rome since Britain was predominantly a non-Catholic country. These reservations have been gradually abolished only in the 20th century.

Acquisitions policy At present restricted to central diocesan archives, but no relevant deposits are refused.

Major collections Records of organization of Catholics in the London District (Home Counties) and correspondence with other areas, 16th–19th centuries;

papers of some agents abroad (especially Roman), recovered *c*1815; administration and correspondence of Westminster diocese, 1850– (except 1865–92); records of Bishops' Meetings, 1865–1945.

Deposited records of St Edmund's College, Ware, school and seminary, chiefly 1794–*c*1950.

Non-manuscript material Small pamphlet collection; a few plans and elevations; photographs and scrapbooks concerning most cardinals of Westminster.

Finding aids Various lists and indexes.

Facilities Photocopying, generally of 19th- and 20th-century material. Microfilming of earlier material can sometimes be arranged.

Publications P. Hughes: 'The Westminster Archives', *Dublin Review*, cci (1937) [gives an account of papers earlier than mid-19th century, but further material of this period has been discovered]

Archives of St Edmund's College, Royal Commission on Historical Manuscripts (1972)

504   Westminster Medical School

Address   17 Horseferry Road
London SW1P 2AR

Some deposited collections are held but no information is available. Westminster Hospital employs a part-time archivist, Mrs Brenda Weedon, at All Saints' Hospital, Austral Street, West Square, Southwark, London SE11.

505   Westminster School Archive and Library

Address   17 Dean's Yard
London SW1

Telephone   (01) 222 2831

Enquiries to   The Librarian and Archivist

Open   During school terms by appointment only

Access   On application, to researchers with specific enquiries or interests.

Historical background Westminster School has been established on a site adjacent to Westminster Abbey since at least 1361 and its history is closely bound up with the ecclesiastical and political history of Westminster.

Acquisitions policy To extend the collection of books, relics and records connected with the history of the school.

Major collections The school archive: an extensive collection of records and documents concerning the history of the school from its foundation.

Non-manuscript material Prints and photographs of school history.
The Busby Library: a private 17th-century academic library left to the school by Richard Busby, Headmaster, in 1695.
The Greene Library: a collection of first editions of works by Westminster authors.

Finding aids Computerized catalogue and data retrieval system.

506 Whitelands College
Roehampton Institute of Higher Education

Address	West Hill
	Putney
	London SW15 3SN
Telephone	(01) 788 8268
Enquiries to	Archivist, Mr Malcolm Cole
Open	Mon–Fri: times vary according to college terms
	Arrangements for visits preferably by appointment
Access	Generally open to all enquirers; there is a 30-year closure on personal records.

Historical background The college was founded in 1841 by the National Society (Church of England) to be a training institution for women teachers and soon became important in the professional qualification and academic advancement of women generally. It had connections with Baroness Burdett-Coutts (1814–1906) and especially with John Ruskin who gave substantial donations of books, illustrations etc and who inspired the institution of the May Queen Festival in 1881. Ruskin also interested Edward Burne-Jones and William Morris in the decoration of its chapel. The college was in Chelsea from 1841 to 1930. In the 1920s and early 1930s its interests were greatly promoted by Winifred Mercier OBE who moved the college to a building in Putney specially designed by Giles Gilbert Scott. Since 1978 it has been a constituent college of the Roehampton Institute of Higher Education and it is expected that from 1983 RIHE will be a part of the University of Surrey.

Acquisitions policy To enlarge the existing collection by donations from former staff and students of examples of work, mementos, letters, etc.

Major collections Over 3000 student records, 1842–.
College annual reports, 1849–; minute books and account books of governing body.
Guild of old students: annuals and complete records, 1881–.

Documents covering all aspects of college development (administrative, financial, curricular, social) especially 1870–.

Non-manuscript material Extensive photographic collection.
May Queen collection, 1887–.
Gifts from Ruskin of books, illustrations, pictures, etc, and other donations from former staff and students to college and its chapel.
Some educational equipment of historical interest.
Specimens of students' work (e.g. in needlework).

Finding aids Extensive additional material in process of being catalogued.

Facilities Photocopying. Photography.

Publications H. Henstridge: *Whitelands College Archive Catalogue* (London, 1979)
M. Cole: *History of Whitelands College,* (London, 1982).

507 Wiener Library and Institute of Contemporary History

Address   4 Devonshire Place
                London W1N 2BH

Telephone   (01) 636 7247/8

Enquiries to   Librarian, Mrs C.S. Wichmann

Open   Mon–Fri: 10.00–5.30

Access   Accredited researchers, who may become members on payment of a moderate fee.

Historical background The Wiener Library collection was founded by Dr Alfred Wiener in Amsterdam in 1933 and brought to London in 1939. It covers totalitarianism, the history of Germany since 1914 and Jewish history. Most of the books were transferred to Tel Aviv University in 1980, but much of its unique material is available on microfilm. The Institute of Contemporary History and Wiener Library is recognized as an educational charity.

Acquisitions policy To build on existing collections covering the rise of the Nazis and the subsequent history of Europe.

Major collections Eye-witness and Fate of Survivors reports.
Collection on the Nazi Party in Spain.
Gestapo files and Himmler papers.
*c*40,000 International War Crimes Tribunal prosecution documents.
(Most material is on microfilm.)

Non-manuscript material Press Archives: over a million cuttings drawn from an international range of newspapers and covering a wide range of subjects relating to events in Europe and other countries before, during and after World War II; also

includes a special collection of files covering biographical information on several thousand individuals considered relevant to the Library's holdings.
Ephemeral pamphlets, leaflets and brochures.
(Most material is on microfilm.)

Finding aids   Guides and indexes.

Facilities   Photocopying. Microfilm reader/printer.

Publications   Various reference works including:
I. Wolff and H. Kehr (eds.): *Wiener Library Catalogue Series* (1949–78) [7 vols]
The Wiener Library Bulletin

508   The Worshipful Company of Barbers of London

Address   Barber-Surgeons' Hall
                   Monkwell Square
                   Wood Street
                   London EC2Y 5BL

Telephone   (01) 606 0741

Enquiries to   Clerk, Mr Brian W. Hall

Open   Strictly by prior arrangement with the Clerk

Access   To approved researchers on written application.

Historical background   The earliest direct reference to the Company of Barbers is the record of the presentation of Richard le Barbour before the Court of Aldermen in 1308. In 1462 the Company received a Charter of Incorporation from King Edward IV, which deals mainly with the practice of surgery in the City and suburbs; the first Barbers' Hall was built in Monkwell Street. In 1540, by Act of Parliament, the Barber-Surgeons' Company and the Fellowship of Surgeons were joined, one of the most important events in the history of surgery in England. The association lasted until 1745 when the two companies separated. In World War II the hall was destroyed; rebuilding was completed in 1969. Some records have been transferred to Guildhall Library (*see* entry 349).

Acquisitions policy   Additions to the Library by gift or purchase are mainly books relating to the history of London, the livery companies, and biographical information particularly of members of the Company who contributed to the progress of surgery.

Major collections   Minute Books of the Court of Assistants, 1550–.
Account Books, 1603–.
Names of Masters and Wardens, 1308–.
Inventories of possessions.

Non-manuscript material   The small library contains books devoted to the history of surgery and barbery and of the craft guilds.
Portraits of Masters and a few photographs.

Finding aids   List of records of the Company.
Transcripts of the Court Minutes so far as they have been prepared are indexed.

Publications   S. Young: *Annals of the Barber-Surgeons* (London, 1890)
J. Dobson and R. Milnes-Walker: *Barbers and Barber-Surgeons of London* (London, 1979)

509   The Worshipful Company of Goldsmiths

Address   The Library
Goldsmiths' Hall
Foster Lane
London EC2V 6BN

Telephone   (01) 606 8971

Enquiries to   The Librarian

Open   Mon–Fri: 10.00–5.30 by appointment

Access   Generally open to bona fide researchers.

Historical background   The Library was established after World War II to provide access to Company records.

Acquisitions policy   All relevant material on hallmarking, assaying, and the precious metals as functional or decorative works of art.

Major collections   Company records including Wardens' Accounts, 1339–, Court Minutes, Books of Ordinances, Estate documents.
Trial of Pyx records.
London Assay Office records.

Non-manuscript material   Philip Hardwick drawings of the Hall.
Edward Spencer metalwork designs.
Omar Ramsden workbooks.
Twining collection: material on regalia throughout the world.
Trade papers from 1950s.
Photographs; slides; films.

Finding aids   Card catalogue.

Facilities   Limited photocopying.

Publications   *The Early History of the Goldsmiths' Company*
Exhibition catalogues [list available from Librarian]

510   The Worshipful Company of Leathersellers

Address	15 St Helen's Place
	London EC3A 6DQ
Telephone	(01) 588 4615
Enquiries to	The Clerk
Open	Strictly by appointment only
Access	On a restricted basis following discussion with the Clerk.

Historical background   The Leathersellers' Company appears to have been the successor of two earlier and minor fraternities which existed in the early 13th century. Reference to a Fraternity of Leathersellers appears in 1372. Articles for the regulation of the craft were applied for in 1398, and in 1444 the Leathersellers obtained a Charter of Incorporation. The Company has possessed five halls and has provided technical education since 1909 with the establishment of the Leathersellers' Technical College, re-established as the National Leathersellers' College in 1951.

Acquisitions policy   No set policy. The Company relies on the goodwill of members of the profession and families who present items of historical interest.

Major collections   Black's *History* (*see* 'Publications') lists the following: minutes, 1608–; Warden's accounts, 1471–; Books of wills, 1470–1799; apprenticeship books, 1629–; registers for freedom, 1630–; livery books, 1706–; charters and ordinances.

Publications   W.H. Black: *History of the Antiquities of the Worshipful Company of Leathersellers of the City of London* (London, 1871) [includes facsimiles].

511   The Worshipful Company of Mercers

Address	Mercers' Hall
	Ironmonger Lane
	London EC2V 8HE
Telephone	(01) 726 4991
Enquiries to	Archivist, Miss Anne F. Sutton
Open	Mon–Fri: 9.30–5.00, by appointment only
Access	Approved readers.

Historical background   The Worshipful Company of Mercers is the premier City livery company and one of the ancient merchant guilds of London. The word 'mercer' derives originally from the French word for merchant but it later became associated particularly with the trade in luxury goods especially cloth. The records start in 1347 but the Company is certainly older. From an early date the Mercers administered estates in land and money left to them by wealthy members and non-members such as Richard Whittington, Dean Colet, the founder of St Paul's School, Sir Thomas Gresham, the founder of the Royal Exchange and Gresham College, and the Earl of Northampton. These charities were and are for the poor and for educational purposes.

Acquisitions policy To acquire material closely related to the history of the Company and its members by purchase, permanent loan or donation.

Major collections Records of the Mercers' Company and of the Charitable Estates in its care.

Non-manuscript material A small collection of books printed 'at' the Mercers' Chapel London.

Finding aids Various lists and catalogues.

Facilities Limited photocopying.

Publications J. Watney: *Some Account of the Hospital of St. Thomas of Acon... and of the Plate of the Mercers' Company* (London, 1892; 2/1906)
————: *An Account of the Mistery of Mercers of the City of London* (London, 1914)
L. Lyell and F. Watney (eds): *The Acts of Court of the Mercers' Company 1453–1527* (Cambridge, 1936)
J. Imray: *The Charity of Richard Whittington, 1424–1966* (London, 1968)

512 The Worshipful Company of Stationers and Newspaper Makers

Address Stationers' Hall
London EC4

Telephone (01) 248 2934

Enquiries to Hon. Archivist, Miss Robin Myers

Open Mon and Wed: 9.30–4.00 by appointment;
other days by special arrangement

Access Approved researchers on written application.

Historical background A Stationers' Guild dates from 1403, and was incorporated by royal charter in 1557. Membership was and is open to those working in the book and allied trades. Until the end of the 17th century, membership was limited to those working and living in the City. Until 1695 all permitted books had to be entered in the Company's register of copies; thereafter until 1911, entry constituted copyright entitlement. In 1603 the Company started a publishing venture known as the English Stock, which came to an end in 1961, with monopoly to print almanacs and several other so-called 'privileged books'. The hall dates from 1674, the Company's first hall having been burnt down in the Great Fire of 1666.

Acquisitions policy   To augment the primary collection with secondary material and to acquire material related to the history of the Company or to individual firms or members connected with it; by donation or deposit or by purchase where possible.

Major collections   The records of the Company, 1554–, including:
Charters of Incorporation and Letters Patent;
Decrees and ordinances;
Membership rolls (apprentice, Freemen, Livery and Court registers).
Minutes of the Court, Court books and 'Waste Books'.
Account books etc, relating to the English Stock.
Registers of publications entered at Stationers' Hall 1554–1842, thereafter to 1923 at the Public Record Office.

Non-manuscript material   Printed Livery lists (various from 1721).
Indexes of registers, 1842–1911.
A library of c2000 volumes, started in 1974, of 'books about books' with a bias towards secondary material relating to the Company and other city livery companies.

Finding aids   Various lists and indexes.

Facilities   A privately produced microfilm of much of the pre-1800 records is available in the British Library, the Bodleian, and the University Library, Cambridge.

Publications   A.W. Pollard: 'Catalogue of Records at Stationers' Hall', *The Library* (March, 1926)
S. Hodgson: 'Papers recently found at Stationers' Hall', *The Library* (1944)

513   Zoological Society of London

Address   Regent's Park
                 London NW1 4RY

Telephone   (01) 722 3333

Enquiries to   Librarian, Mr R. Fish

Open   Mon–Fri: 9.30–5.30

Access   By permission of the Secretary.

Historical background   The Society was founded in 1826. Most of the correspondence, etc, for past years was destroyed during World War II.

Acquisitions policy   Important back files from various departments of the Society are added to the archives.

Major collections Administrative records and documents from 1826, including minutes; scientific meetings; Zoological Club records, 1866–1927; Certificates of Election of Fellows, 1829–31, 1870–; account books; Daily Occurrence Books for Regent's Park and Whipsnade.
c3000 letters, mainly concerning administrative matters, 19th century.
Sir Hugh S. Gladstone's collection of autographs of naturalists.
[Other individuals' collections are principally non-MS material.]

Non-manuscript material Paintings, drawings etc.
List of Fellows.
Zoo Guides.

Facilities Photocopying. Photography.

Publications Annual Report

514 Louth Naturalists' Antiquarian and Literary Society

Address The Museum
4 Broadbank
Louth
Lincolnshire

Enquiries to Secretary and Curator, Mr W.R.C. Simpson (0507) 603026

Open By arrangement; archival material is housed elsewhere

Access Bona fide researchers.

Historical background The Society was formed in 1884 and the museum was formally opened in 1910 by private subscription. The Society owns the Mansion House, leased to the local library, where some of the archives are held.

Major collections Miscellaneous collection of MS material, mostly relating to the history of the town, includes Court Rolls for the Manor of Louth, 12th–17th centuries.

Finding aids Parts of the collection have been catalogued.

515 Kent Archives Office

Address County Hall
Maidstone
Kent ME14 1XQ

Telephone (0622) 671411 ext. 3363/3312

Enquiries to County Archivist, Mr W.N. Yates

Open   Mon: 9.00–7.30
                   Tues–Thurs: 9.00–4.30

Historical background The Office was established in 1933. It also acts as the Diocesan Record Office for Rochester and Canterbury (archdeaconry of Maidstone). There are branch offices at Folkestone Library (*see* entry **197**) and Ramsgate Library (*see* entry **596**).

Major collections Usual local authority record holdings and deposited collections including the following which have a wider significance:

Correspondence of Frederick North, fifth Earl of Guildford, principally concerning activities as Governor of Ceylon, 1798–1805.

Wykeman Martin MSS; including correspondence relating to American affairs, 18th century.

Cornwallis (Mann) MSS, including correspondence of Charles, Marquis Cornwallis as Governor General of India, later Lord Lieutenant of Ireland, 1786–1804.

Sackville of Knole MSS, including correspondence about the Young Pretender, 1746; military papers of Lt-Col. Sir Francis Whitworth concerning Gibraltar and West Indies, 1777–1807.

Mackeson MSS: correspondence from John Mackeson while in the army in India, 1801–3 and in West Indies, 1807–14.

Papers of Sir Jeffrey, first Lord Amherst, covering his military career in Europe, America and after 1764 in England.

Von Anacker MSS: family and official papers relating to their diplomatic work in the Imperial Service, 18th and 19th centuries.

Talbot MSS, including diaries of Lady Caroline Stuart Wortley, 1814–8; travel diaries of J.G. Talbot and others, 19th–20th centuries.

Garnett MSS, including military correspondence of General Robert Garnett, 1841–64.

Papers of Charles, Baron Hardinge of Penshurst (1858–1944).

Papers of George Harris, first Baron Harris, covering his life in India and the Seringapatam Campaign, 1789–1800.

Romney MSS, including correspondence of Sir John, first Baronet, 1656–83.

Papers of Thomas Papillon (1623–1702), London merchant and politician, and his Huguenot family.

Business and personal correspondence of Sir Mark Wilks Collett, Bart, especially about the American cotton market, 1816–1905.

Pratt MSS, including political correspondence of Sir Charles Pratt, first Earl Camden (1714–94), Lord Chancellor; and John Jeffreys Pratt, second Earl and first Marquess, 1795–1829.

United and Cecil Club records, 1882–1961.

Sir John Rodgers, Bart, MP for Sevenoaks, 1950–79, official and family papers.

Rowney of the Mote MSS, including estate papers relating to St Kitts and slavery.

Extensive correspondence with many eminent figures is included in the following collections:

Faunce Delaune MSS.

Knatchbull and Banks MSS, including correspondence relating to Jane Austen's and Sir Joseph Banks's families.

Sir William Knollys, treasurer and controller of household of Prince of Wales, 1863–77.

Lady Rose Weigal (*d* 1921) and family.

Rt Hon. J.H. Thomas, MP (1874–1949).

Cecil-Maxse MSS, mainly relating to Violet Georgina Maxse, married to Lord Edward Cecil (1894) and Viscount Milner (1921).

De l'Isle MSS: Sydney family of Penshurst, 14th century–.

Stanhope of Chevening MSS: official, literary and scientific papers of the seven Earls Stanhope, with family and estate papers, including most of the letters from the fourth Earl of Chesterfield to his son, 1738–68.

Facilities   Photocopying. Photography. Microfilming. Microfilm reader.

Publications   *Guide to Kent Archives Office* (1958); *First Supplement 1957–68* (1971); *Second Supplement 1969–80* (1982)
Handlist of County Council Records 1889–1945 (1972)

516   Kent Biological Archives and Records Centre

Address   Natural History Section
                   Maidstone Museums & Art Gallery
                   St Faith's Street
                   Maidstone
                   Kent ME14 1LH

Telephone   (0622) 54497

Enquiries to   Keeper of Natural History, Mr E.G. Philp

Open   Mon–Fri: 10.00–5.00
                   Some Sats by appointment only

Access   Restricted to bona fide applicants.

Historical background   The archive was started in 1971 to keep records of all natural history in the present administrative county of Kent.

Acquisitions policy   Any records concerning any branch of natural history are accepted provided that they relate to Kent. Photographs of habitats and species are kept and a collection of MS material has also been started.

Major collections   Local naturalists' notebooks and other MSS.

Non-manuscript material   c1000 photographs and photographic slides of natural history habitats and species.

Finding aids   Records before 1971 are dealt with as historical records and recorded under species headings. All records for 1971 onwards are treated as recent records and are filed under species and locality headings.

517 Chetham's Library

Address	Long Millgate Manchester M3 1SB
Telephone	(061) 834 7961
Enquiries to	The Librarian
Open	Mon–Fri: 9.30–5.00
Access	Material available on request. Readers are asked to provide references. The building can be visited by the public during opening hours.

Historical background Founded in 1633 by Humphrey Chetham, a Manchester merchant, as a free public library for 'the use of scholars . . .', it was recognized by Royal Charter in 1665; founded with Chetham's school (now the School of Music).

Acquisitions policy The Library concentrates on the history and topography of north-western England.

Major collections A varied collection, including some early English MSS, and others acquired from the Byrom and Crossley collections. There are also MSS relating to local history.

Non-manuscript material c31,100 broadsides and tracts, including the Chetham Popery tracts.
c2000 photographic slides; engravings.
Scrapbooks (various) relating to the 18th- and 19th-century history of Manchester; local newspapers for the past 200 years.
122 incunabula.

Finding aids Catalogues, indexes and lists available; the collection is continuously researched and indexed.

Facilities Photocopying. Photography by arrangment.

Publications H. Lofthouse: 'Unfamiliar Libraries: 1. Chetham's Library', *The Book Collector*, v/4 (1956), 323
G.H. Tupling: 'A Selection from the List of Historical Manuscripts in the Chetham Library' *Bulletin of Historical Research* x (1932–3), 69

518 City of Manchester Archives Department

Address	Manchester Central Library St Peter's Square Manchester M2 5PD
Telephone	(061) 236 9422, ext 269

Enquiries to   Archivist, Miss J.M. Ayton

Open   Mon: 9.00–12.00; 1.00–9.00
Tues–Fri: 9.00–12.00; 1.00–5.00

Access   Available for consultation unless restricted by the terms of the deposit.

Historical background   The Manchester Libraries were founded in 1852. The Local History Department assumed responsibility for archives and local MS collections in 1957. A separate Archives Department has been in existence from 1963. In 1958 it was recognized as a manorial repository; from 1968 for various records under the Public Record Act, 1958; and in 1972 as the Diocesan Record Office for Manchester (parish records). Prior to the mid–1950s other records were acquired within a wide area around Manchester.

Acquisitions policy   Records of the local authority and organizations within the City of Manchester.
Parish records for the Diocese of Manchester.
Methodist records of circuits and chapels within Manchester and Stockport Methodist District (excluding Stockport).
Records of the Society of Friends Hardshaw East Monthly meeting and preparative meetings.

Major collections   Manchester Branch of the National Union of Women's Suffrage Societies, 1867–1919; papers of Mrs. Millicent Garrett Fawcett, LLD, on Women's Suffrage etc, 1871–1919.
Manchester Chamber of Commerce Minutes, 1794–1964.
Records of the Strutt Mills at Derby, Milford and Cromford, Derbyshire, 1780–1936, and Samuel Greg's Quarry Bank Mill, Styal, Cheshire, 1788–1937.
Papers of Dr William Farrer, editor of Victoria County History of Lancashire, 16th–20th centuries.
Letters, mostly from politicians, to George Wilson, Chairman of the Anti-Corn Law League, 1827–85; letters to John Benjamin Smith, MP, 1832–74.
Records of the Lancashire, later the National Public School Association, 1848–62.
Records of churches in the Diocese of Manchester, 16th-20th centuries; records of circuit and chapels in the Manchester and Stockport district, 18th-20th centuries; records of Hardshaw East monthly and preparative meetings, 17th–20th centuries.
Records of many Manchester Jewish organizations.

Non-manuscript material   Prints, photographs, broadsides and photographs are located in the Local History Department.

Finding aids   Lists and calendars for individual collections. Name, place and subject indexes to the calendars.

Facilities   Photocopying. Photography. Microfilm/fiche readers.

519   Greater Manchester Record Office

Address	56 Marshall Street New Cross Ancoats Manchester M4 5FU
Telephone	(061) 247 3383/3893
Enquiries to	County Archivist, Mr M.J.W. Willis-Fear
Open	Mon–Fri: 9.30–4.30, preferably by appointment

Historical background   Greater Manchester Council was founded in 1974 on local government reorganization, and the Record Office was established in May 1976. Close liaison is maintained with the ten districts in the Council, seven of whom have record offices or local studies centres with substantial archive holdings. By agreement, the Council looks after collections of national and regional importance, or which cover more than one district.

Major collections   Usual local authority record holdings and deposited collections of which the following have a wider significance:
Family papers, including Lord Wilton's family and estate papers relating to Heaton Park, Manchester, and estates in Wrinehill, Cheshire/Staffordshire, and Battesley, West Yorkshire, 1304–1970s; archives of the Assheton family of Middleton, c1300–1830s.
Canal records, including archives of the Manchester Ship Canal, 1883–1970s; archives of Rochdale Canal Company, 1793–1880s.
Architectural records, 19th and 20th centuries.
Business archives, including records of National Vulcan Insurance Company, Manchester, c1860s–1950s; records of Robinsons of Ramsbottom, Bury, bleachers and dyers, 1900–70s.
c100,000 engineering drawings.

520   John Rylands University Library of Manchester

Address	University of Manchester Deansgate Manchester M3 3EH
Telephone	(061) 834 5343
Enquiries to	Keeper of Manuscripts, Miss Glenise A. Matheson
Open	Mon–Fri: 9.30–5.30, preferably by appointment Sat: 9.30–1.00, by appointment only
Access	Approved researchers on written application.

Historical background   The Library was formed by the merger in 1972 of the Library of the University of Manchester (founded 1851) and the John Rylands Library (founded 1900). MS collections are housed in the former John Rylands Library in Deansgate, with the exception of the University's own archives and the *Manchester Guardian* archive, which are at the University Library, Oxford Road.

Acquisitions policy   To strengthen existing collections by purchase, donations or deposits.

Major collections   Oriental collections: including papyri, Hebrew (400 codices and c10,000 fragments); Arabic, Persian and Turkish codices (c2000); Indian, SE Asian and Far Eastern collections in 30 languages.

Western MSS: medieval MSS, many from libraries of famous collectors, particularly rich in Latin MSS of early Germanic and Italian provenance.

Charter Rooms: extensive deeds, genealogical and family papers and other material, mainly relating to Cheshire, Lancashire, Derbyshire, Yorkshire, Warwickshire, Lincolnshire and Suffolk, 12th–20th centuries.

Major collections include the following:

Clinton Papers, with ancillary collections relating to Peninsula War and Napoleonic period.

Crawford Muniments, with papers of Alexander, sixth Earl of Balcarres.

Melville and Pitt Papers and much other material concerning British rule in India.

Papers of Field Marshal Sir Claude Auchinleck (1884–1980).

Thrale-Piozzi MSS relating to Johnson circle (3000 items).

Correspondence of John Ruskin and his circle (2000 letters).

Collections of British artists, especially correspondence of Holman Hunt and Pre-Raphaelites.

Papers of modern writers and actor/producers, including Basil Dean, director.

Papers of John Dalton (1766–1844), scientist.

Archives of businesses, especially textile industry, in particular Samuel Oldknow, early cotton industry records, late 18th century–.

Archival collections from Harley Victoria Methodist College, the Unitarian and Congregational Colleges of Manchester and the Moravian Collection.

Manchester Guardian archive.

University Archive, with papers of a number of academics, including Professor T.F. Tout (1855–1929).

Extensive autograph letter collection.

See separate entry (**522**) for Methodist Archives and Research Centre archives, which are held in the John Rylands Library.

Non-manuscript material   Maps, plans etc, and all supporting materials of a major university library.

Finding aids   Lists and indexes of some collections.

Facilities   Photocopying. Photography. Microfilming. Microfilm/fiche reader/printer.

Publications   Many published handlists and catalogues [publications list available]
Current major accessions recorded in the Library *Bulletin* [twice yearly]

521 Manchester Polytechnic Library

Address	All Saints Building Oxford Road Manchester M15 6BH
Telephone	(061) 228 6171
Enquiries to	Librarian, Mr I. Rogerson
Open	Term: Mon–Thur: 9.00–9.00; Fri: 9.00–4.45 Vacation: Mon–Fri: 9.00–4.45
Access	Approved external readers on written application.

Historical background Manchester Polytechnic was created in 1970 when the Regional College of Art, John Dalton College of Technology and the Manchester College of Commerce merged. Didsbury, College of Education and Hollings College were also brought into the Polytechnic in 1977.

Acquisitions policy To strengthen existing undergraduate research collections in subject areas taught in the Polytechnic and to acquire specialized materials where necessary.

Major collections Barnett Freedman Archive: substantial correspondence, books illustrated by and dustwrappers designed by Barnett Freedman (1901–58).
Jimmy Dean Archive: correspondence and working documents of an active socialist, 1930s–1950s.
Parry Archive: original illustrations, books illustrated and written by Charles James Parry (1824–94).

Non-manuscript material 500,000 monographs, 2240 current serials, 17,000 slides.

Facilities Photocopying. Microfilm reader/printer.

Publications I. Rogerson: *Sir Frances Meynell and the Nonesuch Press* (1979)
E. Green: *The pictorial cover 1960–1980* (Harmondsworth, 1981)

522 Methodist Archives and Research Centre

Address	John Rylands University Library of Manchester Deansgate Manchester M3 3EH
Telephone	(061) 834 5343
Enquiries to	Mr David W. Riley
Open	Mon–Fri: 9.30–5.30 Sat: 9.30–1.00

Access Approved readers on written application.

There is an embargo placed on certain MS material and written permission for access to these items must first be obtained from the Secretary of the Methodist Church, Rev. Kenneth G. Greet.

Historical background Established in 1961 by the Methodist Church, the Centre was formerly housed in Epworth House, City Road, London. In 1977 the Collection was transferred to Manchester and deposited in JRULM. The Collection remains the property of the Methodist Church and consists of books and MSS devoted to the religious history of the denomination and the doctrinal theological controversies relating thereto.

Acquisitions policy To strength existing primary and secondary collections in the history of Methodism and allied subjects by purchase and donation.

Major collections J.J. Colman Collection: surviving diaries and sermon notebooks of John Wesley (1703–91).

E.S. Lamplough Collection: letters of John Wesley and other members of the family. Preachers' Letters and Portraits Section: *c*50,000 letters of Methodist ministers, mainly 18th and 19th centuries, and *c*100 of their diaries and journals.

J.T. Wilkinson Collection: 11,500 items, over 4000 letters of Professor A.S. Peak (1865–1929), and other documents relating to the history of Hartley Victoria College and to Primitive Methodism.

National and district, but not Circuit, records.

No genealogical records, no baptismal or burial records.

Non-manuscript material 18th-century editions of Wesley's works (2000 vols); Charles Wesley's library (500 vols); John Fletcher's library (130 vols).

6000 pamphlets.

Over 5000 periodicals. 3000 hymn books. 4000 circuit plans.

Finding aids The Methodist Archives and Research Centre Information Folder can be purchased from the Connexional Archivist, Rev. William Leary, c/o Methodist Church Property Division, Central Hall, Oldham Street, Manchester M1 1JQ. Detailed catalogues and finding aids are available for consultation in the Deansgate Building of the Library.

Facilities Photocopying. Microfilms. Photography. Colour slides and all other kinds of work can be supplied.

Publications D.W. Riley: 'The Methodist Archives and Research Centre', *Bulletin of the John Rylands University Library of Manchester*, lx, 269; lxii, 3

————: *Proceedings of the Wesley Historical Society*, xli, 139; xlii, 116; xliii

W.F. Swift: *Proceedings of the Wesley Historical Society*, xxxiii, 79

J.C. Bowmer: *Methodist Magazine* (1963), 251, 288, 335, 368, 413, 452; (1964), 9, 50, 104, 128, 172, 217, 249, 293, 330, 377, 413, 457

523   North Western Museum of Science and Industry

Address	97 Grosvenor Street Manchester M1 7HF
Telephone	(061) 273 6636
Enquiries to	Director, Dr R.L. Hills
Open	Mon–Fri: 10.00–5.00, by appointment
Access	Generally open to the public.

Historical background   The Museum was founded in 1969. Collections cover the industries typical of the North West of England and the scientists who worked in this region.

Acquisitions policy   To acquire pamphlets, photographs, drawings etc, which explain or complement the museum's exhibits.

Major collections   Principally non-MSS material.
Also Beyer, Peacock & Co., Locomotive and Machine Tool Builders' records.

Non-manuscript material   Clapperton, Clayton Bleadle and Schieland collections of early watermarks.
Engineering drawings of all mill engines built by Lancashire Firms, c1870–1930.
Engineering drawings of steam, drop and pneumatic hammers, c1870–1930.
J.B. Green collection of hand-made paper samples, 1840–1920.
Catalogues and pamphlets of engineering firms (mainly firms based in the North West of England), c1890–1950.
Photographic collections including cars bodied by J. Cockshoots of Manchester, 1890–1939; steam locomotives, 1960s.
Collections of printed cotton samples, 1795–1930.
Collection of books particularly important in the fields of photography, paper-making and electrical engineering.

Finding aids   Various lists available.

Facilities   Photocopying. Photography. Microfilm/reader.

524   University of Manchester Institute of Science and Technology (UMIST)

Address	PO Box 88 Manchester M60 1QD
Telephone	(061) 236 3311
Enquiries to	The Librarian

Open   Term: Mon–Fri: 9.00–8.45
                    Sat: 9.00–11.45
                    Vacation: Mon–Fri: 9.00–5.00
                    Sat: 9.00–11.45

Access   Generally open to the public.

Historical background   Founded as the Manchester Mechanics' Institution in 1824,
    it was renamed Manchester Technical School in 1883, and Manchester Municipal
    School of Technology in 1902. It was incorporated as the Faculty of Technology in
    the University of Manchester in 1903, renamed Manchester Municipal College of
    Technology in 1918, and Manchester College of Science and Technology in 1955.
    It was awarded a Royal Charter as an independent university in 1956 and renamed
    University of Manchester Institute of Science and Technology in 1966.

Acquisitions policy   Material to support the teaching and research of the Institute.

Major collections   UMIST records (not yet fully arranged or catalogued); some
    departments retain their own archives as well.
    Records of the National Federation of Building Trade Operatives.

Non-manuscript material   Joule Collection: library of the Manchester scientist J.P.
    Joule (1818–89).
    UMIST theses.
    The Department of History of Science and Technology has began an oral history
    collection for medicine in the North-West.

Facilities   Photocopying. Microfilm/fiche reader/printers.

Publications   The Department of History of Science and Technology has published a
    series of pamphlets listing health service records extant in the region.

525   National Coal Board Archive Centre

Address   200 Lichfield House
                    Mansfield
                    Nottinghamshire NG18 4RG

Telephone   (0623) 22681, ext. 291

Enquiries to   Head of Archives Centre, Mr F.H. Clews
                    Chief Record Officer, Mr J. Barlow

Access   Bona fide inquirers

Historical background   The records are public records under the Public Records
    Act. Certain pre-nationalization records (up to 1947) were distributed to
    relevant county record offices (lists of these deposits are kept at the Archive
    Centre). The Centre acts as an intermediate repository for records pending their
    transfer to the Public Record Office (*see* entry **441**).

526 Margate Library Local History Collection

Address	Central Library Cecil Square Margate Kent CT9 1RE
Telephone	(0843) 23626/22895
Enquiries to	The Librarian
Open	Mon–Fri: 9.30–6.00 Sat: 9.30–5.00
Access	Generally open to the public.

Historical background   The basis of the Margate Local History Collection was the bequest of a local antiquary, Dr Arthur Rowe, in 1926. It consisted of every kind of material relevant to the development of Margate which he was researching in order to write and illustrate a parish history. This has continued to be augmented by purchases and donations.

Acquisitions policy   To acquire material relating to Margate by purchase, donation and loan.

Major collections   Rowe MSS: part of Rowe Collection documenting streets, buildings, local families, sea bathing, archaeology.
Pridden MSS: a description of the Isle of Thanet in Kent, by Rev. John Pridden, 1780–90, a fair copy and rough draft, including 100 original drawings; c100 letters of John Anderson relating to the Founders of the Sea Bathing Hospital; pedigrees of Thanet families (fair copy available on microfilm).
Edward White's MS extracts from Kent newspapers, archives, State and Domestic Papers, parish registers, gravestones; W.J. Mercer's scrapbooks and indexes.
Letters and documents, account and minute books from local dignitaries and officials relative to the history and government of Margate, the Theatre Royal, local Boards and charities, and businesses.

Non-manuscript material   Rowe Collection: over 2000 items relating to Margate, including books, pamphlets, programmes, maps, illustrations, plans, photographs, bills, posters.
Parker Collection: over 10,000 items relating to Kent, including books, pamphlets, maps, 7000 prints and 1000 illustrations.
Other items include press cuttings, illustrations and ephemera, scrapbooks covering Margate and Kent, photographs, postcards, correspondence relating to Margate, Broadstairs and Ramsgate, and many guide books and directories.

Finding aids   Catalogue. Some original indexes. The collection is being exhaustively re-catalogued.

Facilities   Photocopying. Photography by arrangement. Microfilm reader.

527   Derbyshire Library Service
Local Studies Department

Address	County Offices
	Matlock
	Derbyshire DE4 3AG
Telephone	(0629) 3411 ext. 6840
Enquiries to	Librarian, Mrs J. Radford
Open	Mon–Fri: 9.00–5.00
	Sat: 9.30–1.00, by appointment only
Access	Generally open to the public.

Historical background   The Local Studies Department started as the Derby Collection at St Mary's Gate Central Lending Branch. The collections were moved to Matlock in 1966 and housed in a branch library; they were moved to the County Offices in 1969.

Acquisitions policy   To strengthen and enlarge existing primary and secondary collections on the history of the county of Derbyshire and on environmental studies.

Major collections   Peach Collection: MS and printed play, film and radio scripts of L. du Garde Peach, Derbyshire dramatist.
Barmasters Library: includes, in addition to printed material, MSS, account books and ledgers relating to lead-mining industry in Derbyshire.

Non-manuscript material   Wolley MSS (British Museum Additional MSS 6666–6718) on microfilm, covering Derbyshire; MSS 6676–6686 relate to the Derbyshire lead-mining industry.
Census returns for Derbyshire and some small portion of surrounding counties, 1841–71 (on microfilm).
Newspapers: *Derbyshire Times*, 1854–; *Derbyshire Courier*, 1829–51 (on microfilm).
c1500 illustrations covering all aspects of Derbyshire life.
Maps, historical and modern, of the county (various scales).

Finding aids   Various lists and indexes. Card index to Wolley MSS.

Facilities   Photocopying. Microfilm/fiche reader/printer.

Publications   *Catalogue and Indexes of the British Museum Additional MSS 6676–6686*, Derbyshire County Library (1977)
Derbyshire Local Studies Collections: a Guide to Resources, Derbyshire Library Service (rev. 1982)
List of Library publications available on request.

528   Derbyshire Record Office

Address	County Offices Matlock Derbyshire DE4 3AG
Telephone	(0629) 3411 ext. 7347
Enquiries to	County Archivist, Miss J.C. Sinar
Open	Mon–Fri: 9.30–1.00; 2.00–4.45 Sat and evenings by arrangement

Historical background   The office was officially established in 1962, although a few collections had been deposited previously. It also acts as the Diocesan Record Office for Derby. Administrative assistance is given to Derby, Chesterfield, Glossop and Swadlincote libraries.

Major collections   Usual local authority record holdings and deposited collections of which the following have a wider significance:
John Taylor, first publisher to University of London, early 19th century.
Economic surveys of the Hundred of Scarsdale, mid-17th century.
Fitzherbert collection, including Treby papers concerning the Titus Oates plot; and papers of Lord St Helens (1753–1839).
Estate papers of Harpur-Crewe of Calke, 12th–20th centuries.
Several collections of Civil War papers.
Engineering company records, late 18th–20th centuries.
National Coal Board pre-vesting date records.

Facilities   Photocopying. Photography. Microfilm reader. Microfilming.

529   Merthyr Tydfil Central Library

Addres	High Street Merthyr Tydfil Mid-Glamorgan CF47 8AF
Telephone	(0685) 3057
Enquiries to	Arts Officer, Mr David Francis
Open	Mon–Fri: 9.00–6.30 Sat: 9.00–12.00
Access	Generally open to the public.

Historical background   The Central Library opened in 1935.

Acquisitions policy   Primary and secondary material relating to the Merthyr Tydfil area.

Major collections   Borough Council minutes and County Borough Council and Education minutes, 19th–20th centuries.
New County Borough Council minutes, 19th century.

Rate books and rate account books of the Iron Masters, 19th century.

Parish minutes, local Board of Health minutes and Urban District Council minutes (in care of Glamorgan Archive Service, *see* entry **106**).

Dowlais Iron Company letters (at Dowlais Library, Church Street, Dowlais, Merthyr Tydfil).

Non-manuscript material   Photographic collection.

Maps, including Ordnance Survey maps of the Merthyr Tydfil area, 1832–, and later surveys.

Extensive collection of pamphlets and photocopied material.

Merthyr Express, 1912–54 (incomplete), 1954– (microfilm).

Finding aids   Material is filed by subject with a separate author/title index.

Facilities   Photocopying. Microfilm/fiche reader.

Publications   *Guide to the Local History Collection* (1976)
New bibliography [in preparation]

530   British Steel Corporation
Records Services Section

Address   Northern Region Records Centre
Unit F2, Commerce Way
Skippers Lane Industrial Estate
South Bank, Middlesbrough
Cleveland TS6 6UT

Telephone   (0642) 467144

Enquiries to   Eastern Regional Manager, Miss J. Hampson

Covers the north-east of England and Sheffield. For enquiries covering more than one region write to Director, Secretariat, at the Corporation's Head Office, 33 Grosvenor Place, London SW1. For other information in common with each Records Centre *see* entry **687**.

531   Cleveland County Archives Department

Address   81 Borough Road
Middlesbrough
Cleveland TS1 3AA

Telephone   (0642) 210944

Enquiries to   County Archivist, Mr D.H. Tyrell

Open   Mon–Thurs: 9.00–1.00; 2.00–5.00
                  Fri: 9.00–1.00; 2.00–4.30

Historical background   The office was established in 1974 following the creation of
   Cleveland County, comprising the former County Boroughs of Teesside and
   Hartlepool and parts of the former counties of Durham and North Riding of
   Yorkshire. Very few collections had been deposited before this. The department
   also acts as the Diocesan Record Office for York (Cleveland parish records).

Major collections   Usual local authority record holdings and deposited collections,
   all of purely local interest.
   Sound archives of Radio Cleveland from 1971.

Facilities   Photocopying. Photography. Microfilm/fiche reader. Microfilm printers,
   by arrangement.

Publications   *Cleveland County Archives, Genealogical Sources* [continually re-
   vised]

532   Rochdale Libraries
Local Studies Collection

Address   Middleton Area Central Library
                  Long Street
                  Middleton
                  Manchester M24 3DU

Telephone   (061) 643 5228

Enquiries to   Assistant Librarian, Mrs J.E. Scott
                  or
                  The Local Studies Librarian at Rochdale Library (*see* entry **608**).

Open   Mon, Thurs: 9.30–8.00
                  Tues, Fri: 9.30–5.30
                  Wed: 9.30–1.00; 2.00–5.00
                  Sat: 9.30–1.00; 2.00–4.00

Access   Generally open to the public.

Historical background   The dynamic growth of Rochdale, Middleton and Heywood
   during the 19th century produced a wealth of material relating to the area. Prior to
   1974 the substantial local collections of Heywood, Middleton and Rochdale were
   located at the Central Libraries in those areas and on local government
   reorganization it was decided that each should retain a separate collection under
   the general supervision of a Local Studies Librarian based at Rochdale.

Acquisitions policy   The collection of documentary material relating to all aspects of
   life in the area of the Metropolitan Borough of Rochdale and its previously
   independent constituent authorities.

Major collections Local Administrative Records: early administrative records including highway rates, Poor Law administration and administrative material from the constituent authorities of the Metropolitan Borough; includes Middleton Poor Book, 1838, and Sheffield Rental, 1784.
Church Records: church rates, leys, tithe commutation maps, plans, deeds etc.

Non-manuscript material Complete runs of local newspapers – original and microfilm copies.
Books, pamphlets, audio-visual material, photographs, maps, plans, broadsheets, political handbills, theatre posters.

Finding aids Calendar of archival material. Newspaper index.

Facilities Photocopying. Microfilm/fiche readers.

Publications *Introduction to Local Studies Collections* (1981)

533 Clwyd Library Service

Address   Headquarters Library
              Civic Centre
              Mold
              Clwyd CH7 6NW

Telephone   (0352) 2121 ext. 480

Enquiries to   The County Librarian

Local History Collection of non-MS material.

534 Montrose Museum

Address   Panmure Place
              Montrose
              Angus DD10 8HE

Telephone   (0674) 3232

Enquiries to   Curator, Mr Norman Atkinson

Open   April–Sept: Mon–Sat: 10.30–1.00; 2.00–5.00
              Oct–Mar: Mon–Fri: 2.00–5.00; Sat: 10.30–1.00
              July–Aug: Mon–Fri: 2.00–5.00; Sat: 10.30–1.00; Sun: 2.00–5.00
              Prior notice needed for access at weekends

Access   Generally open to the public on written application.

Historical background The Museum was built and opened by Montrose Natural History and Antiquarian Society in 1842. From 1975 it has been part of Angus District Libraries and Museums.

Acquisitions policy Any local material.

Major collections Payroll of Forfar and Kincardine Militia, 1803. Rifle Volunteer papers.
Miscellaneous local voluntary and friendly society records, 18th and 19th centuries.
Log of whaling ship *Snowdrop*, 1907.
Autograph collection includes Sir Walter Scott (1771–1832); Alfred, Lord Tennyson (1809–92); Richard Chevenix French; William Harrison Ainsworth (1805–82); Alex Burness ('Bokhara Burness') (1805–41); Joseph Bonaparte; Admiral Sir Charles Napier (1786–1860).

Non-manuscript material Local maps and plans, 17th–19th centuries.

Finding aids Archives list.

Facilities Photocopying by arrangement.

535 Montrose Public Library

Address   Pell Place
                  Montrose
                  Angus

Telephone   (0674) 3256

Enquiries to   Librarian, Miss M. Stephen

Open   Mon–Sat: 10.00–6.00

Access   Generally open to the public on written application.

Historical background The Library was opened in 1902 as Montrose Free Library. From 1975 it has been part of Angus District Libraries and Museums.

Acquisitions policy Any local material.

Major collections Montrose Royal Lunatic Asylum and Dispensary, miscellany, 1810–1948.
Local trades, voluntary, friendly societies and charities records, 18th-20th centuries.
Forfarshire Gold Cup (Montrose Races) records, 1820–27.
Subscription Library and Trades Library records, 1810–1904.
Genealogical collection, families of Mudy, Scott, Straton and Walker, 12th–19th centuries.

Non-manuscript material Local maps and plans.
Local published monographs.
Rules, regulations and proceedings of local societies and institutions.
Local periodicals.

Finding aids   Archives list.

Facilities   Photocopying by arrangement.

536   Northumberland County Central Library

Address   The Willows
Morpeth
Northumberland NE61 1TA

Archives are neither held nor collected.

537   Midlothian District Library

Address   Fisherrow School
South Street
Musselburgh
Lothian EH21 6AU

Telephone   (031) 665 2931

Enquiries to   The Assistant Director (Libraries)

Open   Mon–Thurs: 9.00–5.00
Fri: 9.00–3.45

Access   Generally open to the public.

Historical background   Established as the County Library in 1921 under the Education (Scotland) Act (1919), it continued to expand until local government reorganization in 1975, when it was renamed Midlothian District Library and was cut to approximately half its previous size. Much material has been transferred to Edinburgh District Archives (*see* entry **170**).

Acquisitions policy   The Library attempts to acquire by purchase, gift or otherwise items relating to its area in whatever form they appear.

Major collections   Local History of Midlothian District, with a small but significant collection of MS material of a very diverse nature, including family material, diaries etc, through to items such as County Council Minutes, 1910–43, 1970–75; District Council Minutes thereafter; School Log Books (some back to 1870); School Board letter-books and cash books.

Non-manuscript material   Maps and plans; prints and photographs; a small collection of slides.

Finding aids   Bibliographies, including some in MS. Catalogues of material. A few years of local newspapers indexed etc.

Facilities   Photocopying. Microfilm/fiche reader.

538   Neath Antiquarian Society

Address	Gwyn Hall Neath West Glamorgan
Telephone	(0639) 50048 (Librarian's home)
Enquiries to	Mrs S.A Evans, 28 Creswell Road, Neath SA11 1HE
Open	By appointment
Access	Approved readers only.

Historical background   The Society was founded in 1923 by a number of local people, including the late Mr Glen A. Taylor, archaeologist and antiquarian.

Acquisitions policy   Acceptance of any local material through loan, donation or purchase.

Major collections   Neath Borough records to the 19th century.
Gnoll Estate documents, ledgers etc.
Eaglesbush Estate material.
Neath Abbey material.

Non-manuscript material   Maps and plans of locality. Topographical books.

Finding aids   Card catalogue (in process).

Publications   Transactions of the Society [annual]

539   Newark District Council Museum

Address	Appletongate Newark Nottinghamshire NG24 1JY
Telephone	(0636) 702358
Enquiries to	The Curator, Mr H.V. Radcliffe
Open	Mon–Fri: 10.00–5.00 Sat: 10.00–1.00, by appointment
Access	Generally open to the public.

Historical background   Established in 1912 as the Museum of the Borough of Newark on Trent, the collection passed, under local government re-organization in 1974, to the Newark District Council.

Acquisitions policy   Acquisitions consist of ephemera circulated in the District, items relating to local government and local material accumulating from activities of the staff.

Major collections   Newark Borough records, 17th to 20th centuries.
Newark Improvement Commissioners Minutes, 1851–74.
Newark Rural District Council, clerk's files, 1894–1953.
Newark Urban Sanitary Authority/Borough deposited plans, 1875–1970.
Southwell Urban District Council deposited plans, 1934–70.

Non-manuscript material   Pamphlets of local interest.
W.N. Nicholson & Sons Ltd, agricultural engineers, Newark: printed catalogues, photographs and negatives, *c*1860–1967.
Negatives and photographs of the locality.
Negatives of illustrations from the *Newark Advertiser*, 1949–78.

Finding aids   Author, subject and topographical card catalogues.

Facilities   Photocopying. Photography. Microfilm/fiche reader.

Publications   *Additions to the Local History Collection*, (1975/76; 1976)

540   Newcastle upon Tyne City Libraries
Local Studies Collection

Address   Central Library
                   Princess Square
                   Newcastle upon Tyne
                   Tyne and Wear NE99 1MC

Telephone   (0632) 610691

Enquiries to   Inquiry Hall (visitors)
                   or
                   Local Studies Department (postal)

Open   Mon–Thurs: 9.00–9.00
                   Fri, Sat: 9.00–5.00

Access   Generally open to the public.

Historical background   The Mechanics' Institute formed the basis of the Central Library. The Collection was founded in 1884 to include all local material (books, photographs, archives etc). In recent years most of the archives have been transferred to the appropriate Record Offices.

Acquisitions policy   Archive material is no longer collected unless it has connections with the history of the Library itself (e.g. Mechanics' Institute minute books).

Major collections   Mechanics' Institute minute books, 1834–.
T. and G. Allan Collection: Tyneside song MSS, 1860s.
Bell family collections: Seymore Bell plans, charts, etc, 18th–20th centuries; T. Bell material about the River Tyne, 1844–86; papers relating to printing, 19th century.

Literary and other correspondence of Wilfred Gibson, poet, 1930–39.

Gowland MSS relating to estates and collieries in Durham, early 18th century (4 vols).

MSS of Joe Wilson, songwriter, c1850s.

c100 letters relating to Durham Collieries, 1838–57.

Early letters and papers relating to Stockton and Darlington Railway.

Non-manuscript material   Thomas Bewick (1769–1829) Collection, including engravings, original blocks, many illustrations.
Clark Music Library: theatre and concert playbills and programmes, 1860–1925.
Civil War tracts.
Genealogical Collection.

Finding aids   Name and classified catalogues.

Facilities   Photocopying. Microfilm/fiche reader/printer.

Publications   *Bewick Collection Catalogue*
List of Parish Register Transcripts

541   Newcastle upon Tyne Polytechnic

Address   The Library
                   Ellison Buildings
                   Ellison Place
                   Newcastle upon Tyne
                   Tyne and Wear NE1 8ST

No archives are held.

542   Northumberland Record Office

Address   Melton Park
                   North Gosforth
                   Newcastle upon Tyne
                   Tyne and Wear NE3 5QX

Telephone   (0632) 362680

Enquiries to   County Archivist, Mr R.M. Gard

Open   Mon: 9.00–9.00
                   Tue–Thur: 9.00–4.45
                   Fri: 9.00–4.15

Historical background   The Council accepted a few archives before the appointment of the first Archivist in 1959. The office, which was formally established in 1962, also acts as Diocesan Record Office for Newcastle. There is a Branch repository at Berwick upon Tweed (*see* entry **50**).

Major collections   Usual local authority record holdings and deposited collections.

Facilities   Photocopying. Photography. Microfilming. Microfilm reader.

Publications   List of Documents of Public Interest filed in the Office of the Clerk of the Peace for the County (1922; suppl. 1959).

543   Tyne and Wear Archives Department

Address   Blandford House,
                   West Blandford Street,
                   Newcastle upon Tyne
                   Tyne and Wear NE1 4JA

Telephone   (0632) 326789

Enquiries to   County Archivist, Mr W.A.L. Seaman

Open   Mon, Wed–Fri: 8.45–5.15
                   Tues: 8.45–8.30

Historical background   The Department was established with local government reorganization in 1974, taking over holdings from Newcastle City Archives, Sunderland Library and local authority material. Pre-1974 Gateshead material remains *in situ*. The department administers the North Tyneside branch Record Office at North Shields (*see* entry **552**).

Major collections   Usual local authority record holdings and deposited collections, of which the following have a wider significance:
Papers of Sir W.G. Armstrong & Co [later Armstrong Whitworth, then Vickers], Elswick, Newcastle upon Tyne, relating to engineering and armaments, 1847–1928.
Papers of Sir Joseph Wilson Swan about the invention of incandescent electric light bulbs, the improvement of photographic processes, etc, 1863–1959.
Joseph Cowen, politician and newspaper proprietor, correspondence, etc, 1929–1900.
Messrs Merz & McLellan, Newcastle, consulting engineers; reports, minutes, specifications, photographs etc, 1900–47.
Sir Charles Parsons' plans of the *Turbinia*, 1893–1904.
A.J. Fenwick collection of circus material, 1773–1974.
Messrs Ralph Beilby and Thomas Bewick, Newcastle engravers, financial records, 1752–1881.

Facilities   Photocopying and photography by arangement. Microfilming.

544　University of Newcastle upon Tyne Library

Address　　　Newcastle upon Tyne
　　　　　　　Tyne and Wear NE1 7RU

Telephone　　(0632) 328511

Enquiries to　Special Collections Librarian, Mr Alistair Elliot

Open　　　　Term:
　　　　　　　Mon–Fri: 9.00–9.00 (arrive 9.00–5.00)
　　　　　　　Sat: 9.00–4.30
　　　　　　　Vacation:
　　　　　　　Mon–Fri: 9.00–5.00
　　　　　　　Sat: 9.00–1.00

Access　　　By written application to Special Collections Librarian.

Historical background　Founded as the College of Physical Science under the aegis of Durham University in 1871, the University finally became an independent body in 1963, after changing its name several times.

Acquisitions policy　Very selective strengthening of MS materials.

Major collections　Papers of four Trevelyans: Sir Walter Calverley (1797–1879), Sir Charles Edward (1807–86), Sir George Otto (1838–1928), Sir Charles Philips (1870–1958).
Papers of Walter Runciman, first Viscount Runciman of Doxford (1847–1937); Bernard Bosanquet (1848–1923) and Helen Bosanquet (1860–1925); Gertrude Bell (1872–1947).
Papers of Frederick Whyte (1867–1941), publisher, translator and biographer of W.T. Stead and William Heinemann.
Papers of Jack Common (1903–68), novelist and journalist.
Travel diaries and book MSS of Thomas Hodgkin (1831–1913), historian.
Other MSS include medieval items; a 17th-century poetic miscellany; 19th-century letters; 20th-century literary material.

Non-manuscript material　Robert White collection of border history and ballads; 19th-century ephemeral literature, chapbooks and broadsides.
Newcastle Cathedral books.
Burman collection of Alnwick-printed books.
Joseph Cowan tracts on political, social and economic topics (150 vols).
Hindson-Reid collection of 19th-century Newcastle woodblocks.
John Bell's material on local printing.

Facilities　Photocopying. Photography. Microfilm equipment.

Publications　*The Trevelyan and the Runciman papers* [out of print]
Handlists of the Bosanquet, Whyte, Common and Hodgkin material
The Gertrude Bell papers [out of print]
B.C. Raw has described MS 1 *Lives of the Saints* at length (1961) [pubd separately]

F.W. Ratcliffe: 'Chapbooks with Scottish imprints in the Robert White collection . . .', *Bibliotheck*, iv (1964), 88

C.J. Hunt: 'Scottish ballads and music in the Robert White Collection . . .', *Bibliotheck*, v (1967), 138

F.M. Thomson: 'A Newcastle collection of wood blocks', *The Book Collector*, xvii (1968), 443

545   Business Statistics Office Library (BSO)

Address   Cardiff Road
Newport
Gwent NPT 1XG

Telephone   (0633) 56111 ext. 2399

Enquiries to   The Librarian

The G.R. Porter Collection comprises UK statistical material held by the BSO, which was combined with the Royal Statistical Society Library and archive in 1973. It is named after George Richardson Porter (1792–1852), who supervised the establishment of the Statistical Department of the Board of Trade in 1834 and helped form the Statistical Society. It is a collection of historical statistics, almost all of which were published through normal Government channels. There are no plans to acquire archives. The G.R. Porter Library Catalogue is available.

546   Gwent County Library

Address   Central Library
John Frost Square
Newport
Gwent NPT 1HZ

Telephone   (0633) 65539/211376

Enquiries to   Reference Librarian, Mrs H.B. Strong

Open   Mon, Tue, Wed: 9.30–6.00
Thurs: 9.30–5.00
Fri: 9.30–7.00
Sat: 9.30–4.00

Access   Generally open to the public.

Historical background   Newport Public Library opened in 1870. An extensive general reference library and local collection was built up over 100 years. In 1974 much archival material was transferred to Gwent County Record Office (*see* entry **135**).

Acquisitions policy MSS are occasionally acquired by donation only.

Major collections Chartist riots, verbatim reports of trials affecting Newport and district (30 vols).
Mary Delany (1700–88) correspondence with well-known figures of the day including Fanny Burney.
Correspondence of Sir Charles Hanbury Williams (1708–59), satirist and diplomat, 1750s.

Non-manuscript material Maps.

Finding aids Card catalogues.

Facilities Photocopying. Microfilm reader.

547   **Isle of Wight County Record Office**

Address   26 Hillside
                 Newport
                 Isle of Wight PO30 2EB

Telephone   (0983) 524031, ext. 132

Enquiries to   County Archivist, Mr C.D. Webster

Open   Mon, Tues, Thur, Fri: 9.30–5.00
                 Wed: 9.30–8.00

Historical background The Record Office was founded in 1958. It also acts as the Diocesan Record Office for Portsmouth (Isle of Wight parish records).

Major collections Usual local authority record holdings and deposited collections of local interest.

Facilities Photocopying.

Publications *Archives of Hampshire and the Isle of Wight*, Hampshire Archivists Group (1966) [typescript]
Poor Law, Hampshire Archivists Group (1970)
Transport, Hampshire Archivists Group (1973)
Education, Hampshire Archivists Group (1977)

548   **Ulster Polytechnic Library**

Address   Shore Road
                 Newtownabbey
                 Co. Antrim BT37 0QB

No archives are held.

549   North Yorkshire County Record Office

Address   County Hall
Northallerton
North Yorkshire DL7 8SG

Telephone   (0609) 3123 ext. 455

Enquiries to   County Archivist, Mr M.Y. Ashcroft

Open   By appointment
Mon, Tues, Thurs: 9.00–5.00
Wed: 9.00–9.00
Fri: 9.00–4.30

Historical background   The present Office was established in 1974 with local government reorganization; previously the Office had covered the old North Riding area. The first archivist was appointed in 1949, although records had been collected from 1938. York Archives (*see* entry **707**) is an associate office and holds all church records. It also acts as the Diocesan Record Office for Bradford, Ripon and York (parish records).

Major collections   Usual local authority record holdings and deposited collections.

Facilities   Photocopying. Photography. Microfilming. Microfilm reader/printer.

550   Northampton Museum

Address   Central Museum
Guildhall Road
Northampton NN1 1DP

Telephone   (0604) 39131

Enquiries to   Keeper of the Boot and Shoe Collection, Miss J.M. Swann

Open   Mon–Sat: 10.00–6.00, by appointment

Access   Generally open to the public on application.

Historical background   The County Museum was established in 1865. Since 1873 it has collected, in addition, objects related to shoes and shoemaking worldwide, though the greater part of the collections still relates to shoes as worn in the UK and the history of shoemaking in Northamptonshire.

Acquisitions policy   Objects related to the history of Northamptonshire, and in the shoe department to continue to acquire material related to the history of shoes and shoemaking worldwide.

Major collections   Accounts and account books.
Apprenticeship indentures.

Documents relating to shoe unions, and education.
Shoe designs.

Non-manuscript material Pictures, prints and photographs of shoemakers, factory exteriors, shoe shops and transport.
Shoe price lists and catalogues.
Shoe tool and machinery catalogues, handbooks.
Advertisements.

Finding aids Card indexes of the above. Card indexes of shoemakers, bucklemakers, lastmakers, machinery makers. History of shoemaking by Northamptonshire parishes.

Facilities Photocopying. Photography.

Publications J.M. Swann: *Catalogue of Shoemaker Pictures and Works of Art* (1975)

551   Northamptonshire Record Office

Address   Delapre Abbey
                Northampton NN4 9AW

Telephone   (0604) 62129

Enquiries to Chief Archivist, Mr P.I. King

Open   Mon, Tues, Wed, Fri: 9.15–4.45
                Thur: 9.15–7.45
                Sat: 9.00–12.15
                Office may close 1.00–2.00 without prior notice; documents required Thurs evening, Sat. morning and weekdays 12.00–2.00 should be ordered in advance

Historical background The Northamptonshire Record Society founded and ran an office from 1920 to 1951. Since then it has been administered by the County Council. The office also acts as the Diocesan Record Office for Peterborough. Peterborough.

Major collections Usual local authority record holdings and deposited collections of which the following have a wider significance:
Bridgewater estate and canal accounts, 1759–1806.
Exchequer tellers' accounts, 1568–86.
Militia records of various forces, particularly c1790–1815.
Naval records of Admiral P. Rye, c1791–1815.
Correspondence of Rev. C. Hartsdhorne, antiquary, 1818–47; and Dr Joan Wake (d 1974).
Diaries of Lady Louisa Knightley, 1856–1913, and Lord Dover 1814–33.
Diplomatic papers of Sir Thomas Cartwright (1795–1850) and Sir Fairfax Cartwright (1857–1928).

Political papers of Duke of Shrewsbury, *c*1694–1700; Edmund Burke, 1764–97; 4th and 5th Earls Fitzwilliam 1766–1857; W.C. Cartwright *c*1860–1910.

Facilities   Photocopying. Microfilming. Photography (subject to delays).

552   Tyne and Wear Archives Department

Address   Local Studies Centre
                   Howard Street
                   North Shields
                   Tyne and Wear NE30 1LY

Telephone   (0632) 582811

Enquiries to   County Archivist, Mr W.A.L. Seaman (at Newcastle upon Tyne
                   Office, *see* entry **543**)

Open   Mon, Wed–Fri: 9.00–1.00; 2.00–5.00
                   Tues: 9.00–1.00; 2.00–7.00

Historical background   The archives are based on old library collections (mostly Tynemouth Library). The office was established with local government reorganization in 1974.

Major collections   Usual local authority record holdings and deposited collections.

Facilities   Photocopying. Photography and microfilming by arrangement. Microfilm reader.

553   Merchant Taylors' School

Address   Sandy Lodge
                   Northwood
                   Middlesex HA6 2HT

Telephone   (65) 21850

Enquiries to   The Headmaster

Open   By appointment

Access   On application to the Headmaster.

Historical background   Merchant Taylors' School was founded in 1561. Documents relevant to the early history of the School are at Merchant Taylors' Hall (*see* entry **411**).

Major collections   'Probation Books', 1933–.
    School Registers, 1933–.
    Information about pupils, 1933–.

Non-manuscript material   Goad Library.
  School Magazines.

Finding aids   Index kept in the school library at Sandy Lodge.

Publications   F.W.M. Draper: *Four Centuries of Merchant Taylors' School* (London, 1962).

554   Norfolk County Libraries Headquarters

Address   County Hall
                Martineau Lane
                Norwich
                Norfolk NR1 2DP

Archives are neither held nor collected.

555   Norfolk Record Office

Address   Central Library
                Norwich
                Norfolk NR2 1NJ

Telephone   (0603) 611277, ext.262

Enquiries to County Archivist, Miss Jean M. Kennedy

Open   Mon–Fri: 9.00–5.00
                Sat: 9.00–12.00

Historical background   The office was founded in 1963, taking over from the Archives Dept. of Norwich Library. It acts as the Diocesan Record Office for Norwich and Ely (deaneries of Feltwell and Fincham).

Major collections   Usual local authority record holdings, and deposited collections, mainly of purely local interest.
  Houses muniments of Norwich Dean and Chapter up to 1900.

Facilities   Photocopying. Photography. Microfilming. Microfilm reader.

Publications   P. Rutledge: *Guide to the Great Yarmouth Borough Records* (1973)

556   Norwich Cathedral
Dean and Chapter's Library

Address   The Close
                   Norwich
                   Norfolk NR1 4BH

Telephone   Cathedral Office: (0603) 20715

Enquiries to   The Canon Librarian

All MSS have been deposited in Norfolk Record Office (*see* entry **555**), but the library maintains a collection of slides and photographs of the cathedral architecture and personnel and has a collection of pamphlets on theology and politics, *c*1625–1750.

557   University of East Anglia Library
Holloway Collection of Modern Cultural Records

Address   University of East Anglia
                   Norwich
                   Norfolk NR4 7TJ

Telephone   (0603) 56161, ext. 2413

Enquiries to   Senior Assistant Librarian, Mr John Kimber

Open   Term: Mon–Fri: 9.00–10.00
                   Sat: 9.00–5.00
                   Sun: 2.00–7.00
                   Open most of the year

Access   Generally available to scholars.

Historical background   The Library of Contemporary Culture Records was founded in 1970. Originally an independent registered charity administered by a Board of Trustees, it has recently been acquired by the University of East Anglia. It represents a valuable conspectus of cultural life in Britain at the present, and gathers together ephemera that would otherwise be dispersed or destroyed.

Acquisitions policy   It is hoped to develop and expand the collection.

Major collections   A voluminous collection of largely ephemeral material relating to contemporary cultural activity (broadly defined) from approximately 1965. It covers all parts of the country (excluding London) and a wide range of subjects including art, bookselling, librarianship etc. Contains primarily material emanating from local festivals, the local poetry society, art associations etc.

Non-manuscript material   Printed material including posters, broadsheets, pamphlets, programmes, catalogues, files of relevant magazines and accumulations of the arts features of national newspapers. Some photographs.

Finding aids   Card index.

Facilities   Microfilm/fiche reader.

558   Nottinghamshire County Council Leisure Services

Address   Central Library
Angel Row
Nottingham NG1 6HP

Telephone   (0602) 412121

Enquiries to   The Local Studies Librarian

Local History Collection of non-MS material.

559   Nottinghamshire Record Office

Address   County House
High Pavement
Nottingham NE1 1HR

Telephone   (0602) 54524

Enquiries to   Principal Archivist, Mr A.J.M. Henstock

Open   Mon, Wed, Thur: 9.00–4.45
Tues: 9.00–7.15
Fri: 9.00–4.15
First and third Sat in each month 9.30–12.45

Historical background   The office was formally established in 1949 although some archives were collected from an earlier date. It acts also as the Diocesan Record Office for Southwell.

Major collections   Usual local authority record holdings and deposited collections of which the following have a wider significance:
Portland Papers (development of London, 17th and 18th centuries).
Foljambe Papers (include charters and correspondence of Sir George Savile, MP, mid-18th century).
Edge collections (household accounts, bills etc).

Facilities   Photocopying. Photography. Microfilming. Microfilm reader.

Publications   P.A. Kennedy: *Guide to the Nottinghamshire County Record Office* (1960)

560 Trent Polytechnic Library

Address   Dryden Street
              Nottingham NG1 4F2

No archives are held.

561 University of Nottingham Library
Manuscripts Department

Address   University of Nottingham
              University Park
              Nottingham NG7 2RD

Telephone   (0602) 506101
              The Secretary and general enquiries, ext. 3440
              The Keeper of Manuscripts, ext. 3437
              The Assistant Keeper of Manuscripts, ext. 3436

Enquiries to   Keeper of the Manuscripts, Mrs M.A. Welch

Open   Mon–Fri: 9.00–5.00, by appointment

Access   Open to the public on application. Restrictions on modern records varying between 30 and 100 years, depending on the type of material.

Historical background   Nottingham University College began collecting MSS in the 1930s after the appointment of the first professional Librarian in 1931. The first archivist was appointed in 1947, which led to the development of a separate MSS department within the University Library. Nottingham gained full University status in 1948.

Acquisitions policy   To acquire additions to existing collections and acquisitions of others in related fields, mainly by donations and deposits, but occasionally by purchase.

Major collections   Family collections: title deeds and settlements, manorial and estate records (court rolls, compoti, accounts, rentals, surveys, maps and plans); correspondence (estate, political, personal) and other papers covering banking, business and other interests, including Chamier, Clifton, Drury-Lowe, Galway, Manvers, Mellish, Middleton, Newcastle, Portland, Wrench and Kirke families.
Ecclesiastical Records: Church of England (Archdeaconry of Nottingham), Unitarian, Baptist, United Reformed Church (Congregational/Presbyterian).
Literary Collections: Restoration and 18th-century verse (Cavendish and Harley material in Portland Collection); Henry Kirke White; Coventry Patmore; D.H. Lawrence.

Hospital Records of those hospitals in the Nottinghamshire Area Health Authority (Teaching) Nottingham District.

Water Authority: records of the former Trent River Authority and its predecessors and other bodies amalgamated with it such as Hatfield Chase Drainage Authority and Brigg Court of Sewers.

Business Records, mainly of firms connected with the lace industry.

Trade union records, including those of the Amalgamated Society of Lacemakers.

Specialized Collections such as those of the 17th-century collection of Francis Willoughby, naturalist and patron of John Ray (a natural history collection within the Middleton [Willoughby family], collection); meteorological records; and Russian and British posters of World War II.

Altogether there are over 2,000,000 MSS, 12th–20th centuries.

Non-manuscript material Included in the MSS collections are photographic material; printed pamphlets; posters; printed sermons; hymn books and related material.

The MSS Department forms part of the Nottingham University Library. Collections in the Special Collections (printed) and Local History sections of the Library often complement those in the Manuscripts Department.

Finding aids Hand-lists can be consulted in the Department, in the National Register of Archives section of the Historical Manuscripts Commission, in the copyright Libraries and in the local (i.e. Nottinghamshire, Derbyshire and Lincolnshire) record offices. Copies are also available for sale from the Department. More detailed calendars have been compiled for a small number of collections, or section of collections. These can be consulted in the Department as can the few indexes of personal and place names which exist.

Facilities Photocopying. Photography. Microfilming.

Publications *The University of Nottingham, Manuscripts Department of the University Library*, Information leaflet no.13.

The University of Nottingham, Report of the Keeper of the Manuscripts [pubd biennially]

562   Local Interest Centre

Address	Greaves Street
	Oldham
	Lancashire OL1 1DN
Telephone	(061) 678 4654
Enquiries to	Curator, Mr Julian M. Hunt
Open	Mon, Weds, Thurs, Fri: 10.00–7.00
	Tues: 10.00–1.00
	Sat: 10.00– 4.00

Access　　　　Generally open to the public.

Historical background　The Local Interest Centre opened in 1972, taking over the existing local history library and general museum. From 1974 it also became a depository for archives of local authority and private institutions within Oldham.

Acquisitions policy　To collect archives, printed matter and objects relating to the history of Oldham.

Major collections　Records of Oldham County Borough and Urban Districts of Chadderton, Crompton, Failsworth, Lees, Royton and Saddleworth.
Rowbottom Diaries and Butterworth MSS, a day to day record of events in Oldham, 1787–1843.

Non-manuscript material　Maps, photographs and microfilms on the history of Oldham.
5000 books; 1000 pamphlets.

Finding aids　Various special indexes and calendars to collections.

Facilities　Microfilm reader.

Publications　Catalogue.

563　　Trafford Borough Council

Address　　　　Library Headquarters
　　　　　　　　Birch House
　　　　　　　　Talbot Road
　　　　　　　　Old Trafford
　　　　　　　　Manchester M16 0GH

Telephone　　(061) 872 6133

Enquiries to　Borough Librarian, Mr J.W.H. Watters

Few archives are held and details are not available.

564　　Ashmolean Museum

Address　　　　University of Oxford
　　　　　　　　Beaumont Street
　　　　　　　　Oxford OX1 2PH

Papers have been transferred to Bodleian Library (*see* entry **565**).

565   Bodleian Library
Department of Western Manuscripts

Address	University of Oxford Oxford OX1 3BG
Telephone	(0865) 244675
Enquiries to	The Keeper of Western Manuscripts
Open	Term: Mon–Fri: 9.00–10.00 Sat: 9.00–1.00 Vacation: Mon–Fri: 9.00–7.00 Sat: 9.00–1.00 Closed: Sundays; New Year Bank Holiday; Good Friday to Easter Monday (inclusive); Encaenia Day; the week beginning with the late summer bank holiday; 24–31 Dec
Access	By reader's ticket. Applicants must present themselves in person, and must have either a letter of introduction from, or an application form filled in by, a responsible person familiar with their work.

Historical background   The Library has had a continuous history since the 1602 refoundation by Sir Thomas Bodley. Early major collections were Greek MSS from William Herbert, third Earl of Pembroke, in 1629 and Archbishop Laud in the 1630s. In the 1920s the Bodleian absorbed other special libraries – Radcliffe Science Library (*see* entry **578**), Indian Institute Library (*see* entry **567**) and Rhodes House Library (*see* entry **579**), but these still have a separate identity. It also acts as Diocesan Record Office for Oxford.

Acquisitions policy   Increasing the strength of existing collections.

Major collections   Vast collections of Greek and medieval MSS and papryi.
   MSS collections of family papers and papers of individuals, including politicians and literary figures.
   Topographical drawings.
   Local history collections.
   Deeds and rolls.
   Music MSS.
   Ecclesiastical records, including Oxford diocesan, probate and parochial records.

Non-manuscript material   Oxford University theses.
   A register of the microfilms of MSS and archives housed in other repositories.

Finding aids   Many unpublished lists and indexes. Departmental Guide to catalogues of Western MSS owned by the Bodleian.

Facilities   Photocopying. Microfilming. Microfilm readers. Typing room. Facility for blind readers.

Publications   Lists of accessions in the following:

Annual Report of the Curators (1888–); *Bodleian Quarterly Record*; *Bodleian Library Record* (1914–); annual reports to Historical Manuscripts Commission.
Summary Catalogue of Western MSS in the Bodleian Library at Oxford, i-viii (1895–1953; repr., 1980) [basic catalogue; for other catalogues see Introduction to vol. i of the reprint].

566   English Faculty Library

Address	University of Oxford
	St Cross Building
	Manor Road
	Oxford OX1 3UQ
Telephone	(0865) 249631
Enquiries to	Librarian, Miss M.J.P. Weedon
Open	By appointment
	Term: Mon–Fri: 9.30–7.00 Sat: 9.30–12.30
	Vacation: Mon–Fri: 9.30–1.00; 2.00–4.00
	Closed: for ten days at Christmas and Easter, on Encaenia Day and for six weeks in August and September
Access	Primarily for members of the University. Other people may be admitted at the discretion of the Library Committee. Application should be to the Librarian giving credentials and special reasons for wishing to use the Library.

Historical background   Founded in 1914 to serve the English School, it is essentially a working collection and has been enriched by gifts and bequests.

Acquisitions policy   It is not Library policy to buy MS material; working papers of scholars are occasionally deposited.

Major collections   E.H.W. Meyerstein (1889–1952): papers, including unpublished works, copies of letters, collections of family photographs, portraits (40 boxes).
Wilfred Owen (1893–1918) Collection includes his personal library, some of his manuscripts (poems, etc), family relics, press cuttings, correspondence about his works, and other papers preserved by his brother, Harold Owen (1897–1971), also an author in his own right; correspondence by or to Wilfred Owen, and later letters from members of his circle or editors (e.g. Siegfried Sassoon (1886–1967) and Edmund Blunden (1896–1974)) to Susan and Harold Owen.
Deposited papers include some of the notes, correspondence, etc of Dr Percy Simpson (also relevant to the history of the Library); Dr K.D. Büllbring (1863–1917); S. Roscoe (1900–77), bibliographer of the Newbery family of booksellers; and Professor H.J. Davis (1893–1967), editor of Swift.

Finding aids   Special handlists for MSS collections.

Facilities   Microfilm readers. Photocopying.

Publications   J. Harker: *The Historical Development of the English Faculty Library, Oxford* (London, 1980)
P. Morgan: *Oxford Libraries outside the Bodleian: a Guide* (Oxford, 2/1980), 169
P. Morgan: *Brief Calendar...* (1965) [available in Bodleian Library]

567   Indian Institute Library

Address   University of Oxford
New Bodleian
Parks Road
Oxford OX1 3BG

The library does not hold archives. All archival material connected with it is either in the Oxford University Archives (*see* entry **575**) or the Department of Western Manuscripts of the Bodleian Library (*see* entry **565**).

568   Magdalen College Archives

Address   University of Oxford
Magdalen College
Oxford OX1 4AU

Telephone   (0865) 241781

Enquiries to Keeper of the Archives, Dr G.L. Harriss

Open   By prior arrangement

Access   On written application, stating the purpose of the research.
A search fee is charged.

Historical background   The College was founded in 1458.

Acquisitions policy   The integration into the College archive of any material relevant to its history, donated or deposited by former members or by the general public.

Major collections   Documents and volumes relating to the College's internal administration from the 15th century to the 20th century.
Deeds and documents relating to acquisition and control of College estates from 12th century to the 20th century.
An artificial collection of literary and personal MSS relating to alumni, and of collegiate, local and national interest.

Non-manuscript material   Prints and photographs relating to the College buildings and to its members.

Finding aids   Late 19th-century typescript catalogue of medieval deeds (arranged by county) by W.D. Macray. Catalogue of the early estate records is in preparation.

Personal and literary MSS catalogued and indexed. Lists and indexes to the College administrative and later estate material in process of compilation.

Facilities   Photocopying.

Publications   J.R. Bloxam: *Register of the Members of St. Mary Magdalen College* (1853–81)[7 vols]
W.D. Macray: *Register of Magdalen College* new series (1894–1915)[8 vols]

569   Middle East Centre
St Antony's College

Address   University of Oxford
Oxford OX2 6JF

Telephone   (0865) 259651 ext. 64

Enquiries to   Archivist, Ms Gillian Grant

Open   Mon–Fri: 9.30–1.00; 2.00–5.15

Access   Approved readers on written application.

Historical background   The collection was begun in 1961 by Elizabeth Monroe and Albert Hourani with the aim of gathering together the papers, both personal and official, of individuals who either served in the Middle East – as senior Government representatives, members of the armed forces etc – or whose main area of concern – as bankers, businessmen, missionaries or travellers – was the Middle East. The collection has expanded rapidly and now contains the papers of well over 200 individuals, covering the period from 1800 to the present day.

Acquisitions policy   To acquire by donation or deposit further collections of private papers of individuals who were involved in the Middle East.

Major collections   H.R.P. Dickson (1881–1959) papers: reports, diaries and correspondence concerning his career as Political Agent in Bahrain, 1919–21; Political Resident in the Gulf, 1928; and Political Agent in Kuwait, 1929–36.
Papers of C.J. Edmonds concerning his service in Iraq, 1915–45, and his study of Kurdistan (topography, language and people), 1915–60s.
H. St John Philby: correspondence, memos, travel diaries, published and unpublished MSS, relating to Transjordan, Iraq, Palestine and Arabia, 1915–57.
Major General Sir E.L. Spears: papers relating to the Spears Mission to Syria and Lebanon, 1941–44.
Jerusalem and East Mission: records covering the mission's work in Palestine, Syria, Iraq, Jordan, Iran, Gulf, Egypt, Sudan, Cyprus and North Africa, 1841–1970s.

Non-manuscript material   Photographic Archive: c10,000 positive prints; 10,000 negatives; 100 albums; 2000 lantern slides and 2000 coloured slides covering all areas of the Middle East, c1860–1960.

Finding aids   Handlists are available for approximately one third of the collections and there is an extensive author and subject index.

Facilities   Photocopying. Photography by arrangement.

Publications   D. Grimwood-Jones (ed): *Sources for the History of the British in the Middle East 1800–1978. A Catalogue of the Private Papers Collection in the Middle East Centre, St Antony's College, Oxford* (London, 1979)

570   Museum of the History of Science

Address   Old Ashmolean Building
                 Broad Street
                 Oxford OX1 3AZ

Telephone   (0865) 243997

Enquiries to   Librarian, Mr A.V. Simcock

Open   Mon–Fri: 10.30–1.00; 2.30–4.00

Access   Available to scholarly readers by arrangement with the Libarian; prior notice of visits is helpful.

Historical background   Along with the collection of scientific instruments of Lewis Evans (1853–1930), with which the Museum was founded in 1924, came the founder's Library of c1000 books and 120 volumes of MSS on the subjects of his collection – early scientific instruments, especially sundials, and associated techniques. The first Curator of the Museum, R.T. Gunther (1869–1940), built up a Museum Library around this core, and it has continued to develop by purchase, gift and deposit. The manuscript collections and iconographic collection (prints, photographs and printed ephemera) have developed in the same way.

Acquisitions policy   MSS are occasionally purchased but more usually deposited or given, on the subject of scientific instruments, history of science, and other themes relating to the displays, activities and history of the Museum.

Major collections   c800 volumes, files or bundles, including L.H. Dudley Buxton MSS containing important material relating to Charles Babbage (1712–1871).
The R.T. Gunther Archive relating to the early history and activities of the Museum during Gunther's Curatorship (1924–40).
The Radcliffe Observatory MSS.
The H.E. Stapleton collection relating to Islamic alchemy.
(The archives of the Royal Microscopical Society are at present kept in the Library, under the care of the Society's Honorary Archivist, who is a member of the Museum staff.)

Non-manuscript material   Associated with the general collection of books is a large collection of offprints and pamphlets, mostly modern, and 115 volumes of the

Radcliffe Tracts, offprints and pamphlets mostly of the 18th century and early 19th century.

The iconographic and printed ephemera collection includes prints and photographs of scientists, scientific instrument-makers, scientific instruments and apparatus; a few drawings, paintings, and early photographs; printed handbills, advertisements, lecture notices and syllabuses.

Finding aids   Catalogue and index of the manuscript collections.

Facilities   Photocopying. Photography can be arranged. Microfilm/fiche reader.

571   Nuffield College Library

Address   University of Oxford
                 Nuffield College
                 Oxford OX1 1NF

Telephone   (0865) 248014

Enquiries to   The Librarian

Open   Mon–Fri: 9.30–1.00; 2.00–6.00
                 Sat: 9.30–1.00

Access   Bona fide researchers.

Historical background   The College was founded in 1937 as a graduate college in the social sciences.

Acquisitions policy   To serve the research needs of members of the College.

Major collections   College records including Nuffield College Social Reconstruction Survey, and Nuffield Trust for the Special Areas
Records of Fabian Society and Guild Socialism.
Papers, including Lord Cherwell (1886–1957); William Cobbett (1762–1835); G.D.H. Cole (1889–1957); Sir Stafford Cripps (1889–1952); Lord Gainford (1860–1943); Sir Hubert Henderson (1890–1952).

Non-manuscript material   Books, pamphlets, journals, government publications relating to the social sciences.

Finding aids   Detailed lists of some collections and catalogues of most others.

Facilities   Photocopying. Microfilm/fiche readers.

572   Oxford Polytechnic Library

Address   Headington
                 Oxford OX3 0BP

No archives are held.

573   Oxfordshire County Record Office

Address	County Hall New Road Oxford OX1 1ND
Telephone	(0865) 815203
Enquiries to	County Archivist, Miss S.J. Barnes
Open	Mon–Thur: 9.00–1.00; 2.00–5.00 Fri: 9.00–1.00; 2.00–4.00

Historical background   The Office was formally established in 1936.

Major collections   Usual local authority record holdings and deposited collections mainly of local interest.

Facilities   Photocopying. Photography. Microfilming.

Publications   *Oxfordshire County Record Office and its records* (1938)
Summary Catalogue of the Privately Deposited Records in the Oxfordshire County Record Office (1966)

574   Oxfordshire Health Authority Archives

Address	The Warneford Hospital Warneford Lane Headington Oxford OX3 7JX
Telephone	(0865) 245651, ext. 282/208
Enquiries to	Archivist, Mrs B. Parry-Jones
Open	By prior appointment only
Access	Approved readers on written application. 30-year closure on administrative records and 100-year closure on medical material.

Historical background   The Oxfordshire Health Authority assumed active responsibility for the conservation of its archives by introducing the part-time services of an archivist in 1969. The records, including ancient deeds relating to endowments, of all hospitals within the Authority's catchment area have been listed and are generally housed in their hospitals of origin, under the supervision of the archivist. The hospitals include two Public Subscription Infirmaries (founded 1770 and 1869), one Public Subscription Asylum (founded 1826), one County Pauper Lunatic Asylum (founded 1846) and a range of Cottage Hospitals and specialized units (late 19th century and early 20th century).

Acquisitions policy   Any material relating to hospitals within the Oxfordshire Health Authority or to members of its staff, including obsolete records passed on internally and requiring preservation, and gifts or deposits from any source which have direct relevance to the history of these hospitals.

Major collections   Archives of the following hospitals:
Radcliffe Infirmary, 1757–1971.
Warneford Hospital (formerly Radcliffe Asylum), 1567–1963.
Littlemore Hospital (formerly Oxfordshire County Lunatic Asylum), 1846–60.
Horton Hospital (formerly Infirmary), 1869–1974.
Victoria Cottage Hospital, Thame, 1891–1969.
Brackley Cottage Hospital, 1876–1968.

Non-manuscript material   Paintings, prints and photographs of medical, nursing and administrative staff and of hospital wards and sites.

Finding aids   Lists for all collections.

Facilities   Photocopying.

Publications   A.H.T. Robb Smith: *A Short History of the Radcliffe Infirmary* (1970)
B. Parry-Jones: *The Warneford Hospital, 1826–1976* (1976)
———— : 'Peter Hollins at the Warneford Hospital', *Leeds Arts Calendar*, no. 88 (1981)

575   Oxford University Archives

Address   Bodleian Library
Broad Street
Oxford OX1 3BG

Telephone   (0865) 244675 ext. 345/479

Enquiries to   Keeper of the Archives, Mr T.H. Aston
Material from the University Archives is read in Duke Humfrey reading room in the old Bodleian Library.

Open   Term: Mon–Fri: 9.00–10.00; Sat: 9.00–1.00
Vacation: Mon–Fri: 9.00–7.00; Sat: 9.00–1.00
The staff of the University Archives are only on duty and records can only be fetched Mon–Fri: 9.00–5.00. Having been fetched however records can be read during library opening hours.

Access   Requires a Bodleian reader's ticket. Certain classes of records require a written application to the Keeper. All records are closed for 30 years and personal information in certain classes for longer.

Historical background   The date of the first extant University charter is 1214. Since then the University has preserved records such as charters, deeds, financial documents and records of students, which safeguarded its rights and privileges.

Until recently however less formal working papers were not kept in the archives. The first Keeper of the Archives was elected in 1634 and he and his successor transferred the records from the old Congregation House adjoining St Mary's church to the lower of the two uppermost rooms in the tower in the old Bodleian Library quadrangle. Expansion led to the acquisition of the upper room in the tower for the archives in 1854 and the accommodation in other university buildings more recently. The archives are supervised by the Delegates of Privileges, a body first appointed in 1768 to safeguard the rights of the University.

Acquisitions policy   Acquisitions are restricted to the records of the University and its departments and personal working papers directly related to these.

Major collections   University charters, grants of privilege and title deeds.
University statutes.
Records of students.
Records of the University's legislative and executive bodies.
Financial records.
Records of the Chancellor's jurisdiction.
Departmental records (e.g. registry, University museum).
Records of the Oxford Delegacy of Local Examinations.

Non-manuscript materials   Plans of the Nottingham Park Estate, Nottingham, 19th and 20th centuries.
Plans of the University museum and the Taylor Institution, 19th and 20th centuries.
Drawings and photographs of the restoration of the Sheldonian Theatre, 1935–7, 1958–63.

Finding aids   Handlist to contents of lower archive room; lists of most other collections; indexes to some of these lists; detailed index to Chancellor's Court records, 1594–1639, 1654 (in preparation).

Facilities   Shared with Bodleian Library. Photocopying. Photography. Microfilm/ fiche reader/printer.

Publications   *Corpus Statutorum Universitatis Oxoniensis* (Oxford, 1768) [with additions]
J. Griffiths: *Index to Wills and other Testamentary Records of the Chancellor's Court* (Oxford, 1862)
J. Griffiths: *Statutes of the University of Oxford codified in 1636* (Oxford, 1888)
R.L. Poole: *Lecture on the History of the University Archives* (Oxford, 1912)
S. Gibson: *Statuta Antiqua Oxoniensis* (Oxford, 1931)
T.H. Aston and D.G. Vaisey: 'University Archives', P. Morgan *Oxford Libraries outside the Bodleian* (Oxford, 2/1980)
[Most of the pre-1485 University records and some 16th- and 17th-century material has been published by the Oxford Historical Society]

576   Pitt Rivers Museum
Balfour Library

Address	University of Oxford Parks Road Oxford OX1 3PP
Telephone	(0865) 512541, ext. 602
Enquiries to	Librarian, Mrs E.J.M. Edwards
Open	Term: Mon–Fri: 9.00–12.30; 2.00–5.00 Vacation: Mon–Fri: 9.00–12.30; 2.00–4.00 MS and Photograph collections by appointment
Access	Senior Members and Research Students of the University of Oxford. Undergraduate students taught in the Department of Ethnology and Prehistory. Others at the discretion of the Librarian.

Historical background   The Library is named after Henry Balfour, first curator of the Museum, who left his personal library of over 10,000 volumes and pamphlets to the Museum on his death in 1939. This collection forms the core of the Balfour Library. The Library has a dual function, as the research library of the Pitt Rivers Museum, one of the world's major ethnographic collections, and as the teaching and research library of the University Department of Ethnology and Prehistory. The subject coverage is ethonography, anthropology, prehistoric archaeology, religion, music, travels and pre-industrial technology/material culture.

Acquisitions policy   To strengthen existing collections to meet the teaching and research needs of the Museum and Department. Material is added by purchase, exchange, donation and bequest.

Major collections   Henry Balfour (1863–1939): diaries and annotated writings.
Miss B. Blackwood (1889–1975): field notes and correspondence.
Sir Baldwin Spencer (1860–1929): correspondence, notes and other papers.
Prof. Sir Edward B. Tylor (1832–1917): correspondence and notes.
Col. R.G. Woodthorpe (1845–98): diaries and sketches.
Various other smaller collections of MSS of anthropological interest.

Non-manuscript material   Photographic Archive: An important collection of *c*30,000 items of anthropological interest dating from the 1860s onwards. The whole world is represented but the collection is particularly strong on Oceania, Assam and south-western USA. Collections include Prof. E. Evans-Pritchard (Nuer and Azande), Miss B. Blackwood (Melanesia), and J.H. Hutton and J. Mills (Naga).

Finding aids   Various catalogues, lists and indexes. Cataloguing work is still in progress.

Facilities   Photocopying. Photography. Microfiche reader.

Publications   E. Edwards and L. Williamson: *World on a Glass Plate: Early*

Anthropological Photographs from the Pitt Rivers Museum (1981) [a selection of photographs from the archive with descriptions of ethnographic content]

577   Pusey House Library

Address   Pusey House
St Giles
Oxford OX1 3LZ

Telephone   (0865) 259519/257117

Enquiries to   Custodian of the Library, Rev R. McCarthy

Open   Mon—Fri: 9.00—5.00
Sat: 9.00—1.00
Subject to alteration out of University term

Access   Bona fide researchers on written application.

Historical background   The Library was founded as a Memorial Library after the death of E.B. Pusey (1800–82) by his friends, who bought Pusey's own library for the purpose. It was joined with the Theology Faculty Library in the late 1950s, although the two libraries remain distinct administratively and financially. In harmony with Pusey's own interests, the Library concentrates upon patristics, church history, Victorian church sources and liturgy.

Acquisitions policy   To strengthen the areas noted above, as well as to augment the extensive 19th-century pamphlet collection.

Major collections   Papers and correspondence of various important figures and organizations involved in the High Church movement: the basis is c120 vols of E.B. Pusey's own correspondence, original and transcribed, (compiled for his *Life of E.B. Pusey*) and a collection by and relating to John Henry Newman.
Also: Liddon papers; papers of Philip Pusey (1799–1855); Edward Churton (1800–74) and William Ralph Churton (*d* 1828); W.K. Hamilton (1808–69); C. Marriott (1811–58); R. Scott (1811–87); H.A. Woodgate; the English Church Union; the Association for the Promotion of the Unity of Christendom etc.
Papers of 20th-century Anglican figures, including C.H. Turner, Darwell Stone, N.P. Williams, Sidney Lesley Ollard.

Non-manuscript material   21,500 19th-century pamphlets centring around the Tractarian Movement (many are bound into vols).
Theological Library (*see* 'Historical background') of which c60,000 items belong to Pusey House.

Finding aids   Lists and provisional author catalogue for much of the MS material. Pamphlets are catalogued by author, title, and subject, in three separate indexes, with a complete handlist.

Facilities   Photocopying.

Publications   J.A. Fenwick: *Nineteenth-century Pamphlets at Pusey House: an Introduction for the Prospective User by Father Hugh* (1961)

578   Radcliffe Science Library

Address   University of Oxford
Parks Road
Oxford OX1 3QP

Telephone   (0865) 244675 (Bodleian switchboard)
(0865) 254161 (direct line)

Enquiries to   Keeper of Scientific Books, Dr D.F. Shaw

Open   Term: Mon–Fri: 9.00–10.00
Vacation: Mon–Fri: 9.00–7.00
Closed: the week beginning with the late summer Bank Holiday; 24 Dec–1 Jan inclusive

Access   Bona fide researchers.

Historical background   The Radcliffe Science Library is the scientific, medical and mathematics library of Oxford University and a department of the Bodleian. It was first housed in the Radcliffe Camera (1749–1860) which was designed for the original Radcliffe Library by James Gibbs. In 1861 it was transferred to the University Museum and in 1901 was brought to its present site. In 1927 the Radcliffe Trustees presented the Library and its collection of books and periodicals to Oxford University.

Acquisitions policy   Collections of scientific or medical papers are accepted if appropriate.

Major collections   Radcliffe records: MSS and printed material relating to the Radcliffe Library and Radcliffe Librarians; a major part relates to Sir Henry Acland (1815–1900), Regius Professor of Medicine in the University of Oxford.
Pharmaceutical recipè books by William Bostock of Oxford, c1895.

Non-manuscript material   c250,000 scientific theses from European universities, 1884–1930 and 1970–.
Portraits of Oxford medical men and scientists.
Natural history paintings and drawings of birds, animals and flowers, mainly from the 18th and 19th centuries.
Coloured drawings, illustrative of costume etc of the natives of Japan.
Small collection of computer manuals acquired by Professor G. Strachey.

Finding aids   Radcliffe records index and handlist.

Facilities   Photocopying. Microfilm/fiche readers.

Publications   *Annual Report* [included in Annual Report of the Curators of the Bodleian Library].

579   Rhodes House Library

Address   South Parks Road
                Oxford OX1. 3RG

Telephone   (0865) 255762

Enquiries to   Librarian, Mr A.S. Bell

Open   Term: Mon–Fri: 9.00–7.00; Sat: 9.00–1.00
                Vacation: Mon–Fri: 9.00–5.00; Sat: 9.00–1.00
                Follows Bodleian Library timetable for closure at Christmas, Easter,
                and in early September. Intending vacation readers are advised to
                write for information.

Access   Approved readers holding Bodleian reader's ticket or short-term
                ticket available at Rhodes House Library. Suitable credentials
                required and written application in advance preferred.

Historical background   A dependent library of the Bodleian, founded by the Rhodes
    Trustees in 1929 and housing, in their Oxford headquarters, the post-1760
    Bodleian Library printed book and manuscript collections relating to the political,
    economic and social history of the British colonies and Commonwealth
    (excluding India, Pakistan, Bangladesh and Burma), the USA, and Africa.

Acquisitions policy   Development of existing holdings as a collecting point for
    administratively affiliated archive surveys; solicitation of gifts and deposits (and
    some purchases) in continuation of established practice.

Major collections   MS collections relating to areas mentioned above, notably the
    personal papers of former British colonial officials and Development
    administrators have been gathered through the Oxford Colonial (and
    Development) Records Projects, and the Library houses the papers of
    organizations such as the Anti-Slavery Society, the Fabian Colonial Bureau, and the
    African Bureau.
    Substantial holdings relating to Cecil John Rhodes (1853–1902) and his family; Sir
    Thomas Fowell Buxton (1786–1845) and Charles Roden Buxton (1875–1942);
    papers of Arthur Creech Jones (1891–1964); Sarawak materials include papers of
    the Brooke family and their associates.

Finding aids   Handlists of individual collections distributed by the Historical
    Manuscripts Commission.

Facilities   Photocopying in library. Other photographic services at Bodleian.
    Microfilm/fiche readers. Audio-equipment for oral history collections.

Publications   *Manuscript Collections of Africana in Rhodes House Library* (1968;
    suppls 1971, 1978)
    Manuscript Collections (1970, suppl. 1978) [excluding Africana]
    P.M. Hugh: 'The Oxford Colonial Records Project and Oxford Development
    Records Project', *Journal of the Society of Archivists* vi/2 (1978), 76

580   University of Oxford
Department of Educational Studies Library

Address   15 Norham Gardens
                 Oxford OX2 6PY

No archives are held.

581   Paisley College of Technology Library

Address   High Street
                 Paisley
                 Strathclyde PA1 2BE

Telephone   (041) 887 1241

Enquiries to   Chief Librarian, Mr H.C. Maclachlan

Open   Term: Mon–Fri: 9.10–7.00
                       Sat: 9.30–12.30
                 Vacation: Mon–Fri: 9.10–5.00

Access   Upon satisfactory identification and approval of need.

Historical background   The College was founded in 1900, as Paisley Technical College with the Paisley Government School of Art and Design (*fd*1842) as a constituent. It was granted the status of a Central Institution in 1950, when the art courses were dropped and development concentrated on technology. The Library was established in 1963.

Major collections   A collection of estimates and contracts relating to the construction of *c*25 Scottish railway companies, donated to the College in 1967, at the time of closure of St Enoch's Station, Glasgow.

Non-manuscript material   Maps and plans relating to above material.

Publications   *Calendar of Scottish Railway Documents*

582   Perth and Kinross District Archive

Address   Sandeman Library
                 16 Kinnoull Street
                 Perth
                 Perthshire PH1 5ET

Telephone   (0738) 23320/23329

Enquiries to   Archivist, Mr S.J. Connelly

Open Mon–Fri: 9.30–5.00, by appointment

Access Generally open to the public.

Historical background The Archive was established as a result of the reorganization of local government in Scotland in 1975, the first appointment of a permanent archivist being made in 1978. The Archive is principally concerned with the preservation of the former local authority records which now vest in Perth and Kinross District Council, or which vest in Tayside Regional Council, but are held on indefinite loan in Perth.

Acquisitions policy To locate local authority records for preservation in the district archive and to act as a place of deposit for the records of various local businesses, institutions, families and individuals.

Major collections Records of the City and Royal Burgh of Perth, 1210–1975.
Records of the burghs of Aberfeldy, Abernethy, Alyth, Auchterarder, Blairgowrie and Rattray, Coupar Angus, Crieff, Kinross and Pitlochry, 1708–1975.
Records on indefinite loan from Tayside Regional Council: County of Perth, 1650–1975; County of Kinross, 1738–1975; County of Perth and Kinross, 1930–75.

Non-manuscript material Reports, posters, photographs, maps and plans.

Finding aids Descriptive lists are available for the main series of records. Lists are in course of preparation for the papers of various local authority bodies and some private deposits.

Facilities Photocopying. Microfilm/fiche readers.

583 Perth Museum and Art Gallery

Address George Street
Perth
Tayside PH1 5LB

Telephone (0738) 32488

Enquiries to The Keeper

Open Mon–Sat: 10.00–1.00; 2.00–5.00
By appointment only

Access Generally open to the public.

Historical background The nucleus of the collections was the Literary and Antiquarian Society Collection, built up from 1784. In 1822 part of the present museum was erected; opened in 1824. In 1902 a separate collection built up by the Perthshire Society for Natural Sciences was transferred to local authority ownership, as was the Literary and Antiquarian Society collection in 1914. All of the collections were amalgamated in the 1824 building, which was extended and reopened in 1935. The museum has three sections: Human History, Fine and Applied Art, and Natural Sciences.

Acquisitions policy   The archives are no longer being actively added to, but the Museum retains interest in material associated with Perth and the Kinross District.

Major collections   Records of the Museum and of the Literary and Antiquarian Society Collection, mainly antiquarian tracts and papers.
Local history material, including Guildry book, a history of the guilds.
Records of members of the Perthshire Society of Natural Sciences.

Non-manuscript material   A few plans, mostly of Perth.
Photographic collection (100,000 glass negatives).
Scottish paintings.

Finding aids   The National Register of Archives (Scotland) has made lists of the collection. Photographic collection well indexed.

Facilities   Photocopying. Photography.

584   Trinity College Library

Address   Trinity College
                Glenalmond
                Perth
                Tayside

No archives are held.

585   Peterborough Cathedral

Address   Prebendal House
                The Precincts
                Peterborough
                Cambridgeshire PE1 1XX

Telephone   (0733) 69441

Enquiries to Canon T.R. Christie

Virtually all MSS and early printed books are on loan to Cambridge University Library (*see* entry 87).

586   Peterborough Museum and Art Gallery

Address	Priestgate Peterborough Cambridgeshire
Telephone	(0733) 43329
Enquiries to	Curator, Mr M.D. Howe
Open	Mon–Fri: 8.45–5.00, by prior appointment only
Access	Bona fide researchers. In the case of Clare MSS proof of bona fides will be requested.

Historical background   The Museum was founded by the Peterborough Museum Society in 1879 and taken over by the City Council in 1968. The Peterborough Museum Society still retains the local history archive collection; apply to Priory Road, Peterborough.

Acquisitions policy   The Museum now collects material of local interest (i.e. within Greater Peterborough area), although collections held in Museum cover a wider area).

Major collections   Archaeological records of excavations (mostly 20th century).
Natural History material (acquired in connection with Natural History Resources Centre).
Papers and MSS of John Clare (1793–1864).
Norman Croft Collection: Napoleonic prisoner of war work records, including order of day books, accounts of court martials, land tenure agreements, inventories, 1797–1816.
Very few local government records (those are retained in town hall).
Small collection of local archives.

Non-manuscript material   Photographs; playbills; maps from 1820; topographical collection.

Facilities   Photocopying and photography by arrangement only.

Finding aids   Card indexes

Publications   M. Grainger: *Catalogue of Clare MSS in the Peterborough Museum*

587   Devon Library Services

Address	Plymouth Central Library Drake Circus Plymouth Devon

Telephone	(0392) 77977 (Exeter Central Library)
Enquiries to	The Area Librarian
Open	Mon–Fri: 9.00–9.00
	Sat: 9.00–4.00
Access	Generally open to the public. Prior enquiry advisable.

Historical background   Devon Library Services was formed from a number of separate library authorities on local government reorganization in 1974. Two of these authorities, Exeter and Plymouth, were established in the 19th century and had considerable MS collections. They both suffered losses in World War II and their archives are now administered by West Devon Record Office (*see* entry **589**). Any MSS in Devon Library Services are non-archival in nature and relatively few in number. They are mainly in the local studies collections in Plymouth and Exeter Central Library (*see* entry **192**).

Acquisitions policy   To acquire non-archival MSS which reflect the development of Devon and the South West of England.

Major collections   A small number of MSS, including antiquarian notes and the collections of Sabine Baring-Gould (1834–1924) on folksongs and parish history.

Non-manuscript material   Extensive collections of illustrations, newspaper cuttings, files, ephemera, maps.
A collection of theses on Plymouth.

Facilities   Photocopying. Microfilm/fiche reader/printers. Photography by arrangement.

Publications   Some material included in A. Brodett: *The Devon Union List* (Exeter, 1977)

588   Plymouth Polytechnic

Address	Drake Circus
	Plymouth
	Devon PL4 8AA

No archives are held.

589   West Devon Record Office

Address	Clare Place
	Coxside
	Plymouth
	Devon PL4 0JW

Telephone	(0752) 264685
Enquiries to	Area Archivist, Miss E.A. Stuart
Open	Mon–Thurs: 9.30–5.00
	Fri: 9.30–4.30
	Sat (2nd of every 2nd month): 9.30–12.00
	There is a daily or annual charge.

Historical background   The Office was set up in 1952 as a section of the Plymouth Central Library which was administered. by the City Council. Since 1974 it has come under West Devon County Council. It also acts as the Diocesan Record Office for Exeter (parish records).

Major collections   Usual local authority record holdings and deposited collections.

Facilities   Photocopying. Photography. Microfilming. Microfilm reader.

Publications   C.E. Welch: *Guide to the Archives Department of Plymouth City Libraries. Part 1: Official Records* (1962)

590   The Polytechnic of Wales Library

Address	Pontypridd
	Mid Glamorgan CF37 1DL

There are no deposited collections. Internal records are held.

591   Poole Borough Council

Address	Civic Centre
	Poole
	Dorset BH15 2RU
Telephone	(0202) 22066
Enquiries to	Hon. Borough Archivist, Mr I.K.D. Andrews,
	(Town Clerk and Chief Executive Officer)
	or
	Secretary, Mrs. J.E. Jessop
Open	Mon–Thur: 8.30–5.15
	Fri: 8.30–4.45, by appointment
Access	Approved students after written application.

Historical background   Poole Borough Council houses its own archive, dating back to its first Charter in 1248. The Council were trustees of the quays until the late 19th century and so the records are of particular value to students of port trade.

Acquisitions policy   To acquire by gift, loan or purchase any material which can be regarded as, or was formerly part of, the Borough archive, or which adds a dimension to it (e.g. family records or title deeds of local relevance).

Major collections   Those relevant to the archive of a chartered borough.

Corporate records and minute books and deeds, as well as those of the Court of Record, Petty Sessions and Quarter Sessions (Poole was a County incorporate from 1568 to 1974).

Certain other material with local connections has been deposited with, or bequeathed to, the Council, including not only local title deeds, but research material on the Newfoundland trade on which the prosperity of the town was established.

Records of merchant families.

Non-manuscript material   Photographic, art, archaeology, books, posters, ephemera, map, film and sound collections (which are not borough archive by definition, but which are relevant to all aspects of the locality) are maintained separately at Poole Guildhall Museum.

Finding aids   Recently calendared material (approximately 10,000 entries) on index cards. Further material yet to be calendared on MSS records. Photocopies of some documents and a copy of the calendar of archives are available for other students at Poole Reference Library, Arndale Centre, Poole, and the Guildhall Museum, Market Street, Poole.

Facilities   Photocopying. Photography by arrangement.

Publications   Calendar of archive (4 vols pubd), also lodged in the National Register of Archives.

592   Portsmouth City Records Office

Address   3 Museum Road
                   Portsmouth
                   Hampshire PO1 2LE

Telephone   (0705) 829765

Enquiries to   City Records Officer, Miss S.E. Peacock

Open   Mon–Wed: 9.30–12.30; 2.00–5.00
                   Thurs: 9.30–12.30; 2.00–7.00
                   Fri: 9.30–12.30; 2.00–4.00

Historical background   The Records Office was established in 1960. It also acts as the Diocesan Record Office for Portsmouth.

Major collections   Usual local authority record holdings and deposited collections of local interest.

Facilities   Photocopying. Photography. Microfilming.

Publications   *Guide to Collections Part I: Church Records* (1977)

593   Portsmouth Polytechnic Library

Address   Cambridge Road
                 Portsmouth
                 Hampshire PO1 2ST

No archives are held.

594   Lancashire Record Office

Address   Bow Lane
                 Preston
                 Lancashire PR1 8ND

Telephone   (0772) 54868, ext. 3039

Enquiries to   County Archivist, Mr K. Hall

Open   Tues: 10.00–8.30
                 Wed–Fri: 10.00–5.00

Historical background   The Record Office was established in 1940. It is also the Diocesan Record Office for Blackburn, part of Liverpool and part of Bradford.

Major collections   Usual local authority record holdings and deposited collections of local interest.

Facilities   Photocopying. Photography. Microfilming.

Publications   R. Sharpe France: *Guide to Lancashire Record Office* (2/1962)
    Handlist of Genealogical Sources (5/1980)

595   Preston Polytechnic

Address   Library and Learning Resources Service
                 St Peter's Square
                 Preston
                 Lancashire PR1 7BB

Telephone   (0772) 22141, ext. 2321

Enquiries to   Polytechnic Librarian, Mr J.R. Edgar

Open   Term: Mon–Thurs: 9.00–9.00; Fri: 9.00–8.00
                 Vacation: Mon–Thurs: 9.00–5.30; Fri: 9.00–5.00

Access   Written application preferred.

Historical background Preston Institute for the Diffusion of Knowledge was founded in 1828. It was later known as the Avenham Institution until reformed in 1882 as the Harris Institute. This became Harris College in 1956 and Preston Polytechnic in 1973. The Preston Municipal Observatory, founded in 1881, was incorporated into the Polytechnic in 1974.

Acquisitions policy   To collect all material likely to be relevant to the understanding of the history and development of the Polytechnic and its predecessors.

Major collections Astronomical and meteorological records for Preston, 1881–1960s.
Index registers of all Harris Institute/College students, 1882–1965.
MSS of committee minutes, 1828–1920s.

Non-manuscript material   All prospectuses and reports, 1928–.
Photographs and ephemera. Early library catalogues. Oral history video tapes.

Facilities   Photocopying. Photography.

Publications   G. Timmins and others: *Preston Polytechnic: the Emergence of an Institution, 1828–1978* (Preston, 1979)

596   Kent Archives Office
North East Kent Branch

Address   Ramsgate Library
                 Guildford Lawn
                 Ramsgate
                 Kent CT11 9AY

Telephone   (0843) 53532

Enquiries to   Archivist-in-charge, Miss Charlotte Hodkin

Open   By appointment

Historical background   The branch office opened in autumn 1982. The collections comprise material relating to Thanet transferred from Margate, Broadstairs, and Ramsgate libraries, from the previous local authorities which were superseded by Thanet District Council following local government reorganization in 1974, and from the Kent Archives Office at Maidstone (*see* entry **515**).

Major collections   Usual local authority record holdings and deposited collections.

Facilities   Photocopying by arrangement. Microfilm reader.

597   BBC Written Archives Centre

Address   Caversham Park
            Reading
            Berkshire RG4 8TZ

Telephone   (0734) 472742, ext. 280/1/2

Enquiries to Written Archives Officer, Mrs J.M. Kavanagh

Open   Tues–Fri: 9.45–1.00; 2.00–5.00, by appointment

Access   By written appointment giving full details of the nature of the
            enquiry. Correspondence 1922–62 open for research. Unrestricted
            access to programme records, programmes-as-broadcast, news
            bulletins and scripts. Certain charges are made.

Historical background   The Centre was established in November 1970 as the
    repository for the Corporation's early papers.

Acquisitions policy   Non-current records of the Corporation including regional
    records, BBC publications, papers of prominent BBC figures.

Major collections   Correspondence, minutes and reports covering all areas of the
    BBC's activities – administration, technical development, audience research, and
    programmes, including correspondence with outside contributors. Programmes-
    as-broadcast, news bulletins, scripts.

Non-manuscript material   Plans and illustrations, technical handbooks, microfilm
    holdings. BBC publications including *Radio Times* (with regional volumes), *The
    Listener*, *World Radio*, *London Calling*, BBC Schools Publications, BBC Symphony
    Concert Programmes, BBC Promenade Concert Programmes and Monitoring
    Services, *Daily Digest* (later the *Summary of World Broadcasts*).

Finding aids   Various lists and indexes.

Facilities   Photocopying. Microfilm readers. Canteen.

598   Berkshire County Libraries

Address   Shire Hall
            Shinfield Park
            Reading
            Berkshire RG2 9XD

Archives are neither held nor acquired.

599   Berkshire Record Office

Address	Shire Hall Reading Berkshire RG2 9XD
Telephone	(0734) 875444, ext.3182
Enquiries to	The County Archivist
Open	Mon: 2.00–5.00 Tues–Wed: 9.00–5.00 Thurs: 9.00–9.00 Fri: 9.00–4.30

Historical background   The Record Office was established in 1948. It also acts as the Diocesan Record Office for Oxford (archdeaconry of Berkshire).

Major collections   Usual local authority record holdings and deposited collections of local interest.

Facilities   Photocopying. Photography. Microfilming.

Publications   F. Hull: *Guide to the Berkshire Record Office* (1952)
M.F. and S. Bond: *Handlist of Records Preserved in the Muniment Rooms of the Royal Borough at New Windsor* (1973)

600   Douai Abbey

Address	Upper Woolhampton Reading Berkshire RG7 5TH
Telephone	(073 521) 3163
Enquiries to	The Archivist
Open	Mon–Fri, by appointment
Access	Bona fide researchers.

Historical background   The English Benedictine Community of St Edmund was founded in Paris in 1615. After the French Revolution it moved to Douai where it remained until 1903 when it settled at Woolhampton. Since 1818 there has been a school for boys. The bulk of pre-1800 documents were confiscated by the French Government.

Acquisitions policy   Microfilms of the lost records are obtained when possible.

Major collections   A few records of the Community and of the English Benedictine Congregation, 1619–1800.

Records of Community and School, 1818–.

Records of pastoral work of the Community in various parts of England and Wales, also Mauritius and Australia.

Finding aids   Various lists and indexes available.

Facilities   Photocopying. Microfilm/fiche reader.

601   Institute of Agricultural History and Museum of English Rural Life

Address   University of Reading
Whiteknights
Reading
Berkshire RG6 2AG

Telephone   (0734) 875123 ext. 475

Enquiries to   Archivist, Mr David Phillips

Open   Mon–Fri: 9.30–1.00; 2.00–5.00, by prior appointment
Closed: between Christmas and New Year

Access   Generally open to the public. A user's card may be issued for study of research collections over a long period. One week's notice is required for consultation of agricultural co-operative society records and certain deposits of national agricultural organizations records. Restrictions on some deposited collections.

Historical background   The Museum of English Rural Life was founded within the University of Reading in 1951 and opened to the public in 1955, moving to its present buildings in 1964. In 1968 the Institute of Agricultural History was established to co-ordinate and extend teaching and research in agricultural history; to collect, preserve and publish records, documents and other relevant material; and to maintain the Museum of English Rural Life. Results of a survey of farm records made in the 1970s may be consulted at the Institute.

Acquisitions policy   To collect material concerned with English agriculture, with an emphasis on agricultural technology, engineering and organization.

Major collections   Trade Records Collection: business records of over 30 agricultural engineering, servicing and processing firms; technical and advertising literature issued by c3000 UK and foreign firms, 19th century–.
National Agricultural Organization Records: records of Royal Agricultural Society of England (*fd* 1838), including archives of the Board of Agriculture and Internal Improvement, 1793–1822; National Union of Agriculture and Allied Workers, 1906–40s; National Farmers' Union, 1909–43; Country Landowners' Association, 1907–58; Royal Agricultural Benevolent Institution, 1880s–1960s; Council for the

Protection of Rural England, 1930s–70s; Agricultural Apprenticeship Council, 1949–74.

Agricultural Co-operative Society records, mostly 20th century.

General collections, including personal papers of agricultural writers and scientists.

Farm records, 18th–20th centuries, are housed at Reading University Library (*see* entry **602**): enquiries should be made to University Archivist in the first instance.

Non-manuscript material   Engineering drawings, catalogues and ephemera.

Photograph Library, including collections of agricultural organizations and farming journals, from mid-19th century (over 250,000).

Finding aids   Lists and catalogues for all principal deposits. Specialized indexes for certain collections.

Facilities   Photocopying. Photography. Microfilming. Microfilm reader.

Publications   *Historical Farm Records, as Summary Guide* ... (Reading, 1973)

602   University of Reading
Department of Archives and Manuscripts

Address　　University of Reading
　　　　　　Whiteknights
　　　　　　Reading
　　　　　　Berkshire RG6 2AE

Telephone　(0734) 874331, ext. 60

Enquiries to　Keeper of Archives and Manuscripts, Dr J.A. Edwards
　　　　　　Assistant Keeper of Archives and Manuscripts, Mr Michael Bott

Open　　　Mon–Fri: 9.00–1.00; 2.00–5.00, preferably by appointment

Access　　Generally open to the public. Certain records restricted.

Historical background　Established as a department of the Library in 1966 on the appointment of Dr J.A. Edwards. Expanded in the 1970s to include Assistant Keeper and Archives Assistant. Current activities include the establishment of a location register of 20th-century English literary MSS and letters.

Acquisitions policy　To acquire literary and historical MSS related to teaching and research in the University of Reading. To preserve University archives through the operation of a records management system.

Major collections　Records of British publishing and printing: 12 collections of which major ones include George Bell & Sons Ltd, Isotype Institute Ltd, Longman Group Ltd, Macmillan & Co Ltd, Routledge & Kegan Paul Ltd, Secker & Warburg Ltd.

Historical farm records: mainly of individual working farmers from every English county, 16th–20th centuries.

Records of contemporary writing: letters and MSS of some 200 authors, 1880–
(largest collection of Samuel Beckett MSS in Europe).
Modern political papers: six collections of 20th-century papers of which most important are those of Waldorf, 2nd Viscount Astor and Nancy, Lady Astor.
University archives: records of University departments and their antecedents and of members of staff, 1860–.

Non-manuscript material   Maps.
Photographs.
Audio-visual material.

Finding aids   Various indexes, catalogues and inventories.

Facilities   Access to all the resources of the University Library including photocopying and photographic services.

Publications   *Accessions of General Manuscripts up to June 1970* (1970)
Historical Farm Records: A Summary Guide to Manuscripts and other material in the University Library Collected by the Institute of Agricultural History (1973)
University of Reading Records Handbook (1977)
J.A. Edwards: *The Samuel Beckett Collection: a catalogue* (1978)
M. Bott and J.A. Edwards: *Records Management in British Universities: a survey with some suggestions* (1978)
J.A. Edwards: *A Brief Guide to Archives and Manuscripts in the Library, University of Reading* (1980)
The Kingsley Read Alphabet Collection: a catalogue (1982)

603   Redditch Public Library

Address   15 Market Place
Redditch
Worcestershire B98 8AR

Telephone   (0527) 63291

Enquiries to   Area Librarian, Mr H.R. Boote

Open   Mon, Thurs, Fri: 10.00–7.00
Tues: 10.00–5.00
Sat: 10.00–4.00, by appointment

Access   Bona fide researchers.

Historical background   Local history material has been collected by the Library since the end of World War II.

Acquisitions policy   Material relating to the history of the area.

Major collections   John English Collection: archives of a needle-trade family from Feckenham, nr Redditch, c1750–c1920.

Non-manuscript material   Newspapers, 1859–; maps 1844–; photographs, *c*1900–. *c*1000 printed books.

Finding aids   Brief contents list of major collections.

Facilities   Photocopying. Microfilm/fiche reader.

604   Cornwall County Library
Local Studies Library

Address   2–4 Clinton Road
Redruth
Cornwall TR15 2QE

Telephone   (0209) 216760

Enquiries to   Local Studies Librarian, Mr G.T. Knight

Local History Collections of non-MS material, including the A.K. Hamilton Jenkin Collection relating to mining in Cornwall.

605   London Borough of Richmond-upon-Thames Libraries Department

Address   Reference and Information Service
Central Library
Little Green
Richmond
Surrey TW9 1QL

Telephone   (01) 940 9125

Enquiries to   Reference Librarian, Miss D. Howard

Open   Mon–Fri: 10.00–6.00
Sat: 9.00–5.00

Access   Generally open to the public. A telephone call in advance is advisable to establish exact location of any given material.

Historical background   The London Borough of Richmond-upon-Thames was formed in 1965 by the amalgamation of the boroughs of Richmond, Twickenham, and Barnes. The local material relating to Richmond and East Sheen, Ham, Kew, Mortlake and Petersham is located at Richmond. There is no borough archivist or archives department and the library is not an official archive depository. Local material relating to Twickenham, The Hamptons, Teddington and Whitton is located at Twickenham District Reference Library. The majority of council records are in the custody of the Chief Executive and Town Clerk's Department, Municipal Offices, Twickenham TW1 3AA (telephone: (01) 892 4466).

Acquisitions policy Very little money is available each year to spend on the purchase of local history material which comes on the market, but anything significant is obtained when possible. A number of additions are donations from members of the public or from other council departments which do not wish to keep older materials.

Major collections Local government records, including rate books, Richmond vestry minutes and workhouse records, 19th and 20th centuries.
School records; miscellaneous collections of deeds (many still uncatalogued).
Richmond Cemetery burial records.
Douglas Sladen Collection of cuttings and letters from literary persons, 1888–1921 (74 vols).

Non-manuscript material Maps, 1635–.
c1000 playbills, mainly for Theatre Royal, Richmond, 1765–1884.
Photographs, prints, postcards; newscuttings and microfilms of local newspapers; copies and microfilms of census returns, 1841–71.
Ionides Collection: topographical paintings, drawings and engravings of Richmond, Twickenham and Lower Thames area (housed at Orleans Gallery, Twickenham).

Facilities Photocopying. Microfilm reader. Microfiche reader/printer.

Finding aids National Register of Archives Index to Sladen letters. Card catalogues of prints. Index to playbills. Document register in progress. Map catalogue.

606 Richmond College

Address   University of London
                Queens Road
                Richmond
                Surrey TW10 6JP

No archives are held.

607 Royal Botanic Gardens

Address   Library and Archives Division
                Kew
                Richmond
                Surrey TW9 3AE

Telephone   (01) 940 1171

Enquiries to The Chief Librarian and Archivist

Open   Mon–Thurs: 9.00–5.30
                Fri: 9.00–5.00

Access On written application

Historical background A Botanic Garden at Kew was begun in 1759 by Princess Augusta. The gardens of the Royal Estates at Kew became a Department of the Crown in 1840. They have been successively managed by the Commissioners of Woods and Forests (1841–51), the Board of Works (1851–1903) and, since 1903, the Board of Agriculture (later Ministry of Agriculture, Fisheries and Food). The buildings in the Royal Botanic Gardens, including Kew Palace, are maintained by the Department of the Environment. The Library was set up in 1852; it was approved as a place of deposit for the Gardens' own records in 1962, under section 4 of the Public Records Act 1958.

Acquisitions policy Official papers are selected according to Public Record Office rules. Other papers are accepted if relevant to Kew's plant collections and research.

Major collections Archives include over 250,000 letters from all over the world, also modern registered files, field notebooks, diaries etc; most date from 1840 onwards.

Notable are the papers of Sir William Jackson Hooker (1785–1865), his son Sir Joseph Dalton Hooker (1817–1911), George Bentham (1800–1884); correspondence with overseas botanic gardens and Departments of Agriculture and Forestry, especially in colonial territories.

Fewer papers relating to the Gardens before 1840 survive: most of the papers of the Superintendents William Aiton (1731–93) and his son William Townsend Aiton (1766–1849) were burnt in 1849; some were rescued, including Inwards and Outwards books and Records books, 1793–, and correspondence with Kew Collectors, e.g. Francis Masson and others; there are some papers of Sir Joseph Banks (1743–1820).

Non-manuscript material 3000 periodicals; 120,000 printed books; 140,000 pamphlets; 10,000 microforms; 175,000 illustrations; 10,000 maps; 500 portraits. *Kewensia*; nurserymen's catalogues.
Sound archive.
Large collection of plant illustrations, including many originals, e.g. the Church, Roxburgh, Tankerville and Curtis's *Botanical Magazine* collections.

Finding aids General author and subject catalogues. Inventory and Public Record Office lists. Name index of correspondents. Artists name index.

Facilities Photocopying. Photography. Microfilm/fiche readers.

Publications G.D.R. Bridson and others: *Natural History Manuscript Resources in the British Isles* (London, 1980) [RBG Kew entries, nos. 269.1–269.387]
Royal Botanic Gardens Bibliography 3. Kew Gardens: Selected References on the History of the Royal Botanic Gardens (Kew, 1980) [6pp.]

608   Rochdale Libraries
Local Studies Collection

Address   Rochdale Area Central Library
                 Esplanade
                 Rochdale
                 Lancashire OL16 1AQ

Telephone   (0706) 47474 ext. 423

Enquiries to   Local Studies Librarian, Mr John Cole

Open   Mon, Tues, Thurs, Fri: 9.30—8.00
                 Wed: 9.30—5.00
                 Sat: 9.30—4.00

Access   Generally open to the public.

Historical background   The dynamic growth of Rochdale, Middleton and Heywood
   during the 19th century produced a wealth of material relating to the area. The
   town of Rochdale in particular was fortunate in that the early pioneers of the
   Library Service were keenly interested in the development of the area and helped
   to acquire a large amount of material which formed the basis of the Local
   Collection. Prior to 1974 the substantial Local Collections of Heywood, Middleton
   and Rochdale were located at the Central Libraries in those areas and upon local
   government reorganization it was decided that each should retain a separate
   collection under the general supervision of a Local Studies Librarian based at
   Rochdale (*see also* Middleton Area Central Library, entry **532**; Heywood Area
   Central Library, entry **244**).

Acquisitions policy   The collection of documentary material relating to all aspects of
   life in the area of the Metropolitan Borough of Rochdale and its previously
   independent constituent authorities.

Major collections   Local Administrative Records: early administrative records
   including highway rates, Poor Law administration and administrative material from
   the constituent authorities of the Metropolitan Borough.
   Church Records: church rates, leys, tithe commutation maps, plans, deeds, etc;
   Methodist archives.
   Family Records: material relating to local families, including manorial records,
   deeds, indentures etc.
   Trade Union Records: records of the Rochdale Operative Cotton Spinners
   Association; the Rochdale Weavers, Winders and Beamers Association.
   Canal Documents: material relating to the construction of the Rochdale Canal.

Non-manuscript material   Complete runs of local newspapers (original and
   microfilm copies).
   Books, pamphlets, audio-visual material, photographs, maps, plans, broadsheets,
   political handbills, theatre posters.

Finding aids   Calendar of archival material.

Facilities   Photocopying. Microfilm/fiche readers.

Publications   *Introduction to Local Studies Collections* (1981)

609   Rochester Bridge Trust

Address   The Bridge Chamber
5 Esplanade
Rochester
Kent ME1 1QE

Telephone   (0634) 46706/43457

Enquiries to   Bridge Clerk, Mr G.A. Reeve

Open   By arrangement

Access   Archives are not readily available to the public, but may be consulted by bona fide scholars, with the approval of the Rochester Bridge Trust.

Historical background   In 1399 Sir Robert Knolles and Sir John de Cobham, prominent local men, gave and collected endowments in money and lands and obtained a Patent of Incorporation to ensure a responsible administration of the Rochester Bridge. A new bridge was built and two Wardens appointed, who with the help of a Court of Assistance administered the bridge. This arrangement still pertains. The bridge was specifically excluded from the provisions of the Trunk Roads Act of 1946. The Wardens were appointed *ex officio* Presidents of the New College of Cobham when it was refounded under the will of William Brooke, Lord Cobham, a descendant of the original founder, and College records are therefore lodged with those of the bridge, forming a distinct series. Deposits of certain papers have been made with the Guildhall Library, Essex County Record Office and Kent Archives Office (*see* entries **349**, **117** and **515** respectively).

Acquisitions policy   Working papers of the Trust.

Major collections   Rochester Bridge:
Administrative records from the early 15th century.
Wardens Accounts from 1391, including rentals of Bridge lands and inventories of tools, boats, furniture etc, 17th–18th centuries.
Records about maintenance and construction of the Bridge, including technical reports, correspondence etc, 1561–, and reports by George Dance, James Rennie, Robert Smirke and Thomas Telford, early 19th century.
Rentals and surveys 1506–.
Legal records, 1529–1835, and records relating to maintenance of property other than the Bridge 1740–.
Estate deeds, including documents for property elsewhere.
Manorial records.

New College of Cobham: Administrative records including payment to pensioners, 1599–; accounts, 1599–; bonds, 1599–1877; nominations, certificates and material concerning elections, 1632–1890; estate deeds and surveys.

Non-manuscript material   Maps.
Plans, 1780–1932.
Photographs and drawings.

Publications   E.S. Scroggs: *Rochester Bridge Trust and the New College of Cobham, Kent: Guide to Classification and Indexing of Records at the Bridge Chamber, Rochester* (1954)

————: 'The records of Rochester Bridge and The New College of Cobham', *Archives*, ii/12 (1954), 183

610   Rochester Diocesan Registry

Address   The Precinct
                  Rochester
                  Kent ME1 1SZ

Telephone   (0634) 43231/2, 47067

Enquiries to   The Diocesan Registrar

The Diocesan records may be seen by appointment.

611   London Borough of Havering

Address   Central Library
                  St Edward's Way
                  Romford
                  Essex RM1 3AR

Telephone   (70) 46040, ext. 355. After 5.00 and Sat: (70) 44297

Enquiries to   The Reference and Information Librarian

Open   Mon–Fri: 9.30–8.00
                  Sat: 9.30–5.00

Historical background   Until 1965 Havering was part of the County of Essex and much archive material relating to the area is therefore to be found at the Essex Record Office (*see* entry **117**). However, a small collection of items is held at Romford.

Acquisitions policy   To obtain further archives relevant to the area where possible and also to acquire copies of those deposited in other collections such as the Essex Record Office (mainly in microfilm form).

Major collections Parish Rate Books for selected areas (especially Romford), 19th century.
Council Minute Books for Hornchurch UDC; Romford UDC; Romford Borough; Romford Local Board of Health, 1851–89.
Liberty of Havering Treasurer's Book, 1835–43.

Non-manuscript material Microfilm copies of items held at the Essex Record Office including one of the Romford Workhouse Guardians, Minutes and S. Divisional Parliamentary Committee for Essex, Minute Book, 1643–56.
*c*2200 pamphlets, posters and post cards/illustrations.
Two newspaper cutting books with some 19th century items.
Maps and plans.

Finding aids Lists and indexes available.

Facilities Photocopying. Microfilm/fiche readers.

Publications *Romford Record*, nos. 1–14 (1969–82)
Subject Index to Romford Record, nos. 1–13
Subject Index to Havering Review, nos. 1–10
Guide to Local Population Figures

612 Rotherham Libraries, Museums and Arts

Address The Brian O'Malley Central Library and Arts Centre
Walker Place
Rotherham
South Yorkshire S65 1JH

Telephone (0709) 2121 ext. 3119

Enquiries to Principal Librarian, Mr D. Hardwick

Open Mon, Tues, Thurs, Fri: 10.00–4.45
Sat: 9.00–12.30

Open Generally open to the public.

Historical background The Library was administered by Rotherham County Borough until 1974 and then, after local government reorganization, began collecting material relating to the new Metropolitan Borough.

Acquisitions policy Collecting material connected with the area of Rotherham Metropolitan Borough.

Major collections Local government archives of Rotherham Metropolitan Borough Council and the former constiuent authorities of Rotherham County Borough, Rotherham Rural District Council, and the Urban District Councils of Kiveton Park, Maltby, Swinton and Rawmarsh.
Non-conformist records.

Non-manuscript material Photographs and other illustrations of the area.
   Oral history tapes.
   Pamphlets, press cuttings, newspapers, maps.

Facilities Photocopying. Microfilm/fiche reader.

613 Rugby School

Address   Temple Reading Room
                 Rugby School
                 Barby Road
                 Rugby
                 Warwickshire

Telephone   (0788) 73959

Enquiries to   Librarian, Mrs P.J. Macrory

Open   Term: Mon–Fri: 9.00–4.00, by appointment

Access   Approved readers on written application. All research undertaken
                 by the School will be charged for.

Historical background Founded by Lawrence Sheriff in 1567. Originally a free
   grammar school for local boys, it began to attract pupils from further afield during
   the late 17th century, and 100 years later was an established public school. Dr
   Thomas Arnold (1795–1842) and Dr Frederick Temple (1821–1902), later
   Archbishop of Canterbury, were among the 19th-century headmasters. The game
   of rugby football originated at the school. Old Rugbeians include W.S. Landor
   (1775–1867), Matthew Arnold (1822–88), A.H. Clough (1819–61), Thomas
   Hughes (1822–96), Rupert Brooke (1887–1915), Lewis Carroll (1832–98),
   Arthur Ransome (1834–1922), and William Temple (1881–1944).

Acquisitions policy Items connected with the school.

Major collections Arnold MSS: letters, diaries and notebooks of Dr Thomas Arnold.
   Rupert Brooke Collection: MS poems and Scrap Book given by Mrs Brooke. Various
   items associated with Brooke's schooldays.
   School Records: registers, governing body papers, collections of boys' letters etc;
   the earliest date from the 1670s, most from 1750.
   Rugby football: MSS and drawings concerning the early history of the game.

Non-manuscript material Photographs, 1861–. Portraits of headmasters and
   distinguished Rugbeians. Natural History Society: published reports, 1867–, and
   supporting collections.

Finding aids Various lists available.

Facilities Photocopying and photography, by arrangement.

614 Saffron Walden Town Council

Address   7a Hill Street
               Saffron Walden
               Essex CB10 1EH

Telephone   (0799) 27661

Enquiries to   Mr M.D. White

Open   Mon–Fri: 9.00–5.00, by appointment

Access   Approved readers on written application.

Historical background   The Borough of Saffron Walden was granted its first charter in c1236. Saffron Walden Town Council was formed in 1974.

Acquisitions policy   Anything relating to Saffron Walden Town Council and of general interest concerning Saffron Walden.

Major collections   Borough Council and court records, c1236–1974.
Town Council records, 1974–.
Charity minutes and papers.

Non-manuscript material   Drawings, paintings, prints of Saffron Walden mainly late 19th and early 20th centuries.

Finding aids   Index available from the Town Clerk.

Facilities   Photocopying available on request.

615 The Hay Fleming Reference Library

Address   St Andrews Branch Library
               Church Square
               St Andrews
               Fife

Telephone   (0334) 73381

Enquiries to   The Branch Librarian
               or
               The District Librarian, North East Fife District Library, County Buildings, Cupar, Fife

Telephone   (0334) 53722

Open   Mon, Tues, Wed, Fri: 10.00–7.00
               Thurs, Sat: 10.00–5.00

Access   Generally open to the public.

Historical background   David Hay Fleming (1849–1931), a native of St Andrews and
an eminent historian and critic, built up a substantial personal library for his own
research and studies. On his death the collection was bequeathed to the town of St
Andrews to form the nucleus of a public reference library and further the study of
Scottish history. The main scope for the collection is Scottish history, literature,
theology and the local history of St Andrews. The Library is administered on a day-
to-day basis by the staff of North East Fife District Library Service and is managed by
a Management Committee of Trustees.

Acquisitions policy   The terms of David Hay Fleming's will stipulated that 'the
proceeds of the endowment spent in increasing the said library shall be mainly
devoted to the purchase of works bearing directly or indirectly on the civil,
political, ecclesiastical and social history of Scotland and on the antiquities of
Scotland'. A few important works were purchased each year. Archival material is
occasionally acquired by donation.

Major collections   David Hay Fleming Collection: research notebooks,
correspondence, press cuttings, proofs of publications, local historical records and
broadsheets.
Collections of Church of Scotland sermons.
Title and legal documents, 1467–1595.
Ecclesiastical documents, 1613–58.
Papers relating to the financial effects of the town of St Andrews, 1614–1702.
Titles to lands in the town, 1622–1724.
Papers of local trades, including wrights, tailors, weavers.
Congregational rolls of churches.

Non-manuscript material   c13,000 printed books and pamphlets, early photographs
and postcard views of St Andrews.
Prints, maps and plans of historical buildings.
Press cuttings.
Broadsides and antiquarian material.

Finding aids   Many collections are listed by the National Register of Archives
(Scotland) in their list NRA(S) 1882. MS index to correspondence.

Facilities   Study area in main reference library. Photocopying by prior arrangement.

Publications   H.M. Paton: *David Hay Fleming, Historian and Antiquary* (1934)
A. Rodden: 'The Hay Fleming Reference Library, St Andrews', *SLA News* cxxii
(1974), 109, [precis of a paper given at St Andrews to the Dundee Branch of the
Library Association, 3 April 1974]

616 St Andrews University Library
Manuscripts Department

Address   St Andrews University
North Street
St Andrews
Fife KY16 9TR

Telephone   (0334) 76161, ext.514

Enquiries to   Keeper of Manuscripts, Mr R.N. Smart

Open   Term: Mon–Fri: 9.00–12.00; 2.00–5.00. Sat: 9.00–12.00, by prior arrangement
Vacation: Mon–Fri: 9.00–12.00; 2.00–5.00
Visitors from a distance are advised to give forewarning

Access   Bona fide researchers.

Historical background   A few manuscripts from the medieval religious house and college libraries of St Andrews survive, but the greater portion has been acquired in the 19th and 20th centuries.

Acquisitions policy   To acquire manuscripts with a local connection and scholarly material of or relating to members of the University. The Library is also interested in material to support teaching and research in the University.

Major collections   Western manuscripts: a miscellaneous collection of over 100,000 Codex manuscripts, letters and documents dating from the early middle ages onwards. It is strong in material of local and University interest, scientific correspondence of the 19th and 20th centuries and papers relating to the Roman Catholic Modernist Movement. Includes papers of Sir James Donaldson (1831–1915), James David Forbes (1809–68), Baron Friedrich von Hugel (1852–1925), Sir D'Arcy Wentworth Thompson (1860–1948), and Wilfrid Ward (1856–1916).
Oriental manuscripts: Small collection of c100 volumes, mostly in Arabic, Persian or Turkish – contains some especially fine copies of the Qu'ran.

Non-manuscript material   Photographs: Valentine Ltd, 120,000 images, British Isles, 1878–1967; G.M. Cowie 60,000 images, Press Photography, Fife, 1930–81.
Miscellaneous collections, 70,0-00 images, zoology, Turkey, Italian architecture, Canada, Fife, Continental scenery, farm animals, art photography, Highland scenery, 1839–.

Finding aids   Unpublished inventories and descriptive lists for particular parts of the collection. Name indexes available for both manuscripts and photographs.

Facilities   Photocopying. Photography. Microfilm/fiche reader/printer.

Publications   *St. Andrews University Library, an illustrated Guide* (St Andrews, 1948)
R.N. Smart: *An Index to the Correspondence and Papers of James David Forbes*

(1809–1868) and also to some Papers of his son George Forbes (St Andrews, 1968)

See also

Historical Manuscripts Commission Report, ii (1871), 208

J.D. Pearson: *Oriental Manuscripts in Europe and North America* (Zug, 1971)

Notes of recent additions to the collection will be found in the annual issues of the National Register of Archives *Lists of Accessions to Repositories* since 1956

617   St Andrews University Muniments

Address   St Andrews University
North Street
St Andrews
Fife KY16 9TR

Telephone   (0334) 76161 ext. 514

Enquiries to   Keeper of Muniments, Mr R.N. Smart

Open   Term: Mon–Fri: 9.00–12.50; 2.00–5.00
Sat: 9.00–12.00, by prior arrangement
Vacation: as above, but closed on Sat

Access   Generally open to the public. Visitors from a distance are advised to give forewarning.

Historical background   The University was founded in 1411; St Salvators College in 1450; St Leonard's College in 1512; St Mary's College in 1538; United College in 1747 and University College was conjoined in 1897 (erected into the University of Dundee in 1967). Although there has been continuous provision for custody of the records since the foundation, the muniments department only dates from 1892.

Acquisitions policy   Only the official records of the University and its constituent parts are acquired. Certain other archival collections are held on deposit.

Major collections   Apart from the University's own records the records of the following former burghs of North East Fife District are held on deposit from the Keeper of the Records of Scotland: Anstruther, Auchtermuchty, Crail, Cupar, Elie and Earlsferry, Falkland, Kilrenny, Ladybank, Newburgh, Newport, Pittenweem, St Andrews, St Monance, and Tayport.
Dundee Royal Infirmary Minutes, 1793–1902.

Non-manuscript material   Pictures, medals, and a wide miscellany of objects relative to the University's history.

Finding aids   Typescript guide; separate name indexes to the College papers, Acta Rectorum, Senatus Minutes and other series.

Facilities   Photocopying. Photography. Microfilm/fiche reader/printer.

Publications   No general published guide, but see
   Historical Manuscripts Commission Report, ii (1871), 206
   R.G. Cant: *The University of St. Andrews: A Short History* (Edinburgh, 1970)
   See also the introductions to
   J.M. Anderson: *Matriculation Roll of the University of St. Andrews 1747–1897*
   (Edinburgh, 1905)
   ————: *Early Records of the University of St. Andrews 1413–1579* (Edinburgh,
   1926)
   A.I. Dunlop: *Acta Facultatis Artum Universitatis Sancti Andree, 1413–1588*
   (Edinburgh, 1964)

618   St Helens Local History Library

Address   Central Library
                   Gamble Institute
                   Victoria Square
                   St Helens
                   Merseyside WA10 1DY

Telephone   (0744) 24061 ext. 2234

Enquiries to   Local History Librarian and Archivist, Mr R.L. Hart

Open   Mon–Fri: 9.00–6.00
                   Sat: 9.00–1.00

Access   Generally open to the public.

Historical background   The Borough Library Service was established in 1872. A
   separate Local History and Archive Library was established in 1974 to expand
   existing collections in the Reference Library and to implement an active archive
   policy to deal with local government records on reorganization.

Acquisitions policy   Records of the St Helens Borough Council are stored where
   appropriate. Donations of other records are accepted. Other records are acquired
   when known to be at risk.

Major collections   Records of the Borough Council and historic constitutents,
   1845–1980.
   Poor Law papers for the Township of Parr, 1688–1828.
   Sherdley estate papers, 1477–1900 (c1500 items).
   Records of Grundy's Ironmongers, 1913–1970.
   Total archive holdings c250,000 items.

Non-manuscript material   Maps, local newspapers, 1859–.
   c8000 books and pamphlets relating to St Helens, Lancashire, and local history in
   general.

Finding aids   Index to most archive collections. Newspaper index.

Facilities   Photocopying. Microfilm/fiche readers.

Publications   Frequent leaflet guides to types of material (e.g. *Genealogical Sources*).

619   Judicial Greffe

Address	States Building
	Royal Square
	St Helier
	Jersey
	Channel Islands
Telephone	(0534) 77111 ext 142/143
Enquiries to	The Judicial Greffier
Open	Mon–Fri: 10.00–1.00; 2.00–5.00

Access   Public Registry: members of the public during office hours on payment of a prescribed fee.
Royal Court records: members of the public by prior arrangement with the Judicial Greffier only. Permission is not automatically granted. Some records (e.g. criminal matters) are not available for consultation.
Probate Registry: not open to unsupervised inspection by members of the public.

Historical background   The Judicial Greffe is a civil service department which, among other responsibilities, has custody of records although this is not a primary function.

Acquisitions policy   The department houses only the documents of the Court.

Major collections   Three major categories of documents as follows:
Public Registry, containing deeds of sale and conveyance, mortgage, etc, of real property, 1602–; wills of real estate, 1851–; powers of attorney.
Records of the Royal Court, comprising all acts etc, of the Royal Court and other related documents.
Probate Registry, containing wills of personal estate, from c1660–; letters of administration, 1848–.

Finding aids   Indexes to relevant Court books.

Facilities   Photocopying of some Court records.

620   La Société Jersiaise

Address   9 Pier Road
                 St Helier
                 Jersey
                 Channel Islands

Telephone   (0534) 75940

Enquiries to   Hon. Secretary, Mrs W.E. Macready

Open   Mon–Sat: 10.00–5.00, by appointment.

Access   Bona fide researchers.

Historical background   La Société Jersiaise was founded in 1873 for the study of the
    history and the language of the Island, the conservation of antiquities and the
    publication of historical documents etc. It has since increased its activities to
    encompass the study of all aspects of natural history and has a very comprehensive
    library and a museum.

Acquisitions policy   To increase the value of existing collections and to make them
    more attractive. Some material is purchased but a great many collections come by
    donation.

Major collections   Records of the Society, including minutes and lists of members.
    Large amount of MS material, chiefly relating to the history of Jersey, but also
    covering natural history and geology.

Non-manuscript material   Maps; photographic and iconographic collections.

Facilities   Photocopying.

Publications   Annual Bulletin

621   Norris Library and Museum

Address   The Broadway
                 St Ives
                 Huntingdon
                 Cambridgeshire PE17 4BX

Telephone   (0480) 65101

Enquiries to   Curator, Mr R.I. Burn-Murdoch

Open   May–Sept:
                 Tues–Fri: 10.00–1.00; 2.00–5.00
                 Sat: 2.00–5.00
                 Sun: 2.00–5.00

                    Oct–April:
                    Tues–Fri: 10.00–1.00; 2.00–4.00
                    Sat: 10.00–12.00

Access   Bona fide researchers.

Historical background   The Library and Museum opened in 1933, according to the
   terms of the will of Herbert Ellis Norris (1859–1931). Norris assembled a large
   collection of antiquities, both historical and archaeological, which he left, together
   with a substantial trust fund to pay for a building to house them and to allow for
   future maintenance, to St Ives Borough Council. The present Town Council
   continues to administer the Library and Museum as Trustees. Norris collected
   material from the former county of Huntingdonshire (technically abolished in
   1974). Since 1933 other collections of a similar scope have been added to his
   foundation, notably those of the Huntingdonshire Literary and Scientific Institution
   (1840–1959). The present Norris Library and Museum houses material from every
   part of Huntingdonshire and every period of history.

Acquisition policy   Material relating to all parts of Huntingdonshire and all periods of
   history and pre-history. There is a small accessions fund for the Library. The
   Museum is dependent on gifts.

Major collections   Variety of MS material, including various legal documents, wills,
   etc, 16th–18th centuries.
   Field survey of St Ives, 17th century.
   MSS by John Clare (1793–1864).
   Many minute books, etc relating to local government and local charities, 19th
   century.
   Notes by local historians and antiquarians, notably S. Inskip Ladds, Ely Diocesan
   architect and editor of Victoria County History of Huntingdonshire.

Non-manuscript material   Pamphlets etc relating to the Civil War period, and to
   Cromwell, in Huntingdonshire.
   Runs of local newspapers, including 19th–century editions.
   Maps, including Saxton, Speed, Blaeu, 16th–18th centuries.
   Photographs, postcards, prints, paintings and drawings of local scenes; various
   periods.
   General collection of books relating to all aspects of the history of
   Huntingdonshire.

Finding aids   Comprehensive card index in preparation.

Facilities   Limited photocopying by arrangement. Photography by arrangement.
   Microfilm reader of sorts.

622   The Greffe

Address	The Royal Court House
	St Peter Port
	Guernsey
	Channel Islands
Telephone	(0481) 25277
Enquiries to	Her Majesty's Greffier, Mr K.H. Tough
Open	Mon–Fri: 9.00–1.00; 2.00–4.00
Access	Written application should be made to Her Majesty's Greffier. A letter of introduction is recommended.

Historical background   As the record office of the Royal Court of Guernsey the Greffe has existed in various forms throughout the history of the Royal Court, which is first referred to in a document of 1179.

Acquisitions policy   All Island judicial and legislative records. Deposits of private collections and documents relating to Guernsey accepted.

Major collections   Virtually all records prior to 1948 are in French and a command of that language is essential for all serious students researching at the Greffe.
Contemporary copies of charters granted to the Bailiwick, 1394–.
Judicial records of the Royal Court of Guernsey, 1526–.
Legislative records, 1553–.
Records of land conveyance etc, 1576–.
Records of the States of Guernsey, 1605–.
Registers of Births, Marriages and Deaths, 1840–.
Wills of Real Property from 1841 when it first became possible to make Wills of realty (Wills of Personality are held by the Ecclesiastical Court).
Surviving records of the German Feldkommandantur, 1940–45 (some 300 files, in German).
Private collections deposited by local families (especially the de Sausmarez papers).
Transcripts of documents elsewhere especially Mont St Michel Collection (originals of which were destroyed when Departmental Archives at Saint-Lo (Manche) were bombed in 1944).

Finding aids   Typescript calendar of all single documents may be consulted at the Greffe.

Facilities   Photocopying.

Publications   Complete list of bound volumes published by the List and Index Society (1969) [vol. ii in the Society's special series]
Brief calendar of single documents under the Bailiwick Seal, primarily from the period 1350–1600 (1978) [as vol. xi in the same series]

For a general introduction see
J.C. Davies: 'The Records of the Royal Court,' *La Société Guernesiaise, Transactions*, xvi (1956–60), 404

623   La Société Guernesiaise

Address   Le Courtil à L'Herbe
                 Route des Bas Courtils
                 St Sauveur
                 Guernsey
                 Channel Islands
Telephone   (0481) 63410

Enquiries to   The Hon. Secretary (Le Secrétaire)

Open   On demand

Access   Members only.

Historical background   La Société Guernesiaise is a society of natural science and local research founded in 1882 to encourage interest in all aspects of Guernsey's natural and local history, geography and geology. It has a small library of local books which members can consult by arrangement. It does not hold historical documents or records, family history etc. These are kept by the Island Government in its record office, the Greffe (*see* entry **622**).

Acquisitions policy   Purchase, donations and deposits.

Major collections   Diaries and accounts of Island life written in Guernesiais.

Non-manuscript material   Survey maps of the Island.
    Local books, 1600–.
    Transactions, bulletins and periodicals of most French historical and archaeological societies.
    Report and Transactions of La Société Guernesiaise, 1882–.
    Herbarium, 1790 [Island plants].
    Modern herbarium, zoological collections.

Finding aids   Comprehensive index to the Report and Transactions.

Publications   The Report and Transactions, published annually since 1882
    La Dictiounnaire Angllais-Guernesiais

624   The Salford Museum of Mining

Address   Buile Hill Park
                 Eccles Old Road
                 Salford
                 Greater Manchester M6 8GL

Telephone	(061) 736 1832
Enquiries to	Keeper of Industrial Archaeology, Mr G. Preece
Open	By appointment only, Mon–Fri: 10.00–12.30; 1.30–5.00 Sun: 2.00–5.00
Access	Generally open to the public.

Historical background   The Museum opened in 1906 with Natural History Collections. Mining interest began in the late 1950s and the museum was completely re-displayed and opened as the Mining Museum in 1980.

Acquisitions policy   To collect, display or make available anything relating to the Lancashire/Cheshire coalfields, including items relating to social history.

Major collections   Business archives of John Wood Ltd and Walker Bros Ltd of Wigan, including c5000 drawings, letter-books, specification books, c1890–1940. Large collections of National Coal Board underground layout plans relating to South Lancashire collieries (c300).

Non-manuscript material   Several thousand books and journals relating to all aspects of coal mining. Extensive photographic archive of local collieries.

Finding aids   Some lists and indexes.

Facilities   Photocopying and photography to order.

625   University of Salford Library

Address	University of Salford Salford Greater Manchester M5 4WT
Telephone	(061) 736 5843
Enquiries to	Librarian, Mr A.C. Bubb
Open	Term: Mon–Fri: 9.00–9.00; Sat: 9.00–12.00 Vacation: Mon–Fri: 9.00–9.00
Access	All members and employees of the University; other persons admitted for reference and private study at the discretion of the Librarian. Access to Bridgewater Estates Papers only granted by permission of the Directors of Bridgewater Estates Ltd.

Historical background   The Library was founded in 1957 by the amalgamation of the collections of the various departments of the Royal College of Advanced Technology, Salford, which became the University of Salford in 1967.

Acquisitions policy   Reflects subjects taught and research conducted at the University. Also special collections relating to local subjects and authors.

Major collections Bridgewater Estates Papers, collection of correspondence etc (*c*480 files) covering history of Bridgewater Estates Ltd, Worsley, 1890–1923.

Non-manuscript material Walter Greenwood Collection: typescripts and printed copies of this local author's novels and plays. Also related press cuttings, programmes, photographs and association copies.

Finding aids Special card catalogue of Bridgewater Estates Papers, with subject index.
Greenwood Collection included in main book catalogue (on microfiche).

Facilities Photocopying. Microfilm/fiche readers.

626 Salisbury Cathedral
Chapter Archives

Address 6 The Close
Salisbury
Wiltshire

Enquiries to Librarian and Keeper of the Muniments, Miss S.M. Eward

Open Mon–Fri: 10.00–12.30; 2.15–4.00, by appointment

Access Bona fide researchers on written application.

Historical background Salisbury Cathedral was commenced in 1220 and has had a continuous history since that date.

Major collections Dean and Chapter archives from the medieval period onwards.

Finding aids Brief general catalogue.

627 Salisbury District Council Muniment Room

Address Council House
Bourne Hill
Salisbury
Wiltshire

Records were transferred to Wiltshire Record Office (*see* entry 674) in 1982.

628 North Yorkshire County Library
Eastern Division

Address   Central Library
Vernon Road
Scarborough
North Yorkshire YO11 2NN

Telephone   (0732) 64285

Enquiries to   The Assistant County Librarian (postal enquiries)
or
The Divisional Organizer, Reference and Information Services
(telephone)

Open   Mon–Thurs: 10.00–5.30
Fri: 10.00–7.00
Sat: 10.00–4.00

Access   Admission to Local History Room on production of library ticket or other identification. Archive material generally available to the public on request.

Historical background   The Local History Collection was founded in 1930. Archives are acquired by deposit, solicited and unsolicited.

Acquisitions policy   To accept deposit of relevant material within accommodation limits and where the donor wishes material to remain in Scarborough.

Major collections   School log-books, minute books etc, from Scarborough and the immediate area, *c*1870–*c*1950 (*c*120 vols).
Scarborough town rate-books, 1837–1900 (*c*150 vols).
Minutes and accounts of Scarborough Harbour Commissioners, 1752–1904 (20 vols); Scarborough Cliff Bridge Company, 1826–1920; Spa (Scarborough) Ltd, 1920–37.
Minutes and accounts of several local societies, 19th and 20th centuries.
Minor collections of family papers, indentures, property deeds, ships logs etc.

Non-manuscript material   *c*700 prints, topographical, 18th and 19th centuries. Photographs, topographical and local subjects.

Finding aids   Descriptive typescript catalogues of archive holdings (compiled 1968, not updated).

Facilities   Photocopying. Microfilm/fiche readers.

629 The Oates Memorial Library and Museum and The Gilbert White Museum

Address   The Wakes
Selborne
Alton
Hampshire GU34 3JH

Telephone   (042 050) 275

Enquiries to   Curator, Dr J.E. Chatfield

Open   March–October: Tues–Sun: 12.00–5.30, by appointment
Closed Mondays except public holidays in season

Access   Access to reserve collections by advance appointment with the Curator. There is no librarian on the staff.

Historical background   The Museum is housed in the Wakes, the former home of the Rev. Gilbert White. The house was purchased by Robert Washington Oates in 1954 and the dual museums opened in 1955. It is a private museum funded by the Oates Memorial Trust. The Wakes passed out of the White family in 1839 and at this time any remains of Gilbert White's possessions were scattered. The museum deeds include very few items prior to 1844. The collection of White's personal items and documents are therefore limited since most of these were already placed in museums by 1955. The bulk of the manuscript collection is on loan from the Holt-White family. Robert Washington Oates provided the museum with a range of notebooks and drawings by members of the Oates family.

Acquisitions policy   To acquire further MSS relevant to Gilbert White and his work and relating to Lawrence Oates, the Antarctic Expedition and Frank Oates in Africa. Additions to the collections are made by donations and purchase, but the museum relies entirely on grant aid for the latter.

Major collections   Gilbert White Collection: original MS of *The Natural History of Selbourne*; record of wine and beer brewing 1771–93; account book, 1758–93, and memoranda; Thomas White's personal copy of the first edition of *The Natural History of Selborne*, reputedly bound in the skin of Gilbert White's dog.
Holt-White family documents: including an account book of Gilbert White, 1745–65; sermons; household receipts; various letters to Gilbert White from members of the family. Various White family papers, 1678–1820, including personal letters, legal documents, MS notebooks, estate papers, family wills and settlement deeds, Selborne tithes.
Oates Collection: Frank Oates (1840–75): original notebook from the journey in America and Africa together with a small collection of ethnographic items. Lawrence Oates (1880–1912): original letters and papers from his childhood and early military career in South Africa, Egypt and India. A comprehensive collection of printed material relating to the Scott Polar Expedition and Lawrence Oates's death.

Non-manuscript material   A few items of Gilbert White personalia.

Oates family portraits, old newspapers relating to Antarctic Expedition, paintings by members of the Oates family.

Finding aids   Person index and catalogue of the Holt-White collection.

Facilities   Photocopying.

630   Borders Regional Library

Address	St Mary's Mill
	Selkirk
	Borders TD7 5EU
Telephone	(0750) 20842
Enquiries to	Regional Librarian, Mr A. Carter
Open	By appointment
	Mon–Thurs: 8.30–5.00
	Fri: 8.30–4.30
Access	Generally open to the public.

Historical background   Records have been drawn from holdings of education and library authorities which had enjoyed pre-1975 independent existence within the area now constituting the Borders Region. The Local Collection contains both books and archives and is in process of being rehoused at St Mary's Mill.

Acquisitions policy   Items of Borders area interest which can strengthen the collection are added as opportunity offers.

Major collections   Records of pre-1975 counties:

Berwickshire records include burials, 1808–1891; parochial and poor relief, 1773–1930; school boards, 1873–1931; Burgh of Duns Police Commissioners, 1842–1901; Eyemouth Harbour Trust, 1794–1964; Berwickshire Coast Disaster Fund, 1881–1896; Burgh of Duns Baillie Court, 1732–1789; Duns Skinners and Glovers Trade, 1695–1839.

Peeblesshire records include burials, 18th–20th centuries; inventories and cartularies, 1684–1975; Turnpike Road Trustees, 1760–1890; Peebles Town Council, 1799–1975; Peebles Burgh Court, 1770–1937.

Roxburghshire records include Heritors' Records, 1758–1884; valuation rolls, 1788–1975; Turnpike Road Trustees and successor bodies, 1793–1926.

Selkirkshire records include poor relief, 1753–1881; Lieutenancy, 1797–1961; valuation rolls, 1785–1791; Stent Roll, Burgh of Selkirk, 1752–1770.

Duns Area Library: Berwickshire Collection, 17th–19th centuries (c800 items).

Feuars of Duns papers relating to burgh life, 18th and 19th centuries.

Non-manuscript material   Small collections held at other large branch libraries. Usual local history collection of non-MS materials.

Finding aids   Scottish Record Office Lists. Indexes to Duns Area Library Berwickshire Collection.

Facilities   Photocopying.

631   The John Allwood International Exhibition Collection

Address   Hortondene
Ightham
Sevenoaks
Kent TN15 9HH

Telephone   (0732) 882654

Enquiries to   Mr John Allwood

Open   By prior appointment

Access   Approved readers on written application.

Historical background   A specialist collection on the history of exhibitions and world affairs, 1851–, with additional information on other national and British exhibitions, medieval fairs and allied events. A private collection built up to supplement the Royal Society of Arts (*see* entry 466) collection on the subject.

Acquisitions policy   Necessarily restricted by its privately available funding, the collection sets out to increase the availability of source material on the ephemeral world of exhibitions.

Major collections   International Exhibitions and World Fairs (*c*1000 MSS).
Medieval Fairs (*c*20 MSS).

Non-manuscript material   Posters, souvenirs, tickets, stamps, stickers, and other ephemera connected with exhibitions. Colour slides and monochrome photographs of exhibitions and exhibits. Bibliographies to other international collections on this subject.

Finding aids   Catalogued by date and event. The owner's own knowledge of a collection that is consulted by many users with very varying requirements.

Facilities   Photocopying. Photography.

Publications   John Allwood: *The Great Exhibitions* (London, 1977)

632 Centre for English Cultural Tradition and Language

Address	University of Sheffield Western Bank Sheffield South Yorkshire S10 2TN
Telephone	(0742) 78555, ext.4211
Enquiries to	The Archivist
Open	Mon–Fri: 2.00–5.00, by appointment
Access	Bona fide scholars.

Historical background The Centre was established as the Survey of Language and Folklore in 1964 as part of the English Language Department. It has close links with Departments of Folklore, English and Linguistics at the Memorial University of Newfoundland.

Acquisitions policy The Centre relies greatly on voluntary help from local representatives and correspondents in collection of material: MSS, photographs, tape recordings, printed books and ephemera relating to folklore, folklife, language and cultural tradition.

Major collections Richard Blakeborough MSS, late 19th century.
Local business archives.
Russell Wortley collection of folk dance and song; card index of examples of language and folklore usage; original student monographs.

Non-manuscript material Tape Archive collection of c2300 tape recordings, including c700 of Newfoundland folklore. Edgar Wagner and AKA film collections, examples of wide range of artefacts relating to folklife and traditional industry.

Finding aids Handlist of Blakeborough and Wortley MSS. Catalogue of student monographs in progress.

Facilities None at Centre itself. Can be arranged through University Library and other departments.

Publications *Lore and Language* (1969–) [biannual Centre publication]
Occasional publications
A series of guides and bibliographies is in preparation.

633 Sheffield City Libraries Archives Division

Address   Central Library
Surrey Street
Sheffield
South Yorkshire S1 1XZ

Telephone   (0742) 734756

Enquiries to   Archivist, Dr D. Postles

Open   Mon: 9.30–5.30; also to 8.30 on the first Mon of each month, by prior appointment
Tues–Fri: 9.00–5.30
Sat: 9.00–1.00; 2.00–4.30
Readers are requested to telephone one week in advance to order documents.

Historical background   The Library had acquired a small collection of documents of local interest by 1912; the Jackson Collection was received in the same year and the archive collections have continued to accumulate since then. Until the early 1960s the collections were mainly private, of local families, businesses and solicitors, but since then substantial deposits of parish, Public and Local Authority records have been received. From the beginning, MSS relating to an area within a 30-mile radius of the centre of Sheffield, covering the southern half of the West Riding of Yorkshire and North Derbyshire were collected. There was no County Record Office for the West Riding, nor, until 1962, for Derbyshire. Since Local Government reorganization in 1974 only MSS relating to the area of the Metropolitan District of Sheffield, or additions to existing collections from outside that area, are normally accepted. The Archives Division also acts as the Diocesan Record Office for the archdeaconry of Sheffield.

Major collections   Usual local authority record holdings and deposited collections of which the following have a wider significance:
Wentworth Woodhouse Muniments, including correspondence and papers of Thomas Wentworth, first Earl of Strafford, the second Marquis of Rockingham (1730–82); the second Earl Fitzwilliam (1748–1833); and Edmund Burke (1729–97).
Muniments of Spencer Stanhope of Cannon Hall; Vernon Wentworth of Wentworth Castle; Crewe of Fryston Hall.
Correspondence and papers of Edward Carpenter (1844–1929) and H.J. Wilson, Liberal MP, 1885–1912.
Arundel Castle MSS: the Duke of Norfolk's Sheffield, Derbyshire and Nottinghamshire estate papers, maps and plans.
Bacon Frank Collection, including papers of the Talbot Earls of Shrewsbury, 1549–1617.
Fairbank Collection: over 4500 maps and plans of Sheffield and South Yorkshire, with related notebooks and surveys, c1736–1848.

Yorkshire Engine Company records, including photographs and plans of arrangement of locomotives, 1865–c1960.
Collection of local architects' plans and drawings, 19th and 20th centuries.
Sheffield City Council deposited building plans.

Facilities   Photocopying. Photography. Microfilming. Microfilm/fiche readers.

Publications   R. Meredith: *Guide to the Manuscript Collections in the Sheffield City Libraries* (1956; suppl. (accessions 1956–76), 1976)

634   Sheffield City Polytechnic Library

Address	Psalter Lane Sheffield South Yorkshire S11 8UZ
Telephone	(0742) 56101, ext. 30
Enquiries to	Site Librarian, Mr John Kirby
Open	Term: Mon–Thurs: 9.00–9.00; Fri: 9.00–5.00 Vacation: Mon–Fri: 9.00–5.00
Access	Generally open to the public on application to Site Librarian

Historical background   The Psalter Lane Site of the Sheffield City Polytechnic is the present form of the Sheffield School of Art which was founded as the Government School of Design (Sheffield) in 1843. The Library acts as a repository for the records of the School of Art until its amalgamation to form Sheffield Polytechnic in 1969.

Acquisitions policy   To acquire any material relating to the Sheffield School of Art.

Major collections   Subscription lists and documents relating to the Sheffield School of Art.

Non-manuscript material   Drawings, sculpture, slides and photographs relating to the School of Art. Annual reports, prospectuses etc. Published material on artists connected with the school.

Finding aids   General index to the collection. Index of names of pupils and staff, 1843–1900 (1900–69 in preparation).

Facilities   Photocopying. Microfilm/microfiche readers. Slide projectors.

635 Sheffield University Library

Address	University of Sheffield Western Bank Sheffield South Yorkshire S10 2TN
Telephone	(0742) 78555, ext. 4328
Enquiries to	The Archivist
Open	By previous appointment Term: Mon–Thur: 9.00–9.30; Fri: 9.00–5.00 Sat: 9.00–12.30 Vacation: Mon–Fri: 9.00–5.00; Sat: 9.00–12.30
Access	Bona fide researchers, preferably by written application. University records are subject to a 30-year closure and certain other records are restricted.

Historical background Sheffield University received its charter in 1905 and the MS collections have been acquired from 1907 onwards by donation, purchase and deposit. The official University archives including the records of the institutions which merged to form the University date from 1833 and have been administered from the Library since 1974.

Acquisitions policy The principal area of acquisitions relates to the University itself and persons and institutions associated with it. Other, mainly local, records are acquired where there is no conflict of interest with the neighbouring local authority repositories.

Major collections Hartlib MSS: an internationally important 17th-century collection relating to education, intellectual history, religious movements, agricultural improvements and scientific inventions.
Mundella Papers: Correspondence of a Gladstonian Liberal Cabinet Minister, 1860s–90s.
Hewins Papers: Correspondence and papers of leading protectionist economist, founder of the London School of Economics, secretary of the Tariff Commission, Conservative MP and junior minister, 1880s–1930s.
Official University Archives: Records of Firth College (*fd* 1879), the Sheffield Medical School (*fd* 1829), the Sheffield Technical School (*fd* 1886) and the University of Sheffield (1905–).

Non-manuscript material Official University Archives include collection of photographs and plans.

Finding aids Lists available of Hartlib and Mundella collections together with some of the smaller archives. Hewins list in progress. Partial lists and indexes available for official University Archives.

Facilities Photocopying. Photography.

636   South Yorkshire County Record Office

Address	Cultural Activities Centre
	Ellin Street
	Sheffield
	South Yorkshire S1 4PL
Telephone	(0742) 29191
Enquiries to	County Archivist, Mrs C.M. Short
Open	Mon–Thurs: 9.00–1.00; 2.00–5.00
	Fri: 9.00–1.00; 2.00–4.00
	Sat and evenings by arrangement

Historical background The Office was established in 1974 and opened in 1976. Before that there was no formal repository in West Riding, although archives were collected by Leeds City Library and Sheffield City Library (*see* entries **281** and **633** respectively) which still hold their collections.

Major collections Usual local authority record holdings and deposited collections of which the following have a wider significance:
Personal and political papers of John Mendelson, MP for Penistone, *c*1940–78.
Records of South Yorkshire Police, 1831–1975.
Correspondence relating to Barnsley Canal, 1820–50.
Early industrial films from the late 1920s.

Facilities Photocopying. Photography. Microfilming. Microfilm reader/printer.

637   Shropshire Libraries
Local Studies Department

Address	Until mid-1983:
	St Mary's Hall
	St Mary's Place
	Shrewsbury
	Shropshire
	After mid-1983:
	Castle Gates
	Shrewsbury
	Shropshire
Telephone	(0743) 61058
Enquiries to	Local Studies Librarian, Mr A.M. Carr
Open	Mon, Wed, Sat: 9.30–12.30; 1.30–5.30
	Tues, Fri: 9.30–12.30; 1.30–7.30

Access   Generally open to the public, by prior arrangement.

Historical background   The major part of the MS collection was acquired by Shrewsbury Public Library, 1882–1974.

Acquisitions policy   The Department no longer collects original MSS as this is the function of the Shropshire Record Office (*see* entry **638**). All other material (maps, photographs, newspapers, etc) is acquired.

Major collections   Shropshire Local History: *c*20,000 MS items relating to the whole country.
Lily F. Chitty Collection (Shropshire Archaeology and Local History).

Non-manuscript material   Watercolours and drawings by J. Holmes Smith and others, including *c*400 watercolours of Shropshire Churches etc, 1830–50.
Shropshire Photographic Archive (*c*18,000 prints, 10,000 negatives).
Large collection of microfilm copies of Shropshire MS material in the Public Record Office, British Library, House of Lords Records Office, etc.
Transcripts of all Shropshire Parish Registers to 1812.
Large collection of printed material on Shropshire.

Finding aids   Various lists and indexes available.

Facilities   Photocopying. Photography. Microfilm/fiche readers.

Publications   *A List of Wills and Marriage Settlements in the Local History Collection of the Shrewsbury Public Library* (1958)
Railway Plans in the Local Studies Department, Shropshire Libraries (1978)

638   Shropshire Record Office

Address   The Shirehall
Abbey Foregate
Shrewsbury
Shropshire SY2 6ND

Telephone   (0734) 222406/7

Enquiries to   County Archivist, Mrs M.T. Halford

Open   Mon–Thur: 9.00–12.40; 1.20–5.00
Fri: 9.00–12.40; 1.20–4.00

Historical background   The Office was established in 1946, but the County has collected and cared for its records since the end of the 19th century. The Office is also the Diocesan Record Office for Hereford (archdeaconry of Ludlow) and Lichfield (archdeaconry of Salop).

Major collections   Usual local authority record holdings and deposited collections. Houses the Shrewsbury Borough Archives except the charters and burgers rolls.

Facilities   Photocopying. Microfilming. Microfilm reader.

Publications   M.C. Hill: *Guide to the Shropshire Records* (1952)

639   Solihull Metropolitan Borough Public Libraries

Address   Central Library
                 Homer Road
                 Solihull
                 West Midlands B91 3RG

Telephone   (021) 705 4917/18/19

Enquiries to   Local History Librarian, Mrs S. Bell

A local history collection has existed since 1974 and is designed to provide a general coverage of those areas within the Solihull Metropolitan Borough. It includes maps, photographs, newspapers, books and a few archives, although the majority are deposited at the County Record Office, Warwick (*see* entry **685**).

640   Southampton City Record Office

Address   Civic Centre
                 Southampton
                 Hampshre SO9 4XL

Telephone   (0703) 23855 ext. 251

Enquiries to   City Archivist, Miss S.D. Thomson

Open   Mon–Fri: 9.00–1.00; 1.30–5.00; evenings by arrangement

Historical background   The Office was established in 1953. It also acts as the Diocesan Record Office for Winchester (Southampton parish records).

Major collections   Usual local authority record holdings and deposited collections of which the following have a wider significance:
Molyneux MSS, including letters on astronomy and scientific experiments, 1681–1713.
Cobb MSS: Smyth and Gee families, including letters from the Duke of Kent, 1808–20, and papers about New Brunswick, Canada, 1820s.
South Coast Engineering and Shipbuilding Employers' Association records, c1902–78.

Facilities   Photocopying. Photography.

Publications   *Southampton Records I: A Guide to the Records of Southampton*

Corporation and Absorbed Authorities. . . (1964)
Archives of Hampshire and the Isle of Wight, Hampshire Archivists' Group (1966)
[typescript], *Poor Law* (1970), *Transport* (1973), *Education* (1977).

641　Southampton University Library
Archives and Manuscript Collection

Address　　　　The Library
　　　　　　　　University of Southampton
　　　　　　　　Southampton SO9 5NH

Telephone　　　(0703) 559122 ext. 335

Enquiries to　　The Sub-Librarian (Special Collections)

Open　　　　　Mon–Fri: 9.00–5.00

Access　　　　Members of the University and all bona fide students and
　　　　　　　　researchers.

Historical background　Southampton University, founded in 1952, was based at the
　Hartley Institution which became University College in 1902.

Acquisitions policy　Transfer of the archives of the University. Other archives and
　artificial collections and individual MSS bought only when requested by
　departmental staff for research and teaching.

Major collections　Archives of Hartley Institution, from 1862; University College,
　from 1902; Southampton University, from 1952.
　Papers of the 1st Duke of Wellington, (1769–1852).
　James Parkes (1896–1981) archive relating to Judaism.
　Records of National Association of Divisional Executive for Education; Joint Four
　Secondary Teachers' Associations; Hampshire Field Club and Archaeological
　Society.

Finding aids　Card index to Accessions Register. Handlists of the major collections.

Facilities　Photocopying. Microfilming.

Publications　G. Cheffy: *Dr L.F.W. White Memorial Collection of the records of the
　National Association of Divisional Executives for Education* (1975) [Southampton
　University Library Occasional Paper, no. 5]
　G. Hampson: *Records of the University of Southampton* (1980) [Southampton
　University Library Occasional Paper, no. 7]

642   Essex Record Office
Southend Branch

Address	Central Library
	Victoria Avenue
	Southend-on-Sea
	Essex SS2 6EX
Telephone	(0702) 612621 ext. 49
Enquiries to	Branch Archivist, Mr J.R. Smith
Open	Mon–Thurs: 9.15–5.15
	Fri: 9.15–4.15

Historical background   This branch office of Essex Record Office, (*see* entry **117**), was established in 1974.

Major collections   Usual local authority record holdings and deposited collections.

Facilities   Photocopying. Photography. Microfilming. Microfilm reader.

643   Sefton Metropolitan Borough
Libraries and Arts Service

Address	Town Hall
	Lord Street
	Southport
	Merseyside PR8 1DA
Telephone	(0704) 33133 (Reference Library; Southport Library)
	(051) 928 6487/8 (Crosby Library)
	(051) 933 4508 (Bootle Library)
	(0704) 27547 (Botanic Gardens Museum)
Enquiries to	Miss J. Tarbuck (Southport)
	Mr R. Hull (Crosby)
	Mrs J. Jenkins (Bootle)
	Mr G. Burrows (Botanic Gardens Museum)
Open	Mon, Tues: 10.00–5.00
	Wed, Fri: 10.00–8.00
	Thurs, Sat: 10.00–1.00

Historical background   Sefton Metropolitan Borough was formed after local government reorganization in 1974. It combined the areas of Bootle, Crosby, Southport and parts of the West Lancashire district.

Major collections   Local history collections of a parochial nature are held at each

library; of particular interest are:
Cheetham Collection (at Southport)
Howard Collection (at Botanic Gardens Museum).

Facilities   Photocopying. Microfilm reader/printer.

644   The Royal Marines Museum

Address   RM Corps Secretariat
Royal Marines Eastney
Southsea
Hampshire PO4 9PX

Telephone   (0705) 822351, ext. 6186

Enquiries to   The Director

Open   Mon–Fri: 10.00–4.30, by appointment

Access   Bona fide researchers.

Historical background   In 1963 it became necessary to establish a reference library
and archive repository for the use of the Royal Marines Historian and Museum, and
a certain amount of money was made available for the purchase of items by the
Commandant General Royal Marines. This was supplemented by gifts from
individuals. In 1965 a number of military and naval reference books were
transferred to the museum from the Royal Marines Officers' Mess Library at
Plymouth. This was the first of such transfers. Meanwhile the Commandant
General's grant continued, which provided the basis for further purchases. More
recently, the museum has been able to acquire items from its Ministry of Defence
grant, and published material from the Education Branch of the Ministry of
Defence. In addition, items are occasionally added to the collection as a result of
donation or bequest.

Acquisitions policy   To strengthen the collection by the acquisition of both modern
and antiquarian material, by purchase, donation or bequest.

Major collections   MSS: an extensive collection of personal diaries and letters;
official correspondence, and orders.

Non-manuscript material   A very large collection of historical and modern
photographs with a bearing on the history of, and the present-day Royal Marines.
An extensive collection of supporting published material, in the form of books,
articles, and newspaper cuttings.

Finding aids   Various indexes.

645 South Tyneside Central Library
Local History Department

Address   Catherine Street
              South Shields
              Tyne and Wear NE33 2PE

Telephone   (0632) 568841 ext. 270

Enquiries to Assistant Librarian (Local Studies), Mr D. Johnson

Open   Mon–Thurs: 10.00–7.00
              Fri: 10.00–5.00
              Sat: 10.00–4.00

Access   Generally open to the public.

Historical background   South Shields Public Library was opened in 1874 and in 1879 a Local History Collection was started. On local government reorganization in 1974, South Shields Public Library became South Tyneside Central Library, which meant that the area was expanded from specifically South Shields to cover Jarrow, Hebburn, The Boldons, Cleadon and Whitburn.

Aquisitions policy   Consolidation of existing holdings.

Major collections   Mainly MS items on Northumberland, Durham, and Tyne and Wear, with intensive coverage of the South Tyneside area.

Non-manuscript material   Kelly Collection: *c*2000 posters representing work in South Shields, 1790–1880.
*c*3000 photographs and 10,000 negatives including: Flagg Collection, an amateur photographer and historian's work, *c*1925–*c*1950; Cleet Collection, a professional photographer's work on the slums of South Shields in the 1930s; Jarrow March Collection, the work of various professional photographers on this event; Willits Collection, an amateur photographer's work in the 1890s and 1900s; Parry Collection, the work of a firm of professional photographers, 1900–50.

Finding aids   Most of the photographs have been catalogued and indexed; it is hoped that this work will be completed and that cataloguing and indexing of posters will be started as soon as the latter have been laminated.

Facilities   Photocopying. Photography. Microfilm readers.

646 Southwell Minster

Address   Southwell
              Nottinghamshire NG25 0JP

Enquiries to The Honorary Librarian

Open   Weekdays, by prior arrangement

Access   Approved readers on written application.

Historical background   Cathedral Library re-created at the restoration in 1660.

Acquisitions policy   None, except for local history and publications relevant to Southwell Minster and the diocese.

Major collections   Chapter records from the 14th century onwards. Bishops' transcripts of parish registers in diocese of Southwell.

Non-manuscript material   Local photographs.

647   Spalding Gentlemen's Society

Address   The Museum
                  Broad Street
                  Spalding
                  Lincolnshire

Telephone   (0775) 4658

Enquiries to   Hon. Curator, Mr N. Leveritt

Open   By appointment with the Hon. Curator, the Hon. Secretary or the Librarian

Access   By arrangement with officers – visitors wishing study facilities will be asked for a reference.

Historical background   One of oldest learned societies, founded by Maurice Johnson, FSA (1688–1755), in 1710. Early members included notable 18th-century figures. Discussion of politics and religion banned under the founder's ruling.
With the exception of the Ashmolean, the museum is the oldest in the UK.

Acquisitions policy   By gift and purchase as appropriate.

Major collections   Manorial and local government records including several medieval illuminated charters and MSS.
Fens drainage records.

Non-manuscript material   Four portfolios of prints, drawings and plans, 1754.
Society's library created by the gift of a volume from every new member.
Maps

Publications   *Annual Report*
Various histories including:
Nichol's *Bibliotheca Topographica Britannica* (1790) [history of early days of Society with list of members]

648 Staffordshire Record Office

Address   County Buildings
             Eastgate Street
             Stafford ST16 2L2

Telephone   (0785) 3121 ext.7910

Enquiries to   County Archivist, Mr F.B. Stitt

Open   Mon–Thurs: 9.00–1.00; 2.00–4.45
             Fri: 9.00–1.00; 2.00–4.15
             Sat: 9.30–1.00, at William Salt Library, by arrangement

Historical background   The Record Office was established in 1947; before then
   records were collected by the William Salt Library. The office also acts as the
   Diocesan Record Office for Lichfield (parish records of the archdeaconry of
   Stafford). Assistance is given to Stoke-on-Trent Central Reference Library. The
   William Salt Library, Stafford (*see* entry 649) and Lichfield Joint Record Office (*see*
   entry 291) are dependent repositories.

Major collections   Usual local authority record holdings and deposited collections
   including the following which have a wider significance:
   Dartmouth family collection, includng papers of the Legge family who held various
   government appointments including Secretary of State for the Colonies and
   Admiral of the Fleet, 17th–18th centuries.
   Hatherton collection, including political papers of the first Lord Hatherton (1791–
   1863), Chief Secretary to the Lord Lieutenant of Ireland, 1833–4.
   Business records of Birmingham Rail, Carriage and Wagon Works, with worldwide
   connections, 19th century.

Facilities   Photocopying. Photography and microfilming by arrangement. Microfilm
   reader.

649 William Salt Library

Address   Eastgate Street
             Stafford
             Staffordshire

Telephone   (0785) 52276

Enquiries to   Librarian, Mr F.B. Stitt

Open   Tues–Thurs: 9.30–12.45; 1.45–5.00
             Fri: 9.30–12.45; 1.45–4.00
             Sat: 9.30–1.00

Access   Generally open to the public.

Historical background   Founded in 1872 and based on collections of William Salt (1808–1863), member of a Stafford banking family. The Library is administered by Trustees, but since 1935 its connection with the Staffordshire County Council has become close, at first by grant and since the creation of the Staffordshire Record Office in 1947, also by sharing of staff – the County Archivist acts as William Salt Library Librarian.

Most of the collections deposited with (or loaned to) the Library earlier this century are now housed in Staffordshire County Record Office (*see* entry **648**).

Major collections   William Salt MSS Collection: reflects his interests and contains a considerable number of autograph letters, only some of which have Staffordshire connections. Many transcripts of Staffordshire material in the Public Record Office, British Library, College'of Heralds, much of which is still unpublished (e.g. the Staffordshire entries in the Thomason Tracts and Dr Burney's newspapers).

Subsequent donations (and loans) still in the Library include Anglo-Saxon charters, the Parker Jervis (of Meaford) papers and a large solicitor's collection, Hand, Morgan & Owen of Stafford.

Non-manuscript material   The original collection of William Salt includes printed books, pamphlets, broad-sheets, drawings and engravings and other ephemera relating to Staffordshire, together with other items of a conventional 19th-century collector.

Staffordshire Heraldry (2 vols).

Over 3000 topographical drawings and prints and also engraved drawings of personalities.

Finding aids   Various lists and indexes. Some MS material is still in the process of being catalogued.

Facilities   Photocopying. Photography, by appointment in special circumstances only.

650   Tameside Local Studies Library

Address   Stalybridge Library
                Trinity Street
                Stalybridge
                Greater Manchester SK15 2BN

Telephone   (061) 338 2708/3831

Enquiries to Librarian, Ms Alice Lock

Open   Mon–Fri: 9.00–8.00
                Sat: 9.00–4.00

Access   Generally open to the public.

Historical background   The Tameside Local Studies Library was set up in Stalybridge in 1976. It took over the local history collections of the libraries of the local authorities which preceded Tameside.

Aquisitions policy   To collect all kinds of printed, illustrative and MS material related to the Tameside area: Ashton, Audenshaw, Denton, Droylsden, Dukinfield, Hyde, Longdendale, Mossley and Stalybridge.

Major collections   Records of the local authorities which preceded Tameside, and of some local organizations, for example churches (including non-conformist), schools, trade unions, mechanics' institutes; also some hospital, local business, family and individuals' records.

Non-manuscript material   c1250 maps of the Tameside area, Lancashire and Cheshire, 1577–.
Photographs, from the 1860s; engravings, from the 1790s; slides (all relating to people and places in Tameside).
Pamphlets and broadsides from the 1790s.
c30 tape-recorded interviews with elderly residents of Tameside.
Recordings of local singers and musicians.
Microfilms of local newspapers, census returns and parish registers.

Finding aids   Typescript guide to the archive collection, with detailed calendars of individual collections. Card catalogue of book-stock, photographs, maps, broadsheets. Index of the *Ashton Reporter*. (All in process of compilation.)
Index of streets in the census returns.

Facilities   Photocopying. Photography. Microfilm/fiche readers.

651   Central Regional Council Archives Department

Address   Old High School
Spittal Street
Stirling FK8 1DG

Telephone   (0786) 3111 ext. 466

Enquiries to   Archivist, Mrs Constance L. Brodie

Open   Mon–Fri: 9.00–5.00

Historical background   The office was established in 1975 with local government reorganization. Some material is still retained by appropriate departments in district offices. Stirling Burgh records have been transferred from the Scottish Record Office.

Major collections   Usual local authority record holdings and deposited collections, all primarily of local interest.

Facilities   Photocopying. Photography by arrangement.

652   University of Stirling Library

Address   University of Stirling
                 Stirling
                 Central FK9 4LA

Telephone   (0786) 3171

Enquiries to   Librarian, Mr P.G. Peacock
                 John Grierson Archive, Mrs C. Rowlinson
                 All other collections, Mr D.S. Mack

Open   Term: Mon–Fri: 9.00–10.00
                 Sat: 9.30–12.30
                 Sun: 2.00–9.00
                 Vacation: Mon–Fri: 9.00–5.00

Access   Available to all.

Historical background   The University was founded in 1967. The Library supervises access to Leighton Library Dunblane Collection in the Rare Books Department of the University Library.

Acquisitions policy   Interested in acquiring material relating to Scottish literature, especially from the 19th century. MSS mostly acquired as gifts or bequests.

Major collections   John Grierson Archive: personal papers, writings on documentary film of John Grierson (1898–1972) with related material.
W. Tait Collection: covering left-wing political matters, 1883–1943.
Hometown Fish Farm records, 1873–1978.
William Drummond & Sons Limited, Seed Merchants' records, 1818–1976.
Leighton Library MSS Collection, 16th–20th centuries (c80 MSS).

Non-manuscript material   Material included in collections above.

Finding aids   Grierson Archive: list of contents and card index.
NRA (Scotland) lists of other collections.

Facilities   Photocopying. Photography.

Publications   F. Hardy: *John Grierson Archive List of Contents* (1978)
G. Willis: *The Leighton Library, Dunblane: Catalogue of Manuscripts* (Stirling, 1981)

653   Metropolitan Borough of Stockport
Archives Service

Address   Central Library
Wellington Road South
Stockport
Cheshire SK1 3RS

Telephone   (061) 480 2966/3038

Enquiries to   Archivist, Miss Miriam Critchlow

Open   Mon–Fri: 9.00–8.00
Sat: 9.00–12.00
Appointment advisable for evenings (5.00–8.00) and Sats

Access   Generally open to the public. Restrictions on some records. Contact in advance of visit preferable.

Historical background Active collecting, focused on the County Borough area, began in the 1960s to supplement documents already held by the Library. In 1974 the Archives Service took over the records of the disbanded Urban Districts included in the new Metropolitan Borough: Bredbury and Romiley, Cheadle and Gatley, Hazel Grove and Bramhall, Marple.

Aquisitions policy Acquisition of records relating to any aspect of life in the area of the Metropolitan Borough.

Major collections Local government records for the area.
Records of Stockport Sunday School, 1784–1970.
Records of Christy & Co. Ltd, hat manufacturers, 1773–1969.
Records of the Bradshaw-Isherwood estate, 1274–1919.

Finding aids Calendars for part of the holdings.

Facilities Photocopying. Photography. Microfilm readers.

Publications Guide to Calendars [in preparation]

654   Western Isles Islands Council (Comhairle Nan Eilean)

Address   Sandwick Road
Stornoway
Western Isles PA87 2BW

Telephone   (0851) 3773

Enquiries to   Director of Administration and Legal Services, Mr Douglas Sinclair

Open	Mon–Thurs: 9.00–5.30
	Fri: 9.00–5.00
Access	By written application.

Historical background   Comhairle Nan Eilean is a multi-purpose single-tiered local authority (except Police and Fire) created on local government reorganization in 1975, combining the Ross and Cromarty and Inverness-shire parts of the outer Hebrides.

Aquisitions policy   Maintenance of local authority records for the Western Isles.

Major collections   Minute books of the following:
Stornoway Town Council, 1863–1975 (under all forms of name).
Western Isles Islands Council (Comhairle Nan Eilean), 1974–.
Stornoway Road Trustees, 1866–1901 (also under later form of name).
Dean of Guild Court, 1947–65.
D.L. Robertson Trust, 1930–.
Stornoway Young Men's Mutual Association, 1871–8.
Lewis Coffee House Committee, 1878–1910.
Ross and Cromarty and Inverness-shire District Councils, 1930–70.
Parochial Boards/Parish councils, 1890s–1930.
Education District Sub Committees, 1927–1970s.
Also: Housing registers, 1931–.
Abstracts of accounts (Stornoway Burgh), 1901–60.
Valuation rolls (Stornoway Burgh and Lewis Parishes), 1947–67.

Finding aids   Partial indexes to Stornoway Town Council minutes and Western Isles Islands Council minutes, for internal use.

Facilities   Photocopying by arrangement.

655   Western Isles Libraries (Comhairle Nan Eilean)

Address	2 Keith Street
	Stornoway
	Western Isles PA87 2QG
Telephone	(0851) 3064
Enquiries to	Chief Librarian, Mr A.M. Morrison
Open	Mon, Wed, Thurs: 10.00–5.30
	Tues, Fri: 10.00–7.30
	Sat: 10.00–12.30
	Evenings and Sat by arrangement
Access	Generally open to the public following written or telephone enquiry.

Historical background   The Town Council Library until 1964, then Ross and Cromarty Branch Library until 1975, the Stornoway library is now the headquarters for the whole of the Western Isles.

Aquisitions policy   Building up local history and Gaelic collections including archive material.

Major collections   School log-books of schools in the Western Isles now closed.
Lewis School Board minute books, 1873–1919.
Aircraft movement log-books for Stornoway and Benbecula, 1972–5.
Western Isles Islands Council (Comhairle Nan Eilean) agendas and minutes, 1974–.
Barvas parish rent ledgers, 1854–1920.

Non-manuscript material   T.B. Macaulay photographic collection; other miscellaneous photographs, postcards, slides.
Newspapers: *Stornoway Gazette*, 1917–40 (on microfilm), 1940– (bound vols);
West Highland Free Press, 1972–; *Highland News*, 1893–5, 1897–1922, 1927–9.

Finding aids   Local history catalogue. Partial subject index being compiled.

Facilities   Photocopying by arrangement. Microfilm reader.

656   Shakespeare Birthplace Trust Records Office

Address   Guild Street
                   Stratford-upon-Avon
                   Warwickshire

Telephone   (0789) 4016

Enquiries to   Director, Dr Levi Fox

Open   Mon–Fri: 9.30–1.00; 2.00–5.00
                   Sat: 9.30–12.30 (except before Bank Holidays)

Access   Bona fide researchers.

Historical background   The Records Office was founded in the early 1860s, primarily as a repository for Shakespearean and allied material, but this limited objective was eclipsed at an early date on the rapid accumulation of documents relating to Stratford-upon-Avon and the surrounding district. It also acts as the Diocesan Record Office for Stratford and Shottery parishes.

Acquisitions policy   Until about 1945, the Record Office acted as a repository for any material from the locality which became available for deposit; as a result, not only Stratford-upon-Avon, but most places in Warwickshire and many in the neighbouring counties of Gloucestershire, Worcestershire and Oxfordshire are represented in the collections. Since c1945, with the expansion of neighbouring county offices, most acquisitions relate only to Stratford-upon-Avon and its immediate hinterland.

Major collections   Stratford-upon-Avon Borough Muniments.
Manorial records.
Warwickshire family collections: Ferrers of Baddesley Clinton; Throckmorton of Coughton Court; Gregory-Hood of Stivichal; Willoughby de Broke of Compton Verney; Leigh of Stoneleigh Abbey; Archer of Umberslade.
Robert Bell Wheler collection: antiquarian papers, *c*1800–20.

Non-manuscript material   Large collection of topographical views (photographs, prints, drawings).
Local history and family history library, with standard reference collection on local history sources including local newspapers.

Finding aids   Summary list of accessions reproduced by NRA and available in major libraries. Separate collections listed in typescript, and indexed in card catalogue for persons, places and subjects.

Facilities   Photocopying. Photography. Microfilm/fiche reader.

Publications   J.O. Halliwell: *A descriptive Calendar of the Ancient Manuscripts and Records in the Possession of the Corporation of Stratford-upon-Avon* (1863)
L. Fox: 'Shakespeare's Birthplace Library, Stratford-upon-Avon', *Archives*, v, (1961) 90

657   Borough of Sunderland Libraries Department

Address   Central Library
Museum and Art Gallery
Borough Road
Sunderland
Tyne and Wear SR1 1PP

Archives were transferred to Tyne and Wear Record Office (*see* entry **543**) in 1974.

658   Peter Liddle's 1914–18 Personal Experience Archives

Address   Sunderland Polytechnic
St Mary's Building
Chester Road
Sunderland SR1 3SD

Telephone   (0783) 76191, ext. 21

Enquiries to   Mr Peter Liddle

Open   By appointment, on most days throughout the year; closed weekends. A charge may be made.

Access   Generally open to the public.

Historical background   The collection dates from 1964 and has been based within Sunderland Polytechnic since 1967 serving as a principal source of original material for student work on World War I and for researchers interested in all areas of personal experience at that time. An attempt to secure appropriate institutionalisation of the collections, but still under Mr Liddle's curatorship, is being actively sought.

Acquisitions policy   By donation. Any original documentary material in the form of letters, diaries, artwork, scrapbooks, official papers and also maps, books, artefacts, souvenirs, weapons, uniforms relating to 1914–18 and the period immediately before and after World War I. Also manuscript, typescript and tape-recorded recollections of personal experience in any aspect of the War. The Domestic Front and Conscientious Objection are areas considered as significant as the fighting fronts. Mr Liddle will do any necessary travelling to facilitate help in the collection of material or making of tape-recordings.

Major collections   The 1914–18 papers and/or recollections of over 3500 veterans (many men and women of outstanding eminence). A special feature of the archives is that there is first hand evidence of the early active service careers of about 150 men who later rose to the highest army, navy and air force ranks. The same can be claimed for outstanding politicians, scientists, business men and men of the arts and of sport. The war in the air, at sea, Gallipoli and conscientious objection are among the areas most comprehensively covered but of special interest is the material relating to less well-documented aspect of the war, such as German East Africa, Dunsterforce, the Caspian Naval Force and British internment in Russia.

Non-manuscript material   More than 2000 books.
Large newspaper collection of national, local, army and navy, and foreign issues with many unusual specialist items, including trench news sheets. Map collection for all the fighting fronts.
Museum collection of uniforms, weapons, souvenirs and various artefacts. Tape-recorded recollections of all areas of personal experience in the war with the social background and pre-1914 working experience of the man or woman being interviewed. Those interviewed include Harold Macmillan, Henry Moore, Lord Shinwell, Fenner Brockway as well as a number of marshals of the Royal Air Force, Field Marshals and an Admiral of the Fleet.

Finding aids   Leaflets fully listing individuals represented in archive. With the exception of the French and German material, everything is fully listed in the General and Special Area catalogue. For army service, a special aspects catalogue specifically lists original document references. There is a similar catalogue for the RFC, RNAS and RAF and one is to be prepared for the Royal Navy and Mercantile Marine. The tape-recording collection is card indexed and there are appropriately subdivided listings for the newspapers, maps and museum collections.

Facilities   Research work area available. Some facility for photograph and document copying.

Publications   'The First World War: Teaching and Research', *Teaching History* (May, 1974)
Men of Gallipoli (1976)
'Recollections of the Great War', *Journal of Oral History* (1979)

659   Sunderland Polytechnic Library

Address   Chester Road
                   Sunderland
                   Tyne and Wear SR1 3SD

Sunderland Polytechnic Library does not hold any archival or MSS material. At present it houses Peter Liddle's Collection (*see* entry **658**).

660   Sutton Central Library

Address   St Nicholas Way
                   Sutton
                   Surrey SM1 1EA

Telephone   (01) 661 5050

Enquiries to   Local History Librarian, Miss June Broughton
                   or
                   Principal Librarian, Reference and Information Services, Mr Clewett

Open   Tues–Fri: 9.30–8.00
                   Sat: 9.30–5.000
                   Appointment preferred

Access   Generally open to the public.

Historical background   The library sevice began in 1935; a collection of local history material was started in the 1940s. Following local government reorganization in 1965 the present Local History Collection was formed by the amalgamation of the collections for Beddington and Wallington, Sutton and Cheam, and Carshalton.

Acquisitions policy   To accept whatever material is offered on the history of the locality generally.

Major collections   Records of predecessor authorities, including rate books, 18th–20th centuries; vestry minutes, 18th and 19th centuries; churchwardens' accounts, 1764–1833; school log and punishment books, 1871–; valuation lists, 1806–1963. Court rolls for the manor of Sutton, 1720–1905, and the manor of Carshalton, 19th and 20th centuries, with transcripts from 1346.

Carshalton Charities records, 1766–1939.

Sutton Congregational Church minutes, 1870–1960.

Phillips Collection relating to the Carew family of Beddington, 15th–17th centuries.

Dr Peatling Collection relating to Carshalton, including notes, pamphlets and cuttings, and transcriptions, 20th century.

River Wandle Collection of deeds relating to fishing rights and milling, 17th–20th centuries.

Non-manuscript material   Croydon Airport Collection, 1915–.

Photographs and glass negatives, 1860–; 5,000 slides; *c*500 paintings, drawings and prints.

Transcripts of Beddington parish registers (those for other parishes have been published).

Early editions of Surrey maps.

Newspapers 1863–; cuttings collection; microfilms of newspapers and census returns.

Films and tapes, including Sutton weekly talking newspaper 1976–, and interviews and talks

Finding aids   Brief finding list. Calendar of Philips papers. Indexes to streets and buildings; newspapers (1976–); biography (mainly Sutton and Cheam).

Facilities   Photocopying. Microfilm reader/printer.

Publications   Local History publishing programme [details on application].

661   Royal Institution of South Wales

Address   Victoria Road
                 Swansea
                 West Glamorgan SA1 1SN

The Institution's archive collection has been deposited at the University College of Swansea (*see* entry **665**).

662   South Wales Miners' Library

Address   50 Sketty Road
                 Uplands
                 Swansea
                 West Glamorgan SA2 0LG

Telephone   (0792) 29859/298366

Enquiries to   Tutor/Librarian, Dr Hywel Francis

The Library, opened in 1973, is part of University College Swansea (*see* entry **665**). The College houses the South Wales Coalfield Archive and enquiries should be directed there. A full description of its historical origins can be found in H. Francis: 'The Origins of the South Wales Miners' Library', *History Workshop*, no. 2 (Autumn 1976).

663   Swansea Central Library

Address   Alexander Road
                   Swansea
                   West Glamorgan SA1 5DX

Telephone   Central Library: (0792) 54065/6
                   Reference Library: (0792) 55521

Enquiries to   County Librarian, Mr B. Thomas (at Headquarters)
                   or
                   Local History Librarian, Mr John V. Hughes

Open   Mon–Wed, Fri: 9.00–700
                   Thurs, Sat: 9.00–5.00

Access   Generally open to the public.

Historical background   The Central Library was opened in 1887. Archival material has been collected from that date and is held in the Reference Library.

Acquisitions policy   Any local history material is collected.

Major collections   Most collections and documents relate to local history in the Swansea area. They include the following:
Edward Hughes MSS: accounts and receipts of a local business, mainly 18th century.
W. Mansel Collection: MSS relating to Cwnbran newspaper and Swansea theatres.

Non-manuscript material   W.J. Davis papers concerning adult education in Swansea, mainly pamphlets.
Microfilm copies of old Welsh MSS relating to the area.

Finding aids   Handlist.

Facilities   Photocopying. Microfilm reader.

Publications   A.F. Peplow: *Manuscript Collections at Swansea Public Library* (reproduced typescript, undated, c1957)

664   Swansea City Council
City Archives

Address   Guildhall
                 Swansea
                 West Glamorgan SA1 4PE

Telephone   (0792) 50821 ext. 2115/2122

Enquiries to   City Archivist, Dr J.R. Alban

Open   Tues, Wed: 9.30–12.45; 2.15–4.30
                 Appointments to consult MSS are not necessary, but preferred.

Access   Bona fide researchers. Written application needed for consultation
                 of cine films and sound archives.

Historical background Before 1835 the care and custody of the records were the responsibility of the Portreeve and after that date of the Town Clerk. In the 1840s the older records were arranged and repaired by the antiquarian George Grant Francis. During the 1920s an Honorary Borough Archivist was appointed, but from 1932 until 1974 the Council's Estate Agent had a responsibility for historical records. Since 1974 an archivist, attached to the staff the Chief Executive and Town Clerk's Department, has had charge of the records and responsibility for the management of modern departmental records. In 1968 the medieval charters and most of the early minute books were transferred to the Library of the University College of Swansea (*see* entry **665**).

Aquisitions policy Care and custody of the records of the City Council and its departments.

Major collections Official records of the City Council and its predecessor authorities, 18th–20th centuries.

Non-manuscript material *c*25,000 photographic items including prints, negatives, slides, printing blocks etc, relating to the Swansea area, from mid-19th century.
*c*110 cine films of important civic events, 1936–.
Sound Archive: *c*130 tape recordings of work experience in local industries in the Lower Swansea Valley; agricultural life in Gower; war; women in society etc.
Collection of pamphlets, secondary works, and general reference works on the history of the locality.

Finding aids Lists and descriptive lists of most processed classes. General subject index in progress.

Facilities Photocopying. Photography. Access to microfilm/fiche reader when required. Facilities for viewing cine films and listening to tapes (strictly by appointment only).

Publications *Air Raids on Swansea* (1981) [document resources pack]
   J.R. Alban: *Calendar of Swansea Freemen's Records* (1982)

665 University College Library, Swansea

Address   Singleton Park
               Swansea
               West Glamorgan SA2 8PP

Telephone   (0792) 205678 ext. 7316

Enquiries to   Archivist, Mr David Bevan

Open   Mon–Fri: 9.00–5.00, preferably by appointment

Access   Bona fide readers on written application.

Historical background   The Manuscript Department of the Library has been built up over the last two decades.

Acquisitions policy   To strengthen existing holdings of trade union and political papers from the South Wales Coalfield and of the records of the historical metallurgical industries of the Swansea region.

Major collections   South Wales Coalfield Archive: c300 separate collections of trade union, political, co-operative and personal collections from the South Wales Coalfield.
Industrial records: archives of the main metallurgical firms of the Swansea region; and of the Mumbles Railway.
Local collections: Swansea municipal records, including medieval charters and most administrative records (mainly minutes), c1530–c1800; church and chapel records; family, estate and topographical papers of the Royal Institute of South Wales.

Non-manuscript material   Large collections of local material.
Large print and photographic collection (in the Royal Institution of South Wales, see entry 661).
Sound archives (in the South Wales Miners' Library, see entry 662).

Finding aids   Descriptive lists of individual collections (some in course of preparation).

Facilities   Photocopying. Photography. Coalfield Archive material cannot be photocopied.

Publications   D. Bevan: Guide to the South Wales Coalfield Archive (1980)

666 Wiltshire Library and Museum Service

Address   Swindon Divisional Library
               Regent Circus
               Swindon
               Wiltshire SN1 1QG

Telephone	(0793) 27211
Enquiries to	The Divisional Librarian
Open	Mon–Fri: 9.00–9.00
	Sat: 9.00–5.00
Access	Generally open to the public. Visitors who wish to use microfilm readers should telephone beforehand.

Historical background The public library service in Wiltshire comprises (since 1974) the former Wiltshire County Library, Swindon Borough Library (successor to the Great Western Railway Mechanics' Institute Library) and Salisbury City Library.

Acquisitions policy Archival material is not now acquired, such material being directed to the Wiltshire Record Office (*see* entry **674**).

Major collections Goddard family documents: *c*2700 items pertaining to the Goddard family's interests and estates mostly in Swindon and north Wiltshire, 14th–20th centuries (mostly since the 17th century).
Wiltshire and Berkshire canal papers: ledgers, accounts, maps and deeds, 1793–1908.
Alfred Williams MSS: MSS of published and unpublished works by the Swindon poet and author, including his folksong collection, letters and his own library of books.
Great Western Railway papers: 58 administrative and miscellaneous items relating to the locomotive works and the Great Western Railway generally.

Non-manuscript material Local studies material in various media (including illustrations, maps, ephemera, newspapers and a few sound recordings as well as books and periodicals) are collected and maintained principally in four collections, at Devizes, Salisbury, Swindon and Headquarters at Trowbridge (*see* entry **674**).
1841–1871 Census enumerators' books (on microfilm): most Wiltshire returns may be made available at Swindon Headquarters or certain other libraries by prior arrangement.
Certain official records (principally minute books) of the Old and New Swindon Local Boards and UDCs, and the Great Western Railway Medical Board Fund Society have been microfilmed and are available at Swindon. The original material is in the Wiltshire Record Office.

Finding aids A computerized union catalogue of local studies holdings in preparation.

Facilities Photocopying. Microfilm/fiche readers. Paper print-out copies from certain microfilms may be made by arrangement.

Publications The Goddard documents have been catalogued in two volumes (1960 and 1969), to be reprinted soon. Bibliographies of published material about Wiltshire to 1920 (1929) and 1920–1960 (1975) have been published by Wiltshire County Council.

667 Hydrographic Department

Address   Ministry of Defence
                   Taunton
                   Somerset TA1 2DN

Telephone   (0823) 87900 ext. 276

Enquiries to   The Curator

Open   By appointment
                   Mon–Fri: 9.00–4.30

Access   On application to and approval by the Curator.

Historical background   The Department was established in 1795 and has acquired documents of varying worth for navigational purposes.

Aquisitions policy   Continual addition of the results of modern hydrographic surveys and other worldwide information sent to the Department in the interests of safer navigation.

Major collections   Royal Navy hydrographical surveys, including surveys by James Cook (1728–79) and George Vancouver (1758–98), with sailing directions and correspondence from the 18th century.

Non-manuscript material   Record copies of cancelled Admiralty charts, catalogues, sailing directions and all Hydrographic Department publications.

Finding aids   Catalogues. Indexes.

Facilities   Photocopying. Photography. Slides. Microfilm/fiche reader.

668 Somerset County Council Local History Library

Address   The Castle
                   Castle Green
                   Taunton
                   Somerset TA1 4AD

Archives are neither held nor collected.

669 Somerset Record Office

Address   Obridge Road
                   Taunton
                   Somerset TA2 7PU

Telephone	(0823) 87600/78805
Enquiries to	County Archivist, Mr D.M.M. Shorrocks
Open	Mon–Thurs: 9.00–4.50 Fri: 9.00–4.20 Sat: 9.15–12.15, by appointment

Historical background   Archives were first housed in a repository in 1929, with a professional archivist appointed in 1935. County Council records are housed at Shire Hall, Taunton. The Office also acts as the Diocesan Record Office for Bath and Wells.

Major collections   Usual local authority record holdings and deposited collections including the following which have a wider significance:
Dickinson MSS: merchants' accounts etc relating to Jamaica and trade with the Americas and the Baltic, 18th century.
Tudway MSS concerning the family estate on Antigua, late 17th–20th centuries.
Helyar MSS: Jamaican estate papers, c1660–1713.
Phelips MSS: political papers, mainly of Sir Robert Phelips, early–mid-17th century.
Papers of: William Kirkpatrick relating to India, 1787–1811; John Strachey, historian and scientist, early 18th century; Sir William Joliffe, politician, 1845–66; Edward Lear, 1847–86; John Braham, singer, early 19th century; Chichester Fortescue, Lord Carlingford, politician, 1854–90.

Facilities   Photocopying.

Publications   *Interim Handlist of Somerset Quarter Session Documents and other official Records* (1947)
Proceedings, Somerset Archaeological and Natural History Society [includes annual lists of main MS accessions]

670   Telford Development Corporation

Address	Priorslee Hall Telford Shropshire TF2 9NT
Telephone	(0952) 613131
Enquiries to	Archivist

Virtually all material falls within the 30-year rule and is not open to the public. The Corporation will cease to exist by c1990 and the final place of deposit for its papers has yet to be decided.

671   Tonbridge Central Library

Address   Avebury Avenue
                   Tonbridge
                   Kent TN9 1TG

Telephone   (0732) 352754/350479

Enquiries to   The Area Librarian

Open   Mon, Tues, Thur: 9.30–7.00
                   Wed, Fri: 9.30–6.00
                   Sat: 9.30–5.00

Access   Generally open to the public upon prior application.

Historical background   The Public Library started in Tonbridge in 1882 but most archival material has only been collected within last 20 years.

Acquisitions policy   To strengthen existing collection relating to the Tonbridge area, although the Library does not seek to compete with local County Record Office.

Major collections   Minutes of Tonbridge Local Board, 1870–94, Tonbridge Urban District Council, 1895–1970.
Census returns for Tonbridge/Malling Division, 1841, 1851, 1861, 1871.
Some items from local families including wills.

Non-manuscript material   Pamphlets, posters, etc relating to the Tonbridge area.

Finding aids   Indexes.

Facilities   Photocopying. Microfilm reader.

672   Treorchy Library and Administrative Centre

Address   Station Road
                   Treorchy
                   Rhondda
                   Mid Glamorgan CF42 6NN

Telephone   (0443) 773204

Enquiries to   Borough Librarian, Miss E. Davies

Open   Mon–Thurs: 9.30–5.30
                   Fri: 1.00–8.00
                   Sat: 9.00–12.00

Access   Generally open to the public.

Historical background   The Library Acts were adopted in 1933 but the service, consisting of small premises and two staff, was not commenced until 1939.

Major collections Various MSS and archival collections of local history interest, including Welsh Congregational Church records.

Non-manuscript material Music scores and literature in the Welsh collection.

Finding aids Local history catalogue.

Facilities Photocopying. Microfilm reader.

673 Wiltshire Library and Museum Service Headquarters

Address Bythesea Road
Trowbridge
Wiltshire BA14 8BS

Telephone (02214) 3641

Enquiries to The Director

The archaeological sites and monuments record for Wiltshire is maintained on a computer database, with over 2000 archival aerial photographs of archaeological features. Its use is restricted to bona fide researchers.
Manuscript material is held at Swindon Divisional Library (*see* entry 666).

674 Wiltshire Record Office

Address County Hall
Trowbridge
Wiltshire BA14 8JG

Telephone (02214) 3641 ext. 3500

Enquiries to County Archivist, Mr K.H. Rogers

Open Mon, Tues, Thurs, Fri: 9.00–12.30; 1.30–5.00
Wed: 9.00–12.30; 1.30–8.30

Historical background The Office was established in 1947. Previously, the Wiltshire Archaeological Society collected material and this was incorporated in 1947. The Salisbury Diocesan Office was closed in 1980 and the great majority of records was transferred to Wiltshire Record Office. Salisbury District Council Muniment Room records were transferred in 1982. The office also acts as the Diocesan Record Office for Salisbury (parish records) and Bristol (Wiltshire parish records).

Major collections Usual local authority record holdings and deposited collections.

Facilities Photocopying. Photography and microfilming by arrangement. Microfilm reader/printer.

Publications   M.G. Rathbone: *Guide to the Records in the Custody of the Clerk of the Peace for Wiltshire* (1959)
P. Stewart: *Guide to County Council, Poor Law and other Official Records...* (1961)
Guide to Private Records (1969) [typescript]
Guide to the Records of the Bishop, the Archdeacons of Salisbury and Wiltshire ... (1973)

675   Cornwall County Library

Address   County Hall
                 Station Road
                 Truro
                 Cornwall TR1 3UN

Local History collections were amalgamated in 1974 and are held in Redruth Local History Library (*see* entry **604**).

676   Cornwall County Record Office

Address   County Hall
                 Truro
                 Cornwall TR1 3AY

Telephone   (0872) 73698

Enquiries to   County Archivist, Mr P.L. Hull

Open   By appointment only
                 Tues–Thurs: 9.30–1.00; 2.00–5.00
                 Fri: 9.30–1.00; 2.00–4.30
                 Sat: 9.00–12.00
                 Closed: every Bank Holiday, the preceding Sat and the day following the Bank Holiday

Historical background   The Office was established in 1951 with the appointment of an archivist. It also acts as the Diocesan Record Office for Truro.

Major collections   Usual local authority record holdings and deposited collections, primarily of local interest.

Facilities   Photocopying. Photography and microfilming by arrangement. Microfilm reader.

Publications   *Brief Introduction to Sources* (1979)
Summary list of parish registers, 1981 [updated regularly]
Handlists: *Family History Sources; History of a House*

677   The Royal Institution of Cornwall

Address   The County Museum
                   River Street
                   Truro
                   Cornwall

Telephone   (0872) 72205

Enquiries to   Curator and Archivist, Mr H.L. Douch

Open   Mon–Sat: 9.00–1.00; 2.00–5.00

Access   Generally open to the public.

Historical background   Founded in 1918, the Institution sponsored a museum since its foundation. The muniment room was added in 1936 to house the Charles Henderson collection of deeds. The Courtney Library, strong in all aspects of local history and related subjects, is also administered by the Institution.

Acquisitions policy   Since the establishment of the County Record Office (*see* entry 676) the Institution no longer collects archives.

Major collections   Charles Henderson collection (pruned from Estate Offices of Cornish families).

Non-manuscript material   Local newspapers (*Royal Cornwall Gazette*, 1801–1951; *West Briton* 1810–56; etc).
Microfilms of parish registers (about half the ancient parishes, mainly those in the West).
Large collection of Cornish photographs.
Recent purchase of a large private library on Methodism in Cornwall.

Finding aids   Lists to all archive collections. Place name and (partial) personal name indexes.

Facilities   Photocopying. Microfilm/fiche readers.

Publications   *The Annual Journal of the Institution* [contains reports and articles on aspects of Cornish history, topography etc]

678   Brunel University

Address   Uxbridge
                   Middlesex UB8 3PH

Telephone   (0895) 37188 ext. 547

Enquiries to   Archivist, Mr R.W.P. Wyatt

The University developed from the College of Advanced Technology, Acton, London, and received its Royal Charter in 1966. It has minutes and other records of the University from c1960.

679   Hillingdon Borough Libraries

Address   22 High Street
                   Uxbridge
                   Middlesex UB8 1JN

Telephone   (0895) 50600

Enquiries to   Local Studies Librarian, Miss M. Pearce

Open   Mon–Fri: 9.30–8.00
                   Sat: 9.30–5.00

Access   Generally open to the public.

Historical background   The Hillingdon Borough Libraries consists of part of the area previously administered by the Middlesex County Council and encompasses Northwood, Hayes and Harlington, and Yiewsley and West Drayton. The archives and local history collection have been built up with the full involvement of the Uxbridge Local History and Archives Society.

Acquisitions policy   All material relating to constitutent parts of the present borough, but including adjoining parts of Buckinghamshire (not in depth).

Major collections   Principally non-MSS material; also Council and Committee minutes covering constitutent parts of the borough (mostly 20th century).

Non-manuscript material   Maps and plans covering mainly the area of the present borough (300–400 items, 17th–20th centuries).
Illustrations, chiefly photographs, covering the present borough (c5500 items, mostly 20th century).
Press cuttings relating to present borough (27 vols).
Library of Society of Friends, Uxbridge (older part of collection 96 vols covering the 17th century to the early 20th century).
Complete files of all local newspapers (some on microfilm).

Finding aids   Handlist of local history materials held at Uxbridge Library (Rev. 1979). Card index.

Facilities   Photocopying. Microfilm/fiche reader/printer.

680 Wakefield Metropolitan District
Department of Archives and Local Studies

Address   Library Headquarters
Balne Lane
Wakefield
West Yorkshire WF2 0DQ

Telephone   (0924) 371231

Enquiries to   Principal Local Studies Officer and Archivist, Mr John Goodchild

Open   Mon: 9.30–7.00
Tues–Fri: 9.30–5.00
Second Sat in month: 9.30–4.00, other times by arrangement
Appointments desirable

Historical background The office was established in 1975; it also houses the Goodchild Loan MSS which were collected for many years before this. Large collections from Wakefield Corporation Library and West Riding County Library were taken over also in 1975. The Department supervises access to Pontefract Borough MSS at Pontefract Municipal Buildings.

Major collections Usual local authority record holdings and deposited collections. Especially good collection of papers and records relating to local industrial and transport history.

Facilities Photocopying. Photography. Microfilm readers.

Publications *Wakefield District Archives: a Handlist for Students, Part I: Manuscripts relating to Local Social Life* (1976)
Various other publications on regional historical themes.

681 West Yorkshire Record Office

Address   Registry of Deeds
Newstead Road
Wakefield
West Yorkshire WF1 2DE

Telephone   (0924) 367111 ext. 2352

Enquiries to   County Archivist, Mrs E.K. Berry
or
By post: West Yorkshire Record Office, County Hall, Wakefield, West Yorkshire WF1 2QW

Open   Mon–Fri: 9.00–5.00 Sat: 9.00–4.00 (or by arrangement)

Historical background The Office was established in the Department of

Administration in 1974 and houses records of West Riding Quarter Sessions, West Riding County Council and West Riding Registry of Deeds. It administers Yorkshire Archaeological Society collections at Leeds and acts as the Diocesan Record Office for Wakefield (parish records, including Wakefield Cathedral).

Major collections Usual local authority record holdings and deposited collections including the following which has a wider significance:
British Waterways Board records, 1652–1976.

Facilities Photocopying. Photography. Microfilming. Microfilm reader.

682 Walsall Metropolitan Borough Archives Service

Address Walsall Library and Museum Services
Central Library
Lichfield Street
Walsall
West Midlands WS1 1TR

Telephone (0922) 21244 ext. 3111

Enquiries to Archivist, Mrs M. Lewis

Open Mon–Fri: 9.30–7.00
Sat: 9.30–5.00

Access Generally open to the public. Documents should normally be ordered one day in advance.

Historical background The Local Studies Room of Walsall Central Library was established by a local newspaper, *The Walsall Observer*, to mark its centenary in 1968. It housed the Local Studies Library and a collection of miscellaneous MS material acquired over the years by successive librarians. A full Archives Service has been in operation since 1978.

Acquisitions policy To locate, collect and preserve archival and local studies material relating to all aspects of life and work in Walsall.

Major collections Public records: Walsall Quarter Sessions, Magistrates and Coroners' Courts, 19th–20th centuries.
Walsall Hospital records, 19th–20th centuries.
Local government records: Walsall Metropolitan Borough and the superseded Urban Districts of Aldridge, Brownhills, Darlaston, and Willenhall, mainly 19th–20th centuries; records of Walsall Corporation, 17th–20th centuries.
Church records: local non-conformist church records, 18th–20th centuries.
Local organizations: many important collections of records of local businesses, societies and organizations, mainly 19th–20th centuries.

Non-manuscript material c4000 photographs of all parts of the Borough.

Microfilm copies of local newspapers, 1857–.
Large collection of local posters, pamphlets, etc.
*c*250 tape recordings [growing collection] of reminiscences of local residents.

Facilities   Photocopying. Photography. Microfilm/fiche readers.

Publications   Set of ten Guides to sources available for genealogists, students of industry, politics, transport, etc.
Various handlists of Archive Accessions (1972–1980).
M. Lewis: 'The Walsall Metropolitan Borough Archives Service', *Archives*, xiv/64 (1980), 225
Walsall Chronicle (Annual Report of Archives Services Work), No 1 (1979) No 2 (1980) No 3 (1981)

683   The Tank Museum

Address   Bovington Camp
Wareham
Dorset BH20 6JG

Telephone   (0929) 462721 ext. 463

Enquiries to   Curator, Lt-Col. (Retired) G. Forty
or
Assistant Curator/Librarian, Lt-Col. (Retired) K. Hill

Open   Every day of the year except for the two weeks over Christmas and the New Year. The library, archives and photo archives are open only by prior appointment.

Access   By voluntary donation; all visitors are expected to make a modest contribution.

Historical background   Founded after World War I as the Royal Tank Corps Museum, the current Museum embraces all regiments of the Royal Armoured Corps. The Museum exists under the sponsorship of the Ministry of Defence (Army) as both a Corps and a Regimental Museum. The exhibits are the property of the Trustees, who receive no grants of funds from any source towards their upkeep or preservation. The Museum is registered with the Charity Commissioners.

Acquisitions policy   One of the aims is to maintain a repository for items of value associated with the history of armoured fighting vehicles and armoured warfare and encourage historical interest and research.

Major collections   Principally non-MS material (*see* below).
Much documentary archival material on the history of the Royal Tank Regiment and its forbears, and the history of armoured fighting vehicles.
Many pamphlets and vehicle documents of British, and a fair number of foreign, armoured fighting vehicles.

Non-manuscript material Many photographs of armoured fighting vehicles, armoured warfare etc.

The Library contains most regimental histories of the Royal Armoured Corps regiments.

Historical relics, memorabilia and uniforms belonging to the Royal Tank Regiment and its forbears.

Finding aids Apart from a fairly comprehensive index maintained by the Librarian, there is no catalogue or written index available at present.

Facilities Photocopying. Photography.

684   Warrington Library

Address   Museum Street
                   Warrington
                   Cheshire WA1 1JB

Telephone   (0925) 571232

Enquiries to   The Reference Librarian

Open   Mon—Wed, Fri: 9.00—7.30
                   Thurs: 9.00—5.00
                   Sat: 9.00—1.00

Access   On application.

Historical background Warrington Library claims to be the first rate-supported library. Opened on 1 Nov 1848, it has always concentrated on collecting local material. In 1974 the formerly independent Borough Library became part of the Cheshire County Libraries and Museums Service.

Acquisitions policy To strengthen existing primary and secondary collections in Warrington history by purchase, donations or deposits.

Major collections c12,000 MSS including:
Manorial and tithe documents.
Early Poor Law rate and account books; Police Commissioners' minutes.
Town Council minutes and rates books.
Family deeds including the Patten, Harrison and Lyon papers.
Quaker records.
Sibson papers relating to Ashton in Makerfield.

Non-manuscript material c15,000 broadsides consisting of handbills, engravings, photographs, postcards, posters and other ephemera.
c2000 photographs plus negatives of Warrington streets and buildings (Warrington Photographic Survey; in progress since 1973).

Finding aids Catalogue. Indexes.

Facilities Photocopying. Photography and microfilming, by arrangement.

685 Warwick County Record Office

Address Priory Park
Cape Road
Warwick CV34 4JS

Telephone (0926) 493431 ext. 2508

Enquiries to County Archivist, Mr M.W. Farr

Open Mon–Thurs: 9.00–1.00; 2.00–5.30
Fri: 9.00–1.00; 2.00–5.00
Sat: 9.00–12.30

Historical background The Office was established in 1931 and covers the historic county area (excluding, for most purposes, Birmingham, Coventry and Stratford-upon-Avon). It also acts as the Diocesan Record Office for Birmingham (parish records) and Coventry.

Major collections Usual local authority record holdings and deposited collections.

Facilities Photocopying. Photostat. Microfilming. Microfilm reader.

686 Warwickshire County Library

Address Warwickshire Collection
Warwick Library
Church Street
Warwick CV34 4AL

Telephone (0926) 492077, 493431 ext. 2488

Enquiries to The Librarian

Local History Collection of non-MS material covering the County in general. Other libraries throughout the County maintain smaller collections.

687 British Steel Corporation
Records Services Section

Address East Midlands Regional Records Centre
By-Pass Road
Irthlingborough
Wellingborough
Northamptonshire NN9 5QH

Telephone (0933) 650277

Enquiries to   Eastern Regional Manager, Miss J. Hampson
                  (for the South East of England, including London and extending to
                  Birmingham and Scunthorpe)
                  or
                  The Director, Secretariat, British Steel Corporation, Head Office,
                  33 Grosvenor Place, London SW1
                  (for postal enquiries covering more than one region)

Open   Mon–Fri: 9.45–4.15, by appointment
                  Lunchtime closures vary in regions according to local practice.

Access   At discretion of the Regional Manager. 30-year closure.

Historical background   The Records Section was established in 1970 to look after
    the archives of the constituent companies which made up the Corporation on
    its formation in 1967 and to provide a Records Management service to the
    Corporation. The archives and records of the Corporation are now housed in
    five Records Centres: Eastern Region at Wellingborough and Middlesbrough;
    Scottish Region at Glasgow; Western Region at Deeside and Cardiff.

Acquisitions policy   Restricted to records relating to the British Steel Corporation,
    its constituent companies and related bodies.

Major collections   Records of the Scheduled steel companies which made up the
    whole Corporation: Colvilles Ltd, Consett Iron Co. Ltd, Dorman Long & Co.
    Ltd, English Steel Corporation Ltd, GKN Steel Company Ltd, John Summers &
    Sons Ltd, Lancashire Steel Corporation Ltd, Park Gate Iron & Steel Works Ltd,
    Richard Thomas & Baldwins Ltd, Round Oak Steel Works, South Durham Steel
    & Iron Company Ltd, Steel Company of Wales Ltd, Stewarts & Lloyds Ltd, and
    the United Steel Companies Ltd.
    Records of the British Iron and Steel Federation and its predecessor the National
    Federation of Iron and Steel Manufacturers.

Non-manuscript material   Small collections of publications relating to the history
    of the iron and steel industry.

Finding aids   Records Transmittal Lists. Contemporary indexes.

Facilities   Photocopying.

688   Sandwell Public Libraries
Archives and Local History Department

Address   Central Library
              High Street
              West Bromwich
              West Midlands B70 8DZ

Telephone   (021) 569 2416

Enquiries to   Borough Librarian, Mr R.B. Ludgate
or
Reference Librarian Mrs M. Reed

Open   Mon, Fri: 9.00–7.00
Tues, Wed: 9.00–6.00
Thurs, Sat: 9.00–1.00
Prior application preferred

Access   Generally open to the public.

Historical background   Libraries in the West Bromwich area have collected archival material since the mid-19th century. Local history and archive material is housed at West Bromwich, Wednesbury, Tipton and Smethwick district libraries. The library acts as the Diocesan Record Office for Birmingham (rural deanery of Warley; parish records of West Bromwich).

Acquisitions policy   To acquire any documents that become available from industry, local government, or any other source relating to Sandwell.

Major collections   Parish registers.
Local government records.
Methodist records.
Jesson Deeds, 1589–1784.

Non-manuscript material   Maps, including mining maps
Over 8000 photographs (especially Smethwick Library Collection).

Finding aids   Catalogues and indexes.

Facilities   Photocopying. Photography. Microfilming. Microfilm reader.

689   Hampshire County Library

Address   81 North Walls
Winchester
Hampshire

Archives are not held, since anything of an archival nature is directed to Hampshire Record Office (*see* entry 690).

690   Hampshire Record Office

Address   20 Southgate Street
Winchester
Hampshire SO23 9EF

Telephone   (0962) 63153

Enquiries to   County Archivist, Miss R. Dunhill

Open   Mon–Thurs: 9.00–4.45
                        Fri: 9.00–4.15
                        Sat: (2nd and 4th of each month): 9.00–11.55, by appointment

Historical background   The Office was established in 1947. It houses Winchester
    City records and also acts as the Diocesan Record Office for Winchester.

Major collections   Usual local authority record holdings including the following
    deposited collections which have a wider significance:
    Political correspondence of George Tierney senior (1761–1830); first Duke of
    Wellington, 1828–50; third Baron Calthorpe, c1814–30; William Wickham
    c1795–1830; first Baron Bolton (1764–1807).
    Bonham Carter family papers, including correspondence with Florence
    Nightingale, 18th and 19th centuries.
    Lemprière family papers relating to the Channel Islands, 19th century.
    Shelley-Rolls papers, including papers relating to Percy Bysshe Shelley (1792–
    1822).

Facilities   Photocopying. Microfilming. Microfilm reader.

Publications   Hampshire Archivists Group: *Archives of Hampshire and the Isle of
    Wight* (1966); *Poor Law* (1970); *Transport* (1973); *Education* (1977) [typescript]

691   Winchester Cathedral Library

Address   The Close
                       Winchester
                       Hampshire SO23 9LS

Enquiries to   The Rev Canon P.A. Britton, 11 The Close, Winchester, Hampshire
                       SO23 9LS
                       (Telephone (0962) 68580)

Open   April–Sept: Mon–Sat: 10.30–12.30; 2.30–4.30
                       Oct–March: Wed and Sat: 10.30–12.30; 2.30–4.30
                       (days and times subject to alteration)

Access   Bona fide research students on written application with references.

Historical background   The Cathedral was commenced in 1079 and has a con-
    tinuous history from that date.

Major collections   Archives relating to the Priory and the Cathedral from middle
    ages to present day.

Non-manuscript material   One of the oldest book rooms in Europe, including a fine
    17th-century collection.
    Plans and maps.

692   Winchester College Archives

Address   Winchester College
                 Winchester
                 Hampshire SO23 9NA

Enquiries to   The Archivist

Open   By written appointment only, during normal school terms

Access   Approved researchers.

Historical background   Winchester College was founded by William of Wykeham in 1382. His statutes provided for the careful preservation of documents relating to the College's internal administration and to its estates. The oldest documents are still housed in the 14th-century muniment room with its original chests.

Acquisitions policy   To preserve the administrative and educational records of the College.

Major collections   Extensive records of the College's estates, which lay primarily in Hampshire, Wiltshire and Dorset, from the late 14th century (in some cases the records pre-date the foundation).
Nearly complete internal accounts, 1394–.
Assorted educational records, increasingly full from the 18th century.

Non-manuscript material   Maps and plans of the College's estates.
Photographs of College buildings and portraits.

Finding aids   Various lists and indexes available, especially for the records pre-1870. Xerox copies of the main descriptive list are available at the main university and London libraries, and at relevant county record offices.

Facilities   Limited photocopying and photography.

Publications   J.H. Harvey: 'Winchester College Muniments', *Archives*, v, 28 (1962)
S. Himsworth: *Winchester College Muniments*, i (1976); ii, iii (in preparation)
[descriptive list, with indexes by P. Gwyn and others]

693   Eton College Records

Address   South Cloister
                 Eton College
                 Windsor
                 Berkshire SL4 6DB

Telephone   (95) 62937 (telephone enquiries not accepted)

Enquiries to   College Archivist, Mr Patrick Strong

Open   Mon–Fri: 8.00–12.30; 1.30–5.00, by written appointment
                 Closed: ten days at Christmas and at Easter

Access   Graduates welcome. Others may be asked for reference from an accredited scholar. Requests to use records 50–31 years old may be referred to Provost or Bursar. Closure on records 30 years old or less.

Historical background   Eton College was founded in 1440 by Henry VI in a collegiate parish church: the College was soon enlarged to include 70 scholars and 20 commensals (sons of benefactors or friends of the College, paying for board and lodging but educated free). Commensals were the forerunners of the oppidans, fee-paying boarders of the school which has grown up around the College and is administered separately. The Provost had peculiar jurisdiction from 1443 over the College and parish. Provosts were rectors of Eton until 1875, when a separate vicarage was created, but are still the ordinaries of College and lower (junior boys') chapels. Provosts also had testamentary jurisdiction, which petered out in the 1660s, and the power to issue marriage licences to parishioners.

Acquisitions policy   Occasional purchases or gifts of archives some time out of custody.

Major collections   The administrative and financial records only of the College (the Provost and Fellows), 1440–.

Eton College Library collection of post-medieval MSS contains some unofficial or personal papers of former Provosts; Fellows; members of the College; masters or boys in the school.

Some MS books of house, societies' and sporting annals.

Enrolled grants of probate and administrations, 1450s–1660s; and a few 18th-century marriage licences.

Parish registers were transferred to Buckinghamshire Record Office (*see* entry 26) after the Parochial Registers and Records Measure 1978 (microfilms and index to baptism and marriages held).

Finding aids   Eton College Records, vols 1–58, compiled by H.N. Blakiston, Emeritus Archivist (the only set outside Eton is in the library of the Public Record Office; *see* entry 441). The vols are calendars of estates documents, generally to 1871. Further vols in preparation: archives made by the college administration and bursary; additional vols of rediscovered estates documents. Additions to M.R. James: *Catalogue of ... MSS* (Cambridge, 1895); his interleaved office copy. Preliminary list of additional post-medieval MSS.

Facilities   Limited photocopying. Photography, by arrangement. Readers welcome to bring their own cameras; flash bulbs permitted. Microfilm/fiche reader.

Publications   Registers and lists of Etonians, 1441–1919 (all pubd; various years, 1863–1932)[the only source of record of past boys in the school]

For boys after 1919: *Eton Calendar* (pubd each term) [held at British Library and other copyright deposit libraries]; ABC lists in *Eton College Chronicle* (weekly/fortnightly)[held at British Library Newspaper Library]

694 St George's Chapel, Windsor Castle

Address   The Aerary
              Dean's Cloister
              Windsor Castle
              Windsor
              Berkshire SL4 1NJ

Telephone   (0753) 557942

Enquiries to Mrs G. Holmes

Open   By appointment only

Access   Approved readers on written application; 30-year closure rule.

Historical background   The College of St George was founded 1348/50

Acquisitions policy   Occasionally personal papers of retired or deceased members
of the College of St George are preserved. Otherwise internal acquisitions only.

Major collections   Records of the Dean and Canons of Windsor from the foundation
of the College, 1348/50–; some property deeds predate the foundation, the earliest
being of 1140. Records include chapter acts, accounts, attendance books, some
records of the Order of the Garter.

Non-manuscript material   Some maps and plans.
c1200 photographs.

Finding aids   Slip index to recent items (post-1957). Index to photographs.

Facilities   Photocopying. Copies of photographs can be obtained.

Publications   M.F. Bond: *The Inventories of St George's Chapel, Windsor Castle,
1384–1667* (1947)
Rev. E.H. Fellowes and E.R. Poyser: *The Baptism, Marriage and Burial Registers of
St George's Chapel, Windsor* (1957)
J.N. Dalton: *The Manuscripts of St George's Chapel* (1957)
C. Mould: *The Musical Manuscripts of St George's Chapel* (1973)

695 Windsor Muniment Rooms

Address   Guildhall
              High Street
              Windsor
              Berkshire SL4 1LR

Records have been transferred to Berkshire Record Office (*see* entry **599**).

696 Wolverhampton Borough Archives

Address Central Library
Snow Hill
Wolverhampton
West Midlands WV1 3AX

Telephone (0902) 773824/5/6

Enquiries to Archivist, Ms Elizabeth A. Rees

Open Mon–Sat: 10.00–1.00; 2.00–5.00
Sat by appointment only

Access Generally open to the public.

Historical background The Archives service was founded within the Public Libraries Department of Wolverhampton Borough Council in 1978, although some acquisitions had been made before this date.

Acquisitions policy The Archives service accepts and cares for historical documents from both public and private sources, relating to the Metropolitan District of Wolverhampton.

Major collections Records of Wolverhampton Borough Concil, 1777–; Bilston Borough Council and Tettenhall and Wednesfield Urban District Councils, 19th century–1966.
Records of Methodist circuits and churches in Wolverhampton, 18th–20th centuries.

Non-manuscript material A collection of local printed books, pamphlets, newspapers, etc is maintained by the Reference Department of the Library. There is also a large collection of photographs and printed ephemera.

Finding aids Typed lists. Card indexes.

Facilities Photocopying. Photography. Microfilm/fiche readers and reader/printer.

Publications Introductory leaflets on 14 topics [available on request]

697 Wolverhampton Polytechnic

Address Robert Scott Library
St Peter's Square
Wolverhampton
West Midlands WV1 1RH

No archives are held.

698 Hereford and Worcester County Libraries

Address   Loves Grove
               Worcester
               Worcestershire WR1 3BY

Telephone   (0905) 353366

Enquiries to   The Librarian

Open   Mon–Fri: 9.00–5.00, prior contact appreciated

Access   Generally open to the public.

Historical background   Hereford and Worcester County Libraries were formed in 1974 by the amalgamation of the former authority libraries of Hereford City, Herefordshire County, Evesham, Malvern, Redditch, Kidderminster, Worcester City and Worcestershire County.

Acquisitions policy   To provide as comprehensive a service of local information as possible within limited funds.

Major collections   Local history and local industry collections at Worcester City Library, Forgate Street, Worcester, telephone (0905) 353366, and Hereford City Library, Broad Street, Hereford, telephone (0432) 2456/68645.
Needlemaking Collection at Redditch Library, 15 Market Place, Redditch, telephone (0527) 63291/2.

Finding aids   Catalogues of local material.

Facilities   Photocopying. Microfilm/fiche readers.

699 Hereford and Worcester Record Office

Address   Shirehall
               Worcester WR1 1TR

Telephone   (0905) 353366 ext. 3612

Enquiries to   County Archivist, Mr A.M. Wherry

Open   Mon–Fri: 9.15–4.45

Historical background   Hereford and Worcester Record Office was created in 1974 following local government reorganization. Worcester Record Office was established in 1947. Hereford Record Office (*see* entry 241) and St Helen's Record Office (*see* entry 700) are dependent repositories.

Major collections   Usual local authority record holdings and deposited collectons, including several of national standing.

Facilities   Photocopying. Photography. Microfilming. Microfilm readers.

700   St Helen's Record Office

Address	Fish Street Worcester WR1 2HN
Telephone)	(0905) 353366 ext. 3615/6
Enquiries to	Assistant County Archivist, Miss M. Henderson
Open	Mon–Fri: 9.15–4.45

Historical background   The Office was established in 1956 and is a dependent repository of Hereford and Worcester Record Office (*see* entry **699**). It also acts as the Diocesan Record Office for Worcester and gives administrative assistance to Worcestershire Historical Society and Worcestershire Archaeological Society.

Major collectons   Usual local authority record holdings and deposited collections, some of national standing.

Facilities   Photocopying. Photography. Microfilming. Microfilm readers.

701   Worcester Cathedral Library

Address	Worcester Cathedral Worcester WR1 2LG
Enquiries to	Librarian, Canon Jefferey Fenwick, (0905) 24874
Open	By arrangement with the Librarian
Access	Approved readers on written application.

Historical background   Worcester Cathedral has had a continuous history since its foundation as a Benedictine House in 962.

Acquisitions policy   Apart from the muniments the only additions to the collection are books relating to the Cathedral and Diocese of Worcester. There is no purchasing fund.

Major collections   Cathedral Archive and muniments consisting of letter-books, deeds, accounts, chapter act books etc.
c275 medieval MSS which mainly comprised the working library of the monks; some fragments pre-date the monastic community (the Diocese dates from 680).
The University of Birmingham Library is in the process of recording all MS material on microfilm. Positive copies can be obtained on application to the Librarian at Worcester or the Keeper of Special Collections at Birmingham University Library (*see* entry **59**).

Non-manuscript material   c4500 16th–18th century printed books.
Church Music of the 17th–18th centuries.

Finding aids Catalogues for the MSS and printed books. The muniments are being re-catalogued.

702 Borthwick Institute of Historical Research

Address   University of York
St Anthony's Hall
Peasholme Green
York
North Yorkshire YO1 2PW

Telephone   (0904) 642315

Enquiries to Director, Dr D.M. Smith

Open   Mon–Fri: 9.30–1.00; 2.00–5.00, by appointment
Closed: public holidays; short period at Christmas and Easter; fortnight in late August

Access   Bona fide researchers. Restrictions on some modern records.

Historical background The Borthwick Institute is a research institute of the University of York specializing in the study of ecclesiastical history, in particular the administrative and legal history of ecclesiastical institutions within the province of York. It was established in 1953 on the initiative of the York Academic Trust and in 1963 became a department of the newly-established University.

Acquisitions policy The main acquisitions are records of the Church of England in the York diocese (papers of the Archbishops, Archdeacons, Rural Deans, and certain parishes) and related church material.

Major collections York Diocesan Records: records of the Archbishops and their subordinate officials from the 13th century to the present, including probate records, 1389–1858.
Mirfield Papers: records of the Community of the Resurrection at Mirfield and of several prominent members, 19th and 20th centuries.
Quaker Records: archive of the Retreat, York [Quaker-founded mental asylum], 18th century to the present; archives of the Tuke family, 18th and 19th centuries; social survey papers of Seebohm Rowntree, 20th century.
Halifax Archives: archives and political papers of the Wood family, Earls of Halifax, 18th–20th centuries.
Many smaller collections of a non-ecclesiastical nature, including family papers, guild records etc.

Non-manuscript material Gurney Library, 15,000 vols, principally concerned with ecclesiastical history and archive studies. It is a working library (reference only) for use in conjunction with the deposited archives.

Finding aids Typescript calendars, lists and indexes of the principal areas of the collection.

Facilities   Photocopying. Photography. Microfilming. Microfilm/fiche readers.

Publications   D.M. Smith: *Guide to the Archive Collections in the Borthwick Institute* (1973; suppl. 1980)
C.C. Webb: *Guide to Genealogical Sources in the Borthwick Institute* (1981)
The Institute also publishes the following series:
Borthwick Papers [studies concerned with the ecclesiastical history of northern England and aspects of the history and historiography of Yorkshire]
Borthwick Texts and Calendars [editions, calendars, handlists of records]
Borthwick Institute Bulletin [annual report, articles]
Borthwick Wallets [palaeography wallets]

703   Castle Howard

Address   York
North Yorkshire YO6 7BZ

The archives are closed pending the appointment of an archivist.

704   Centre for Southern African Studies
Southern African Archives

Address   University of York
Heslington
York
North Yorkshire YO1 5DD
The Southern African Archives are located in the Borthwick Institute of Historical Research (*see* entry **702**).

Telephone   (0904) 59861 ext.260 (Centre for Southern African Studies)
(0904) 59861, ext.274 (Borthwick Institute of Historical Research)

Enquiries to   The Director, Centre for Southern African Studies (general enquiries)
or
The Director, Borthwick Institute (for appointments to consult the collection)

Open   Mon–Fri: 9.30–1.00; 2.00–5.00
Closed: short periods at Christmas and Easter; the week of the late summer Bank Holiday and the week preceding it.

Access   Bona fide researchers and scholars. Researchers from outside the University should first consult the Director of the Centre or of the

Borthwick Institute; students should have a letter of introduction from their academic supervisor. Some materials are covered by specific conditions laid down by the donors; closure on some items for specified periods. Due acknowledgement should be made if material is used in publications; and the Director of the Centre would appreciate details of all such publications.

Historical background   The Southern African Archives were collected under the Southern African Documentation Project funded by the Leverhulme Trust from October 1974 to September 1977; further work on the collection and the addition of extra items was funded by the SSRC, Jan–Dec 1980. The Documentation Project was established to build up a collection of primary source material on southern Africa, following a suggestion by the poet Dennis Brutus. The collection reflects systematic searching, responses to notices in newspapers and periodicals, chance contacts, and the interests of the Research Fellows involved. Most of the material has come from private individuals and institutions in the UK; it was not the intention to remove progenitorial MSS from southern Africa, though some have been given and others photocopied. In addition to the archival material other donations, more suitable for library use, have been deposited in the University Library.

Acquisitions policy   Donations or deposits which will extend the collection or strengthen existing coverage are welcomed. The regional focus is on southern Africa: Angola, Botswana, Lesotho, Namibia, Malawi, Mozambique, South Africa and related territories, Swaziland, Zambia and Zimbabwe.

Major collections   Papers of Dennis Brutus, poet and anti-apartheid campaigner.
Records and related material of the Capricorn Africa Society.
Tanganyikan papers of Marion, Lady Chesham, mainly 1955–65.
Papers, diaries, correspondence, sermons etc of The Rt Rev. Joost De Blank (1908–68); the collection also includes materials collected by his sister, Miss Bertha De Blank.
Papers of the Rt Hon. Sir Patrick Duncan (1870–1943), noted South African radical.
Political papers of the Rev. William D. Grenfell relating to Angola, and the war of liberation, 1960–77.
Dr Franco Nogueria: papers of Dr Antonio D'Oliveira Salazar (1889–1970), former Prime Minister of Portugal.

Non-manuscript material   South African papersa of Lord Loch (Henry Brougham), High Commissioner in South Africa, 1890–95 (microfilms of the collection which is now in the Scottish Record Office)
Many of the collections contain pamphlets etc.
Some small photographic collections, including an album of photographs of Basutoland.
A few tape recordings, mainly of political material.

Finding aids   Various lists and indexes. Many of the collections fully listed; details available in mimeograph.

Facilities   Photocopying. Photography. Microfilming. Microfilm/fiche readers.

Publications   A. Ross: *Guide to the Tanganyikan Papers of Marion, Lady Chesham* (1975)

T. Lodge (comp.), A.V. Akeroyd and C.P. Lunt (eds.): *A Guide to the Southern African Archives in the University of York* (1979)

T. Lodge (comp.): *A Guide to the papers of Patrick Duncan 1918–1967* [in preparation]

705   National Railway Museum Library

Address   Leeman Road
York
North Yorkshire YO2 4XJ

Telephone   (0904) 21261 ext.33

Enquiries to   Librarian, Mr C.P. Atkins

Open   Tues–Fri: 10.30–5.00, by prior appointment

Access   Readers' tickets available on written application.

Historical background   The Museum was set up in 1975 following the closure of the former British Museum of Transport at Clapham in 1973. It is a part of the Science Museum, London.

The records from the former British Railways Historical Record Office in York are deposited at the Public Record Office (*see* entry **441**) and for Scottish Railways at the Scottish Record Office (*see* entry **188**).

Acquisitions policy   Archival, photographic and other material relating to the collection is welcomed.

Major collections   Several unique MS items including the pocket notebook of Sir Daniel Gooch (1816–90).

Research material of Selwyn Pearce Higgins relating to obscure railways in West Midlands and Welsh Border area.

Photograph albums and notebooks of Eric Mason relating to the Lancashire and Yorkshire Railway.

Personal records of Messrs R.C. Bond.

Rugby Locomotive Testing Station records.

Non-manuscript material   200,000 engineering drawings.

Official glass negatives of several major railway companies covering, mainly, 1880–1950.

Industrial Railway Society Library.

Finding aids   Card catalogue being compiled.

Facilities   Photocopying. Photography. Dyelines.

Publications   C.P. Atkins: 'The National Railway Museum and its photographic collection', *Railway World* (Jan 1982)

706   North Yorkshire County Library
Southern Division

Address   Central Library
                 Library Square
                 Museum Street
                 York
                 North Yorkshire YO1 2DS

Telephone   (0904) 55631/54144

Enquiries to   The Assistant County Librarian (postal enquiries)
                 or
                 The Divisional Organizer, Reference and Information Services (telephone)

Open   Mon–Wed, Fri: 9.00–8.00
                 Thurs: 9.00–5.30
                 Sat: 9.00–1.00

Access   Archive material generally available to public on request in the Reference Library, subject to satisfactory proof of identity.

Historical background   A limited collection of archival material, temporarily held MSS that had been in Guildhall and were placed in York City Archives (*see* entry 707) in 1980.

Acquisitions policy   To direct potential donors of archival material to York City Archives (*see* entry 707).

Major collections   Letters of the Thomas Allis (1788–1875), William Etty (1787–1849) families and Waterton papers, 1841–65.
Note-books on York subjects.
Records of the Knowles family, stained-glass manufacturers in York, late 19th century.

Non-manuscript material   14 films of local interest.
7000 local illustrations.
1000 slides of local interest.

Finding aids   Card catalogue and index available in the York Reference Library.

Facilities   Photocopying. Microfilm/fiche readers.

707   York City Archives

Address	Exhibition Square York North Yorkshire YO1 2EW
Telephone	(0904) 51533
Enquiries to	Archivist, Mrs R.J. Freedman
Open	Tues–Thurs: 9.00–12.30; 2.00–6.00 Mon and Fri by appointment

Historical background   Guildhall civic records and deposited collections were placed in the City Library in 1957 when a record office was opened with a full-time archivist. Following reorganization in 1974 the archives were transferred to the administration of the City and are now housed in premises in the Art Gallery building.

Major collections   Usual local authority record holdings and deposited collections of purely local interest.

Facilities   Photocopying. Photography and microfilming by arrangment.

Publications   R.J. Green: *York City Archives* (1971)

708   York Minster Archives

Address	York Minster Library Dean's Park York North Yorkshire YO1 2JD
Telephone	(0904) 25308
Enquiries to	Archivist, Rev. A.S. Leak
Open	Mon–Fri: 9.00–5.00, preferably by appointment
Access	Approved readers. 50-year closure on administrative records.

Historical background   The Dean and Chapter Archives (from c1150) and the Vicars Choral Archives (from 1252) were transferred from the Minster in 1960 to the newly-built muniment room in the Minster Library. To these two major collections have been added the Hailstone Collection and a number of smaller accumulations.

Acquisitions policy   To continue acquiring contemporary and historical records of the Minster; to house any private collections by donation or deposit relevant to the life and work of the Minster; to strengthen the collection of Yorkshire records based on the Hailstone Collection.

Major collections   Dean and Chapter Archives: a continuous record of the business of the Minster, including its properties in York and Yorkshire and elsewhere, c1150–.

College of Vicars Choral: records of the Vicars Choral of York Minster, from their foundation in 1252 to 1936, when the college ceased to exist as an independent corporation.

Hailstone Collection: by bequest of Edward Hailstone in 1890 the Minster Library acquired this extensive Yorkshire collection comprising archival material from the middle ages to modern times, and antiquarian material from the 18th and 19th centuries.

Various smaller collections of private papers, notably of Archbishop Garbett, Archbishop Sharp, Dean Purey-Cust, and Dean Milner-White; also a wide variety of Additional MSS.

Non-manuscript material   Pamphlets (especially Civil War tracts); maps and plans (Yorkshire); architectural drawings (York Minster); prints and drawings (Yorkshire, topographical and biographical); photographs (York Minster); newspapers (mainly Yorkshire), 18th and early 19th centuries.

Finding aids   Various lists and card indexes.

Facilities   Photocopying. Photography. Microfilm/fiche readers.

Publications   Outline list of Dean and Chapter Archives is given in:
First Report of the Historical Manuscripts Commission (1870), 97
J. Burton: *Monasticon Eboracense* (York, 1758), ix
G. Lawton: *Collectio rerum ecclesiasticarum de diocesi Ebor* (1842), ii
Many individual documents have been published in various vols of the Surtees Society and elsewhere [a typescript list is being revised for publication]

Select Bibliography

Aldridge, T.M. *Registers and Records, Sources of Information* (London, 3/1976)

Armstrong, N. *Local Collections in Scotland* (Paisley, 1977)

Aslib Directory *A Guide to Sources of Information in Great Britain and Ireland* (London, Vol. I 1977, Vol. II 1980)

Baldock, R.W. *A Survey of Southern African Manuscripts in the United Kingdom* (London, 1976)

Barrow, M. *Women 1870–1928: A Select Guide to Printed and Archival Sources in the United Kingdom* (London, 1981)

Beal, P. (comp.) *Index of English Literary Manuscripts, Vol. I 1450–1625* (London, 1980; Vols. II-V in preparation)

Bridson, G.D.R., Phillips, V.C. and Harvey, A.P. *Natural History Manuscript Resources in the British Isles* (London and New York, 1980)

Brink, A. (ed.) *The Libraries, Museum and Art Galleries Year Book* (Cambridge, 1981)

British Records Association, *Archives* 1949–

Camp, A.J. *Wills and their Whereabouts* (London, 4/1974)

Cockerell, H.A.L. and Green, E. *The British Insurance Business, 1547–1970: An Introduction and Guide to Historical Records in the United Kingdom* (London, 1976)

Cook, C. (comp.) *Sources in British Political History 1900–1951* (London, 1975–8)

Cox, J. and Padfield, T. *Tracing your Ancestors in the Public Record Office* (London, HMSO, 1981)

Crick, B.R. and Alman, M. *A Guide to Manuscripts Relating to America in Great Britain and Ireland*, rev. J.W. Raimo (London, 1979)

Dymond, D.P. *Writing Local History, a Practical Guide* (London, 1981)

Emmison, F.G. and Smith, W.J. *Material for Theses in Local Record Offices and Libraries* (London, 1979)

Evans, H. and M. (eds.) *The Picture Researcher's Handbook: An International Guide to Picture Sources and How to Use them* (London, 2/1979)

Gibson, J.S.W. *Census Returns, 1841, 1851, 1861, 1871 on Microfilm: A Directory to Local Holdings* (Federation of Family History Societies, 1979)

Government Publications *Sectional List 17: Publications of the Royal Commission on Historical Manuscripts* (London, HMSO, published annually)

Sectional List 24: British National Archives (London, HMSO, published annually)

A Guide to the Reports on Collections of Manuscripts of Private Families, Corporations and Institutions in Great Britain and Ireland (London, Royal Commission on Historical Manuscripts, HMSO, 1914–73)

List of Accessions to Repositories (1956 onwards) (London, Royal Commission on Historical Manuscripts, HMSO, 1957–72)

Accessions to Repositories and Reports added to the National Register of Archives (1972–) (London, Royal Commission on Historical Manuscripts, HMSO, 1973–)

Record Repositories in Great Britain (London, Royal Commission on Historical Manuscripts, HMSO, 5/6/7/1973–82)

Manuscript Papers of British Scientists 1600–1940 (London, Royal Commission on Historical Manuscripts, HMSO, 1982)

Henderson, G.P. and S.P.A. (eds.) *Directory of British Associations and Associations in Ireland* (Beckenham, 6/1980)

Hepworth, P. (ed.) *Select Biographical Sources: the Library Association Manuscripts Survey* (London, 1971)

Hewitt, A.R. *Guide to Resources for Commonwealth Studies in London, Oxford and Cambridge, with Bibliographical and Other Information* (London, 1957)

Institute of Historical Research *Bulletin* (London, 1923-66)

Iredale, D. *Enjoying Archives* (Newton Abbot, 1973; 2/1980)

Jones, C.A. *Britain and the Dominions: a Guide to Business and Related Records in the United Kingdom concerning Australia, Canada, New Zealand and South Africa* (Boston, 1978)

Jones, P. Mander *Manuscripts in the British Isles relating to Australia, New Zealand and the Pacific* (Canberra, 1972)

Ker, N.R. *Medieval manuscripts in British libraries* (Oxford, 1969)

Kitching, C.J. *The Central Records of the Church of England: A Report and Survey presented to the Pilgrim & Radcliffe Trustees* (London, 1976)

Library Association *Libraries in the United Kingdom and the Republic of Ireland* (London, 1981)

Library of Congress *British Manuscripts Project: a Checklist of the Microfilms prepared in England and Wales for the American Council of Learned Societies, 1941–1945*, comp. L.K. Born (Washington D.C., 1955)

Line, J. *Archival Collections of Non-book Materials: a Preliminary List Indicating Policies for Preservation and Access* (London, 1977)

521

London Local Libraries *Guide to London Local Studies Resources* (typescript available at Guildhall Library, Museum of London, Public Record Office and London local libraries)

Macleod, R.M. and Friday, J.R. *Archives of British Men of Science* (London, 1972)

Manchester Studies Unit *The Directory of British Oral History Collections* (Colchester, 1981)

Mathews, W. *British Diaries: An Annotated Bibliography of British Diaries Written between 1442 and 1942* (Berkeley and Los Angeles, 1950)

Mathias, P. and Pearsall, A.W.H. (eds.) *Shipping: A Survey of Historical Records* (Newton Abbot, 1971)

Matthews, N. and Wainwright, M.D. *A Guide to Manuscripts and Documents in the British Isles relating to Africa* (Oxford, 1971)

—————*A Guide to Manuscripts and Documents relating to the Far East* (Oxford, 1977)

Mayer, S.L. and Koenig, W.J. *The Two World Wars: A Guide to Collections in the United Kingdom* (London, 1976)

Morgan, P. *Oxford libraries outside the Bodleian: A Guide* (Oxford, 2/1980)

Museums Association *Museums Year Book* (London, published annually)

National Library of Ireland *Manuscript Sources for the History of Irish Civilisation* (Boston, 1970)

Oliver, E. (ed.) British Universities Film Council *Researcher's Guide to British Film and Television Collections* (London, 1981)

Ottley, G. *Railway History: A Guide to Sixty-one Collections in Libraries and Archives in Great Britain* (London, 1973)

Owen, D.M. *The Records of the Established Church in England excluding Parochial Records*, British Records Association Archives and the User No.1 (London, 1970)

Pearson, J.D. *Oriental Manuscripts in Europe and North America: A Survey* (Zug, 1971)

Peek, H.E. and Hall, C.P. *The Archives of the University of Cambridge* (Cambridge, 1962)

Riden, P. *Record Publications on Sale* (London, 1980)

Ritchie, L.A. *Modern British Shipbuilding. A Guide to Historical Records* (London, 1980)

Roberts, S. *et al. Research libraries and collections in the United Kingdom* (London, 1978)

Smith, D.M. *Guide to Bishops' Registers of England and Wales: a Survey from the Middle Ages to the Abolition of Episcopacy in 1646* (London, 1981)

Society of Archivists *Journal* (formerly *Bulletin of the Society of Local Archivists*) 1955–

Society of Genealogists *National Index of Parish Registers* (London, 1968, etc.)

Stephens, W.B. *Sources for English Local History* (Cambridge, 2/1981)

Storey, R.A. and Madden, J.L. *Primary sources for Victorian Studies: A Guide to the Location and Use of Unpublished Materials* (London, 1977)

Tate, W.E. *The Parish Chest: A Study of the Records of Parochial Administration in England* (Cambridge, 3/1969)

Thompson, K. *The Use of Archives in Education: A Bibliography* (Leicester, 1982)

Wainwright, M.D. and Matthews, N. *A Guide to Western Manuscripts and Documents in the British Isles relating to South and South East Asia* (London, 1965)

Wall, J. (comp.) *Directory of British Photographic Collections* (London, 1977)

Walne, P. (ed.) *A Guide to Manuscript Sources for the History of Latin America and the Caribbean in the British Isles* (London, 1973)

General Index to Collections

This index is to the Major Collections and Non-manuscript material sections of the main entries. Readers are directed also to the indexes maintained by the National Register of Archives (*see* List of Useful Addresses).

Key Subject Word List

This list is compiled from a checklist of key subject headings which was sent with the questionnaire. Because of the comprehensive nature of their holdings it was decided to exclude local authority record offices and the following national repositories: British Library (Departments of Oriental and Western Manuscripts), British Museum (National History), Public Record Office, Public Record Office of Northern Ireland, Scottish Record Office, Bodleian Library, Cambridge University Library and the National Libraries of Scotland and Wales.

This list is not intended as an index to collections but rather as a general guide to repositories with holdings of relevance in specific subject areas. However, readers should bear in mind that collections are not normally catalogued or arranged on a subject basis.

An asterisk * indicates that the subject word is additional to the original list, having been suggested by certain repositories as relevant to their holdings: therefore the references given for these words are not comprehensive.